To Ejaz,
with compliments
[signature]
2 August 2006

Festschrift
for Tarmo Pukkila
on his 60th Birthday

Portrait of Tarmo Pukkila painted by Eeva Rihu, 2005.
[Photograph by Simo Puntanen, reproduced with permission from Eeva Rihu and the University of Tampere.]

Festschrift for
Tarmo Pukkila
on his 60th Birthday

Edited by

ERKKI P. LISKI JARKKO ISOTALO
JARMO NIEMELÄ SIMO PUNTANEN
GEORGE P. H. STYAN

Report A 368
Department of Mathematics, Statistics and Philosophy
University of Tampere, Finland
2006

Published by
Department of Mathematics, Statistics and Philosophy
University of Tampere, Finland

Edited by
Erkki P. Liski, Jarkko Isotalo, Jarmo Niemelä, Simo Puntanen,
and George P. H. Styan

1st printing

Typeset by
Jarmo Niemelä

Printed by
Vammalan Kirjapaino Oy
Vammala, Finland, 2006

ISBN-13: 978-951-44-6620-5
ISBN-10: 951-44-6620-9

Preface

Dr. Tarmo Pukkila, former Professor of Statistics and Rector of the University of Tampere, now Director General in the Ministry of Social Affairs and Health, Helsinki, turned 60 on the 26th of March 2006. To celebrate this occasion, the Department of Mathematics, Statistics and Philosophy of the University of Tampere is publishing this *Festschrift* for his 60th birthday.

Following a tabula gratulatoria, this *Festschrift* begins with a conversation with Dr. Pukkila, including some comments on his career, followed by a detailed annotated list of his research publications. Several photographs illustrate these two articles.

The main part of this *Festschrift* comprises 23 invited and refereed papers, prepared by the following colleagues, coauthors, collaborators and friends of Tarmo Pukkila:

Brännäs, Kurt – Umeå University, Sweden

Brillinger, David R. – University of California, Berkeley, USA

Farebrother, Richard William – University of Manchester, England, UK

Granger, Clive W. J. – University of California, San Diego, USA

Kollo, Tõnu – University of Tartu, Estonia

Koreisha, Sergio G. – University of Oregon, Eugene, USA

Koskinen, Lasse A. – Insurance Supervisory Authority, Helsinki, Finland

Liski, Erkki P. – University of Tampere, Finland

Mathew, Thomas – University of Maryland, Baltimore County, USA

Merikoski, Jorma K. – University of Tampere, Finland

Mustonen, Seppo – University of Helsinki, Finland

Nordberg, Leif – Åbo Akademi, Turku, Finland

Oja, Hannu – University of Tampere, Finland

Pukelsheim, Friedrich – University of Augsburg, Germany

Puntanen, Simo – University of Tampere, Finland

Rantala, Jukka – Finnish Centre for Pensions, Helsinki, Finland

Rao, C. Radhakrishna – Pennsylvania State University, University Park USA

Rissanen, Jorma – Tampere University of Technology, Finland, and Helsinki Institute for Information Technology

Scott, Alastair J. – University of Auckland, New Zealand

Sinha, Bikas Kumar – Indian Statistical Institute, Kolkata, India

Sinha, Bimal Kumar – University of Maryland, Baltimore County, USA

Styan, George P. H. – McGill University, Montréal (Québec), Canada

Trenkler, Götz – University of Dortmund, Germany

We plan that this *Festschrift* will be presented to Dr. Pukkila in a Special Session (sponsored by the University of Tampere Foundation) of the Fifteenth International Workshop on Matrices and Statistics, to be held in Uppsala, Sweden, from June 13 through June 17, 2006. We are very grateful to Professor Dietrich von Rosen for arranging this Special Session as a part of the Workshop program.

The Editorial Board for this Festschrift comprises Erkki P. Liski (chair), Jarkko Isotalo, Jarmo Niemelä, Simo Puntanen, and George P. H. Styan. We wish to express our warmest thanks to the contributors to this *Festschrift*: thank you very much! It was a pleasure to collaborate with you. We are also grateful to the City of Tampere and the University of Tampere Foundation for financial support.

All articles have been refereed, and for this, special thanks go the anonymous referees for their valuable work. Tarmo and Helena Pukkila deserve particular thanks for a thorough photo-browsing which yielded many memorable photos appearing in this *Festschrift*. We are also most grateful for the efforts and time that Tarmo Pukkila devoted to editing the conversation article, which appears at the front of this book. And thanks go also to Evelyn M. Styan for her help.

Finally, *Parhaimmat syntymäpäiväonnittelut, Tarmo!*

Erkki P. Liski
Jarkko Isotalo
Jarmo Niemelä
Simo Puntanen
George P. H. Styan
May 2006

Contents

Tabula gratulatoria

Aaltonen Markus, Counsellor of Parliament
Anttila Rauno, Director
Apteekkien Eläkekassa, Pension Fund
Asp Kari, Managing Director
The Association of Pension Foundations / Eläkesäätiöyhdistys-ESY
Backman Heli, Government Counsellor
Elinkeinoelämän Keskusliitto ry / Confederation of Finnish Industries EK:
Fagernäs Leif, Director General, Riski Seppo, Director, Ojala Arto, Director, Laatunen Lasse, Director, Legal Affairs
Eläke-Fennia / Pension Fennia
Eläketurvakeskus / The Finnish Centre for Pensions
Etla / The Research Institute of The Finnish Economy
Federation of Finnish Enterprises: Järventaus Jussi, Managing Director, Vanhanen Rauno, Director, Suominen Risto, Director
Fellman Johan, Professor
Fennia Mutual Insurance Company
Finalm Oy
Finnish Insurance Broker Association
The Finnish Pension Alliance TELA
Finnish Union of Researchers and Teachers
Forss Mikael, Dr. Econ.
Graeffe Gunnar
Haaparanta Leila, Professor
Haikala Klaus, Gardener, Säijä
Hakala Antti, Planning Manager
Haukkanen Pentti, Ph.D., Professor
Heino Aarre, Professor
Hella Heikki, Ph.D.
Hellman Anni, FASF
Hemilä Kalevi, Managing Director, Etera Mutual Pension Insurance Co.
Hohti Paavo, Professor
Huotari Päivi, Managing Director, Farmers' Social Insurance Institution
Huuhtanen Jorma, Director General
Huuhtanen Pentti, Ph.D.
Hylsynen Karin, HDR, Rovaniemi
Härkönen Tarja, Head of Department

Ilmarinen: Puro Kari, Tuomikoski Jaakko, Kivihuhta Sini, Aro Timo, Auvinen Pirkko, Mannonen Hillevi
Inha Jyri, Doctor of Laws, Docent, Legislative Counsellor
Isotalo Jarkko, Researcher
Jakobsson Matti, Rector, University of Vaasa
Jännäri Kaarlo, Director General
Järvinen Pertti and Annikki, professors
Jääskeläinen Pirkko and Tapani
Kallinen Arto, Ph. Lic., FASF
Kannisto Jorma, M.Sc.
Kantola Veikko J., Cabinet Counselor
Kari Matti, Ph.D., Project Director
Kausto Risto, M.Sc., SHV
Kemppainen Kimmo, Entrepreneur
Keskinäinen Vakuutusyhtiö Tapiola
Ketoja Elise, Biometrician
Knuuti Kaarina, Lic. Sc.
Kurki-Suonio Reino, Professor Emeritus
Korpiaho Teija, Senior Officer
Koskenkylä Heikki, Head of Department
Koski Heikki
Koskinen Lasse, Research Director, Insurance Supervisory Authority of Finland
Kultalahti Jukka, Professor
Kultalahti Olli, Professor
Kuluttajien Vakuutustoimisto / The Finnish Insurance Ombudsman Bureau
Kuntien Eläkevakuutus
Kuntoutumis- ja liikuntasäätiö Peurunka / Hallitus: Puhakka Matti, Huunan-Seppälä Antti, Haapa-aho Jussi, Toivio Reino, Valkonen Pirkko, Valve Jaakko, Koskinen Hannu, Pekkonen Mika, Korpi Kalevi
Kärkkäinen Päivi, Director of Programmes
Kässi Tuomo and Kaisa
Laitinen Jussi, Chief Investment Officer
Lankia Eero, Secretary General
Latva-Rasku Paavo, Mayor, Lapua
Lehtinen Uolevi, Professor
Lehto Markku, Permanent Secretary of Health and Social Affairs
Lehtonen Jarmo, Director General, Pharma Industry Finland (PIF)
Lehtonen Risto, Professor
Lemmetty Markku, Director, AKAVA
Leppiniemi Jarmo, Professor
Leppälä Raija
Leveelahti Ilkka, Head of Finance
Lindqvist-Virtanen Carin, M.Sc.

Liski Erkki
Louko Olavi, Technical Director of City of Espoo
Lounatvuori Markku, Chief Legal Counsel
Luoma Martti, Professor Emeritus
Luukkonen Irene, Director
Läärä Esa, Professor
Meklin Pentti, Professor
Mikola Markus, Managing Director
Mäkeläinen Eva-Christina
Mäntynen Annikki, M. Soc. Sc.
National Emergency Supply Agency
Neittaanmäki Pekka, Professor, University of Jyväskylä
Nieminen Mauri, Senior Adviser
Nokian Eläkesäätiö / Nokia Pension Foundation
Nummi Tapio
Nyblom Jukka, Professor
Osuuspankkikeskus
Oulun Osuuspankki
Palm Heikki, Ministerial Adviser
Parjanen Anja and Matti
Parmanne Pertti, Director
Partala Hannu, Managing Director
Penttilä Seppo, Professor
Penttinen Antti, Professor
Perälä Jorma, Master of Political Science
Pesonen Martti, Chief Actuary
Piekka Risto, President, AKAVA
Pietiläinen Seppo, LL.Lic.
Puntanen Simo
Rahiala Markku, Professor
Rahkola Sirkku, Financial Director
Reponen Tapio, Rector, Turun kauppakorkeakoulu
Ronkainen Vesa, M.Sc.
Rosenqvist Gunnar, Professor
Ruuskanen Jukka, Managing Director
Räihä Kari-Jouko, Professor
Salomaa Hely, Director General
Saloranta Seppo
Savolainen Onerva, Chief AC
Sillanpää Juha, Lic. Ph., Lecturer
The Social Insurance Institution
Sonninen Matti, Master of Social Sciences
Sotamaa Yrjö, Rector, Taideteollinen Korkeakoulu (VALKI)
The State Pension Fund Financial Counsellor

Suomen Aktuaariyhdistys ry / The Actuarial Society of Finland
Suomen Kulttuurirahasto / Finnish Cultural Foundation, Regional Fund of South Ostrobothnia
Suvanto Antti, Head of Department
Suvanto Arvi, Financial Counsellor
Tampere Chamber of Commerce and Industry
Tapiola Group
Tapiola Pension
Tapiola Vahinkovakuutusyhtiö
Teräsvirta Timo, Professor
Toimihenkilökeskusjärjestö STTK Säätiö
Turunen Juhani, Senior Officer, Legal Affairs
Uimonen Matti, Ph.D. (Econ) h.c.
University of Helsinki, Department of Mathematics and Statistics
University of Joensuu, Department of Statistics
University of Tampere, Central Administration
University of Tampere, Department of Law
University of Tampere, Faculty of Economics and Administration
University of Tampere, Faculty of Information Sciences
Utriainen Anu and Dinkov Rostislav
Vaden Totte, Chief Psychologist
Vainiomäki Jari, Professor
Vanne Reijo, Head of R&D
Varma Keskinäinen Työeläkevakuutusyhtiö: Vuoria Matti, CEO, President, Hyvärinen Markku, Executive Vice-President
Vehkalahti Kimmo, D.Soc.Sc.
Veijola Risto, M.Sc.
Vesterinen Markku, Senior Executive Vice President
Virtanen Ilkka, Professor
Visakorpi Anja and Jarmo
Vuontisjärvi Alpo, Ounasloma Luxury Cabins
Öller Lars-Erik, Professor

Festschrift for Tarmo Pukkila on his 60th Birthday
Eds. E. P. Liski, J. Isotalo, J. Niemelä, S. Puntanen, and G. P. H. Styan
© Dept. of Mathematics, Statistics and Philosophy,
Univ. of Tampere, 2006, ISBN 978-951-44-6620-5, pages 13–44

A conversation with Tarmo Mikko Pukkila

SIMO PUNTANEN & GEORGE P. H. STYAN

Abstract. Dr. Tarmo Mikko Pukkila, currently Director General in the Ministry of Social Affairs and Health, Helsinki, celebrated his 60th birthday on March 26, 2006. After completing his Master's Degree in Statistics and Mathematics at the University of Tampere in 1971, he worked in the University first as an assistant in statistics and mathematics and then as a senior assistant in statistics and later as a planning manager at the Computer Centre. He completed his Ph.D. degree in 1977. In 1980, he was appointed Professor of Statistics at the University of Tampere.

He has served in numerous administrative positions at the University of Tampere: Head of the Department, Dean of the Faculty, and as Rector from 1987 to 1993. From 1993 onwards, he has served as Director General in the Ministry of Social Affairs and Health, Helsinki.

Dr. Pukkila has authored or coauthored numerous research papers and several books. He has served on several editorial boards and Finnish national committees, and has organized influential international conferences and workshops.

In 1972 he married Helena Nykänen and they have two daughters, Elina and Laura, and one grandson, Vilppu Vaskelainen.

2000 MSC codes: 01A60, 01A65, 01A70, 01A73, 01A74, 62-03.

Key words and phrases: Jerzy K. Baksalary (1944–2005); Biography; Harald Cramér (1893–1985); Morris Herman DeGroot (1931–1989); Gustav Elfving (1908–1984); Finland after World War II; Eino Haikala (1913–1993); Edward James Hannan (1921–1994); International Workshops on Matrices and Statistics; IWMS; Chinubhai Ghelabhai Khatri (1931–1989); Paavo Koli (1920–1968); Paruchuri R. Krishnaiah (1932–1987); Ministry of Social Affairs and Health, Helsinki; Photographs; Statistics and mathematics at the University of Tampere; University of Oregon, Eugene; University of Pittsburgh.

The following conversation took place mainly by e-mail during March and April 2006.

Simo Puntanen

Figure 1. Tarmo Pukkila at home in Espoo, August 2000.

Early years

Tell us about your youth.

"I was born on March 26, 1946, in Vähäkyrö, a small community in the western part of Finland, near Vaasa, about 450 km north of Helsinki. Finland had been in the so-called 'Winter War' (Finnish: *Talvisota*) against the Soviet Union in 1939–1940. This was followed by the 'Continuation War' (Finnish: *Jatkosota*) also against the Soviet Union which lasted from 1941 to 1944. After that Finland was at war against Germany in Finnish Lapland, with the war finally concluded by the Paris peace treaty of 1947. At that time many young men had to serve in the military for as long as five years. My father was one of them. Finland was one of the few European countries which were not occupied during World War II. Finland also remained independent after the war.

Finland was found guilty for the wars against the Soviet Union, and as a result had to pay rather high reparations, which it did mainly with industrial products. Finland also repaid its war debts to the United States, among other countries.

After World War II, Finland was a rather poor country. In the 1950s, at least in the countryside, imported fruits were rare indeed. The war reparations, however, helped Finland develop industrially, especially its metal industry. I think that after the war the Finnish economy and standard of living improved at an astonishingly fast rate.

As in many other countries, in Finland there was a population boom right after the war. The largest age group, comprising 108,000 children, was born in 1947. The 1946 age group was a little smaller. For comparison, we note that nowadays about 55,000 children are born each year. As elsewhere, now also in Finland the population is aging rapidly.

My parents owned a small farm. Farms in the area around Vaasa where I lived were generally small. That meant hard work with low earnings. For this reason I was taught at home that studying is a key to a better life. My older brother became a banker. My younger brother is still living on the farm, but he has another job besides farming.

Living on the farm also meant hard work for me especially in summer time, but also during the winter. In later life I found it very useful that we had to work hard already while we were going to school. It seems that hard work is necessary in almost all areas of human life, but especially in research."

At high school, were you mathematically oriented or were there also other topics that interested you very much?

"At high school I was also interested in languages. At one stage, I thought that I might study Swedish later on at university. One reason for this was that during two summer breaks at high school I worked at a big aluminium factory in Sundsvall, Sweden. At that time I learnt Swedish a little better than was generally possible at high school. And salaries in Sweden were higher than in Finland. There were, therefore, many Finnish schoolboys working in Sweden during the summer. Indeed in the 1960s many Finns emigrated to Sweden. This partially helped solve the employment problems of large age groups in Finland."

The University of Tampere in the late 1960s

Please describe in a nutshell the University of Tampere in the late 1960s.

"The Finnish university network comprises 20 institutions. This large number of universities is partially explained by the fact that there are also universities where the teaching language is Swedish, the other official language in Finland. There are also a few specialized and rather small institutions like the Sibelius Academy. Geographically the university network covers the whole country. The University of Helsinki was founded in 1640. Other Finnish universities are much younger. In Finland the university system was expanded especially in the 1960s and 1970s.

The University of Tampere is one of the younger universities. Its predecessor was founded in Helsinki in 1925. In 1960 it was moved to Tampere. At that time the university had only one faculty, namely the Faculty of Social Sciences. In the first half of the 1960s two further faculties, the Faculty of Humanities and the Faculty of Economics and Administration were created. Then in the 1970s the Faculty of Medicine and the Faculty of Education were added.

The Faculty of Economics and Administration was born in 1965. In this faculty it was possible to study, besides business, economics and administrative sciences, also computer science, mathematics, statistics, and philosophy. One of the ideas was to educate experts for business and administration who would have a good knowledge in the methodological sciences. The Professorship in Computer Science was the first such professorship in the Nordic countries."

That was quite a remarkable event those days. I think the initiative for this professorship came from Seppo Mustonen (*now Professor Emeritus of Statistics at the University of Helsinki*).

"That is true. Professor Mustonen, who was then at the University of Tampere, was indeed a key person in the creation of this Professorship. One of his ideas was to create a new type of faculty in the university. The orientation of the faculty would have been in mathematical sciences without having traditional natural sciences. Unfortunately his idea did not materialize at that time; some other ideas evidently were more important to the university at that time."

Figure 2. Seppo Mustonen with a computer in Tampere 1987. Behind in different rows, Peter Naeve, George P. H. Styan, Tarmo Pukkila, Jerzy K. Baksalary, Friedrich Pukelsheim, John W. Pratt, Bill Farebrother.

I think another influential figure at that time was then-Rector Paavo Koli. Did you know him?

"When I started my university studies in the mid-1960s, Professor Paavo Koli was the Rector of the University of Tampere. At that time Seppo Mustonen was in close cooperation with Rector Koli. Unfortunately for the University of Tampere, Seppo Mustonen moved rather soon to the University of Helsinki, where he was Professor of Statistics until he retired recently.

In Finland at the opening ceremony of the autumn term, university rectors deliver addresses that can then be quoted rather extensively in the media. I personally never met Rector Koli, but I had the pleasure of attending his opening speech in the autumn term of 1966.

He was a very charismatic person. He had three different academic degrees, one in sociology, one in physical education, and one from the Military Academy. At the University of Tampere he was Professor of Sociology. He was a most highly respected military officer and leader during World War II. Indeed a war hero! Unfortunately he passed away already in 1968 at the young age of 48."

How did you end up studying at the University of Tampere?

"Occasionally random events have a rather strong effect on how people make their selections. This has been the case also in my life. One of my friends told me of the possibilities to study mathematics in a new type of environment. So in September 1966 I began my studies at the University of Tampere. At that time a number of students had more than one major. I studied both mathematics and statistics, as well as computer science, and a little bit of economics.

Computer science was a new topic in the 1960s. The first computer was an Elliott 803 B using paper tape as the input and output device. As compared with present computers, the Elliott 803 B was complicated to use. Anyway we learnt programming with it in different programming courses. I still remember my first program that I managed to execute properly. The problem was to write a program that would read a game situation of a chessboard and then give the locations of those squares on the chessboard where there is a white piece threatened by a black one.

I remember my first programming course taught by Reino Kurki-Suonio (now Professor Emeritus of Computer Science and Engineering at the Tampere University of Technology) in a huge auditorium with hundreds of students. He taught me that there are three different levels of learning. At the first level one reads and understands a certain subject, e.g., in a book. A deeper level of learning is needed if somebody tries to teach something to another person. The deepest level is reached when somebody teaches what has been learnt to a computer. Later in my own research I have applied this method to test ideas developed using paper and pencil. For example, some beautiful asymptotic results might be less beautiful when one applies them in cases where one has only a limited number of observations."

When were you hired for the first time in the Department of Mathematical Sciences of the University of Tampere?

"After two years of basic studies I met Eino Haikala, the Professor of Statistics at that time. He asked me to begin as one of his part-time assistants. That was the start of my academic career. After completing my Master's Degree, I was appointed to a permanent assistantship in statistics, 'permanent' then meaning for a three-year time period. That was the time I also first met you, Simo, as well as Erkki Liski, Pentti Huuhtanen, and many others. I might add that my appointment to this assistantship was a result of a specific random event."

Figure 3. Professor Eino Haikala.

Do you recall any particularly inspiring statistics books from those days? You surely became familiar with Harald Cramér's famous book, which was one of Eino Haikala's favourites. This book was first published in Uppsala in 1945.

"I certainly remember Cramér's book *Mathematical Methods of Statistics* very well. In fact during the spring semester of 1968, the second year of my studies, I took the final examination in that course in the summer of 1968. I guess that that examination may have influenced Professor Haikala to ask me to help him when he next gave that course. Still today I think that solving the exercises given in Cramér's book is very rewarding both for younger and older statisticians. Some of the exercises can be reasonably demanding.

As you may know Harald Cramér's grandson Martin Rasmussen is a Medical Doctor in Tampere. It was a quite fascinating coincidence that in 1999 in Tampere (at the 8th International Workshop on Matrices and Statistics), Dr. Martin Rasmussen was an invited speaker in our reception, and that he then met keynote speaker Professor T.W. 'Ted' Anderson, who had been visiting his grandfather in Stockholm[1] in 1947–1948, just over 50 years before! In the opening remarks of his detailed obituary article, Gunnar Blom (1987) notes that Harald Cramér (1893–1985) was a 'great scientist and a good man'."

First international contacts

The visit by Professor Fred C. Andrews in the late 1960s was very influential, is that right?

"Professor Fred C. Andrews of the University of Oregon spent his sabbatical year 1969–1970 at the University of Tampere. This visit was a key to my first visit to the United States in 1982. I completed my compulsory military service in 1972–1973. After that I returned to the university. Instead of statistics I served the year 1973–1974 as an assistant in mathematics. In 1974 I was appointed as a senior assistant in statistics."

The active use of the computer in teaching statistics began in Tampere in 1975. I think you put a lot of energy to computer usage, you even gave your inaugural address for your professorship on that topic in November 1980.

"In the 1970s we were very interested in using computers in teaching statistics. We built computer programs that were used to simulate random events. This interest took me to several conferences in statistical computing, e.g., Leiden in The Netherlands in 1978, Tbilisi in Georgia (then in the Soviet Union) in 1979, Edinburgh in 1980, Lausanne in 1981, Prague in 1984, etc. For me Leiden was particularly important. At that conference I met Professor Peter Naeve from the University of Bielefeld in Germany."

[1] For some interesting comments on Ted Anderson's visit to Sweden see the *Statistical Science* conversation with Morris H. DeGroot (1986).

Figure 4. Tarmo Pukkila receiving award for the Army Service, March 1973.

COMPSTAT

Figure 5. Peter Naeve, Mrs. Naeve, Simo Puntanen and Tarmo Pukkila, COMPSTAT Conference in Edinburgh, 1980.

Thesis, computer centre, Haikala, Rovaniemi

You were also working in the Tampere Computer Centre in the mid-1970s?

"In 1974, I was asked to move temporarily to the Computer Centre of the University of Tampere to work as the Planning Manager. I was on leave from my senior assistantship while I worked there. My duties were to develop time series analytical methods for statistical packages that were extensively used at the university at that time.

The time I worked at the Computer Centre was very beneficial for my later career. At that time I became interested in frequency domain methods in time series analysis. That interest led to my Ph.D. thesis, where I used frequency domain methods in the estimation of autoregressive moving average models. These methods are based on the periodogram ordinates that may have strong bias as the estimates of the corresponding spectrum ordinates. This bias is transmitted in the parameter estimates of the autoregressive moving average models. It can be said that the more the model differs from white noise, the stronger is the bias in the parameter estimates. A similar feature is observed in the Yule-Walker estimates of autoregressive models.

I defended my Ph.D. thesis in 1977. Much later I observed a curious phenomenon in the time-domain Yule-Walker estimates of autoregressive parameters. I observed that the variance of Yule-Walker estimates may increase when the number of observations is increased. Naturally the variances of the estimates will finally begin to decrease when the number of observations is increased. This is because the Yule-Walker estimates are consistent. This observation meant that the variance of a consistent estimate does not necessarily decrease monotonically with an increasing number of observations."

You were the first among your fellow students who completed the Ph.D. degree. It apparently was all very independent work. Not much supervising? Was there any particular main source for your thesis?

"It was really very independent work. Naturally it would have been very useful if I had had somebody to talk with about the topic of the thesis while I worked on it. But this was not the case at that time. However, there were several people in the department and faculty who helped me with practical arrangements concerning my thesis. I would especially like to mention Pertti Järvinen, a professor of computer science. With him, I also used to run in deep forests with a map and compass. Pertti taught me a lot about orienteering, evidently successfully, as I could always find my way back out of forests.

In the beginning of the 1970s I became interested in Box-Jenkins models. The seminal book on time series by Box and Jenkins (1970) inspired me. At that time I studied also frequency-domain methods and I began to wonder whether it might be useful to apply frequency-domain methods to estimate autoregressive moving-average models. The reason is that the likelihood function attains a rather simple form in the frequency domain. Unfortunately the bias in the periodogram ordinates is seen as a bias in the frequency-domain estimates of the parameters."

The important years 1976–1977; recollections from Haikala's farm and Rovaniemi?

"I returned to Statistics from the Computer Centre in 1976. That was the year when Professor Haikala retired. But before that the whole department had the very nice opportunity to meet George P. H. Styan (now Professor Emeritus of Mathematics and Statistics at McGill University), who spent the academic year 1975–1976 on sabbatical leave at the University of Helsinki as a guest of Professor Timo Mäkeläinen.

George Styan visited Tampere in January 1976, and he and the whole statistics group were then invited one evening to the Haikala farm in Säijä near Lempäälä, about 25 kilometres south of Tampere. If I remember correctly the temperature was around −20 Celsius that evening. As always, we enjoyed the warm hospitality of Eino and Marja Haikala at their farm, as so many times before and later.

The following summer of 1976 the Summer University of Lapland organized a small statistics conference in Rovaniemi (near the Arctic Circle) and George Styan was one of the main speakers at that event. In May 2000, 24 years later, the Faculty of Economics and Administration of the University of Tampere was proud to award George an Honorary Doctorate of Philosophy, in part for his 'promotion of research in the University of Tampere'."

You gave a talk about your forthcoming thesis in Rovaniemi?

"Yes I did. If I remember correctly, at the time of the Rovaniemi conference I had all the results for the thesis completed. So it was a nice opportunity for me to try to explain at a conference what kind of results I had obtained in my studies. I might add that the University of Lapland, which was founded in 1979 in Rovaniemi, is the northernmost university in Finland and also in the European Union[2]."

Towards professorship

When were you appointed Professor?

"Following Professor Haikala's retirement, the Professorship in Statistics at the University of Tampere became open and I applied. When I returned home from the Tbilisi conference in 1979, having read the referees' assessments

[2]The University of Tromsø is further north than Rovaniemi but Norway is not a member country of the European Union. Neither is Russia, and there are three universities in Murmansk, which is also further north than Rovaniemi but south of Tromsø. Murmansk is at 68° 59′ N, Tromsø 69° 42′ N, and Rovaniemi 66° 57′ N.

Antti Penttinen

Figure 6. Statisticians in Jyväskylä, 1975. Seppo Mäkelä, Annika Nyström, Vesa Kanniainen, Eija Janhonen, Timo Teräsvirta, Lars-Erik Öller (front row), Kalevi Selkäinaho (back row), Leif Nordberg, Esko Leskinen, Antti Suvanto (front row), Tarmo Pukkila.

of the applicants, I realized that I might be appointed. This happened in 1980 when I received the appointment letter from President Urho Kekkonen (1900–1986). At that time full professors were appointed by the President of the Republic."

Collaboration with Estonia

Your contacts with Estonia?

"I made my first visit to Tallinn in Estonia (then in the Soviet Union) in 1979. I was a member of a group of professors from Tampere. We met Estonian mathematicians, statisticians and economists, among others Professor Leo K. Vyhandu from Tallinn Polytechnic University. In fact I had met Leo Vyhandu already before in Tampere. At that time visitors from Estonia had often made a complicated and time-consuming train trip from Tallinn via Moscow to Helsinki.[3]

My first visit to Tallinn was interesting in that we had a possibility to make a one-day visit by bus to Tartu. At that time Tartu was a closed city for foreigners, who were not allowed to stay overnight in Tartu. Anyway we could visit the University of Tartu, which was founded in 1632, eight years before the University of Helsinki in 1640. At that time both Estonia and Finland were part of Sweden.

In autumn 1983 a group of statisticians from the University of Tampere made a visit to Tallinn. We had many research reports from our department with us. It was a very interesting experience to see a customs officer go through these reports.

Also later I collaborated with the University of Tartu and Estonian statisticians. As Rector and during my insurance supervisory career my cooperation with Estonians has deepened to another level. Insurance supervisors have intensive cooperation with all EU countries, also with Estonia. Nowadays Estonia, like Finland, is a full member of the European Union. Since 1988 we have experienced historic events taking place in Europe. I might add that nowadays there are a number of Finnish students who study, e.g., medicine at the University of Tartu. There is indeed a long history of scientific cooperation between Estonia and Finland."

Umeå & Oregon

Umeå 1982?

"The Finnish university system is such that active professors very soon find themselves taking care of various administrative duties. This happened also

[3]Today there are frequent daily helicopter flights between Helsinki and Tallinn which take just 20 minutes.

to me. Very soon in the beginning of the 1980s I observed that I was at the same time the Head of the Department of Mathematical Sciences and the Dean of the Faculty of Economics and Administration. I felt that continuing in such administrative positions would not have been good for my research at that stage. Fortunately in 1981 I received an offer from the University of Umeå in Sweden. I accepted and then spent four months in the Department of Statistics at Umeå in the spring of 1982. There I met several statisticians, including Professor Uno Zachrisson, the Head of the Department of Statistics, as well as Dr. Anders Westlund, Dr. Hans Nyquist, Dr. Kurt Brännäs, and Dr. Lennart Bondesson.

At least at that time, it was a tradition for there to be two separate departments of statistics at Swedish universities, one for statistics and one for mathematical statistics. The Head of the Department of Mathematical Statistics then was Professor Gunnar Kulldorff.

I very much enjoyed the atmosphere of the University of Umeå. The whole university was internationally oriented with many visitors from overseas. The university offered excellent accommodation and other facilities for foreign visitors and their families. Umeå also offered excellent possibilities for cross-country skiing."

Oregon 1982–1983?

"In May 1982, while we were still in Umeå, I got a phone call from Professor Fred Andrews of the University of Oregon in Eugene. He asked whether I would be willing to come to Oregon to work in the Mathematics Department for the following academic year. After a family discussion I accepted the offer. So, after returning to Tampere from Umeå, we began to arrange to move to the west coast of the United States. Things developed fast and already by the beginning of August 1982, my wife Helena, our two daughters, Elina and Laura, and I had moved to Eugene. Elina was then four years old and Laura just nine months when we travelled to the other side of the globe. Later I realized that our visit to Oregon would be en excellent possibility for me and the family. Oregon is a fantastic place.

In Oregon I met a number of eminent scientists mainly in the Mathematics Department. During our visit the Head of the Department was Professor Theodore Palmer. The President of the University at that time was Professor Paul Olum. While writing this I visited the home pages of the Mathematics Department of the University of Oregon, and I noticed that practically all of the professors I met then are now retired.

For my later career it was extremely important to get to know Professor Sergio Koreisha. At that time Sergio was an Assistant Professor in the Business School at the University of Oregon. Several years ago Sergio was promoted to full professor.

In the fall of 1982 I gave a 500-level course on time series analysis. Sergio came to my class. We were both interested in multivariate vector autoregressive moving-average models. Even in rather simple situations such models can contain a huge number of parameters to estimate. After one lecture Sergio posed the rather difficult problem of identifying nonzero parameters in vector autoregressive models on the basis of observed time series data. That was the start to our long cooperation. Over the years we have published 17 joint papers on this topic, see the next chapter by Puntanen and Styan in this book."

Simo Puntanen

Figure 7. Christian Léger, A. M. Mathai, George P. H. Styan, Harold Ruben, and Tarmo Pukkila in the lounge of the Dept. of Mathematics at McGill University, Montréal, Canada, November 1982.

The years 1983–1985

Remind us about "The First International Tampere Seminar on Linear Statistical Models and their Applications".

"Before leaving for Oregon in the summer of 1982, you, Simo, and I made the important decision to host an international conference in statistics at the University of Tampere in 1983, immediately after my return from Oregon. It was called 'The First International Tampere Seminar on Linear Statistical Models and their Applications' and was held from August 30th to September 2nd, 1983. It was an honour for us to have Professor C. R. Rao as a keynote speaker. One of the important architects of this conference was George Styan, who was the other keynote speaker. In addition, several eminent scientists from different countries attended and gave talks.

The opening address was given by Professor Gustav Elfving (then Professor Emeritus of Mathematics at the University of Helsinki), to whom the *Proceed-*

Figure 8. Nokia 1984: Erkki Liski, Tarmo Pukkila, Sergio Koreisha.

ings, edited by Pukkila and Puntanen (1985), is dedicated. Sadly, Professor Elfving passed way in 1984."

Dr. Jerzy K. Baksalary was invited but he could not come?

"Right. We were very disappointed that Dr. Baksalary (then in the Dept. of Mathematical and Statistical Methods in the Agricultural University of Poznań) could not join us in 1983. The political situation in Europe has changed a lot since those days. But he did visit us in Tampere in 1987 and again in 1990. Sadly Professor Baksalary passed away in 2005."

Did an active collaboration between certain Indian and German statisticians have its roots in the 1983 Seminar?

"The 1983 Seminar was a fantastic experience in many ways. We in Tampere became acquainted with many famous statisticians. On the other hand our guests at the Seminar got to know each other. This led to a later and fruitful cooperation between certain Seminar participants. The Sinha twins: Bikas Kumar Sinha (now Professor of Statistics at the Indian Statistical Institute, Kolkata) and Bimal Kumar Sinha (now Professor of Mathematics and Statistics at the University of Maryland-Baltimore County) became regular visitors to Tampere. And Dr. Erkki Liski (now the Professor of Statistics at the University of Tampere) has had a close collaboration with Professor Götz Trenkler from Dortmund, Germany, just to mention a few names."

Simo Puntanen

Figure 9. Seminar Dinner in Sorsapuiston Grilli in Tampere in 1983: Antti Kanto, Bimal Kumar Sinha (hidden), Gustav Elfving, Helga Bunke (back to camera), Evelyn M. Styan, C. R. Rao, Tarmo Pukkila, Dietrich von Rosen, George P. H. Styan (back row).

Simo Puntanen

Figure 10. Haikala's farm in Säijä in 1983: Gustav Elfving, Bhargavi Rao, Kaisa Huuhtanen, Helena Pukkila, C. R. Rao, and Tarmo Pukkila walking to greet Professor Eino Haikala.

Figure 11. Haikala's farm in 1983: C. R. Rao giving his autographed *Linear Statistical Inference and Its Applications* to Eino Haikala.

You had a big job arranging the 60th Anniversary of the University of Tampere in 1985. How did that go?

"After returning to Tampere from Oregon in the autumn of 1983 I thought that now I would have at last some time to work mainly on teaching and research. I did not have that nice feeling for very long. I think that it was in October when the Rector of the University asked me to chair the organizing committee for the 60th anniversary celebrations of the University. It is possible that I was too fast in my decision to accept. It did not take a long time for me to realize that the request meant that the organizing committee should raise money and to arrange the celebrations. I think that this case was not unique, for surely many people at universities all over the world are faced with similar tasks.

The highlight of the celebrations was the doctoral convocation in May 1985 lasting from Wednesday to Saturday. Besides our own new doctorates receiving their diplomas, top hats and swords, about 20 distinguished scientists and cultural figures were awarded Honorary Doctor's Degrees by various faculties of the University, including Professor C. R. Rao (now Eberly Professor of Statistics at Pennsylvania State University) and Professor Fred C. Andrews (now Professor Emeritus of Mathematics (Statistics) at the University of Oregon) and Dr. Mauno Koivisto (then President of the Republic of Finland).

University of Tampere

Figure 12. The doctoral convocation in Tampere in 1985: Bhargavi Rao, C.R. Rao, Fred C. Andrews, Joyce Andrews, Tarmo Pukkila, Eino Haikala, Erkki Liski.

During this anniversary celebration we also arranged a mathematics competition for graduating Finnish high school students. Half a dozen of the best in the competition got rather valuable prizes including computers. I also made a proposal to the University that the 10 best students would be accepted for mathematical studies without further entrance examinations. It happened that some rather influential professors in the University had expressed as their opinion that the university cannot admit entrance on the basis of a beauty contest! So my proposal was turned down. Although I believed it was a good way to compete for the best students. It seems that a lot of water has flowed after that over the Tammerkoski Rapids, the channel in the centre of Tampere connecting the lakes Näsijärvi and Pyhäjärvi.

It seems that the 60th anniversary celebrations of the University were well received. I think that chairing this organising committee had important implications for my later career."

Pittsburgh 1985–1986

Tell us about Pittsburgh in 1985–1986

"After the 60th anniversary celebrations I was honoured by the invitation of Professor C. R. Rao to the Centre for Multivariate Analysis at the University of Pittsburgh. The invitation led to my visit to the University of Pittsburgh in 1985–1986. Professor Bimal Kumar Sinha picked us all up from the Pittsburgh airport. One year later, it was again Professor Sinha who drove us to the airport for our flight home.

In Pittsburgh I worked with model selection criteria. I developed a new white noise test leading to a new method for time series model selection both for univariate and multivariate time series models. This work led to two joint papers with Professor Paruchuri R. Krishnaiah, the Head of the Center for Multivariate Analysis. Sadly Professor Krishnaiah died just one year later in 1987.

It was very fascinating to work at the Center. There were a lot of foreign visitors there. Professor Rao collaborated with most of them by working with them towards publications. Professor Rao was like a conductor of a top Symphony orchestra. It was Professor Rao who in many cases wrote or finalized papers to be submitted for publication. That was very productive work!

I attended a doctoral-level course on pattern detection which Professor Rao taught. I remember very well how Professor Rao very kindly asked his students to often visit the top floor of the department building. The computer laboratory of the department was located there. So Professor Rao requested his students to try statistical methods also in practice by utilizing computers.

It happened some time in November 1985 that I generalized a three-variate problem to the n-variate case. Before the end of the year Professor Rao trav-

Figure 13. Tarmo Pukkila with his MacPlus in Pittsburgh in May 1986.

elled to India to attend statistical conferences there. After one conference I received a postcard from Professor Rao. In that card he said that that generalization was well received at the conference and that when he returned to Pittsburgh we will write a paper on the problem. A couple of times Professor Rao asked me to take care of his pattern recognition class.

One of the visitors to the Centre during that year was Professor C. G. Khatri. I had the honour to write a joint paper on intraclass correlation coefficients with Professor Rao and Professor Khatri. Professor Khatri died just a few years later in 1989.

Pittsburgh was a very interesting city. Besides the University of Pittsburgh there is also Carnegie Mellon University there. Pretty often I attended Statistics Seminars organized by the Department of Statistics at Carnegie Mellon, where Professor Morris H. deGroot was then the Head of the Statistics Department at Carnegie Mellon. Professor deGroot also died in 1989.

In Pittsburgh I continued my cooperation with Professor Sergio Koreisha and produced several computer programs which I needed in my research. In that sense the year was very fruitful.

In August 1985 I attended the big ASA meeting in Las Vegas. There I met Dr. Jorma Rissanen, a Finn who has made a long and productive career at the IBM Research Laboratory in California. Jorma also visited the University of Pittsburgh while I was there. Later he visited Tampere several times. He is a person who expresses himself in no uncertain terms. I have had numerous interesting discussions with him when he has criticized statistical thinking with strong expressions.

All in all the Academic Year 1985–1986 was a fantastic year for me. I learnt a lot that year. I also got to know many famous statisticians there. Best of all was that I was able to participate in joint research projects."

Tampere, 1986–1987

Remind us about "The Second International Tampere Conference in Statistics".

"Having returned to Tampere from Pittsburgh in the fall of 1986 it was possible to continue the work and complete some manuscripts for publication in the academic year 1986–1987. A big project that year, however, was the Second International Tampere Conference in Statistics. At that time Dr. Kurt Brännäs from Umeå visited our department and helped us with the arrangements for the conference."

Figure 14. Conference poster (by Kalevi Kankaala) in Tampere 1987.

I recall that the final decision to arrange the conference was made already in Vienna, in the spring of 1985. There was a coincidental meeting with Professor E.J. 'Ted' Hannan?

"In fact I met Professor Ted Hannan for the first time at a conference organized by Oliver Anderson in Nottingham in 1979. Ted Hannan also told me about Jorma Rissanen. In the late 1970s I did not know about Jorma's work. Sadly both Ted Hannan and Oliver Anderson are now deceased.

Our group from Tampere made a trip to Vienna in 1985. There we met also Professor Manfred Deistler who had had a long and fruitful cooperation with Ted Hannan. We had again some new big fishes in our network.

The Second Tampere Conference was a bigger event than the conference four years earlier. We were honoured to have Professors T. W. Anderson, George E. P. Box, E. J. Hannan and C. R. Rao to give keynote addresses. Invited papers were presented by Professors A. C. Atkinson, Jerzy K. Baksalary, Knut Condradsen, Takeaki Karya, C. G. Khatri, Seppo Mustonen, Michael D. Perlman, John W. Pratt, Friedrich Pukelsheim, Tarmo Pukkila, Jorma Rissanen, Alastair J. Scott, Bimal K. Sinha, T. P. Speed and George P. H. Styan. About 30 contributed papers were delivered at the conference. The *Proceedings*, edited by Pukkila and Puntanen (1987), comprised just over 700 pages, almost double the number of pages for the 1983 Seminar *Proceedings*.

The conference participants had a Sauna party outside Tampere. In spite of the fact that the conference was held in the beginning of June, the weather in Finland was pretty cold that year. This did not, however, prevent conference participants jumping into the lake from the hot Sauna."

University of Tampere

Figure 15. Conference Dinner in Tampere 1987: T. W. Anderson, Tarmo Pukkila, George P. H. Styan.

University of Tampere

Figure 16. Sauna Party in Tampere 1987: Tarmo Pukkila, Dominique Latour, George P. H. Styan, Knut Conradsen, Heikki Hella, E. J. Hannan.

Simo Puntanen

Figure 17. Nokia 1987: Dominique Latour, Pentti Huuhtanen, Alastair J. Scott, Tarmo Pukkila.

Towards the rectorship in 1987

Rectorship of the University of Tampere: how did it start?

"In October 1986, shortly after I had returned to Tampere from Pittsburgh, a professor of the Faculty of Social Sciences called me. It was known that Professor Jarmo Visakorpi would not be a candidate when the new Rector would be selected in April 1987 for a three-year term. The person who called me suggested that I should be a candidate for the rectorship. I had never thought about that kind of possibility. After serious consideration I decided to be a candidate. At that time the Rector of the University of Tampere was elected by the 30 members of the Council of the University. In the election I won with votes 16–14. So, the election was very close.

My first term started on August 1. But in June 1987 I attended a conference in Hamburg, Germany. The conference participants were newly elected rectors mainly from European countries. The teachers at the conference were already experienced as rectors or were persons with long experience in university administration. At the conference among other things, case studies were dealt with. In one case study the problem was how to handle a situation where students have occupied the university and the Rector's office. That was a real world problem. Such events took place in the 1960s and 1970s in Finland and in many other countries.

University rectors represent their universities. They are visible figures in any society. Often they are asked to give speeches at various types of events and celebrations. This reflects the fact that universities enjoy a high respect in society. In Finland rectors are in close touch with ministries, especially with the Ministry of Education. Parliament members are also an important group that rectors have contact with. In the Finnish system the universities get most of their financing through the state budget. Therefore ministries and politicians are important to rectors. Recently, however, universities have had to raise more and more money from grants and research contracts. Still today there are no fees for our university students. Furthermore students get every month approximately 400 euros from the state for living and accommodation costs. Universities in Finland have no tuition fees for foreigners either.

The rector's work is very international. In 1988 the Ministry of Education launched an excellent project in the area of internationalisation. One of the goals was that in the long run about a third of Finnish university students should have a possibility to study from half a year to one year at a foreign university during their university studies. The Finnish membership of the European Union in 1995 strongly supported the realization of such goals. When we live more and more in a globalised world, international experience is more and more important to university students.

Rectors should promote the well being of the university in all possible ways. It has been observed that universities are important players more generally in society. In many cases innovative universities have generated enterprises around them. It seems that society expects such results from the universities.

In 1990 I was elected to a second three-year term as rector. This time there was no real competition."

Does one get a very different view of academic life from the Rector's office?

"To my mind it is very different. As rector you have to consider the whole university community, not only one subject, and especially not the particular discipline of the rector."

Was there anything in particular you did or did not like in the Rector's job? What's the weakest point (if any) in university administration?

"The life of a university rector is very hectic. Naturally it is a very difficult fact that is almost impossible to take care of your own research. Time is simply limited. You are not any more the boss of your calendar. The secretary will tell the rector where the rector should be at a certain time. It is minute-by-minute work with a lot of travelling to Helsinki to attend meetings.

When I was rector, the statutes were such that the rector did not have much financial power. So the rector had to convince other decision makers orally. Nowadays things have changed."

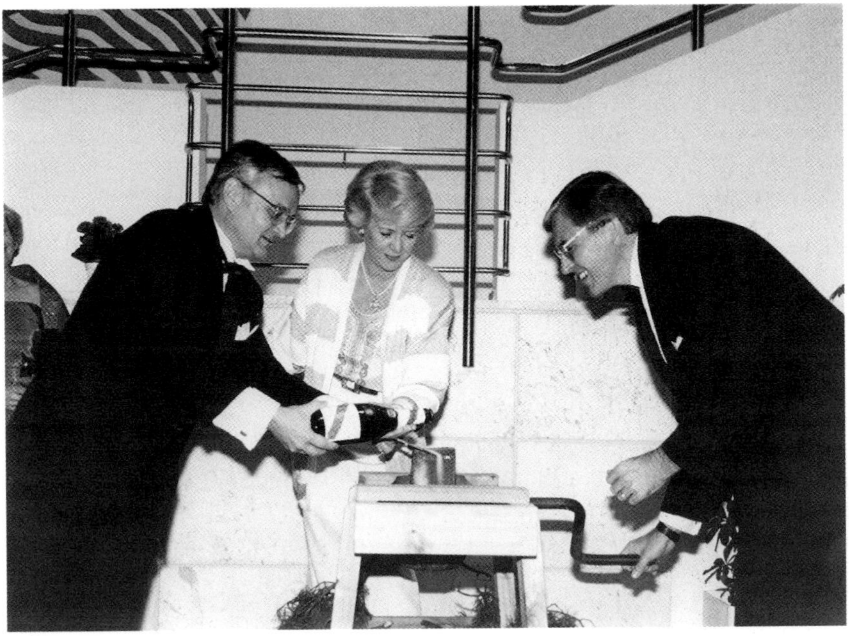

University of Tampere

Figure 18. The doctoral convocation in Tampere in 1990: In the centre: Vigdís Finnbogadóttir (President of Iceland), with Aarre Heino (left) and Tarmo Pukkila.

Jerzy K. Baksalary was visiting Tampere for the academic year 1989–1990. After returning to Poland, he became rector at the University of Zielona Góra. Do you think he was encouraged to accept that job while seeing how you enjoyed the rectorship? You surely talked with Jerzy about his options?

Figure 19. Jerzy K. Baksalary in Dortmund, 2003.

"Professor Baksalary was a very special person. During the year he spent in Tampere, he completed about 40 papers. As far as I know, they have been published in top journals. That is something. He was indeed very efficient in his work.

I do not know whether my rectorship had some effect on Jerzy's rectorship. It is possible. But I may mention one further nice development: Oskar Maria Baksalary, Jerzy's son, spent the academic year 1989–1990 with his parents in Tampere. Then he was just about to start his university studies, and now, over the years he has completed two doctorates (Physics and Mathematics), and I understand that he has been keeping in touch with the Tampere team since then."

One more meeting is particularly important: The International Workshop on Linear Models, Experimental Designs, and Related Matrix Theory that was held in Tampere in August 1990.

"This workshop[4] started a series of annual such events, of which the 15th International Workshop on Matrices and Statistics (IWMS) will take place in Uppsala, Sweden, this June 2006, organised by Professor Dietrich von Rosen. He attended already the 1983 Seminar in Tampere. A small start can lead to lasting events. Often they are called traditions.

When I was the rector I had the possibility to attend a Nordic rectors meeting in Uppsala. It is a very nice city where the University of Tampere has a guest apartment where visitors from Tampere may stay."

And at this 15th IWMS in Uppsala there will be a special session in celebration of your 60th birthday.

[4]Proceedings from this Workshop were published in special issues of *Linear Algebra and its Applications* and the *Journal of Statistical Planning and Inference*, both edited by Jerzy K. Baksakary and George P.H. Styan (1992, 1993).

Figure 20. Sauna Party in Tampere 1990: Can you spot, e.g., Julie Bérubé, Yadolah Dodge, Subir Ghosh, Pentti Huuhtanen, Leena Liski, Monika Pukelsheim, Helena Pukkila, Tarmo Pukkila, C. R. Rao, J. N. Srivastava, Evelyn M. Styan?

Figure 21. Sauna Party in Tampere 1990: Tarmo Pukkila, Ingram Olkin, Dietrich von Rosen, Heinz Neudecker, Erkki Liski, Simo Puntanen, Friedrich Pukelsheim.

University of Tampere

Figure 22. Sauna Party in Tampere 1990: You can find, e.g., Jan Hauke, Yadolah Dodge, Augustyn Markiewicz, Yasunori Fujikoshi, R. Dennis Cook, Tarmo Pukkila, Jorma Merikoski.

To the Ministry of Social Affairs and Health in 1993

Your move to the Ministry of Social Affairs and Health: what's the history behind that?

"In May 1992, I got a phone call from Jorma Huuhtanen, the Minister of Social Affairs and Health. Dr. Jukka Rantala had left the ministry and moved to the position of managing director of Pohjola, a big Finnish insurance company. So the ministry had declared the position of Director General of the Insurance Department open. Minister Huuhtanen asked my opinion on certain candidates for this position. When I met Minister Huuhtanen at the Savonlinna Opera Festival in July 1992, I remembered his phone call in May. I asked him who was selected to the position. He said the position is still open. I was a little surprised. Then at the end of the same year some influential figures contacted me, and they told that I should consider the position. First I said please do not joke! But when they put more and more pressure on me, I finally accepted the offer, and I was appointed to the position in the spring of 1993. However I decided to serve as the Rector to the end of my second term in Tampere. So I started at the Ministry of Social Affairs and Health on August 1, 1993."

How was the beginning of your insurance career?

"A very deep recession hit Finland just before I started at the ministry. The unemployment rate rose very fast from the 1990 figure of 3.5% to almost 20%. I think that it was my second day at the new office that I realized that there was a small life insurance company that will go broke. A couple of weeks later there was a bigger catastrophe waiting around the corner: a whole insurance group was in deep difficulties. In total the first few years as insurance regulator and supervisor meant that I had to take care of six bankruptcies of insurance companies. I remember a discussion with a foreign rector colleague at a meeting when I mentioned that I will start as the insurance supervisor in the beginning of August 1993. He said that I will jump from the frying pan into the fire. I think that broadly speaking he was right."

Can you tell us about the duties of insurance supervision.

"As has become clear, besides the preparation of insurance legislation in 1993, insurance supervision was one of the tasks of the insurance department. In 1999 the Insurance Supervisory Authority was created under the Ministry of Social Affairs and Health. In its decision making concerning supervisory activities, the Insurance Supervisory Authority is independent from the Ministry. Since 1999 I have acted as the chairman of the board of the Insurance Supervisory Authority. Besides that, since 1993 I have been a member of the board of the Financial Supervisory Authority. This means that I have had an excellent possibility to see very closely the supervision of the areas of insurance, banking and securities.

The Insurance department has a very broad area of responsibility to take care of. The department has responsibility for private and social insurance. On the private side the department takes care of the development on of the legislation concerning insurance companies, pension funds, pension foundation, sickness insurance fund, work pension insurance companies, unemployment funds, traffic insurance and patient insurance. On the social side the department takes care of the development of the legislation concerning basic pensions, statutory work pension, accident at work insurance, sickness insurance and unemployment insurance.

After Finland became a member of the European Union, a very close cooperation started. In the European Union, free insurance markets has been created. These markets are based on one licence and on home country supervision. That also means that the legislation concerning such markets is created at the Union level. The new legislation created in this way must be implemented in the legislation of each individual member state."

Any particular research topic that you find important these days?

"One of the biggest challenges of practically all countries is the ageing of the population. In Finland the number of 65 year-old people is about 800,000. By

Figure 23. The doctoral convocation in Tampere in 2000: men in black, Tarmo Pukkila, Simo Puntanen, George P.H. Styan, Erkki Liski, Pentti Huuhtanen, Tapio Nummi, Lasse Koskinen.

the year 2030 this figure will grow by 600,000 to about 1.4 million. It is clear that that kind of development will have a tremendous effect on pensions, health care and old age care systems. But the implications of aging are much deeper than those mentioned. Aging will have its effect on economic growth. It will change the consumption structure of people. Therefore it will probably change also the industrial structure in many countries.

But it is strange that the academic world has not done enough research in this area. That is a pity! Aging is only one important topic that will have a deep impact in all societies.

I hope that one day I will be able to come back to research again. If that would be possible, I would know pretty well what to do according to my research plan. There is really a lot to do."

How does academic life look from the Ministry's office?

"It is interesting to know that we do a lot of research at the Insurance Department of the Ministry. One important topic is the investment strategy of pension assets. There are really a lot of other important research problems in this area. This means that I highly appreciate research work. We cooperate continuously with academic researchers.

The main task of a ministry is the preparation of legislation. The preparation of legislation has a strict and limited timetable. This also means that there is a big difference between the work at a university and the work done at a ministry. A university researcher can work with a problem for years and years. At a ministry that kind of timetable is not possible. I hope that universities would offer solutions to practical problems more than they do nowadays."

What about your leisure time? Any particular hobbies that attract you?

"Unfortunately my leisure time is rather limited. But when I have time I read a lot. I think that the only way to survive in this kind of job is physical training. In summers I bike a lot. In winter I ski as much as possible. I think that cross-country skiing is simply the best form of physical exercise. My present work offers exceptionally good possibilities to travel abroad. That is one of the richnesses of my work."

Acknowledgements

We are most grateful to Tarmo Mikko Pukkila for answering all our questions about his life and work. Special thanks go to Helena Pukkila for her help. Thanks go also to Ilkka and Klaus Haikala, Sami Helle, Antti Penttinen, Soile Puntanen, and Evelyn M. Styan for their help. This research was supported, in part, by the Natural Sciences and Engineering Research Council of Canada.

References

Baksalary, Jerzy K. and Styan, George P. H., eds. (1992). Third Special Issue on Linear Algebra and Statistics. *Linear Algebra and its Applications*, 176, viii + pp. 1-289.

Baksalary, Jerzy K. and Styan, George P. H., eds. (1993). Special issue, papers presented at the International Workshop on Linear Models, Experimental Designs, and Related Matrix Theory. *Journal of Statistical Planning and Inference*, 36 (2,3), ii + pp. 127-432.

Baksalary, O. M. and Styan, G. P. H., eds. (2005). Some comments on the life and publications of Jerzy K. Baksalary (1944-2005). *Linear Algebra and its Applications*, 410, 3-53.

Blom, Gunnar (1987). Harald Cramér 1893-1985. *The Annals of Statistics*, 15, 1335-1350.

Box, George E. P. and Jenkins, Gwilym M. (1970). *Time Series Analysis: Forecasting and Control.* San Francisco: Holden-Day. [Third edition by George E. P. Box, Gwilym M. Jenkins and Gregory C. Reinsel, pub. Prentice Hall, Englewood Cliffs, NJ, 1994.]

Cramér, Harald (1945). *Mathematical Methods of Statistics.* Uppsala: Almqvist & Wiksell. [Paperback reprint edition: Princeton Landmarks in Mathematics and Physics Series, 1999.]

DeGroot, Morris H. (1986). A conversation with T. W. Anderson, *Statistical Science*, 1, 97-105. [Reprinted in *The Collected Papers of T. W. Anderson: 1943-1985* (George P. H. Styan, ed.), vol. 1, pp. xxxv-xliii.]

Pukkila, Tarmo and Puntanen, Simo, eds. (1985). *Proceedings of the First International Tampere Seminar on Linear Statistical Models and Their Applications: University of Tampere, August 30th to September 2nd, 1983.* Report No. A 138, Department of Mathematical Sciences/Statistics, University of Tampere, x + 351 pp.

Pukkila, Tarmo and Puntanen, Simo, eds. (1987). *Proceedings of the Second International Tampere Conference in Statistics: University of Tampere, 1–4 June 1987.* Report No. A 184, Department of Mathematical Sciences/Statistics, University of Tampere, xi + 708 pp.

Puntanen, Simo and Styan, George P. H. (2006). Some comments on the research publications of Tarmo Mikko Pukkila. In *Festschrift for Tarmo Pukkila on his 60th Birthday* (Erkki P. Liski, Jarmo Niemelä, Jarkko Isotalo, Simo Puntanen, and George P. H. Styan, eds.), Dept. of Mathematics, Statistics and Philosophy, University of Tampere, pp. 45–62.

SIMO PUNTANEN
Department of Mathematics, Statistics and Philosophy
FI-33014 University of Tampere, Finland
sjp@uta.fi
http://www.uta.fi/~sjp/

GEORGE P. H. STYAN
Department of Mathematics and Statistics
McGill University, Burnside Hall Room 1005
805 rue Sherbrooke Street West
Montréal (Québec), Canada H3A 2K6
styan@math.mcgill.ca
http://www.math.mcgill.ca/styan/

Festschrift for Tarmo Pukkila on his 60th Birthday
Eds. E. P. Liski, J. Isotalo, J. Niemelä, S. Puntanen, and G. P. H. Styan

Univ. of Tampere, 2006, ISBN 978-951-44-6620-5, pages 45–62

Some comments on the research publications of Tarmo Mikko Pukkila

SIMO PUNTANEN & GEORGE P. H. STYAN

Abstract. We comment on 62 research publications by Tarmo Mikko Pukkila, dated from 1977 through 2004, and identify his 27 coauthors. These 62 publications, which are mainly in time series analysis and statistical computing, are listed with annotations. Following Baksalary and Styan (2005), we define an "authorship matrix" $\mathbf{A} = \{a_{ij}\}$, where $a_{ij} = 1$ if bibliographic entry number i is written with coauthor number j and $a_{ij} = 0$ otherwise. We find that the (doubly-reduced) authorship matrix $\mathbf{A}$ for Tarmo Pukkila is 34×19 and that the matrix $\mathbf{B} = \mathbf{A}'\mathbf{A}$ is reducible and identify four distinct groups of coauthors, which are not linked. The article ends with comments on the eigenvalues and eigenvectors of $\mathbf{B}$.

2000 MSC codes: 01A60, 01A61, 62-03.

Key words and phrases: Authorship matrix; Bibliography; Bibliometrics; Eigenvalues; Eigenvectors; Reducibility; Statistical computing; Time series analysis.

Introduction

Listed in Appendix 1 below are 62 research publications by Tarmo Mikko Pukkila (b. 1946), published from 1977–2004. These publications, which are mainly in time series analysis and statistical computing, include 5 books, 30 articles (plus 2 correction notes [18] and [33]) in research journals, and 24 articles in research collections or edited books. The article [31], originally published in a research journal, has been reprinted in a research collection as [36]. English translations of the titles of the three publications in Finnish are also given in Appendix 1. These 62 publications are arranged chronologically in Appendix 1, and by journal/research collection within year. For entries reviewed by *Mathematical Reviews/MathSciNet* (MR) and/or *Zentralblatt MATH* (Zbl), the review number is given, and for signed reviews, we also give the name of the reviewer.

The 18 research journals in which Tarmo Pukkila has published are listed in Appendix 2 and the 22 research collections/edited books in Appendix 3. Of the 62 publications listed in Appendix 1, 43 are authored jointly with others: there are 27 coauthors (see list in Table 1), of which 8 (identified with group code X) wrote with Pukkila on their own and so as the sole coauthor. This leaves 19 coauthors with 34 entries in Appendix 1.

Table 1. Tarmo Pukkila's 27 coauthors.

Jerzy K. Baksalary	1	Jorma K. Merikoski	1
Heikki Bonsdorff	1	Jukka Nyblom	1
Jan G. De Gooijer	1	Hans Nyqvist	1
Matti Hakama	1	Teivo Pentikäinen	1
Pentti Huuhtanen	2	Martti Pesonen	1
Arto Kallinen	4	Simo Puntanen	10
C. G. Khatri	1	Antero Ranne	2
Sergio G. Koreisha	17	Jukka Rantala	1
Lasse Koskinen	1	C. Radhakrishna Rao	2
Paruchuri R. Krishnaiah	2	Matti Ruohonen	1
Eija-Riitta Lauri	1	Simo Sarvamaa	2
Erkki P. Liski	2	O. Stenman	1
Olavi Manninen	1	Erkki Vilkman	1
Pentti Manninen	1		

We define an "authorship matrix" $\mathbf{A} = \{a_{ij}\}$ as introduced by Oskar Maria Baksalary and Styan (2005) in an article about the life and publications of Jerzy K. Baksalary (1944–2005). This authorship matrix is defined by $a_{ij} = 1$ if bibliographic entry number i is written with coauthor number j and $a_{ij} = 0$ otherwise.

The (doubly-reduced) authorship matrix $\mathbf{A}$ for Tarmo Pukkila 34×19 and is given in Table 2, with the 19×19 matrix $\mathbf{A}'\mathbf{A} = \mathbf{B}$, say, in Table 3a. The diagonal entry b_{jj} of $\mathbf{B}$ represents the numbers of bibliographic entries written with coauthor j $(= 1, \dots, 19)$, while for $j \neq k$ the entry b_{jk} gives the number of entries written with coauthors j and k $(j, k = 1, \dots, 19$ with $j \neq k)$. When $b_{jk} \geq 1$ we say that coauthors j and k are linked, and these linkages are illustrated in Figure 1. We note that the 19 coauthors form four distinct groups, with no linkage between the groups. We denote these four groups as follows:

A: Bonsdorff, Pentikäinen, Pesonen, Ranne, Rantala, Ruohonen, Sarvamaa,

B: Huuhtanen, Kallinen, Koreisha, Liski, Pentti Manninen, Puntanen, Stenman,

C: Khatri, Rao,

D: Lauri, Olavi Manninen, Vilkman.

Table 2. The 34×19 (doubly-reduced) authorship matrix **A**.

publication no.	Bonsdorff	Huuhtanen	Kallinen	Khatri	Koreisha	Lauri	Liski	Olavi Manninen	Pentti Manninen	Pentikäinen	Pesonen	Puntanen	Ranne	Rantala	Rao	Ruohonen	Sarvamaa	Stenman	Vilkman	no of coauthors
6												1								1
7												1								1
10		1	1				1		1			1								5
11												1								1
12												1								1
16		1					1					1								3
20												1						1		2
22												1								1
23												1								1
24					1															1
25												1								1
26			1																	1
27						1		1											1	3
30															1					1
32					1															1
34				1											1					2
35					1															1
38			1		1															2
39					1															1
42					1															1
43			1																	1
46					1															1
47					1															1
49	1									1	1		1	1		1	1			7
50													1				1			2
52					1															1
53					1															1
54					1															1
56					1															1
57					1															1
58					1															1
59					1															1
60					1															1
62					1															1
total	1	2	4	1	17	1	2	1	1	1	1	10	2	1	2	1	2	1	1	52

Table 3a. The 19×19 matrix $\mathbf{B} = \mathbf{A}'\mathbf{A}$, where $\mathbf{A}$ is the 34×19 (doubly-reduced) authorship matrix.

		coauthor #	1	2	3	4	5	6	7	8	9	10	11	12	13	14	15	16	17	18	19
coau-		group	A	B	B	C	B	D	B	D	B	A	A	B	A	A	C	A	A	B	D
thor #	group	coauthor	Bon	Huu	Kal	Kha	Kor	Lau	Lis	OM	PM	Pen	Pes	Pun	Ran	Rant	Rao	Ruo	Sar	Ste	Vil
1	A	Bonsdorff	**1**	0	0	0	0	0	0	0	0	1	1	0	1	1	0	1	1	0	0
2	B	Huuhtanen	0	**2**	1	0	0	0	2	0	1	0	0	2	0	0	0	0	0	0	0
3	B	Kallinen	0	1	**4**	0	1	0	1	0	1	0	0	1	0	0	0	0	0	0	0
4	C	Khatri	0	0	0	**1**	0	0	0	0	0	0	0	0	0	0	1	0	0	0	0
5	B	Koreisha	0	0	1	0	**17**	0	0	0	0	0	0	0	0	0	0	0	0	0	0
6	D	Lauri	0	0	0	0	0	**1**	0	1	0	0	0	0	0	0	0	0	0	0	1
7	B	Liski	0	2	1	0	0	0	**2**	0	1	0	0	2	0	0	0	0	0	0	0
8	D	Olavi Manninen	0	0	0	0	0	1	0	**1**	0	0	0	0	0	0	0	0	0	0	1
9	B	Pentti Manninen	0	1	1	0	0	0	1	0	**1**	0	0	1	0	0	0	0	0	0	0
10	A	Pentikäinen	1	0	0	0	0	0	0	0	0	**1**	1	0	1	1	0	1	1	0	0
11	A	Pesonen	1	0	0	0	0	0	0	0	0	1	**1**	0	1	1	0	1	1	0	0
12	B	Puntanen	0	2	1	0	0	0	2	0	1	0	0	**10**	0	0	0	0	0	1	0
13	A	Ranne	1	0	0	0	0	0	0	0	0	1	1	0	**2**	1	0	1	2	0	0
14	A	Rantala	1	0	0	0	0	0	0	0	0	1	1	0	1	**1**	0	1	1	0	0
15	C	Rao	0	0	0	1	0	0	0	0	0	0	0	0	0	0	**2**	0	0	0	0
16	A	Ruohonen	1	0	0	0	0	0	0	0	0	1	1	0	1	1	0	**1**	1	0	0
17	A	Sarvamaa	1	0	0	0	0	0	0	0	0	1	1	0	2	1	0	1	**2**	0	0
18	B	Stenman	0	0	0	0	0	0	0	0	0	0	0	1	0	0	0	0	0	**1**	0
19	D	Vilkman	0	0	0	0	0	1	0	1	0	0	0	0	0	0	0	0	0	0	**1**

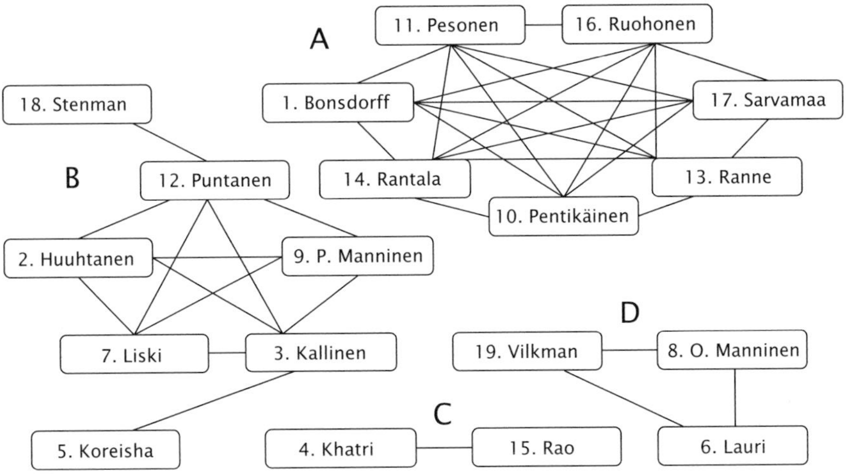

Figure 1. Linkage between Tarmo Pukkila's coauthors and the 4 groups.

Figure 2. C.R. Rao and Tarmo Pukkila thinking of a serious problem in Pittsburgh in May 1986.

Figure 3. Tampere 1987: Tarmo Pukkila and C. G. Khatri exploring photos.

In Table 3b we present the 19×19 matrix $\mathbf{B}$ with the coauthors arranged by group. We write

$$\mathbf{B} = \begin{pmatrix} \mathbf{B}_{\mathrm{A}} & \mathbf{0} & \mathbf{0} & \mathbf{0} \\ \mathbf{0} & \mathbf{B}_{\mathrm{B}} & \mathbf{0} & \mathbf{0} \\ \mathbf{0} & \mathbf{0} & \mathbf{B}_{\mathrm{C}} & \mathbf{0} \\ \mathbf{0} & \mathbf{0} & \mathbf{0} & \mathbf{B}_{\mathrm{D}} \end{pmatrix},$$

where $\mathbf{B}_{\mathrm{A}}$ is 7×7, $\mathbf{B}_{\mathrm{B}}$ is 7×7, $\mathbf{B}_{\mathrm{C}}$ is 2×2, $\mathbf{B}_{\mathrm{D}}$ is 3×3.

In Table 4 we present the 11 nonzero eigenvalues and corresponding eigenvectors of $\mathbf{B}$ (to 4 decimal places), which we computed using the computing environment R due to Ihaka and Gentleman (1996). We note that corresponding to Group A: Bonsdorff, Pentikäinen, Pesonen, Ranne, Rantala, Ruohonen, Sarvamaa, we have

$$\mathbf{B}_{\mathrm{A}} = \begin{pmatrix} 1 & 1 & 1 & 1 & 1 & 1 & 1 \\ 1 & 1 & 1 & 1 & 1 & 1 & 1 \\ 1 & 1 & 1 & 1 & 1 & 1 & 1 \\ 1 & 1 & 1 & 2 & 1 & 1 & 2 \\ 1 & 1 & 1 & 1 & 1 & 1 & 1 \\ 1 & 1 & 1 & 1 & 1 & 1 & 1 \\ 1 & 1 & 1 & 2 & 1 & 1 & 2 \end{pmatrix} = \begin{pmatrix} 1 & 1 \\ 1 & 1 \\ 1 & 1 \\ 1 & 2 \\ 1 & 1 \\ 1 & 1 \\ 1 & 2 \end{pmatrix} \begin{pmatrix} 1 & 1 & 1 & 0 & 1 & 1 & 0 \\ 0 & 0 & 0 & 1 & 0 & 0 & 1 \end{pmatrix},$$

Table 3b. The rearranged 19 × 19 matrix **B** (from Table 3a).

		coauthor #	1	10	11	13	14	16	17	2	3	5	7	9	12	18	4	15	6	8	19
coau-		group	A	A	A	A	A	A	A	B	B	B	B	B	B	B	C	C	D	D	D
thor #	group	coauthor	Bon	Pen	Pes	Ran	Rant	Ruo	Sar	Huu	Kal	Kor	Lis	PM	Pun	Ste	Kha	Rao	Lau	OM	Vil
1	A	Bonsdorff	1	1	1	1	1	1	1	0	0	0	0	0	0	0	0	0	0	0	0
10	A	Pentikäinen	1	1	1	1	1	1	1	0	0	0	0	0	0	0	0	0	0	0	0
11	A	Pesonen	1	1	1	1	1	1	1	0	0	0	0	0	0	0	0	0	0	0	0
13	A	Ranne	1	1	1	2	1	1	2	0	0	0	0	0	0	0	0	0	0	0	0
14	A	Rantala	1	1	1	1	1	1	1	0	0	0	0	0	0	0	0	0	0	0	0
16	A	Ruohonen	1	1	1	1	1	1	1	0	0	0	0	0	0	0	0	0	0	0	0
17	A	Sarvamaa	1	1	1	2	1	1	2	0	0	0	0	0	0	0	0	0	0	0	0
2	B	Huuhtanen	0	0	0	0	0	0	0	2	1	0	2	1	2	0	0	0	0	0	0
3	B	Kallinen	0	0	0	0	0	0	0	1	4	1	1	1	1	0	0	0	0	0	0
5	B	Koreisha	0	0	0	0	0	0	0	0	1	17	0	0	0	0	0	0	0	0	0
7	B	Liski	0	0	0	0	0	0	0	2	1	0	2	1	2	0	0	0	0	0	0
9	B	Pentti Manninen	0	0	0	0	0	0	0	1	1	0	1	1	1	0	0	0	0	0	0
12	B	Puntanen	0	0	0	0	0	0	0	2	1	0	2	1	10	1	0	0	0	0	0
18	B	Stenman	0	0	0	0	0	0	0	0	0	0	0	0	1	1	0	0	0	0	0
4	C	Khatri	0	0	0	0	0	0	0	0	0	0	0	0	0	0	1	1	0	0	0
15	C	Rao	0	0	0	0	0	0	0	0	0	0	0	0	0	0	1	2	0	0	0
6	D	Lauri	0	0	0	0	0	0	0	0	0	0	0	0	0	0	0	0	1	1	1
8	D	Olavi Manninen	0	0	0	0	0	0	0	0	0	0	0	0	0	0	0	0	1	1	1
19	D	Vilkman	0	0	0	0	0	0	0	0	0	0	0	0	0	0	0	0	1	1	1

which has the same nonzero eigenvalues as

$$\begin{pmatrix} 1 & 1 & 1 & 0 & 1 & 1 & 0 \\ 0 & 0 & 0 & 1 & 0 & 0 & 1 \end{pmatrix} \begin{pmatrix} 1 & 1 \\ 1 & 1 \\ 1 & 1 \\ 1 & 2 \\ 1 & 1 \\ 1 & 1 \\ 1 & 2 \end{pmatrix} = \begin{pmatrix} 5 & 5 \\ 2 & 4 \end{pmatrix},$$

which are $\frac{1}{2}(9 \pm \sqrt{41}) \approx 7.7016, 1.2984$.

Corresponding to Group B: Huuhtanen, Kallinen, Koreisha, Liski, Pentti Manninen, Puntanen, Stenman, we have

$$\mathbf{B}_{\mathrm{B}} = \begin{pmatrix} 2 & 1 & 0 & 2 & 1 & 2 & 0 \\ 1 & 4 & 1 & 1 & 1 & 1 & 0 \\ 0 & 1 & 17 & 0 & 0 & 0 & 0 \\ 2 & 1 & 0 & 2 & 1 & 2 & 0 \\ 1 & 1 & 0 & 1 & 1 & 1 & 0 \\ 2 & 1 & 0 & 2 & 1 & 10 & 1 \\ 0 & 0 & 0 & 0 & 0 & 1 & 1 \end{pmatrix}.$$

We find that $\mathbf{B}_{\mathrm{B}}$ has rank 6 (and hence nullity 1), and nonzero eigenvalues (see Table 4) equal to 17.0798, 11.7322, 4.6107, 2.3474, 0.8503, 0.3796 (to 4 decimal places). We have not found an easy way to compute these eigenvalues but it is clear that has rank at most equal to 6 since rows 1 and 4 are identical.

Corresponding to Group C: Khatri, Rao, and to Group D: Lauri, Olavi Manninen, Vilkman, we have

$$\mathbf{B}_{\mathrm{C}} = \begin{pmatrix} 1 & 1 \\ 1 & 2 \end{pmatrix}, \quad \mathbf{B}_{\mathrm{D}} = \begin{pmatrix} 1 & 1 & 1 \\ 1 & 1 & 1 \\ 1 & 1 & 1 \end{pmatrix}.$$

It is very easy to see that $\mathbf{B}_{\mathrm{C}}$ has eigenvalues equal to $\frac{1}{2}(3 \pm \sqrt{5}) \approx 2.6180$, 0.3820 and that $\mathbf{B}_{\mathrm{D}}$ has rank equal to 1 with the single nonzero eigenvalue equal to 3.

In Table 4 we assemble the 11 nonzero eigenvalues of $\mathbf{B}$ in nonincreasing order and present corresponding eigenvectors. For each eigenvector we identify the entry with the largest absolute value and the corresponding coauthor, with whom we associate the eigenvalue. As we see in Table 4, there is a strong (but not perfect) correspondence with the number of joint publications. Within groups, however, the correspondence is essentially perfect.

Table 4. Eigenvalues and eigenvectors associated with Tarmo Pukkila's (doubly-reduced) authorship matrix.

group	eigenvalues	17.0798	11.7322	7.7016	4.6107	3	2.6180	2.3474	1.2984	0.8503	0.3820	0.3796
A	Bonsdorff			−0.3400					−0.2905			
A	Pentikäinen			−0.3400					0.2905			
A	Pesonen			−0.3400					−0.2905			
A	Ranne			−0.4593					0.5376			
A	Rantala			−0.3400					−0.2905			
A	Ruohonen			−0.3400					−0.2905			
A	Sarvamaa			−0.4593					0.5376			
B	Huuhtanen	−0.0093	−0.2738		0.3216			−0.5127		0.0814		0.2281
B	Kallinen	−0.0795	−0.1997		0.7354			0.6270		0.0255		0.1388
B	Koreisha	−0.9966	0.0379		−0.0594			−0.0428		0.0016		−0.0083
B	Liski	−0.0093	−0.2738		0.3216			−0.5127		0.0814		0.2281
B	Pentti Manninen	−0.0072	−0.1519		0.2698			−0.1561		0.0625		−0.9359
B	Puntanen	−0.0177	−0.8826		−0.4044			0.1882		0.1468		−0.0144
B	Stenman	−0.0011	−0.0822		−0.1120			0.1397		0.9801		0.0232
C	Khatri						0.5257				0.8507	
C	Rao						0.8507				−0.5257	
D	Lauri					−0.5774						
D	Olavi Manninen					−0.5774						
D	Vilkman					−0.5774						

Table 4. Continued.

eigenvalues	associated coauthor estimated from eigenvector	coauthor group	number of joint publications with Tarmo Pukkila
17.0798	Koreisha	B	17
11.7322	Puntanen	B	10
7.7016	Ranne, Sarvamaa	A	2, 2
4.6107	Kallinen	B	4
3	Lauri, Olavi Manninen, Vilkman	D	1, 1, 1
2.6180	Rao	C	2
2.3474	Kallinen	B	4
1.2984	Ranne, Sarvamaa	A	2, 2
0.8503	Stenman	B	1
0.3820	Khatri	C	1
0.3796	Pentti Manninen	B	1

Table 4. Continued.

group	eigenvalues	dimension	rank
A	7.7016, 1.2984, 0 (mult. 5)	7	2
B	17.0797, 11.7322, 4.6107, 2.3474, 0.8503, 0.3796, 0	7	6
C	0.382, 2.618	2	2
D	3, 0 (mult. 2)	3	1

Appendix 1. Annotated complete list of research publications by Tarmo M. Pukkila

[1] Tarmo Pukkila (1977). *Fitting of Autoregressive Moving Average Models in the Frequency Domain.* Report No. A 6, Department of Mathematical Sciences, University of Tampere, 129 pp.

[2] T. Pukkila (1978). The utilization of the computer in the teaching of statistics at elementary level. In *COMPSTAT 1978 Proceedings in Computational Statistics: 3rd Symposium held in Leiden 1978*, Physica-Verlag, Vienna, pp. 422–428.

[3] Tarmo Pukkila (1978). Kunnan väkilukuennusteen laatiminen Boxin ja Jenkinsin mentelmällä [Population forecasting using the Box–Jenkins method]. *Kunnallistieteellinen Aikakauskirja*, 2, 22–45.

[4] T. Pukkila (1979). The bias in periodogram ordinates and the estimation of ARMA models in the frequency domain. *Australian Journal of Statistics*, 21 (2), 121–128. [MR547387 (81a:62095), Peter M. Robinson.]

[5] Tarmo Pukkila (1979). *On the Identification of Transfer Function Noise Models with Several Correlated Input Processes Using Frequency Domain Tools.* Acta Universitatis Tamperensis, Series A 110, University of Tampere, [4] + 136 pp. [MR566956 (81d:62103), G. Tintner.]

[6] Tarmo Pukkila, Simo Puntanen (1979). Interactive use of the computer for first university level statistical courses. In *Interactivnye Sistemy Sovetsko-Finskij Simpozium (Tbilisi, 24–27 October 1979), Part II*, Georgian SSR Academy of Sciences (USSR Academy of Sciences) Computing Centre, Moscow, pp. 271–285.

[7] T. Pukkila, S. Puntanen (1980). Computer usage on first statistics courses in the University of Tampere. In *COMPSTAT 1980 Proceedings in Computational Statistics: 4th Symposium held at Edinburgh 1980*, Physica-Verlag, Vienna, pp. 145–151. (Session E1/first paper Education.)

[8] T. Pukkila (1980). Time series analytical operations of SURVO/71. In *COMPSTAT 1980 Proceedings in Computational Statistics: 4th Symposium held at Edinburgh 1980*, Physica-Verlag, Vienna, pp. 602–608. (Session Tl/third paper: Time series analysis.)

[9] Matti Hakama, Tarmo Pukkila (1980). Miesten keuhkosyöpäinsidenssi Suomessa vuonna 2000 [Prediction of lung cancer incidence for men in Finland in the year 2000]. *Duodecim: Lääketieteellinen Aikakauskirja*, 96, 1139–1144.

[10] Pentti Huuhtanen, Arto Kallinen, Erkki P. Liski, Pentti Manninen, Tarmo Pukkila, Simo Puntanen (1980). Tilastotieteen opetuksesta ja tutkimuksesta [On research and teaching of statistics]. In *Juhlakirja Tampereen Yliopiston Taloudellis-Hallinnollisen Tiedekunnan Täyttäessä 15 Vuotta*, Acta Universitatis Tamperensis, Series A 120, University of Tampere, pp. 293–299.

[11] Tarmo Pukkila, Simo Puntanen (1981). The computer as an aid in teaching basic statistics courses at university level. In *Computers in Education: Proceedings of the 3rd World Conference on Computers in Education (IFIP TC-3), Lausanne, Switzerland, July 27–31, 1981*, North-Holland, Amsterdam, pp. 149–156.

[12] Tarmo Pukkila, Simo Puntanen (1982). The use of MATRIX, an interactive computer system for the analysis of matrices, in the teaching of statistics. In *COMPSTAT 1982 Proceedings in Computational Statistics: 5th symposium held at Toulouse, 1982, Part II (Supplement): Short Communications, Summaries of Posters*, Physica-Verlag, Vienna, pp. 223–224.

[13] Tarmo Pukkila (1982). On the identification of transfer function noise models with several correlated inputs. *Scandinavian Journal of Statistics*, 9 (3), 139–146. [MR680909 (84b:62145); Zbl 0508.62080.]

[14] Tarmo M. Pukkila (1982). On the identification of ARMA(p,q) models. In *Time Series Analysis Theory and Practice 1: Proceedings of the International Conference held at Valencia, Spain, June 1981*, North-Holland, Amsterdam, pp. 81–103. [Zbl 0489.62082.]

[15] J.K. Merikoski, T.M. Pukkila (1983). A note on the expectation of products of autocorrelations. *Biometrika*, 70 (2), 528–529. [MR712046 (84m:62116); Zbl 0533.62083.] (Amendment and correction: [19].)

[16] Pentti Huuhtanen, Erkki Liski, Tarmo Pukkila, Simo Puntanen (editorial board) (1983). *Festschrift for Eino Haikala on his Seventieth Birthday.* Acta Universitatis Tamperensis, Series A 153, Department of Mathematical Sciences/Statistics, University of Tampere, xiv + 166 pp.

[17] Tarmo Pukkila (1983). On some practical problems in the identification of transfer function noise models with several correlated inputs. In *Festschrift for Eino Haikala on his Seventieth Birthday*, Acta Universitatis Tamperensis, Series A 153, University of Tampere, pp. 103–117.

[18] J.K. Merikoski, T.M. Pukkila (1984). Amendment and correction to [15]: "A note on the expectation of products of autocorrelations". *Biometrika*, 71 (3), 655.

[19] Tarmo Pukkila (1984). On the distributions of the differences between the estimated autocorrelations and partial autocorrelations at the same lag. *Communications in Statistics: Simulation and Computation*, 13 (4), 463–488.

[20] T. Pukkila, S. Puntanen, O. Stenman (1984). On the possibilities to automate the study of statistical dependence between two variables. In *COMPSTAT 1984 Proceedings in Computational Statistics: 6th Symposium held at Prague 1984, Papers*, Physica-Verlag, Vienna, pp. 249–254.

[21] Tarmo Pukkila, Hans Nyquist (1985). On the frequency domain estimation of the innovation variance of a stationary univariate time series. *Biometrika*, 72 (2), 317-323. [Zbl 0571.62084.]

[22] Tarmo Pukkila, Simo Puntanen (eds.) (1985). *Proceedings of the First International Tampere Seminar on Linear Statistical Models and Their Applications: University of Tampere, August 30th to September 2nd, 1983.* Report No. A 138, Department of Mathematical Sciences/Statistics, University of Tampere, x + 351 pp.

[23] Tarmo Pukkila, Simo Puntanen (1986). The role of the computer in the teaching of statistics. In *Proceedings: The Second International Conference on Teaching Statistics (11–16 August 1986)*, University of Victoria, pp. 163–167.

[24] S.G. Koreisha, T.M. Pukkila (1987). Identification of nonzero elements in the polynomial matrices of mixed VARMA processes. *Journal of the Royal Statistical Society, Series B: Methodological*, 49 (1), 112–126. [Zbl 0615.62116.] (Corrigendum: [33].)

[25] Tarmo Pukkila, Simo Puntanen (eds.) (1987). *Proceedings of the Second International Tampere Conference in Statistics: University of Tampere, 1–4 June 1987.* Report No. A 184, Department of Mathematical Sciences/Statistics, University of Tampere, xi + 708 pp.

[26] Tarmo Pukkila, Arto Kallinen (1987). On the order determination of time series models. In *Proceedings of the Second International Tampere Conference in Statistics: University of Tampere, 1–4 June 1987*, Report No. A 184, Department of Mathematical Sciences/Statistics, University of Tampere, pp. 275–288.

[27] Erkki Vilkman, Olavi Manninen, Eija-Riitta Lauri, Tarmo Pukkila (1987). Vocal jitter as an indicator of changes in psychophysiological arousal (Po 1.7: Acoustics of speech-produced under different circumstances). In *Proceedings XIth ICPhS: The Eleventh International Congress of Phonetic Sciences, August 1–7, 1987, Tallinn, Estonia, U.S.S.R.*, Institute of Language and Literature, Academy of Sciences of the Estonian S.S.R., Tallinn, pp. 188–191.

[28] Tarmo M. Pukkila, Paruchuri R. Krishnaiah (1988). On the use of autoregressive order determination criteria in univariate white noise tests. *IEEE Transactions on Acoustics, Speech, and Signal Processing*, 36 (5), 764–774.

[29] Tarmo M. Pukkila, Paruchuri R. Krishnaiah (1988). On the use of autoregressive order determination criteria in multivariate white noise tests. *IEEE Transactions on Acoustics, Speech, and Signal Processing*, 36 (9), 1396–1403. [Zbl 0656.62099.] (Author's reply to Comments by Sverre Holm: [41].)

[30] Tarmo M. Pukkila, C. Radhakrishna Rao (1988). Pattern recognition based on scale invariant discriminant functions. *Information Sciences: An International Journal*, 45 (3), 379–389. [MR952440; Zbl 0652.62055.]

[31] Tarmo M. Pukkila (1988). An improved estimation method for univariate autoregressive models. *Journal of Multivariate Analysis*, 27 (2), 422–433. [MR970964; Zbl 0659.62108.] (Reprinted as [36].)

[32] Sergio Koreisha, Tarmo Pukkila (1988). Estimation of the polynomial matrices of vector moving average processes. *Journal of Statistical Computation and Simulation*, 28 (4), 313–343. [MR969453 (90k:62192).]

[33] S. G. Koreisha, T. M. Pukkila (1988). Corrigendum to [24]: "Identification of nonzero elements in the polynomial matrices of mixed VARMA processes". *Journal of the Royal Statistical Society, Series B: Methodological*, 50 (1), 155.

[34] C. G. Khatri, T. M. Pukkila, C. Radhakrishna Rao (1989). Testing intraclass correlation coefficients. *Communications in Statistics: Simulation and Computation*, 18 (1), 15–30. [MR1000030 (90f:62178).]

[35] Sergio Koreisha, Tarmo Pukkila (1989). Fast linear estimation methods for vector autoregressive moving-average models. *Journal of Time Series Analysis*, 10 (4), 325–339. [MR1038466; Zbl 0686.62071.]

[36] Tarmo M. Pukkila (1989). An improved estimation method for univariate autoregressive models. In *Multivariate Statistics and Probability: Essays in Memory of Paruchuri R. Krishnaiah*, Academic Press, San Diego, pp. 422–433. [Zbl 0697.62085.] (Reprint of [31].)

[37] Tarmo M. Pukkila (1989). Joint determination of autoregressive order and degree of differencing. In *Statistical Data Analysis and Inference*, Elsevier Science, Amsterdam, pp. 519–531. [MR1089660.]

[38] Tarmo Pukkila, Sergio Koreisha, Arto Kallinen (1990). The identification of ARMA models. *Biometrika*, 77 (3), 537–548. [MR1087844 (91m:62167).]

[39] Sergio Koreisha, Tarmo Pukkila (1990). Linear methods for estimating ARMA and regression models with serial correlation. *Communications in Statistics: Simulation and Computation*, 19 (1), 71–102. [MR1066986; Zbl 0707.62184.]

[40] Tarmo M. Pukkila (1990). The estimation of the variances of sample autocorrelations. *Gujarat Statistical Review*, 17A (Professor Khatri Memorial Volume), 160–168.

[41] Tarmo M. Pukkila (1990). Author's reply to "Comments" by Sverre Holm on [29]: "On the use of autoregressive order determination criteria in univariate white noise tests". *IEEE Transactions on Acoustics, Speech, and Signal Processing*, 38 (10), 1805–1807.

[42] Sergio Koreisha, Tarmo Pukkila (1990). A generalized least-squares approach for estimation of autoregressive moving-average models. *Journal of Time Series Analysis*, 11 (2), 139–151. [MR1046985.]

[43] Arto Kallinen, Tarmo Pukkila (1991). The inverse of the Cholesky decomposition of the autocovariance matrix. In *A Spectrum of Statistical Thought: Essays in Statistical Theory, Economics and Population Genetics in Honour of Johan Fellman*, Ekonomi och Samhälle: Skrifter utgivna vid Svenska Handelshögsoklan 46, Svenska Handelshögsoklan, Helsinki, pp. 113–124.

[44] Jerzy K. Baksalary, Tarmo Pukkila (1992). A note on invariance of eigenvalues, singular values, and norms of matrix products involving generalized inverses. *Linear Algebra and its Applications*, 165, 25–130. [MR1149749 (92m:15006), Shao Kuan Li; Zbl 0743.15005.]

[45] Jukka Nyblom, Tarmo M. Pukkila (1993). Information criterion as a multiple testing procedure. *Journal of Statistical Planning and Inference*, 36 (2-3), 385–397. [MR1234864 (94i:62027), J. A. Melamed.]

[46] Sergio G. Koreisha, Tarmo M. Pukkila (1993). New approaches for determining the degree of differencing necessary to induce stationarity in ARIMA models. *Journal of Statistical Planning and Inference*, 36 (2-3), 399–412. [MR1234865; Zbl 0800.62545.]

[47] Sergio G. Koreisha, Tarmo Pukkila (1993). Determining the order of a vector autoregression when the number of component series is large. *Journal of Time Series Analysis*, 14 (1), 47–69. [MR1212262.]

[48] Jan G. De Gooijer, Tarmo Pukkila (1993). On the expectation of estimators for general ARMA processes. In *American Statistical Association 1993 Proceedings of the Business and Economic Statistics Section* (*San Francisco, California, August 8–12,1993*), American Statistical Association, pp. 164–169. (Revised as [51].)

[49] Teivo Pentikäinen, Heikki Bonsdorff, Martti Pesonen, Tarmo Pukkila, Antero Ranne, Jukka Rantala, Matti Ruohonen, Simo Sarvamaa [Finnish Insurance Modelling Group (FIM-GROUP)] (1994). On stochastic modeling of inflation. In *4th AFIR Actuarial Approach for Financial Risks International Colloquium: April 20–22, 1994, Orlando, Florida, Volume 1*, Society of Actuaries, pp. 589–608.

[50] Tarmo Pukkila, Antero Ranne, Simo Sarvamaa (1994). On the asset models as a part of all company insurance analysis. In *4th AFIR Actuarial Approach for Financial Risks International Colloquium: April 20–22, 1994, Orlando, Florida, Volume 1*, Society of Actuaries, pp. 1471–1501.

[51] J. G. De Gooijer, T. Pukkila (1994). On the expectation of estimators for general ARMA processes. *Statistica* (*Bologna*), 54 (1), 39–50. [MR1324315 (96k:62252), N. Leonenko; Zbl 0830.62080.] (Revision of [48].)

[52] Sergio G. Koreisha, Tarmo Pukkila (1995). A comparison between different order-determination criteria for Identification of ARIMA models. *Journal of Business & Economic Statistics*, 13 (1), 127–131.

[53] Sergio G. Koreisha, Tarmo Pukkila (1995). The identification of seasonal autoregressive models. *Journal of Time Series Analysis*, 16 (3), 267–290. [MR1340570; Zbl 0825.62686.]

[54] Sergio G. Koreisha, Tarmo Pukkila (1996). A new approach for identifying seasonal autoregressive time series forecasting models. In *Aktuarielle Ansätze für Finanz-Risiken: AFIR 1996 Beiträge zum 6. Internationalen AFIR-Colloquium, Nürnberg, 1.–3. Oktober 1996, Band I*, VVW Karlsruhe, pp. 1075–1094.

[55] Lasse Koskinen, Tarmo Pukkila (1996). An application of the vector autoregressive model with a Markov regime to inflation rates. In *Aktuarielle Ansätze für Finanz-Risiken: AFIR 1996 Beiträge zum 6. Internationalen AFIR-Colloquium, Nürnberg, 1.–3. Oktober 1996, Band I*, VVW Karlsruhe, pp. 1095–1108.

[56] Sergio G. Koreisha, Tarmo Pukkila (1998). A two-step approach for identifying seasonal autoregressive time series forecasting models. *International Journal of Forecasting*, 14, 483–496.

[57] Sergio G. Koreisha, Tarmo Pukkila (1998). On the identification of vector autoregressive models. In *Transactions of the 26th International Congress of Actuaries: Birmingham, 7–12 June 1998, Volume 7: Investment*, Faculty of Actuaries in Scotland & Institute of Actuaries, London, pp. 135–156.

[58] Sergio G. Koreisha, Tarmo Pukkila (1999). The selection of the order and identification of nonzero elements in the polynomial matrices of vector autoregressive processes. *Journal of Statistical Computation and Simulation*, 62 (3), 207–235. [MR1703256; Zbl 0919.62107.]

[59] Sergio G. Koreisha, Tarmo Pukkila (1999). A unified methodology for constructing multivariate autoregressive models. In *Multivariate Analysis, Design of Experiments,and Survey Sampling: A Tribute to Jagdish N. Srivastava*, Marcel Dekker, New York, pp. 349–368. [MR1719094; Zbl 1068.62519.]

[60] Sergio G. Koreisha, Tarmo Pukkila (2000). Using the residual white noise autoregressive order determination criterion to identify unit roots in ARIMA models. *Communications in Statistics: Simulation and Computation*, 29 (1), 259–293. [Zbl 0968.62539.]

[61] Tarmo Pukkila (2003). Research and education needs in the area of insurance and financial supervision. In *Statistics, Econometrics and Society: Essays in Honour of Leif Nordberg*, Tutkimuksia Forskningsrapporter Research Reports 238, Statistics Finland, Helsinki, pp. 203–218.

[62] Sergio G. Koreisha, Tarmo Pukkila (2004). The specification of vector autoregressive moving average models. *Journal of Statistical Computation and Simulation*, 74 (8), 547–565. [MR2074612.]

Figure 4. Tampere, Viikinsaari, 1999: Tapio Nummi, Sergio Koreisha, Tarmo Pukkila.

Appendix 2. The 18 research journals in which Tarmo M. Pukkila has published

Australian Journal of Statistics 1
Biometrika 3
Communications in Statistics: Simulation and Computation 4
Duodecim: Lääketieteellinen Aikakauskirja 1
Gujarat Statistical Review 1
IEEE Transactions on Acoustics, Speech, and Signal Processing 3
Information Sciences: An International Journal 1
International Journal of Forecasting 1
Journal of Business & Economic Statistics 1
Journal of Multivariate Analysis 1
Journal of Statistical Computation and Simulation 3
Journal of Statistical Planning and Inference 2
Journal of the Royal Statistical Society, Series B: Methodological 1
Journal of Time Series Analysis 4
Kunnallistieteellinen Aikakauskirja 1
Linear Algebra and its Applications 1
Scandinavian Journal of Statistics 1
Statistica (Bologna) 1

Appendix 3. The 22 research collections and edited books in which Tarmo M. Pukkila has published

Aktuarielle Ansätze für Finanz-Risiken: AFIR 1996 Beiträge zum 6. Internationalen AFIR-Colloquium, Nürnberg, 1.–3. Oktober 1996, Band I (Peter Albrecht, ed.), pub. VVW Karlsruhe, 1996, 2 vol., 1757 pp., ISBN 3-88487-590-6 (Table of contents at http://www.actuaries.org/AFIR/colloquia/Nuernberg/papers.cfm).

American Statistical Association 1993 Proceedings of the Business and Economic Statistics Section (San Francisco, California, August 8–12, 1993), pub. American Statistical Association, 1993, [x] + 458 pp., no ISBN.

COMPSTAT 1978 Proceedings in Computational Statistics: 3rd Symposium held in Leiden 1978 (L.C.A. Corsten, J. Hermans, eds.), pub. Physica-Verlag, Rudolf Liebing KG, Vienna, 1978, 540 pp., ISBN 3-7908-0196-8.

COMPSTAT 1980 Proceedings in Computational Statistics: 4th Symposium held at Edinburgh 1980 (D. Wishart, M.M. Barritt, eds.), pub. Physica-Verlag, Rudolf Liebing KG, Vienna, 1980, 632 pp., ISBN 3-7908-0229-8.

COMPSTAT 1982 Proceedings in Computational Statistics: 5th Symposium held at Toulouse, 1982, Part II (Supplement): Short Communications, Summaries of Posters (H. Caussinus, P. Ettinger, J.R. Mathieu, eds.), pub. Physica-Verlag Ges.m.b.H., Vienna, 1982, 2 vol., ISBN 3-7051-0002-5 (vol. 1), 3-7051-0001-7 (vol. 2).

COMPSTAT 1984 Proceedings in Computational Statistics: 6th Symposium held at Prague 1984, Papers (T. Havránek, Z. Šidák, M. Novák, eds.), pub. Physica-Verlag Ges.m.b.H., Vienna (for the International Association for Statistical Computing (IASC)), 1984, 520 pp., ISBN 3-7051-0007-6.

Computers in Education: Proceedings of the IFIP TC-3 3rd World Conference on Computers in Education, Lausanne, Switzerland, July 27-31, 1981 (R. Lewis, E.D. Tagg, eds.), pub. North-Holland Pub. Co., Amsterdam, 1981, xviii + 876 pp., ISBN 0-444-86255-2.

Festschrift for Eino Haikala on his Seventieth Birthday (Pentti Huuhtanen, Erkki Liski, Tarmo Pukkila, Simo Puntanen; editorial board) Acta Universitatis Tamperensis, Series A 153, University of Tampere, 1983, xiv + 166 pp., ISBN 951-44-1422-5, ISSN 0496-7909.

4th AFIR Actuarial Approach for Financial Risks International Colloquium: April 20–22, 1994, Buena Vista Palace, Orlando, Florida, Volume 1 (James A. Tilley: Chairman, Scientific Committee), pub. Society of Actuaries, 1994, 3 vol., 1540 pp., no ISBN (Table of contents at http://www.actuaries.org/AFIR/colloquia/Orlando/papers.cfm).

Interactivnye Sistemy Sovetsko-Finskij Simpozium (Tbilisi, 24–27 Oktobr, 1979) [*Interactive Systems: Soviet-Finnish Symposium (Tbilisi, 24–27 October 1979)*], *Part II*, pub. Georgian SSR Academy of Sciences (USSR Academy of Sciences) Computing Centre, Moscow, 1979, pp. 217–421, no ISBN.

Juhlakirja Tampereen Yliopiston Taloudellis-Hallinnollisen Tiedekunnan Täyttäessä 15 Vuotta [*Festschrift in Celebration of 15 Years of the Faculty of Economics and Administration of the University of Tampere*], Acta Universitatis Tamperensis, Series A 120, University of Tampere, 1980, 311 pp., ISBN 951-44-1060-2, ISSN 0496-7909.

Multivariate Analysis, Design of Experiments,and Survey Sampling: A Tribute to Jagdish N. Srivastava (Subir Ghosh, ed.), Statistics: Textbooks and Monographs 159, pub. Marcel Dekker, New York, 1999, xviii + 663 pp., ISBN 0-8247-0052-X, ISSN 1040-0672. [MR1722513 (2000g:00088), Zbl 1068.62519.]

Multivariate Statistics and Probability: Essays in Memory of Paruchuri R. Krishnaiah (C. R. Rao, M. M. Rao, eds.), pub. Academic Press, San Diego, 1989, xiv + 567 pp., ISBN 0-12-580205-6. [Reprint of *Journal of Multivariate Analysis*, 27 (1-2), 1988, pp. 1–535 & 28 (2), 1989, pp. 304–330. MR1056087 (90m:62004), Zbl 0697.62085.]

Proceedings of the Second International Tampere Conference in Statistics: University of Tampere, 1–4 June 1987 (Tarmo Pukkila, Simo Puntanen, eds.), Report No. A 184, pub. Department of Mathematical Sciences/Statistics, University of Tampere, 1987, xi + 708 pp., ISBN 951-44-2168-X, ISSN 0356-4231.

Proceedings XIth ICPhS: The Eleventh International Congress of Phonetic Sciences, August 1–7, 1987, Tallinn, Estonia, U.S.S.R, (Tamaz Gamkrelidze, ed.), pub. Institute of Language and Literature, Academy of Sciences of the Estonian S.S.R., Tallinn, 1987, 6 vol., no ISBN.

Proceedings: The Second International Conference on Teaching Statistics [*University of Victoria, 11–16 August 1986*] (Roger Davidson, Jim Swift: Organizing Committee of The Second International Conference on Teaching Statistics, eds.), sponsored by the International Statistical Institute and the University of Victoria, 1986, xiv + 508 pp., ISBN 0-920313-80-9.

Professor Khatri Memorial Volume of Gujarat Statistical Review (Editorial Board: M. Sreehari (Editor), S. K. Mitra, S. R. Patel, K. B. Pathak, Y. S. Sathe, K. R. Shah, M. L. Tiku, A. V. Gajjar (Editorial Secretary)), Gujarat Statistical Association, Ahmedabad, 1990, no ISBN, ISSN 0379-3419.

A Spectrum of Statistical Thought: Essays in Statistical Theory, Economics and Population Genetics in Honour of Johan Fellman (Gunnar Rosenqvist, Katarina Juselius, Kenneth Nordström, Juni Palmgren, eds.), Ekonomi och Samhälle: Skrifter utgivna vid Svenska Handelshögsoklan [Publications of the Swedish School of Economics and Business Administration], pub. Svenska Handelshögsoklan, Helsingfors [Swedish School of Economics and Business Administration, Helsinki], 1991, xii + 276 pp., ISBN 951-555-351-2, ISSN 0424-7256.

Statistical Data Analysis and Inference (Yadolah Dodge, ed.), pub. Elsevier Science Publishers B. V. (North-Holland), Amsterdam, 1989, xii + 617 pp., ISBN 0-444-88029-1. [This collection "contains invited papers presented at the International Conference on Recent Developments in Statistical Data Analysis and Inference in Honor of C. Radhakrishna Rao, held in Neuchâtel, Switzerland, August 21–24, 1989". MR1089619 (91i:62004), Zbl 0732.00019.]

Statistics, Econometrics and Society: Essays in Honour of Leif Nordberg (Rune Höglund, Markus Jäntti, Gunnar Rosenqvist, eds.), Tutkimuksia Forskningsrapporter Research Reports 238, pub. Statistics Finland, Helsinki, 2003, xviii + 246 pp., ISBN 952-467-173-5, ISSN 0355-2071.

Time Series Analysis Theory and Practice 1: Proceedings of the International Conference held at Valencia, Spain, June 1981 (O. D. Anderson, J. G. de Gooijer, Keith D. C. Stoodley, eds.), pub. North-Holland Pub. Co., Amsterdam, 1982, ix + 756 pp., ISBN 0-444-86337-0.

Transactions of the 26th International Congress of Actuaries: Birmingham, 7–12 June 1998, Volume 7: Investment, pub. Faculty of Actuaries in Scotland & Institute of Actuaries, London, 1998, v + 523 pp., ISBN 0-901066-53-2.

Acknowledgements

We are most grateful to Tarmo M. Pukkila for giving us a list of his publications and for providing copies of some hard-to-find items. Many thanks go to Ka Lok Chu for creating Figure 1 and for his help in computing the eigenvalues and eigenvectors in Table 4. Thanks go also to Sergio G. Koreisha, Michelle Kuan, Evelyn M. Styan, and Neda Zare Neyney for their help. This research was supported, in part, by the Natural Sciences and Engineering Research Council of Canada.

References

Baksalary, O. M. and Styan, G. P. H., eds. (2005). Some comments on the life and publications of Jerzy K. Baksalary (1944–2005). *Linear Algebra and its Applications*, 410, 3–53.

Ihaka, R. and Gentleman, R. (1996). R: A language for data analysis and graphics. *Journal of Computational and Graphical Statistics*, 5, 299–314. (See also http://www.r-project.org/)

SIMO PUNTANEN
Department of Mathematics, Statistics and Philosophy
FI-33014 University of Tampere, Finland
sjp@uta.fi http://www.uta.fi/~sjp/

GEORGE P. H. STYAN
Department of Mathematics and Statistics
McGill University, Burnside Hall Room 1005
805 rue Sherbrooke Street West
Montréal (Québec), Canada H3A 2K6
styan@math.mcgill.ca http://www.math.mcgill.ca/styan/

Festschrift for Tarmo Pukkila on his 60th Birthday
Eds. E. P. Liski, J. Isotalo, J. Niemelä, S. Puntanen, and G. P. H. Styan

Univ. of Tampere, 2006, ISBN 978-951-44-6620-5, pages 63–77

Very small samples and additional non-sample information in forecasting

KURT BRÄNNÄS & JÖRGEN HELLSTRÖM

Abstract. Generalized method of moment estimation and forecasting is introduced for very small samples when additional non-sample information is available. Small simulation experiments are conducted for the linear model with errors-in-variables and for a Poisson regression model. Two empirical illustrations are included. One is based on insider trading and the other on private schools in a Swedish county.

2000 MSC codes: 62F10, 62J02, 62P20, 62P25.

Key words and phrases: Generalized method of moments; Additional information; Forecasting; Insider trading; Private schools.

1 Introduction

This paper deals with forecasting in situations when there are only few available observations for the estimation of an underlying econometric model. Such situations are for instance encountered when forecasting aspects of developing or transition economies, when forecasting at regional levels for more developed economies, or when wishing to forecast the future of, say, a new product. Rather than avoiding the use of econometric models for forecasting we wish to improve on the forecasting performance of such models by capitalizing on additional information in the estimation phase.

The paper introduces generalized method of moments (GMM, Hansen 1982) estimation for linear and nonlinear models when the sample size is small and additional non-sample information about the model parameters is likely to be most beneficial. The additional or non-sample information about the parameters is taken to be random and introduced as random linear constraints in the spirit of mixed estimation (ME, Durbin 1953; Theil and Goldberger 1961, and others). The additional information can, e.g., be purely judgemental or obtained by estimating analogous models for other countries, regions or whatever is regarded appropriate. There are other ways of introducing extra information about parameters, e.g., by inequality restrictions or by adopting a Bayesian approach. Such alternative specifications are not considered, but could be developed along the lines of, e.g., Gourieroux and Monfort (1995, ch. 21). The structural model relating the endogenous variable to exogenous ones can in addition to being possibly nonlinear be either static or dynamic.

The general model framework is set in Section 2, while the GMM estimator and the GMM based forecast are introduced in Section 3. Since the linear static model enables a more detailed analytical study, the research on this particular model is briefly reviewed in Section 4. The Poisson regression model provides a slightly more complex illustration. While analytical studies are feasible for some restricted models, such as the linear, they are not feasible for nonlinear models and for models containing, say, errors-in-variables. Section 4 provides Monte Carlo studies of the estimator and forecasting performance for the linear regression model subject to errors-in-variables and for the nonlinear Poisson regression model. Section 5 contributes by two illustrations based on insider trading and on private schools in a Swedish county. A few concluding remarks are saved for the final section.

2 Model

Consider the model

$$y_t = g(\mathbf{z}_t, \boldsymbol{\beta}) + \varepsilon_t,$$

where $\mathbf{z}_t = (y_{t-1}, \dots, y_{t-p}, \mathbf{x}_t, \dots, \mathbf{x}_{t-q}), \boldsymbol{\beta} \in \mathcal{B} \subset \mathbb{R}^k$, and $t = 1, \dots, T$. The mean function $g(.,.)$ may be linear or nonlinear. The random error term, ε_t, is assumed to have zero mean and the covariance matrix of $\boldsymbol{\varepsilon} = (\varepsilon_1, \dots, \varepsilon_T)'$ is $\boldsymbol{\Sigma}$. Note that a full distributional assumption is not made. This model could without substantial difficulty be generalized to a multivariate one.

In a linear and static model to be estimated by ordinary least squares (OLS), we say that the sample is undersized when $T < k$. When this holds true, the Hessian matrix is not invertible. For nonlinear models noninvertibility of the Hessian matrix suggests that the sample is undersized and/or that lack of identification due to an unfortunate parametrization are indicated.

The additional information is provided in the form[1]

$$\mathbf{q} = \mathbf{R}\boldsymbol{\beta} + \boldsymbol{\zeta},$$

where $\mathbf{q}$ is an observed $(m \times 1)$ vector, the $(m \times k)$ matrix $\mathbf{R}$ is given, and $\boldsymbol{\zeta}$ is an unobserved random error with zero mean vector and a given covariance matrix $\boldsymbol{\Omega}$. The m is the number of additional information sources. In addition, we make the assumption that $E(\varepsilon_t \boldsymbol{\zeta}) = \mathbf{0}$.

[1] See, e.g., Kennedy (1991) for an interesting example. A general nonlinear form could be included, but at a cost of some more technical detail.

3 Estimation and Forecasting

The estimation approach is GMM. The feature that makes the present setup different from the conventional one based on (1), is that there are two sets of moment conditions; those based on (1) and those based on (2).

For the model we consider moment conditions of the form

$$\mathbf{m}_1 = T^{-1}\mathbf{U}'(\mathbf{y} - g(\mathbf{Z}, \boldsymbol{\beta})) = T^{-1}\mathbf{U}'\boldsymbol{\varepsilon}.$$

Here, $g(\mathbf{Z}, \boldsymbol{\beta})$ has row elements $g(\mathbf{z}_t, \boldsymbol{\beta})$ and $\mathbf{U}$ is a $(T \times n)$ matrix of instrumental variables, with $n \geq k$. The content of $\mathbf{U}$ should depend on the specification of $g(.,.)$. For instance, in a static model (with $\mathbf{z}_t = \mathbf{x}_t$) the $\mathbf{x}_t$ may serve as its own instrument, while if $\mathbf{x}_t$ is endogenous or measured with error some other instrumental variable vector is required. In the classical setup, $\operatorname{plim} \mathbf{m}_1 = E(\mathbf{m}_1) = \mathbf{0}$ is used to justify the GMM estimator.

For the additional information about the parameter vector, the moment condition is written

$$\mathbf{m}_2 = m^{-1}\mathbf{V}'(\mathbf{q} - \mathbf{R}\boldsymbol{\beta}) = m^{-1}\mathbf{V}'\boldsymbol{\zeta},$$

where $\mathbf{V}$ is an $(m \times p)$ matrix of instrumental variables. In this instance, we norm by the number, m, of additional information sources.

Since $\mathbf{m}_1$ and $\mathbf{m}_2$ are independent by the assumption $E(\varepsilon_t\boldsymbol{\zeta}) = \mathbf{0}$, we may write the GMM criterion on an additive form, yielding

$$\begin{aligned}\hat{\boldsymbol{\beta}} &= \arg\min_{\boldsymbol{\beta}\in\mathcal{B}}\{\mathbf{m}_1'\mathbf{W}_1^{-1}\mathbf{m}_1 + \mathbf{m}_2'\mathbf{W}_2^{-1}\mathbf{m}_2\}\\ &= \arg\min_{\boldsymbol{\beta}\in\mathcal{B}}\{\boldsymbol{\varepsilon}'\mathbf{U}(\mathbf{U}'\boldsymbol{\Sigma}\mathbf{U})^{-1}\mathbf{U}'\boldsymbol{\varepsilon} + \boldsymbol{\zeta}'\mathbf{V}(\mathbf{V}'\boldsymbol{\Omega}\mathbf{V})^{-1}\mathbf{V}'\boldsymbol{\zeta}\}.\end{aligned}$$

The asymptotic covariance matrix of the estimator is then of the form

$$\operatorname{Cov}(\hat{\boldsymbol{\beta}}) = (\mathbf{D}'\mathbf{U}(\mathbf{U}'\boldsymbol{\Sigma}\mathbf{U})^{-1}\mathbf{U}'\mathbf{D})^{-1} + (\mathbf{R}'\mathbf{V}(\mathbf{V}'\boldsymbol{\Omega}\mathbf{V})^{-1}\mathbf{V}'\mathbf{R})^{-1},$$

where $\mathbf{D} = -\partial g(\mathbf{Z}, \boldsymbol{\beta})/\partial\boldsymbol{\beta}'$ is evaluated at estimates.

Since the case of interest is when the sample size is very small, large sample properties of the estimator, such as consistency, can only be taken as very rough approximations. On the other hand, small sample properties are difficult to study except for in some special cases. Small-σ (e.g., Kadane 1971) and related approaches to find approximate properties has not been found useful at this stage. For practical implementation a first stage based on, e.g., the artificial settings $\boldsymbol{\Sigma} = \mathbf{I}$ and $\boldsymbol{\Omega} = \mathbf{I}$ can be used, or $\boldsymbol{\Sigma}$ can be estimated directly by excluding the additional information part. With $\boldsymbol{\beta}$ estimated an estimate of $\boldsymbol{\Sigma}$ can be obtained from the model part and then used together with the given $\boldsymbol{\Omega}$ in a second step. Below, additional light is cast on estimator performance for specialized models.

The h-steps-ahead forecast $\hat{y}_{T+h|T} = E[g(\mathbf{z}^0_{T+h}, \boldsymbol{\beta})|Y_T]$ is evaluated at estimates $\hat{\boldsymbol{\beta}}$, $Y_T = (y_1, \ldots, y_T)$ is the information set, and $\mathbf{z}^0_{T+h} = (y_{T+h-1}, \ldots, y_{T+h-p}, \mathbf{x}^0_{T+h}, \ldots, \mathbf{x}^0_{T+j})$ with $\mathbf{x}^0_{T+j}$, $j = 1, \ldots, h$, is assumed known. For nonlinear dynamic models the evaluation of the conditional expectation may, in practise, be a very difficult problem (e.g., Granger and Teräsvirta 1993, ch. 8).

Using a first order Taylor expansion about the true parameter vector $\boldsymbol{\beta}_0$ and the notation $g^0_{T+h} = g(\mathbf{z}^0_{T+h}, \boldsymbol{\beta}_0)$, the forecast error $\hat{e}_{T+h} = y_{T+h} - \hat{y}_{T+h|T}$ can be written

$$\hat{e}_{T+h} \approx g^0_{T+h} - E(g^0_{T+h}|Y_T) - \frac{\partial E(g^0_{T+h}|Y_T)}{\partial \boldsymbol{\beta}'}(\hat{\boldsymbol{\beta}} - \boldsymbol{\beta}_0) + \varepsilon_{T+h}.$$

From the approximate forecast error we have the general properties:

$$\begin{aligned}
E(\hat{e}_{T+h}) &= E_{Y_T}[E(\hat{e}_{T+h}|Y_T)] \\
&= -E_{Y_T}\left[\frac{\partial E(g^0_{T+h}|Y_T)}{\partial \boldsymbol{\beta}'}(E(\hat{\boldsymbol{\beta}}|Y_T) - \boldsymbol{\beta}_0)\right] \\
V(\hat{e}_{T+h}) &= V_{Y_T}[E(\hat{e}_{T+h}|Y_T)] + E_{Y_T}[V(\hat{e}_{T+h}|Y_T)] \\
&= V_{Y_T}\left[\frac{\partial E(g^0_{T+h}|Y_T)}{\partial \boldsymbol{\beta}'}(E(\hat{\boldsymbol{\beta}}|Y_T)\right] + E_{Y_T}[V(g^0_{T+h}|Y_T)] \\
&\quad + E_{Y_T}\left[\frac{\partial E(g^0_{T+h}|Y_T)}{\partial \boldsymbol{\beta}'}\operatorname{Cov}(\hat{\boldsymbol{\beta}})\frac{\partial E(g^0_{T+h}|Y_T)}{\partial \boldsymbol{\beta}}\right] + \sigma^2,
\end{aligned}$$

where $\sigma^2 = V(\varepsilon_{T+h})$.

For particular models these expressions may be simplified and then easier to interpret. For instance, when there are no lagged endogenous variables and the exogenous variables are fixed, i.e. when $\mathbf{z}^0_{T+h} = (\mathbf{x}^0_{T+h}, \ldots, \mathbf{x}^0_{T+h-q})$, we obtain the predictor $\hat{y}_{T+h|T} = g(\mathbf{z}^0_{T+h}, \boldsymbol{\beta})$ and

$$\begin{aligned}
E(\hat{e}_{T+h}) &= -\frac{\partial g^0_{T+h}}{\partial \boldsymbol{\beta}'}(E(\hat{\boldsymbol{\beta}}) - \boldsymbol{\beta}_0) \\
V(\hat{e}_{T+h}) &= V_{Y_T}[E(\hat{e}_{T+h}|Y_T)] + E_{Y_T}[V(\hat{e}_{T+h}|Y_T)] \\
&= \frac{\partial g^0_{T+h}}{\partial \boldsymbol{\beta}'}\operatorname{Cov}(\hat{\boldsymbol{\beta}})\frac{\partial g^0_{T+h}}{\partial \boldsymbol{\beta}} + \sigma^2.
\end{aligned}$$

If in addition the model is linear in parameters, $\partial g^0_{T+h}/\partial \boldsymbol{\beta}' = \mathbf{z}^0_{T+h}$.

4 Two Special Models

4.1 The Linear Regression Model

Durbin (1953), Theil (1963) and others consider the linear model by augmenting the data set by artificial observations corresponding to the random additional information about parameters.

Suppose we wish to estimate the parameters of the linear model $\mathbf{y} = \mathbf{X}\boldsymbol{\beta} + \boldsymbol{\varepsilon}$, where $\mathbf{y}$ is the T vector of observations on the endogenous variable, $\mathbf{X}$ is the matrix of fixed exogenous variables, $\boldsymbol{\beta}$ is the parameter vector, and $\boldsymbol{\varepsilon}$ is the vector of disturbances with mean zero and known covariance matrix $\boldsymbol{\Sigma}$. The additional information on $\boldsymbol{\beta}$ is available in the form of a random linear constraint.

Combining the two independent sources of sample and extraneous information we have

$$\begin{pmatrix}\mathbf{y}\\ \mathbf{q}\end{pmatrix} = \begin{pmatrix}\mathbf{X}\\ \mathbf{R}\end{pmatrix}\boldsymbol{\beta} + \begin{pmatrix}\boldsymbol{\varepsilon}\\ \boldsymbol{\zeta}\end{pmatrix}.$$

The covariance matrix of the disturbance term is block diagonal with blocks $\boldsymbol{\Sigma}$ and $\boldsymbol{\Omega}$, respectively. The generalized least squares (GLS), the mixed and the GMM (with $\mathbf{U} = \mathbf{X}$ and $\mathbf{V} = \mathbf{I}$) estimators are all equal, such that

$$\hat{\boldsymbol{\beta}}_{\mathrm{ME}} = (\mathbf{X}'\boldsymbol{\Sigma}^{-1}\mathbf{X} + \mathbf{R}'\boldsymbol{\Omega}^{-1}\mathbf{R})^{-1}(\mathbf{X}'\boldsymbol{\Sigma}^{-1}\mathbf{y} + \mathbf{R}'\boldsymbol{\Omega}^{-1}\mathbf{q}).$$

This mixed estimator (ME) is best linear and unbiased with covariance matrix

$$V(\hat{\boldsymbol{\beta}}_{\mathrm{ME}}) = (\mathbf{X}'\boldsymbol{\Sigma}^{-1}\mathbf{X} + \mathbf{R}'\boldsymbol{\Omega}^{-1}\mathbf{R})^{-1}.$$

Note that in the absence of data on $\mathbf{y}$ and $\mathbf{X}$ these expressions reduce to those of a GLS estimator based on only the additional information, while without additional information the conventional GLS estimator emerges. As the variance of the random additional information goes to zero, the mixed estimator approaches the restricted LS estimator (e.g., Fomby et al. 1984, ch. 6) implied by the exact restriction $\mathbf{R}\boldsymbol{\beta} = \mathbf{q}$. On the other hand, as the random restrictions become less certain and assuming that $E(\boldsymbol{\varepsilon}\boldsymbol{\varepsilon}') = \sigma^2\mathbf{I}$, the mixed estimator approaches the ordinary least squares (OLS) estimator. With $\boldsymbol{\Omega}$ known through the external source, restricted versions of $\boldsymbol{\Sigma}$ can be estimated by some two stage procedure. Theil (1963) offers a large sample justification, and Swamy and Mehta (1969) study the finite sample properties.

The predictor of y_{T+h} using mixed estimation and based on known $\mathbf{x}^0_{T+h}$ is $\hat{y}^0_{\mathrm{ME}} = \mathbf{x}^0_{T+h}\hat{\boldsymbol{\beta}}_{\mathrm{ME}}$. The forecast error is $e^0_{\mathrm{ME}} = \mathbf{x}^0_{T+h}(\boldsymbol{\beta} - \hat{\boldsymbol{\beta}}_{\mathrm{ME}}) + \varepsilon_{T+h}$ so that $E(e^0_{\mathrm{ME}}) = 0$, and the forecast error variance is

$$V(e^0_{\mathrm{ME}}) = \sigma^2 + \mathbf{x}^0_{T+h}(\mathbf{X}'\boldsymbol{\Sigma}^{-1}\mathbf{X} + \mathbf{R}'\boldsymbol{\Omega}^{-1}\mathbf{R})^{-1}\mathbf{x}^{0\prime}_{T+h}.$$

When the basic assumptions are satisfied and the additional information is unbiased then forecasting based on ME offers a gain.

If $\mathbf{X}$ or some part of $\mathbf{X}$ is measured with error the mixed estimator will be biased.

Measurement errors appears a real problem for transition and developing economies, with new definitions and measurement practices being put into place. An instrumental variable (IV) or GMM estimator for the linear model is easily obtained but its properties in small samples are largely unknown. The IV estimator and its covariance matrix are of the form

$$\hat{\boldsymbol{\beta}}_{\text{IV}} = (\mathbf{X}'\mathbf{A}\mathbf{X} + \mathbf{R}'\boldsymbol{\Omega}^{-1}\mathbf{R})^{-1}(\mathbf{X}'\mathbf{A}\mathbf{y} + \mathbf{R}'\boldsymbol{\Omega}^{-1}\mathbf{q})$$
$$V(\hat{\boldsymbol{\beta}}_{\text{IV}}) = (\mathbf{X}'\mathbf{A}\mathbf{X} + \mathbf{R}'\boldsymbol{\Omega}^{-1}\mathbf{R})^{-1}$$

with $\mathbf{A} = \mathbf{U}(\mathbf{U}'\boldsymbol{\Sigma}\mathbf{U})^{-1}\mathbf{U}'$ and where $\mathbf{U}$ is the matrix of instrumental variables. For the IV estimator there are equal numbers of variables in $\mathbf{U}$ and $\mathbf{X}$, i.e. $n = k$. The GMM estimator is more general in the sense that it can encompass more variables in $\mathbf{U}$ than in $\mathbf{X}$, i.e. $n \geq k$.

Simulation Experiment

To cast some light on the small sample properties of the GMM estimator for a case of measurement errors in $\mathbf{X}$, and to study coverage probabilities of forecast confidence intervals we perform a small simulation experiment. The assumed models for the generation of data are of the form

$$y_t = \beta_0 + \beta_1 x_t^* + \varepsilon_t \quad \text{and} \quad \mathbf{q} = \mathbf{R}\boldsymbol{\beta} + \boldsymbol{\zeta}.$$

The parameters are set at $\beta_0 = 1$ and $\beta_1 = 0.2$. The unknown x_t^* is generated from an AR(1) model ($x_t^* = 0.7x_{t-1}^* + \nu_t$) and level shifted by adding 5 to x_t^*. The measurement error is introduced as $x_t = x_t^* + \eta_t$ and the instrumental variable is generated as $u_t = 0.7x_t^* + \xi_t$. Additional information about $\boldsymbol{\beta}$ is available with $m = 2, 4, 6, 8, 10$ and 12 so that $\mathbf{R}$ is made up of $m/2$ stacked identity matrices of order two. The random errors ν_t, η_t and ξ_t are generated independently from $N(0,1)$ distributions. The ζ_i, $i = 1, 2$, are generated as $N(0, \sigma_\zeta^2)$ with $\sigma_\zeta^2 = 0.05$ and 0.1, and ε_t as $N(0, 2)$, and mutually independent as well as independent of other error terms. Sample size is varied; $T = 3, 6, 9, 12, 15$ and 18, and 1000 replications are run in each cell. Note that the explanatory power in both models is low. For $\sigma_\zeta^2 = 0.1$ the range of the q_i is for β_i, $i = 0, 1$, approximately 1.26 (using $\sigma_\zeta \approx$ Range/4), while for $\sigma_\zeta^2 = 0.05$ the range is approximately 0.89. For the y_t model a low theoretical R^2 may give a higher estimated R^2 for few rather than for many observations.

Besides estimation by GMM (or equivalently by IV) using the u_t as an instrument, the OLS estimator based on $y_t = \beta_0 + \beta_1 x_t + (\varepsilon_t - \beta_1 \eta_t)$ is applied. The OLS estimator is also used to obtain estimates of σ^2 for GMM estimation.

Some indicative bias and MSE results for β_1 are given in Figure 1. As expected the MSEs of both estimators get smaller as T increases. For the GMM estimator the bias is larger for the larger sample size and small m. An explanation to this lies in the rather low explanatory power of the model. As T increases the less precise model observations become relatively more

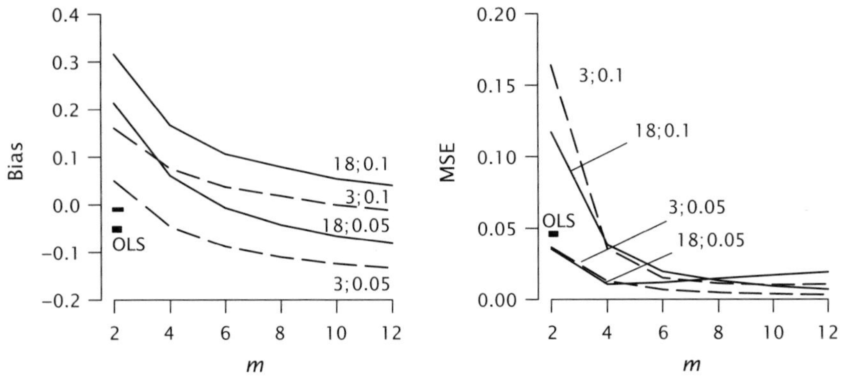

Figure 1. Bias and MSE for β_1 using GMM (solid and dashed lines) and OLS estimation at $T; \sigma_\zeta^2$.

important. Both measures are decreasing in the number of additional information 'observations', m. In terms of bias, OLS is doing better than GMM when this utilizes additional information that is not precise, i.e. when σ_ζ^2 is large. For MSE, the particular extra information used here brings about improvements for all T. The improvement is largest for small T and m. This is the region where improvements are of most value. These conclusions hold for other parameter combinations as well.

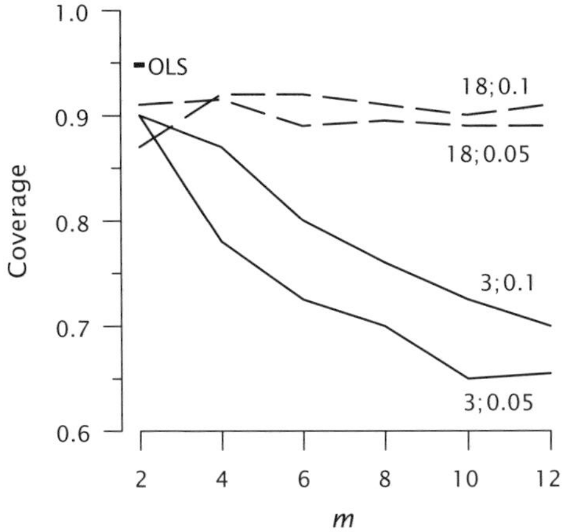

Figure 2. Coverage probabilities for forecast confidence intervals based on GMM (solid and dashed lines) and OLS estimation at $T; \sigma_\zeta^2$.

Figure 2 reports coverage probabilities for forecast confidence intervals. In calculating the intervals quantiles are obtained from the $t(T + m - 2)$-distribution for the GMM estimator and from the $t(T - 2)$-distribution for the OLS estimator. The coverage probabilities for OLS based forecasts are not significantly different from the nominal 0.95 level. For forecasts based on the GMM estimator the discrepancy from the nominal level is significant. Less precise additional information yields coverage probabilities closer to the nominal level and so does a larger T.

4.2 The Poisson Regression Model

The Poisson regression model has both the mean and the variance of independent y_t equal to $\lambda_t = \exp(\mathbf{x}_t\boldsymbol{\beta})$, where $\mathbf{x}_t$ is a vector of exogenous variables. Hence, in this case the ε_t of eq. (1) has variance λ_t, so that heteroskedasticity is an essential feature of the model. A number of different moment restrictions, e.g., those that correspond to the estimators considered by Gourieroux et al. (1984), can be utilized for estimation. We consider restrictions based on the likelihood equation, i.e. $\mathbf{X}'(\mathbf{y}-\boldsymbol{\lambda}) = \mathbf{0}$ with $\boldsymbol{\lambda} = (\lambda_1, \ldots, \lambda_T)'$, to obtain the criterion function

$$(\mathbf{y}-\boldsymbol{\lambda})'\mathbf{X}(\mathbf{X}'\boldsymbol{\Lambda}\mathbf{X})^{-1}\mathbf{X}'(\mathbf{y}-\boldsymbol{\lambda}) + (\mathbf{q}-\mathbf{R}\boldsymbol{\beta})'\mathbf{V}(\mathbf{V}'\boldsymbol{\Omega}\mathbf{V})^{-1}\mathbf{V}'(\mathbf{q}-\mathbf{R}\boldsymbol{\beta}),$$

where $\boldsymbol{\lambda} = \mathrm{diag}(\boldsymbol{\Lambda})$. Since the first order condition is nonlinear in $\boldsymbol{\beta}$ no explicit solution exists. The best forecast can be obtained by specializing a result for serially correlated and overdispersed $y_1, \ldots, y_T$ (Brännäs 1995a) and is here of the simple form λ_{T+h}.

Consider as an example the regressor free case so that λ is constant and $\boldsymbol{\Omega} = \omega\mathbf{I}_m$. Then the natural (in the sense that it still yields a simple linear estimator) criterion to minimize is of the form

$$\sum_{t=1}^{T}(y_t-\lambda)^2/\lambda_0 + \sum_{j=1}^{m} q_j/\omega,$$

where λ_0 is fixed at some initial value. Minimization yields the estimator

$$\hat{\lambda} = \left[\lambda_0^{-1}\sum_{t=1}^{T} y_t + \omega^{-1}\sum_{j=1}^{m} q_j\right]\Big/ u,$$

where $u = T/\lambda_0 + m/\omega$. The estimator has the properties $E(\hat{\lambda}) = \lambda$ and $V(\hat{\lambda}) = \lambda(T/\lambda_0^2 + m/\omega^2)/u^2$.

Hence, the estimator is unbiased and as $\omega \to \infty$, the estimator has a variance approaching that of the maximum likelihood (ML) estimator. For smaller ω the MSE of this mixed estimator may be much smaller than that of the ML estimator. As $\omega \to 0$, the MSE approaches λ/m.

The best forecast is $\hat{\lambda}$ and the forecast variance is equal to $\lambda[1 + (T/\lambda_0^2 + m/\omega^2)/u^2]$. Hence, forecast properties depend on the quality of the additional information in much the same way as the estimator.

Simulation Experiment

To illustrate the properties of the estimator and the forecast for a more general Poisson model we conduct a Monte Carlo experiment. The assumed model is Poisson with

$$\lambda_t = \exp(\beta_0 + \beta_1 x_t).$$

The parameters are set at $\beta_0 = 1$ and $\beta_1 = 0.2$. The x_t is generated as $N(5, 4)$ but kept fixed over the 1000 replications run in each cell, and the sample size is varied; $T = 3$, 6, 9, 12, 15 and 18. The additional information about $\boldsymbol{\beta}$ is available in the form of $\mathbf{q} = \boldsymbol{\beta} + \boldsymbol{\zeta}$, with $m = 2$, 4, 6, 8, 10 and 12. Here, ζ_i, $i = 1, 2$, is generated as $N(0, \sigma_\zeta^2)$, with $\sigma_\zeta^2 = 0.5$ and 1. Note that $\mathbf{q}$ generated this way carries very little information.

Some indicative bias and MSE results for β_1 are given in Figure 3. As expected both the bias and the MSE get smaller as T increases. Both measures are constant or increasing in the number of extra information 'observations', m, for larger sample sizes. In terms of bias, ML is best already at $T = 3$ observations. For MSE the particular extra information used here appears to bring about improvements for all T.

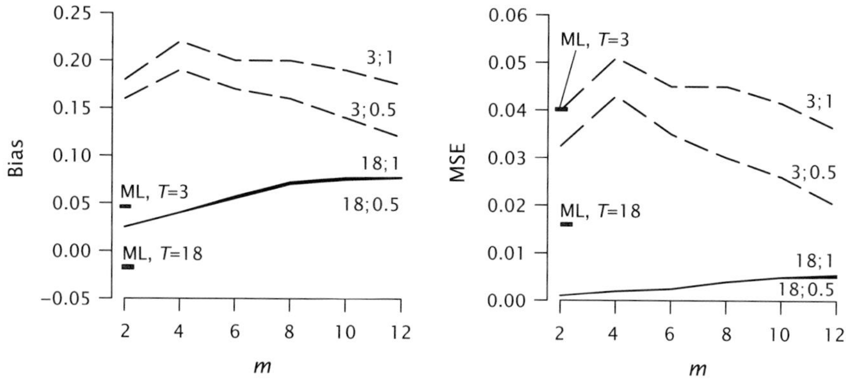

Figure 3. Bias and MSE for β_1 using GMM and ML estimation at $T; \sigma_\zeta^2$.

Figure 4 reports empirical coverage probabilities for forecast confidence intervals based on the normal distribution. Coverage probabilities get closer to the nominal 0.95 level as T increases, while a larger m appears to have a very small effect. On comparison with the ML based forecasts, coverage probabilities based on GMM estimation are higher for $T \leq 9$, while for larger values there are no substantial differences. Coverage probabilities are significantly too small, with the exception of the ML based interval for $T = 18$. The forecasts appear to be (not significantly so) downward biased and to have skewed distributions for small T. Using intervals based on the t-distribution would increase the empirical coverage probabilities.

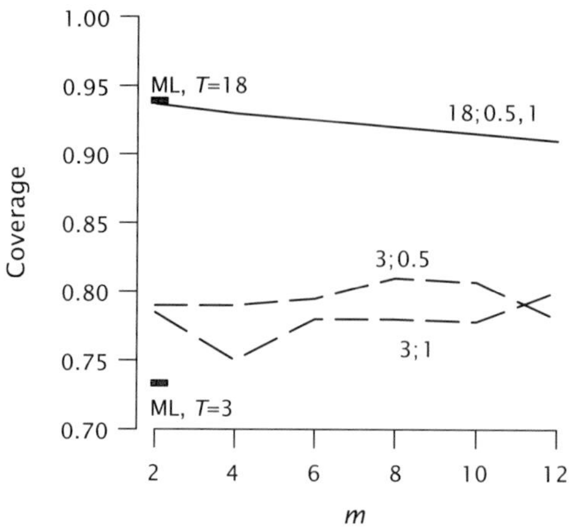

Figure 4. Coverage probabilities for forecast confidence intervals based on GMM and ML estimation at $T;\sigma_\zeta^2$.

5 Empirical Illustrations

5.1 Insider trading

As an illustration of the usefulness of the proposed forecasting and estimation approach we consider modelling the number of suspected cases of illegal insider trades on the financial markets reported to Finansinspektionen[2] in Sweden during 1997–2004. Since the beginning of the 1990s insider trading has been subject to an increasing level of regulation both in Sweden and in the EU. The development in Sweden has gone towards harder requirements concerning the reporting of insider trades and the regulations were particularly reinforced in 2001 (Eklund 2003). Despite this, the number of cases going as far as prosecution have been very few since it has been hard to take legal measures against offences against the insider laws and regulations. As a consequence of this the Swedish legislators are implementing a new legislation during 2005 which will make it easier to prosecute illegal insider traders. Table 1, column one reports estimates from a Poisson model with a parsimoniously specified mean given by

$$\begin{aligned} E(y_t|\mathbf{x}_t) &= \exp(\beta_1 + \beta_2 \ln(\mathrm{tr}_t) + \beta_3 \ln(y_{t-1}) + \beta_4 \ln(p_{t-1})) \\ &= \exp(\beta_1)\, \mathrm{tr}_t^{\beta_2}\, y_{t-1}^{\beta_3} p_{t-1}^{\beta_4}, \end{aligned}$$

where y_t is the number of reported suspected illegal insider trades and the explanatory variables are a trend (tr), the lagged number of reported insider trades (y_{t-1}) and the lagged number of prosecuted cases (p_{t-1}). The model is estimated on data obtained from Finansinspektionen and covers

[2]Finansinspektionen is the Swedish financial supervisory authority.

the years 1997-2004. The lagged number of prosecuted cases does not have a significant effect so that there seem to be no preventive effect. This is an expected effect due to the few number of prosecuted cases. The model may be used to forecast the future number of cases of illegal insider trades. The predicted number, $\hat{\lambda}_{t+h} = \exp(\mathbf{x}_{t+h}\hat{\boldsymbol{\beta}})$, of reported illegal insider trades for the years 2005-2008 are given in Figure 5.[3]

A shortcoming with this forecast is that it is only based on the previous history and does not account for the reinforcement of the legislation concerning insider trading during 2005. Assume that the new legislation will make it easier to take legal measures against insider crimes and that the development will follow the pattern of other economic crimes. Based on the reported number of economic crimes (source: The Swedish National Council for Crime Prevention) 1995-2004 estimates for the above Poisson model is reported in column two. For this sample there seems to be a preventive effect since the number of prosecuted cases has a significant negative impact on the future number of reported economic crimes. Column three reports estimates from a model concerning insider trading using this as extra information concerning the parameter for the number of prosecuted cases. This model shows a negative significant effect for the number of prosecuted cases, hence, a preventive effect from the new legislation is incorporated in the model. A forecast from this model is given in Figure 5.

Table 1. Estimation results for the number of suspected illegal insider trades (s.e. in parentheses).

Variable	Insider	Economic crimes	Insider + Economic crimes
Reported cases$_{t-1}$	−0.799	0.806	−0.536
	(0.258)	(0.024)	(0.204)
Prosecuted cases$_{t-1}$	0.205	−0.594	−0.212
	(0.124)	(0.025)	(0.065)
Trend	−0.098	−0.316	0.384
	(0.222)	(0.021)	(0.127)
Constant	6.947	6.477	5.817
	(0.945)	(0.192)	(0.729)

5.2 Private Schools

Estimates and forecasts for the entry and exit of elementary private schools are given for the county of Västerbotten, Sweden. The sample consists of only 45 observations on 15 municipalities with three annual observations on the number of public schools. Overall there are only a few non-zero observations on the dependent variable. A school finance reform (1991-1992) stimulated

[3]The number of prosecuted cases are predicted with a simple trend model.

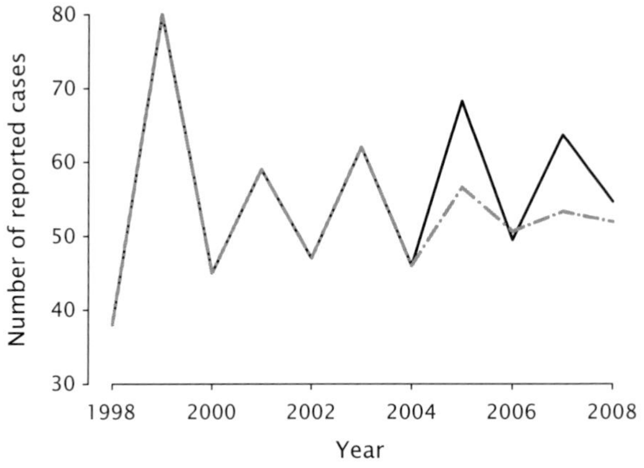

Figure 5. Forecasts of the number of reported illegal insider trades, 2005–2008. Insider (column one in Table 1, solid line) and extra information (column three in Table 1, dot dashed line).

the entry of private schools in Sweden. While the debate on the role of private schools as providers of education is not new, relatively little is known about the economic incentives or disincentives for private schools. Hoxby (1993) found evidence that public schools improve their quality in communities where competition from private schools is strenuous. Downes and Greenstein (1996) shed some light on the determinants of localization choice of private schools in California, 1978–1979.

We model the number of private schools by an integer-valued autoregressive model of order one (e.g., Brännäs 1995b). This model may, e.g., be written on the form

$$y_{it} = \pi_i y_{it-1} + \phi_i + \varepsilon_{it},$$

where y_{it} denotes the number of private schools in the ith municipality at time t, $\pi = 1/(1 + \exp(\theta))$ denotes the survival probability of the existing private schools,[4] ϕ_i is the mean entry and the error term ε_{it} has zero mean. The mean entry ϕ_i could be modelled, e.g., as the mean function of a Poisson variable ($\xi_{it} = \phi_i + \varepsilon_{it}$). In this particular case there appears to be little room for elaborate behavioral models, and we let $\phi_i = \phi + \alpha$ for the largest municipality (Umeå) of the county and let $\phi_i = \phi$ for all other municipalities. In general, ϕ_i could be a function of public school characteristics and the regional demographic structure (Downes and Greenstein 1996, and references therein).

The sample is obtained from the National Board of Education (Skolverket) and covers the calendar years 1992–1994 for 286 Swedish municipalities. Since the model is dynamic there will be only two observations for the two parameters for each municipality. Moreover there is no variation within most

[4] $1 - \pi$ is the exit probability. Note that π is kept constant across municipalities.

of the municipalities while there is more variation across municipalities. The model for Västerbotten was first estimated by nonlinear least squares (NLSQ). Second, extra information was obtained for the θ and ϕ parameters by estimating the model without a dummy variable (cf. α) on other Swedish municipalities and used in a final step for GMM estimation. The estimation results are presented in Table 2 and indicate substantial improvement in estimation efficiency and that the survival probability is very close to one. The mean entry $\hat{\phi}$ is slightly higher when the extra information is used, while $\hat{\alpha}$ is slightly smaller.

Since $\hat{\pi} \approx 1.0$ it follows (Brännäs 1995b) that the best forecast for the number of public schools is the final observation, i.e. $y_{i,1995}$. As $\hat{\phi} = 0.08$ we forecast an entry about every 12 years for the other municipalities. Using $\hat{\phi}$ and $\hat{\phi} + \hat{\alpha}$ as well as their confidence intervals we may obtain the corresponding density function evaluated at $\hat{\phi}$ and $\hat{\phi} + \hat{\alpha}$ as well as at the lower and upper limits of their confidence intervals. We find that for no entries in the next year the probability is between 0.20 and 0.24 for Umeå while between 0.91 and 0.94 for the other municipalities. From these values we easily find probabilities for one or more new private schools. Once a new private school is founded it will according to the model survive.

Table 2. Estimation results for private school models (standard errors in parentheses).

Parameter	Västerbotten		Sweden
	NLSQ	GMM	NLSQ
ϕ	0.07	0.08	0.20
	(0.13)	(0.01)	(0.10)
α	1.43	1.42	—
	(0.52)	(0.05)	
θ	−10.86	−20.30	14.63
	(301.8)	(461.2)	(58.74)

6 Conclusions

The paper has demonstrated that additional information may be incorporated for the estimation of more general models than the previous limitation to linear models have indicated. The additional information may come from different sources. When data is available for corresponding phenomena for other countries, regions, etc. estimation results for these may be utilized using the present framework. An alternative is then obviously to employ a panel data approach instead. The additional information may also take the form of subjective judgemental assessments, which then breaks the ties to panel data estimation.

The Monte Carlo simulations indicate that the use of additional information is most beneficial when the sample size is at its smallest. A realistic goal for forecasting performance in circumstances that we have tried to face in this paper should obviously be placed lower than for cases with long and stable time series data. Using models and clear-cut estimation procedures, we believe, makes it easier to communicate, evaluate and improve on forecasting practise.

Acknowledgements

The authors gratefully acknowledge constructive comments from seminar participants at Umeå University, University of Lisbon, an International Symposium of Forecasting and a Swedish Econometrics Conference on an early version of the paper.

References

Brännäs, K. (1995a). Prediction and control for a time series count data model. *International Journal of Forecasting*, 11, 263–270.

Brännäs, K. (1995b). Explanatory variables in the AR(1) Poisson model. Umeå Economic Studies 381 (revised).

Downes, A. T. and Greenstein, M. S. (1996). Understanding the supply decisions of non-profits: modelling the location of private schools. *RAND Journal of Economics*, 27, 365–390.

Durbin, J. (1953). A note on regression when there is extraneous information about one of the coefficients. *Journal of the American Statistical Association*, 48, 799–808.

Eklund, J. (2003). Varför förbjuda insiderhandel? *Ekonomisk Debatt*, 31, 18–28.

Fomby, T. B., Hill, R. C., and Johnson, S. R. (1984). *Advanced Econometric Methods*. New York: Springer-Verlag.

Gourieroux, C. and Monfort, A. (1995). *Statistics and Econometric Models*. Cambridge: Cambridge University Press.

Gourieroux, C., Monfort, A., and Trognon, A. (1984). Pseudo maximum likelihood methods: applications to Poisson models. *Econometrica*, 52, 701–720.

Granger, C. W. J. and Teräsvirta, T. (1993). *Modelling Nonlinear Economic Relationships*. Oxford: Oxford University Press.

Hansen, L. P. (1982). Large sample properties of generalized method of moment estimators. *Econometrica*, 50, 1029–1054.

Hoxby, C. M. (1993). Do private schools provide competition for public schools? NBER Working Paper 4978.

Kadane, J. B. (1971). Comparison of *k*-class estimators when the disturbances are small. *Econometrica*, 39, 723–737.

Kennedy, P. (1991). An extension of mixed estimation, with an application to forecasting new product growth. *Empirical Economics*, 16, 401–415.

Swamy, P. A. V. B. and Mehta, J. S. (1969). On Theil's mixed regression estimator. *Journal of the American Statistical Association*, 64, 273–276.

Theil, H. (1963). On the use of incomplete prior information in regression analysis. *Journal of the American Statistical Association*, 58, 401–414.

Theil, H. and Goldberger, A. S. (1961). On pure and mixed statistical estimation in economics. *International Economic Review*, 2, 65–78.

KURT BRÄNNÄS
Department of Economics
Umeå University, SE-901 87 Umeå
kurt.brannas@econ.umu.se
http://www.econ.umu.se/personal/kurt_brannas.html

JÖRGEN HELLSTRÖM
Department of Economics
Umeå University, SE-901 87 Umeå
Jorgen.Hellstrom@econ.umu.se
http://www.econ.umu.se/~jorgen.hellstrom/

Festschrift for Tarmo Pukkila on his 60th Birthday
Eds. E. P. Liski, J. Isotalo, J. Niemelä, S. Puntanen, and G. P. H. Styan

Univ. of Tampere, 2006, ISBN 978-951-44-6620-5, pages 79–92

A meandering *hylje**

David R. Brillinger Brent S. Stewart Charles S. Littnan

Abstract. Hawaiian monk seals (*Monachus schauinslandi*) are endemic to the Hawaiian Islands. The species has been declining for several decades and now numbers around 1300. A key hypothesis accounting for the decline is poor growth and survival of young seals owing to poor foraging success Consequently, data have been collected recently on the foraging habitats, movements, and behaviors of Hawaiian monk seals throughout the Hawaiian Islands Archipelago.

Our work here is directed to exploring a data set located on the west side of the main Hawaiian Island of Molokai in our search for a stochastic model of a seal's journey. The work proceeds by fitting a stochastic differential equation (SDE) that mimics some aspects of the behavior of seals by working with location data collected for one seal. The SDE is found by developing a potential function. The estimated times of locations are irregularly spaced and not close together leading to some difficulties of analysis and interpretation. Synthetic plots are generated to assess the reasonableness of the model and suggest departures from it.

2000 MSC codes: 60J60, 62G08, 62M10, 70F99.

Key words and phrases: ARGOS satellite locations; Hawaiian monk seal; Potential function; Spatial locations; Stochastic differential equation; Synthetic plot.

1 Introduction

Tarmo Pukkila has made many contributions to statistics in general and to time series specifically. Figure 1 below shows a particular bivariate time series that will be studied in this paper. We would like to be able to apply some of Tarmos work on ARIMAs to the analysis of this series, but the series is seen to be plagued by various complications including: outliers, unequally spaced time sampling intervals and does not look like any of the usual ARIMAS. What gives some hope in developing an analysis, as we shall see, is that a

*Finnish for seal.

great deal is known about the series context. However surely at later stages Tarmo's work will be applicable and probably applied.

Populations of virtually all pinnipeds (i.e., seals and sea lions) were reduced substantially, and some nearly extinguished, during the 1800s and 1900s by commercial sealers and whalers, poachers, and human fishers who have considered these predators to be competitors for shared marine resources (Reeves et al. 1992; Reeves and Stewart 2005). Most species however, have recovered from those residual small populations and are now relatively robust. There are exceptions however. The Saimaa seal (*Pusa hispida saimensis*), the Ladoga seal (*Pusa hispida ladogensis*), and the Mediterranean (*Monachus monachus*) and Hawaiian (*Monachus schauinslandi*) monk seals are the clearest cases of populations or species that are still at substantial risk of extinction from various causes (e.g., stochastic fluctuation in abundance, environmental change, habitat modification or destruction, reduction in prey, anthropogenic mortality of seals). The Saimaa and Ladoga seals are subspecies of the parent ringed seal species that is widely distributed in the circumpolar Arctic. Both of those species have been confined to inland freshwater lakes for about 9,000 to 10,000 years, the former to the Saimaa lake system in eastern Finland and the latter to Lake Ladoga in Russia near St. Petersburg (Reeves et al. 1992, 2002). Though perhaps never historically exceeding 2000 to 2500 seals, the Saimaa seal declined to around 200 seals by the 1980s, though has evidently increased some recently to around 250 to 300 owing to direct intervention and conservation measures.

Though more numerous and with a less confined distribution than the Saimaa seal, the Hawaiian monk seal now numbers only around 1300 seals in the Hawaiian Island Archipelago, having declined substantially from the 1950s through at least the late 1990s. Because the population is predominately older seals, it is predicted to decline further during the next two decades at least as the number of recruits to the breeding population will be small. This bias towards a mature and aging population is related to poor growth and survival of young seals, evidently owing in part to their poor foraging success, (Craig and Ragen 1999; Baker and Johanos 2004; Stewart et al. 2006). Consequently, data have been collected recently on the foraging habitats, movements, and behaviors of monk seals throughout the Northwestern and main Hawaiian Islands.

This paper studies a three month journey of a juvenile male Hawaiian monk seal, while he foraged and occasionally hauled out ashore. The track started 13 April 04 and ended 27 July 04. He was tagged and released at the southwest corner of Molokai, see Figure 2. He had a satellite-linked radio transmitter glued to his dorsal pelage to document geographic and vertical movements as proxies of foraging behavior. There were 754 locations estimated in all, but many were suspicious. Understanding the foraging behavior and habitat use of the Hawaiian monk seal is critical for clearly identifying the causes for it and instituting management responses to end and reverse

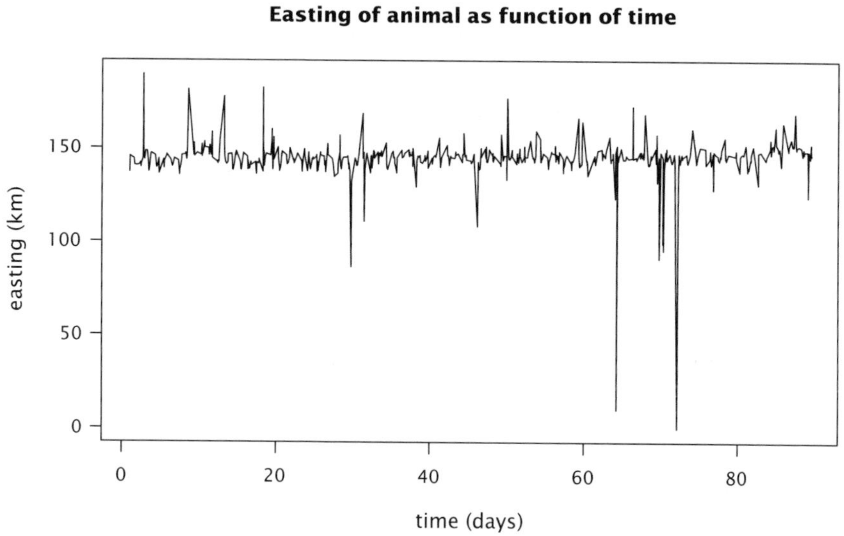

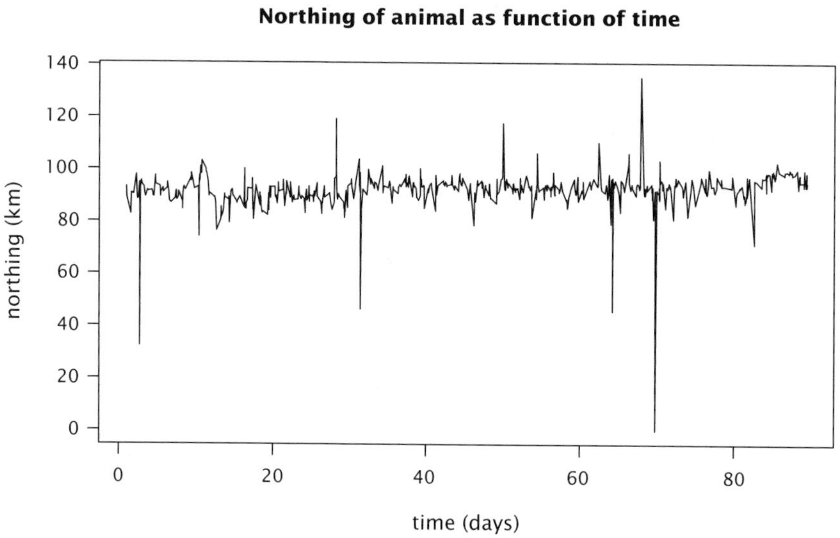

Figure 1. The top graph provides the eastward movement of the seal as a function of time and the bottom the northward component of his movement.

it. There are various specific questions that are relevant to this end:

- "What are the geographic and vertical marine habitats that the Hawaiian monk seals use?"
- "Are there age and sex differences in the habitats seals use when foraging?"
- "Do seals have individual preferences in foraging locations and does an individual vary its behavior over different time scales?"
- "How long is a foraging trip?"

This paper will focus on the first and fourth questions.

The paper Brillinger et al. (2006) presents an exploratory statistical study of the movements of a 4 year old female seal released at the same time and location as the seal of this paper. In those analyses we found that the animal made separate journeys to nearby Penguin Bank. The original intent of our current analyses was to confirm the findings of the first paper using data from another seal. Though we did not confirm those details, we did find that the same general approach of using a potential function proved viable.

A basic tool of the work is a stochastic differential equation. The SDE approach is elaborated in Brillinger et al. (2002). The potential function approach may be found in Brillinger et al. (2001b). There are many references to the literature in those papers. Two particular are Heyde (1994) and Sorensen (1997).

As in the previous paper, we found several difficulties with the data including: outliers, well-separated unequally spaced observations times, map creation, changing coordinates, developing the potential function, observation error (points inland and unreasonable speeds) and carrying out the simulations.

The paper includes the sections: The data and some initial analyses, Gradient functions, Fitting an SDE, Results, Validation, and Discussion.

2 The data and some initial analyses

The study began with a satellite-linked time depth recorder (SLTDR) being glued onto the seal's dorsal pelage. The SLTDR records times and depths of dives and transmits a brief radio frequency signal to a system of near polar earth orbiting satellites managed by the Argos Data Collection and Location Service. Periodic locations of the seal being studied were determined by measurements of Doppler shifts in the reception of successive transmissions. Those locations and accompanying dive data were then communicated daily to us by email.

Associated with a location estimate is a prediction of the location's error (LC or location class). The LC index takes on the values 3, 2, 1, 0, A, B, Z. When LC = 3, 2, or 1 the error in the location is predicted to be 1 km or less.

Errors for locations of LC = 0, A, and B are not predicted by Argos but may often be around 1 km but up to 10 to 20 km on occasion. In this paper when LC is 3, 2, or 1, a location is referred to as well-determined.

Figure 2 (bottom plot) provides locations with LC of value less than 1 and in the top plot those with LC 1 and up. (Later there will be a further restriction that the speed between any two successive location points is less than 259.2 km/day.) The figure is meant to provide an indication of the distinction between well- and poorly-determined points, (i.e. of the impact of the LC value.) One sees that the well-determined points are clustered close to the SW corner of Molokai while the poor ones are some distance offshore and in one case far offshore.

In the work it is convenient to employ UTM coordinates instead of the traditional latitude and longitude. This reduces distortion in the plots, leads to units of km, allows easy interpolation, and generally speaking makes the results more easily interpretable.

Figure 3 provides plots of the well-determined points for 6 successive 15 day periods. The dashed curve is the 200 fathom line which outlines Penguin Bank to some extent. (Penguin Bank is a marine reserve that is attractive to sea life.) The time points are unequally spaced. This means that apparent hotspots may well result from a cluster of time locations rather than a tendency of the animal to return to some particular location.

Figure 4 provides an estimate of the density of the well-determined points as a function of location. The lighter colors refer to the large values. One sees a "hotspot" partly up the coast and the points generally lying in a strip running NE-SW. The hotspot may be simply due to a lot of points being close to each other in time.

The behaviors of many animals are often characterized by circadian (i.e., 24-hour) rhythms. Such behavior was apparent in the movements of elk, see Brillinger et al. (2001a,b, 2002), Preisler et al. (2004), though it was not noticeable in our previous study of a female Hawaiian monk seal, Brillinger et al. (2006).

Figure 5 graphs estimated speeds of the animal based on the well-determined points. A log scale is employed to make the fluctuations more nearly constant. A smooth line has been added to the plot, specifically Cleveland's loess line, see Venables and Ripley (2002). There is a clear suggestion of the animal's moving more rapidly between 0500 and 1000 hr. The speed of the animal at the observation times was estimated by dividing the distance between successive points by the time distance. It is to be noted that there are some gaps in hours of the data. These are caused by the particular orbits of the satellites and complicate the interpretation.

Figure 6 is a plot of successive distances of the animal from the closest point on the coast. In Brillinger et al. (2006) such a plot brought out a number of offshore trips. In the present case one sees that the animal does spend some noticeable time offshore.

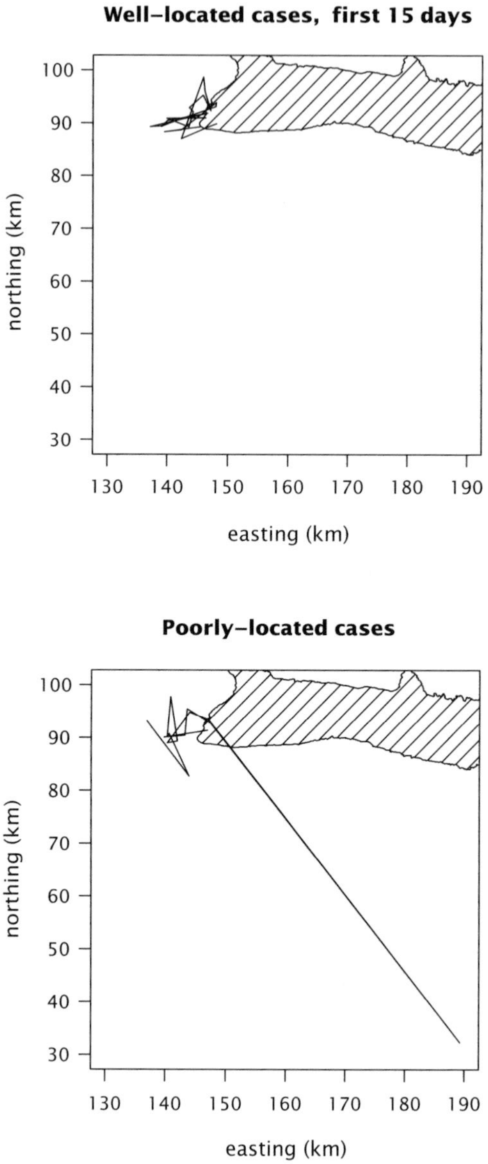

Figure 2. The top figure shows the well-determined points joined by successive lines. The bottom provides the poorly determined points. The hatched in area indicates the island of Molokai. The animal's tracking started at the SW corner of the island.

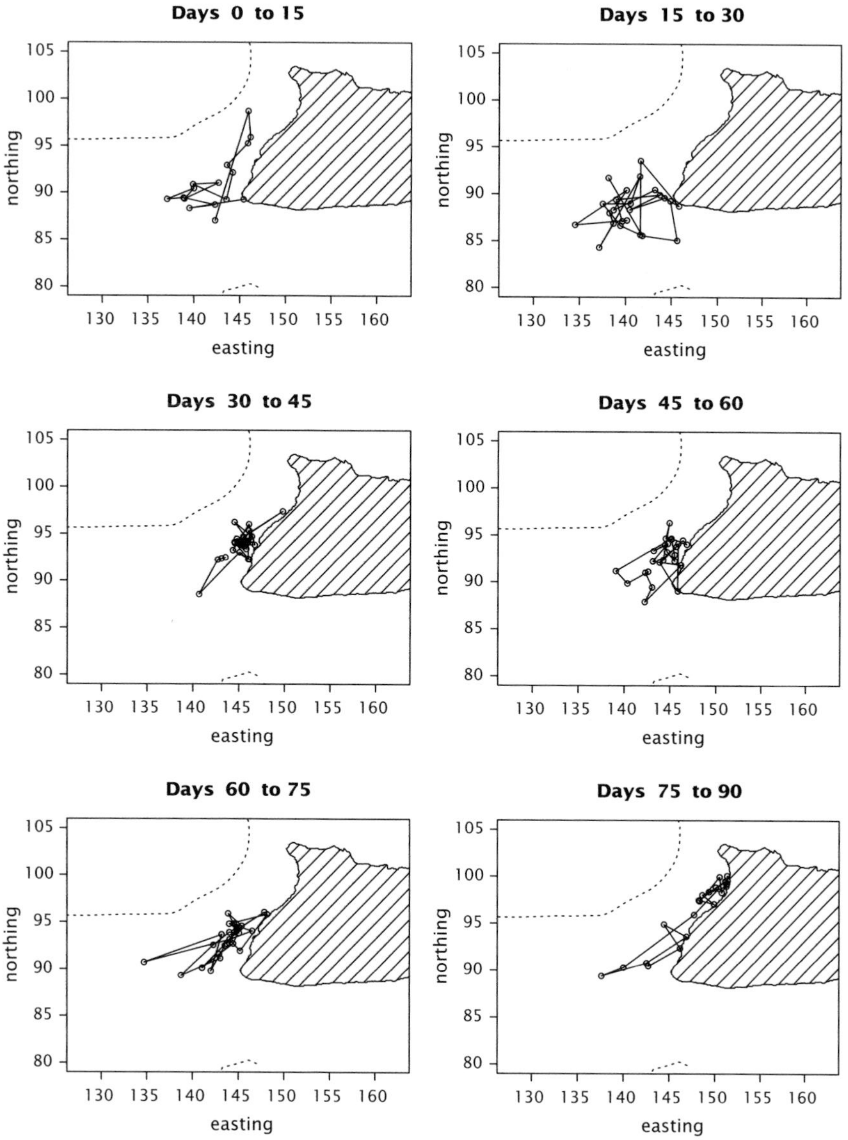

Figure 3. Plots of the well-determined points for six successive 15 day periods. The dashed curve is the 200 fathom line.

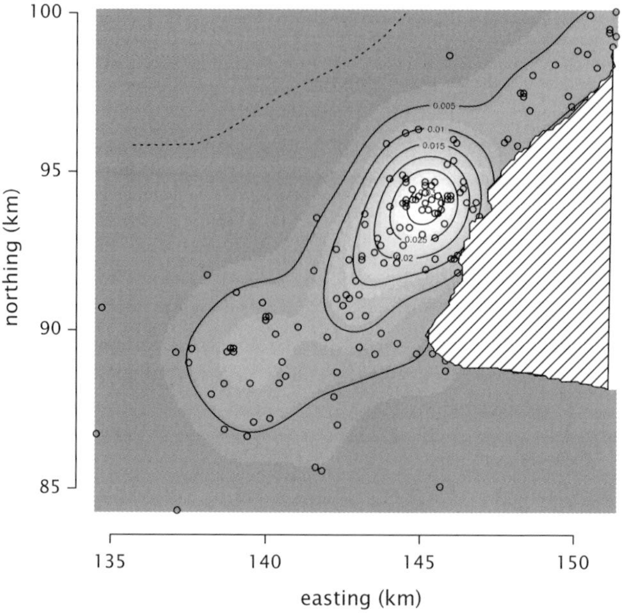

Figure 4. Estimated bivariate density of observed seal locations. Molokai is the hatched region. Lighter coloring corresponds to higher density.

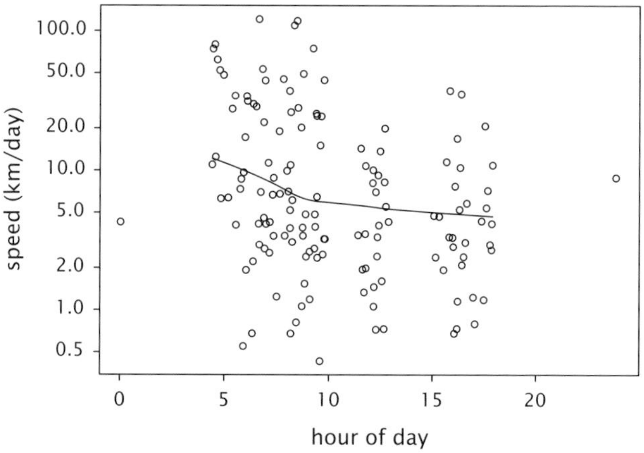

Figure 5. Log-scale plot of estimates of the animal's speed plotted versus time. A loess line has been added. The early morning and late night gaps are due to the satellite's orbit

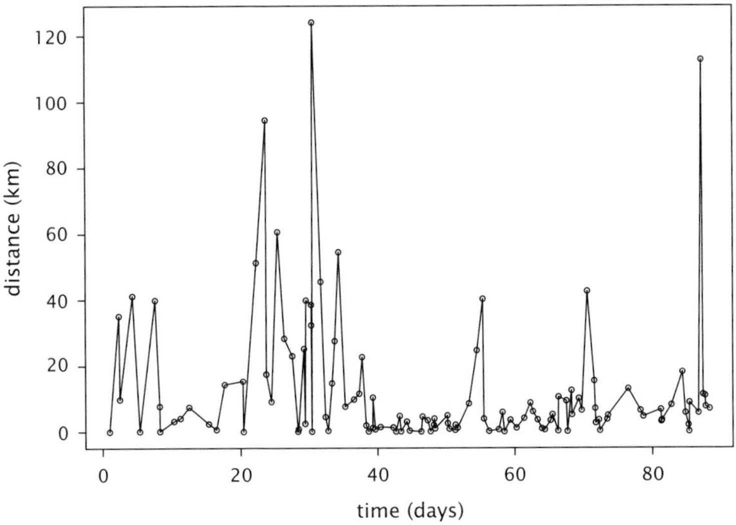

Figure 6. Successive distances of the seal from the shore.

3 Gradient functions

The study of motion, and the statistics of motion, has a long and venerable history. To begin one can note the Newtonian equations of motion

$$d\mathbf{r}(t) = \mathbf{v}(t)\,dt$$

$$d\mathbf{v}(t) = -\beta\mathbf{v}(t) - \beta\nabla H(\mathbf{r}(t), t)\,dt$$

with $\mathbf{r}(t)$ a particle's location at time t, with $\mathbf{v}(t)$ its velocity, with $H(\mathbf{r}, t)$ a potential function, and with ∇ the gradient. The potential function controls a particle's direction and velocity. Regions of attraction and repulsion may be introduced by terms in H. The parameter β represents friction. Nelson (1967) is a reference for this material.

In the case that β is large, the equations become, approximately,

$$d\mathbf{r}(t) = -\nabla H(\mathbf{r}(t), t)\,dt$$

If one adds a stochastic term, and changes the notation slightly, then one obtains the stochastic differential equation,

$$d\mathbf{r}(t) = \boldsymbol{\mu}(\mathbf{r}(t), t)\,dt + \boldsymbol{\Sigma}(\mathbf{r}(t), t)\,d\mathbf{B}(t) \tag{1}$$

Often $\mathbf{B}(t)$ is assumed to be standard Brownian motion. In the planar case with $\mathbf{r} = (x, y)$ the 2-vector $\boldsymbol{\mu}$ contains the partial derivatives H_x, H_y.

The following potential function was suggested for the seal of this paper by Figures 3 and 4,

$$H(x, y) = \beta_{10}x + \beta_{01}y + \beta_{20}x^2 + \beta_{11}xy + \beta_{02}y^2 + C/d_M(x, y) \tag{2}$$

where $d_M(x, y)$ is the shortest distance from the location (x, y) to Molokai. (In the results presented $C = 7.5$ a value suggested by a few trials.) Terms like $C/d_M(x, y)$ are considered in Brillinger et al. (2001b). It has the effect of keeping the animal away from the interior of Molokai. In the computation of Figure 7 below the shortest distance +0.2 was taken for $d_M(x, y)$. The 0.2 was to stabilize the computations. The quadratic in (x, y) allows a broad region of attraction to be present.

4 Fitting an SDE

Stochastic differential equations, such as (1), have been referred to. There has been a substantial amount of work on statistical inference for SDEs, references including Heyde (1994) and Sorensen (1997). Inferential work may be motivated by setting down the Euler approximation

$$\mathbf{r}(t_{i+1}) - \mathbf{r}(t_i) \approx \boldsymbol{\mu}(\mathbf{r}(t_i), t_i)(t_{i+1} - t_i) + \boldsymbol{\Sigma}(\mathbf{r}(t_i), t_i)\mathbf{Z}_i\sqrt{t_{i+1} - t_i} \qquad (3)$$

with the t_i an increasing sequence of time points filling in the time domain of the problem, see Kloeden and Platen (1995). The $\mathbf{Z}_i$ are independent bivariate standard normals and the t_i may be thought of as the times of observation. With the potential function set down above the β parameters appear linearly and so may be estimated by least squares.

Assuming that $\boldsymbol{\mu}(\mathbf{r}, t) = \boldsymbol{\mu}(\mathbf{r})$, and that $\boldsymbol{\Sigma}(\mathbf{r}(t), t) = \sigma^2\mathbf{I}$, one can consider as an estimate of σ^2

$$\hat{\sigma}^2 = \frac{1}{I}\sum_i ||\mathbf{r}(t_{i+1}) - \mathbf{r}(t_i) - \hat{\boldsymbol{\mu}}(\mathbf{r}(t_i))(t_{i+1} - t_i)||^2/(t_{i+1} - t_i) \qquad (4)$$

$i = 1, \ldots, I$ having determined an estimate of $(\beta_{10}, \ldots, \beta_{02})$ by least squares.

5 Results

The model is

$$d\mathbf{r}(t) = \boldsymbol{\mu}(\mathbf{r}(t))\,dt + \sigma d\mathbf{B}(t), \qquad \mathbf{r}(t) \in F \qquad (5)$$

with F a region to be described, with the potential function (2) and with $\mathbf{B}$ bivariate Brownian. The region F is the area between the 200 fathom line and Molokai.

The number of data points in the least squares analysis was 142. The parameter estimates obtained were $\hat{\beta} = (93.53, 8.00, -.47, .47, -.41)$, and $\hat{\sigma} = 4.64$ km.

Figure 7 shows the estimated potential function of (3). The particle (seal) is pulled into the middle of the concentric contours, but the Brownian term pushes it about. The final term of (2) keeps the "animal" off Molokai.

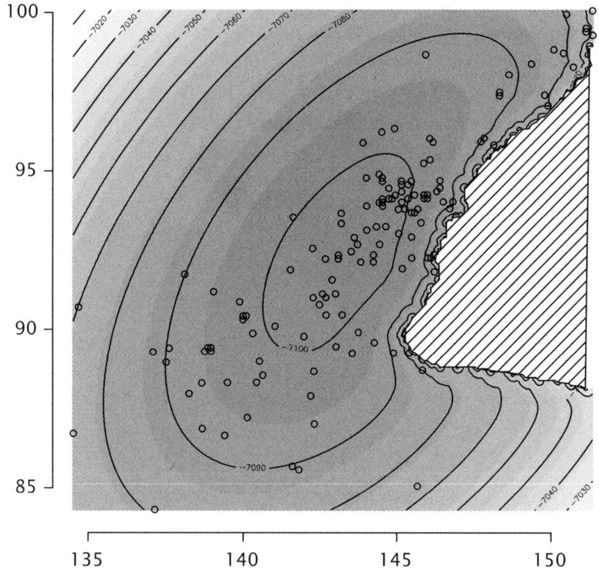

Figure 7. The fitted potential function obtained using the model (2). The darker values are deeper.

6 Validation

Figure 8 shows the results of a simulation of the process (only one was generated) taking the parameter values to be those estimated. The sampling interval $dt = t_{i+1} - t_i$ employed in the numerical integration is 1 hour. The paths were constrained to not go outside the 200 fathom line. The locations at the time points of the data set are the points plotted. This allows direct comparison with the data plot of Figure 3. The variability of Figure 8 is not unlike that of Figure 3.

The plots are "synthetic" in the language of Neyman et al. (1952), Neyman and Scott (1956). They are an exploratory tool for model validation having the possibility of suggesting how to create another model if the resemblance is not good.

Future work includes a study of measurement error, uncertainty, animal interactions and formal validation.

7 Discussion

The work searched out a stochastic model for a seal's trajectory using descriptive methods, classical dynamics and statistical techniques. Developing a pertinent potential function proved an effective manner by which to infer a model for the animal's track. There was preliminary model assessment by looking at pictures of simulations.

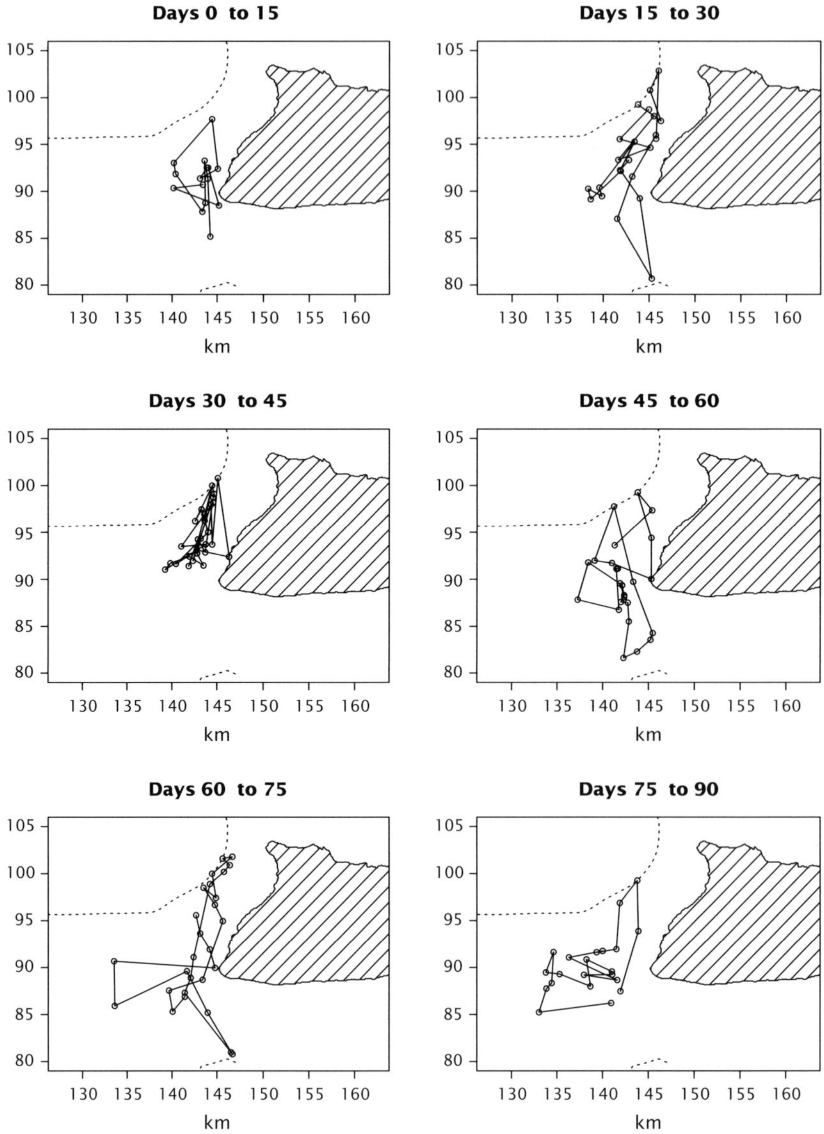

Figure 8. A simulation of the model (5) having fit the potential function (2). The times are those of the data of Figure 3.

It is to be noted that time of day was not included in model in contrast to the work of Brillinger et al. (2001a,b). The work is preliminary and circadian the effect was not considered overly strong. The work again constitutes an exploratory analysis, with the results to be examined with data to be had from other animals.

The key hypothesis accounting for the decline of Hawaiian monk seals in the primary part of their range, the Northwestern Hawaiian Islands, is that growth and survival of juvenile seals is poor owing to poor foraging success (Craig and Ragen 1999; Stewart et al. 2006). Seals in the small but growing population in the main Hawaiian Islands appear to be in better physical condition and grow faster and survive better than those in the Northwestern Hawaiian Islands. The results of the development of descriptive foraging movements of monk seals in the main Hawaiian Islands and of the simulations of movements that incorporate simple attractant and repellent elements may be helpful in further evaluating the differential dynamics. We think that those further studies, directed by these theoretical inquiries, will provide substantial insights into the reasons for the continued declines of monk seals in the Northwestern Hawaiian Islands versus the increases in the main Hawaiian Islands relative to habitat distribution and biological productivity.

Acknowledgements

Phil Spector helped with the use of the statistical package R, Ihaka and Gentleman (1996). The work of David Brillinger was partially supported by the NSF grant DMS-20051127, and that of Brent Stewart by grants from NOAA, PIFSC, and Hubbs-SeaWorld Research Institute.

References

Baker, J. D. and Johanos, T. C. (2004). Abundance of the Hawaiian monk seal in the main Hawaiian Islands. *Biological Conservation*, 116, 103–110.

Brillinger, D. R., Preisler, H. K., Ager, A. A. Kie, J., and Stewart, B. S. (2001a). Modelling movement of free-ranging animals. Technical Report 610, University of California, Berkeley, Statistics Department.

Brillinger, D. R., Preisler, H. K., Ager, A. A. and Kie, J. G. (2001b). The use of potential functions in modeling animal movement. *Data Analysis from Statistical Foundations*. Editor A. K. Mohammed E. Saleh. New York: Nova Science. Pp. 369–386.

Brillinger, D. R., Preisler, H. K., Ager, A. A., Kie, J. G. and Stewart, B. S. (2002). Employing stochastic differential equations to model wildlife motion. *Bulletin of the Brazilian Mathematical Society*, 33, 385–408.

Brillinger, David R., Stewart, B. S. and Littnan, C. L. (2006). Three months journeying of a Hawaiian monk seal. *Lecture Notes in Statistics*. To appear.

Craig, M. P. and Ragen, T. J. (1999). Body size, survival, and decline of juvenile Hawaiian monk seals, *Monachus schauinslandi*. *Marine Mammal Science*, 15, 786–809.

Heyde, C. C. (1994). A quasi-likelihood approach to estimating parameters in diffusion-type processes. *Journal of Applied Probability*, 31A, 283-290.

Ihaka, R. and Gentleman, R. (1996). R: A language for data analysis and graphics. *Journal of Graphical and Computational Statistics*, 5, 299-314.

Jonsen, I. D., Flemming, J. M. and Myers, R. A. (2005). Robust state-space modeling of animal movement data. *Ecology*, 86, 2874-2880.

Kloeden, P. E. and Platen, P. (1995). *Numerical Solution of Stochastic Differential Equations.* New York: Springer.

Nelson, E. (1967). *Dynamical Theories of Brownian Motion.* Princeton: Princeton Press.

Neyman, J. and Scott, E. L. S. (1956). The distribution of galaxies. *Scientific American*, (September), 187-200.

Neyman J., Scott, E. L. S. and Shane, C. D. (1952). On the spatial distribution of galaxies, a specific model. *The Astrophysical Journal*, 117, 92-133.

Palo, J. U., Hyvärinen, H., Helle, E., Mäkinen, H. S., and Väinölä, R. (2003). Postglacial loss of microsatellite variation in the landlocked Lake Saimaa ringed seals. *Conservation Genetics*, 4, 117-128.

Preisler, H. K., Ager, A. A., Johnson, B. K. and Kie, J. G. (2004). Modelling and animal movements using stochastic differential equations. *Environmetrics*, 15, 643-657.

Reeves, R. R., and Stewart, B. S. (2005). *Introduction to Marine Mammals of the World. Walker's Marine Mammals of the World.* The Johns Hopkins University Press. Pp. 1-64.

Reeves, R. R., Stewart, B. S., and Leatherwood, S. (1992). *The Sierra Club Handbook of Seals and Sirenians.* San Francisco: Sierra Club Books.

Reeves, R. R., Stewart, B. S., Clapham, P. J., and Powell, J. A. (2002). *Guide to Marine Mammals of the World.* New York: National Audubon Society, Alfred A. Knopf.

Sorensen, M. (1997). Estimating functions for discretely observed diffusions: a review. *Selected Proceedings of the Symposium on Estimating Functions.* Lecture Notes 32, Institute of Mathematical Statistics. Pp. 305-326.

Stewart, B. S., Antonelis, G. A., Yochem, P. K. and Baker, J. D. (2006). Foraging biogeography of Hawaiian monk seals in the northwestern Hawaiian Islands. *Atoll Research Bulletin.* In Press.

Venables, W. N. and Ripley, B. D. (2002). *Modern Applied Statistics with S, Fourth Edition.* New York: Springer.

DAVID R. BRILLINGER
Statistics Department, University of California, Berkeley, CA 94720-3860
brill@stat.berkeley.edu
http://stat-www.berkeley.edu/users/brill/

BRENT S. STEWART
Hubbs-SeaWorld Research Institute
2595 Ingraham Street, San Diego, CA 92109
http://www.hswri.org/research/scientistDisplay.cfm?sciID=7

CHARLES L. LITTNAN
Pacific Islands Fisheries Science Center
NOAA Fisheries, 2570 Dole Street, Honolulu, HI 96822

Festschrift for Tarmo Pukkila on his 60th Birthday
Eds. E. P. Liski, J. Isotalo, J. Niemelä, S. Puntanen, and G. P. H. Styan

Univ. of Tampere, 2006, ISBN 978-951-44-6620-5, pages 93–100

On the trail of Trotter's 1957 translation of Gauss's work on the theory of least squares

RICHARD WILLIAM FAREBROTHER

Abstract. In this article I trace the history of three attempts made between 1978 and 1982 to obtain a copy of Trotter's (1957) English translation of Gauss's work on the Theory of Least Squares.

1 Introduction

For almost forty years, a 1957 Princeton University technical report entitled 'Gauss's Work (1803–1826) on the Theory of Least Squares' was the only source of an English translation of much of Gauss's work in this area. This translation by Hale F. Trotter was cited several times by Churchill Eisenhart (1968) in his biographical article on Carl Friedrich Gauss for the *International Encyclopedia of the Social Sciences.*

In the early 1970s I read Eisenhart's (1968) article; however, by 1978 I had clearly forgotten the details of this reference, and the present article traces the history of my attempt to obtain a copy of Trotter's report. Note that, for the convenience of readers, I have set the Latin phrases in the earlier letters in italics although there were none in the originals.

2 First Period 1978–79

In 1978 I had started work on a history of the method of least squares and related fitting procedures and felt the need to have access to an English translation of Gauss's work in this area. I therefore wrote to Robin L. Plackett of the University of Newcastle-upon-Tyne On 6 March 1978:

> I should like to read the Princeton English translation of Gauss's *Theoria Combinationis Observationum Erroribus Minimis Obnoxiae* (1821). Do you have the reference?

The top copy of this letter soon came back to me with the annotation:

> I seem to recall that the translator was Hale F. Trotter, but no confirmation from card index and he is not in ASA directory. Suggest that you try G. S. Watson.

Following this suggestion, I wrote in the same terms to Geoffrey S. Watson of Princeton University on 13 March 1978, but received no reply. After an interlude of two months, I therefore wrote to the Librarian of Princeton University on 24 May 1978:

> In the later 1950s Gauss's *Theoria Combinationis Observationum Erroribus Minimis Obnoxiae* (1821) was translated into English by someone at Princeton University. I believe the translation was issued as a discussion paper by the Department of Statistics. A colleague suggests that the author was Hale F. Trotter.
>
> Do you think you could let me have the correct reference as I should like to order it on Inter-Library loan?

The near-coincidence of dates noted below suggests that this letter of 24 May 1978 may have served to elicit a reply to my letter of 13 March 1978, for Hale F. Trotter wrote to me on 28 June 1978:

> Professor Watson passed your enquiry about the english translation of Gauss' work on least squares on to me some time ago. I must apologise for letting it get buried under other papers and not attended to promptly.
>
> I did the translation (a hasty and not very polished job) in 1957, and it was issued as a dittograph report. No copies are now available. I have heard that it can be obtained on microcard from the AEC (Atomic Energy Commission) as AEC T. R. 3049.

About a month later, I also received a direct response dated 24 July 1978 from Frederick L. Arnold, the Reference Librarian at Princeton University:

> I'm sorry to be so long in replying to your letter of 24 May, 1978. I finally have the enclosed reply from Professor Trotter. I'm sure these Technical Reports are available through [the British Library at] Boston Spa.

Enclosed with this letter was a copy of a more detailed memorandum from Hale F. Trotter dated 29 June 1978:

> Mr Farebrother sent an enquiry earlier to Prof. Watson, who passed it on to me. I had forgotten about it, but I have now sent him the information about AEC T. R. 3049. The translation referred to was done by me in 1957 and issued as Technical Report #5 of the Statistical Techniques Research Group at Princeton. It was in fact a translation of a french translation by J. Bertrand published in 1855 of which the Fine Hall Library had (and presumably still has) a copy.
>
> In addition to the *Theoria Combinationis* ... (first part 1821, second part 1823, supplement 1826) it contains extracts from *Theoria Motus*

> *Corporum Coelestium* (1809), *Disquisitio de ellementis ellipticis Palladis* (1803–09), ...
>
> I still have *a* copy 183 8½ by 11 dittoed (purple) pages, not very suitable for reproduction. The translation is somewhat hasty and decidedly unpolished.
>
> I believe that it is available on microcard (film?) from the AEC as AEC T.R. (Technical Report?) 3049 but I have never tried to order a copy myself.

[In passing, note that the dates Trotter employs in the title of his report are explained in this document. However, the dates 1803–09 should not have been used in this way as they actually refer to the years of the observations on the asteroid Pallas.]

Armed with all this information, I approached the Inter-Library Loans Department of the John Rylands University of Manchester Library who reported almost a year later on 28 May 1979 that:

> The British Library have been unable to supply locations for this work. Other likely sources have been tried without success.

3 Second period 1979–80

Some time before the completion of these inter-library loan enquiries, I decided to follow up the suggestion in Trotter's letters myself by obtaining the address of the U.S. Atomic Energy Commission. I have a note dated "29.2.79" from Denise Kelly of the Schuster Laboratory at the University of Manchester, in which she says that:

> ...its address up to 1974 when it ceased to exist as one body and split into three was
>
> Information Office
US Atomic Energy Commission
Washington D.C. 20545

After some further delay occasioned by the wording of this note, I must have written to the Atomic Energy Commission, and they must have referred me to Microinfo Ltd., Newman Lane, Alton, Hampshire, England, (the UK agent for the National Technical Information service), for I wrote to this address on 5 March 1980:

> Please would you send me details of Atomic Energy Commission technical report 3049 "Gauss's work on least squares" written by Hale F. Trotter of Princeton University in 1957.

and received a prompt reply from Mrs H.M. Cuff of their Order Processing Department dated 10 March 1980:

> Thank you for your letter of 5 March regarding the price and availability of NTIS publications. We regret that the report you require, "Gauss's Work on Least Squares", is only available from the Library of Congress.
>
> If you wish, we can apply direct to the Library of Congress for you and obtain the report at a cost of £13.35. If you require us to order it for you, please quote the report number TT 5912019 in your confirmation.
>
> We look forward to receiving your further instructions.

I wrote a note of thanks to Mrs Cuff on 14 March 1980:

> Thank you for your letter of 10 March 1980. I have asked the University Library to order a copy of report TT 5912019.

This second application to the inter-library loans Department of the John Rylands University of Manchester Library resulted in the receipt of a copy of Trotter's report from Youngstown University Library on 3 June 1980. However, I do not recollect having made much use of this report as my father died on 9 June 1980 and, by then, I was reasonably confident of my command of the material in the French edition published by Bertrand (1855).

4 Third Period 1981–82

With the successful outcome of this phase of my enquiry, there was a second interlude of some sixteen months in my pursuit of this reference. However, in the autumn of 1981, the anticipated completion of the manuscript of a book on the history of the method of least squares and related fitting procedures prompted my renewed concern with the general availability of Trotter's translation; for I did not feel entitled to refer all potential readers to the single copy of this work in the Library at Youngstown University. I therefore followed up another lead by writing to the Library of Congress, Washington D. C., on 22 October 1981:

> I am writing a book on the history of least squares which features Hale F. Trotter's paper 'Gauss's Work (1803–1826) on the Theory of Least Squares' as a major reference. Please would you confirm that it is available as Report TT5912019 from the Library of Congress.

I received a reply dated 18 December 1981 from James L. Johnson, Technical Information Specialist in The Science and Technology Division of The Library of Congress:

> This refers to your letter of Oct. 30, 1981, in which you asked for assistance in locating a technical report "Gauss's Work (1803–1826) on the Theory of Least Squares." We were unable to identify your request.
>
> If you have any further information concerning this report, we would be happy to search further.

I wrote again at greater length on 4 January 1982:

> Thank you for your letter of December 18, 1981.
>
> I have written a book on the history of least squares which features Hale F. Trotter's paper "Gauss's Work (1803-1826) on the Theory of Least Squares" as a major reference. I should therefore like to be able to tell the reader where he may obtain a copy.
>
> The paper was originally issued in 1957 as technical report 5 of the Statistical Techniques Research Group of Princeton University. The author informed me that it was reissued by the Atomic Energy Commission as technical report 3049. I also contacted NTIS, Alton, Hants GU34 2PG, England who told me that it was only available from the Library of Congress as report TT5912019.
>
> Do you think you could trace it for me?

I received the following reply from him dated 2 April 1982:

> This refers to your request of January 4, 1982, in which you asked for assistance in locating a technical report, "Gauss's Work (1803-1826) on the Theory of Least Squares."
>
> This report was not made available to the Library of congress. However, we have identified this report as AD 142693 in the Defense Technical Information Center report collection. Therefore, we suggest that you contact:
>
> > Defense Technical Information Center
> > Cameron Station
> > Alexandria, Virginia 22314
>
> We regret that we could not assist you further.

I then wrote to the Defense Technical Information Center on 21 April 1982:

> I have written a book on the history of least squares which features Hale F. Trotter's paper "Gauss's Work (1803-1826) on the Theory of Least Squares" as a major reference. Please would you confirm that it is available from you as report AD142693.

Much to my surprise, I received a reply dated 6 May 1982 from A. M. Trudgeon in the Scientific Information Office of the British Defence Staff at the British Embassy in Washington D. C.:

> Your request to the Defence Technical Information Center was returned to us.
>
> DTIC provides its services only to organisations engaged in research and development under US Government contracts or grants and registered with them to receive Department of Defense scientific and technical information services.
>
> The document you requested, AD 142693 "Gauss's Work (1803-1826) on the Theory of Least Squares" is under the cognisance of the Department of the U. S. Army and is unclassified but has limited distribution.

> It is suggested that you contact the Ministry of Defence and supply a "need-to-know" for the requirement of this document. They may be able to help you.
>
> Ministry of Defence (Procurement Executive)
> Defence Research Information Centre
> Room 401, Station Square House
> St Mary Cray, Orpington, Kent. BR5 3RE
>
> Sorry we cannot help you here.

I then wrote to the address given in this letter, and received a reply dated 9 August 1982 from Mrs I. U. Johnson (for Head/DRIC)

> AD 142693
> *Gauss's work (1803–1826) on the theory of least squares*
>
> Thank you for your letter dated 14 May 1982 requesting a copy of the report referenced above.
>
> I regret to inform you that after extensive enquiries it has been found that the document is not currently available in the UK and as stated by the British Defence Staff, Washington, application for its release by the US authorities can only be made when substantiated by a UK Government Defence 'need-to-know'.
>
> This information must be accompanied with details of your current contract/project/research programme, and confirmed by the relevant MOD Project Officer associated with the contract.
>
> Due to the restrictions imposed upon the report any reader who indicates an interest in obtaining a copy would therefore need to provide the necessary information, as indicated above, before release could be considered providing the US authorities agree to release the report to the UK MOD.

5 Final Period 1999–2000

I would have taken delivery of this last letter on my return from Australia at the end of September 1982. As I had already managed to obtain a copy of the report itself from Youngstown University and seemed to be making no progress on this front, I abandoned any further attempt and wrote to Hale Trotter of Princeton University on 14 October 1982 listing the three sources mentioned above, but adding the Computer Science Department, Stanford University, as Gene H. Golub had advised me that they had a copy. Further, if I had remembered the original source of this reference, then I should have been able to add the name of Churchill Eisenhart of the National Bureau of Standards, Washington D. C.

In the Preface to Farebrother (1999), which grew out of the manuscript completed before December 1981, I summarised my experience in the following terms:

> For a long time I tried to obtain a copy of H. F. Trotter's (1957) translation of Gauss's work on the method of least squares, but eventually I established that the only available edition was distributed by the U. S. Army who were not willing to let me have a copy without security clearance. I therefore thought it simpler to brush up my school French and duplicate Trotter's work by translating the necessary material myself from Bertrand's (1855) edition of this work.

In December 1998 I spoke to John S. Chipman of the University of Minnesota about the difficulties I had experienced in this regard. On 13 January 1999 he wrote to me in a spirit of true friendship:

> By the way, we spoke about the good but 'top-secret' translation of Gauss; at the risk of being prosecuted for espionage, I will be glad to send you a copy.

Later, in a letter dated 25 August 1999 enclosing a copy of his review of my book, H. Leon Harter wrote:

> I'm somewhat mystified by the difficulty that you experienced in obtaining a copy of Trotter's (1957) translation of Gauss's work. I have a copy which I inherited from Paul R. Rider, my mentor and predecessor as head of the Statistics Research Group at the USAF Aerospace Research Laboratories. Our group was on the initial distribution list for reports prepared by the Princeton University Statistical Techniques Research Group under contract with the U. S. Army. I find no indication on my copy that the report bore a security classification; perhaps distribution to foreign nationals was restricted.

I clearly overstated the case in the preface to my book, but the documents from 1982 quoted above establish that this report is effectively restricted to persons with the necessary defence contacts.

On 18 October 1999 I was asked to write the successor to Eisenhart's article on Gauss for the 2001 edition of the *International Encyclopedia of the Social and Behavioural Sciences.* As part of my preparation for this work, I obtained a copy of Eisenhart's (1968) article on 13 January 2000, and finally discovered how I had known that there was an English translation of Gauss's work on the theory of least squares when my search began in 1978.

As a postscript to this account, I should note that the development of modern electronic data bases makes enquiries of the type outlined above relatively easy. Given the author's name alone, a search on the database 'WorldCat', available at many academic libraries, reveals seventeen library locations in the United States and one in Canada for this work. Ironically,

Princeton University Library is one of the sources identified in this way. The current Princeton Library catalogue shows that it now holds at least two copies of Trotter's report in pamphlet form and one on microfilm although it presumably held none in 1978.

References

Bertrand, J. L. F. (1855). *Méthode des Moindres Carrés: Mémoires sur la Combinaison des Observations par Ch.-Fr. Gauss.* Paris: Mallet-Bachelier.

Eisenhart, C. (1968). Carl Friedrich Gauss (1777–1855). In *International Encyclopedia of the Social Sciences* (Vol. 6). Ed. D. Sills. New York. Pp. 75–81.

Farebrother, R. W. (1999). *Fitting Linear Relationships: A History of the Calculus of Observations 1750–1900.* New York: Springer-Verlag.

Trotter, H. F. (1957). Gauss's work (1803–1826) on the theory of least squares. Technical Report 5, *Statistical Techniques Research Group*, Princeton University.

RICHARD WILLIAM FAREBROTHER
11 Castle Road, Bayston Hill, Shrewsbury, United Kingdom
bill.farebrother@manchester.ac.uk
http://les.man.ac.uk/ses/staff/bf/

Festschrift for Tarmo Pukkila on his 60th Birthday
Eds. E. P. Liski, J. Isotalo, J. Niemelä, S. Puntanen, and G. P. H. Styan

Univ. of Tampere, 2006, ISBN 978-951-44-6620-5, pages 101–113

Building econometric models with large data sets

Clive W. J. Granger & Yongil Jeon

Abstract. Economists and other researchers encounter large data sets in their day-to-day activities. However, current forms of statistical and econometric procedures may not be adequate or appropriate for a large data set. This paper considers the impact of large data sets on the econometric modelling process. Having large scaled data allows us to refine our modelling and estimation techniques, although increased data availability does not necessarily provide feasible solutions to many unsolved research problems. This paper discusses modelling issues that occur with linear regression models, time series settings, causality, and panel data sets when using a large data set.

Key words and phrases: Large data sets; Econometric modelling.

1 Introduction

It is becoming more common-place for economists to encounter large data sets, as is also happening in many other fields. It is, then, often found that the traditional statistical and econometric procedures proposed in the standard textbooks are no longer adequate or appropriate. Two previous papers by Granger (1998) [denoted G1] and Granger (2003) [denoted G2] have considered the various types of large data sets that might be found in economics and some of the consequences for basic statistical and econometric procedures. In this paper, we go beyond these previously discussed areas and consider the impact of having large data sets on the econometric modelling process. Since model selection is a broad subject to discuss, we plan to touch just a few of the main points concerned with it. Our discussion concentrates on the amount of data and pays no attention to the data quality, which is a separate and very important question. It will be seen that having lots of data allows us to appreciate and refine our modelling and estimation techniques without being concerned about having insufficient information.

Where a sample size is indicated, the standard notation is to use K for a thousand together with M for a million and B for a billion. So that K times K = M, K times M = B and thus 2M times 3K equals 6B. A large sample of size

n will be at least $n = 10\text{K}$ and more likely $n = 50\text{K}$ or greater. In this paper, we will mostly be concerned with M's.

In G1, it is pointed out that any statistical technique that is $O(1/n)$ will become irrelevant for large samples. This comment includes concepts such as 'small-sample adjustments', bias adjustments such as the jackknife, the AIC and BIC model selection criteria and measures of relative efficiency. In a standard ordinary least squares (OLS) regression, the t-tests, F-tests and chi-squared tests will take simple asymptotic forms so that the t- and chi-squared statistics go to the normal distribution and F-statistic to the value unity. We will escape the 'degrees of freedom' question for these tests as they all go to very large values that may not be in the tables and are no longer relevant.

Procedures that are designed to effectively expand the data set, such as the bootstrap and Bayesian estimation methods will be of little relevance as there is no more data needed. For purposes of inference, perhaps the biggest losses for most researchers are the standard confidence intervals, such as those based on the commonly used 95% and 99% levels. G1 states that "virtually all specific null hypotheses will be rejected using present standards". For example, if you test that "the mean = 6," it will always be rejected, whereas a hypothesis encompassing a wider set of possible values such as "the mean is in the range 5 to 7" may not be.

As previously stated, in this paper attention is turned to the process of modelling when there is plenty of data. Initially, we discuss the standard linear regression model which forms the main framework of most modern econometrics textbooks and is also very widely used in practice. Later consideration is given to a number of other models and situations.

2 The linear regression model

The usual regression model takes the form:

$$Y_t = c + \sum_{j=1}^{k} b_j X_{j,t} + \varepsilon_t \qquad \text{for } t = 1, \ldots, n \tag{2.1}$$

where Y_t is called the 'dependent variable', the $X_{j,t}$'s are the 'independent variables' and ε_t is the 'error term'. In this regression, Y_t will be taken to be a single variable, but possibly a time series is considered. Y_t could be a vector of series, but that is a rather complicated case with which to start the discussion. The "explanatory" terms, $X_{j,t}$'s, are also time series, k in number. In practice, we do not know the value of k nor what variables to include in the $X_{j,t}$'s. That is what the process of modelling should tell us.[1]

[1] It can also be noted that a linear form has been used for the equation, presumably based on an "assumption of convenience", which is probably not itself based on any deep economic theory.

Several econometrics textbooks indicate this model. Here, quotations are from Wooldridge (2003). The standard questions considered are: how well can one estimate the parameters b, are these estimates near the 'true value', how well does the full model fit and can we say that it is better than some alternative model? The answers may depend on the type of estimation that is used, such as the Ordinary Least Squares (OLS) or Maximum Likelihood (ML) procedures. The results of interest here are essentially of two types; the first considers what happens to the estimated model as n increases up to a 'moderate size', and the second type considers the asymptotic case as n becomes very large. Although both are interesting, we will naturally concentrate on the latter.

Wooldridge (2003, pp. 149–151) in discussing the application of OLS to systems or panels derives results of the form:

$$(\text{estimated } b) - (\text{true } b) = \frac{W}{\sqrt{n}} \tag{2.2}$$

where W is some normally distributed random variable with a specified variance matrix, b is a vector and n is the sample size. Thus, as n increases, the estimated b draws closer to its true value in some specific sense. It is seen that as n gets very large, we get an excellent estimate of b. It follows that if a particular $X_{j,t}$ does not belong in the set of explanatory variables, then its corresponding b_j value will tend to zero. Conversely, any $X_{j,t}$ that does belong in the explanatory set should get a non-zero b_j. However, as there is virtually no uncertainty left (except in the residual), the t-value around the true b is almost zero and the F-statistic for the equation is one. The equation now looks like a dry stick, with true non-zero b_j's attached to some explanatory variables and all other variables dropped from the right hand side. If other sets of explanatory variables were considered, other equations of the same form would result but with different R^2. The alternative equations would be compared and the best one is chosen as that having the highest R^2. No test is required.

Equation (2.2) is a consistency result as discussed by Wooldridge in his section 5.1 (from page 166). There are also plenty of examples of OLS estimates that are inconsistent estimates. For example, Wooldridge on his page 169 has a discussion about what is essentially an omitted (explanatory) variable bias. When this occurs, the estimated b does not tend to the true b. The resulting equation is still a dry stick without any associated stochastic terms, but presumably with a lower R^2 value.

The Lagrange Multiplier (LM) test for exclusion restrictions is potentially important and is discussed by Wooldridge on page 175. In the regression (2.1), there are k included explanatory variables ($X_{j,t}$'s) along with m other variables ($Z_{j,t}$'s) that are candidates for inclusion. The null hypothesis being considered is: if they had been included, would they all have zero estimated coefficients? The test is based on two regressions:

(a) regress Y_t on the basic set of k explanatory variables ($X_{j,t}$'s), producing a residual u_t

(b) regress u_t on all of the $k + m$ possible explanatory variables ($X_{j,t}$'s and $Z_{j,t}$'s), producing an equation with measure of goodness of fit R_u^2

The test statistic is

$$\mathrm{LM} = n \cdot R_u^2 \tag{2.3}$$

The decision about this statistic is to compare it to the appropriate critical value in a chi-squared distribution with m degrees of freedom. Note that m is at the choice of the investigator.

In theory, if the only relevant explanatory variables are the first k then the theoretical value for R_u^2 should be zero and so LM should be zero. However, if any of the new m variables have any connection to Y_t, then R_u^2 will take some positive value and LM will be large if n is large. The possibility of getting spurious relationships seems to be substantial. A simulation of this situation is discussed in the next section.

3 A simulation of the LM test and regression case

In the simple time series case for the regression shown in (2.1), Y_t will be some series being modelled. $X_{j,t}$'s could be one or two possible explanatory series, possibly lagged once, and a few lags of Y_t and of the $X_{j,t}$'s. The other possible m explanatory series could be other series and further lags of those already used. The availability of lag terms in the context of time series increases the chances of being able to model the dynamics of the system which include seasonal effects, business cycles and other long-run movements. It also increases the chances of generating spurious lagged relationships.

A spurious regression may come from two different types of misspecifications. One is adding irrelevant variables and the other is dropping relevant variables when we search over different model specifications. Our simulations in this section will show that the basic 'spurious regression' results hold the same for all sample sizes! Thus, if you have a pair of highly autocorrelated series which are independent of each other in an OLS regression you are likely to obtain a spurious relationship regardless of sample size.

The dependent variable Y_t is generated from $Y_t = \sum_{j=1}^{k} X_{j,t} + \varepsilon_t$, for $t = 1, \ldots, n$, as we explained in Section 2, and all the $X_{j,t}$'s have a coefficient of 1. Each $X_{j,t}$ is generated independently from an AR(1): $X_{j,t} = \alpha X_{j,t-1} + \zeta_t$, $j = 1, \ldots, k$, with a white noise of ζ_t and $\alpha = 0.7$ is chosen for each series. We can consider a further set of explanatory variables $Z_{j,t}$, $j = k + 1, k + 2, \ldots, k + m$, which are each generated in the same way as the $X_{j,t}$'s. The $Z_{j,t}$'s are *not* used to generate the Y_t, but a researcher would not know this fact and could ask if they should be included.

A standard test, such as the LM test, assumes that we know some of the actual $X_{j,t}$'s, but in practice this is usually not true. The question is: does the LM test (which has a good reputation) perform well in complicated and large sample situations? Four simulations were run to answer this question;

(i) a simple model with a small sample; that is, $m = k = 5$, $n = 400$

(ii) a simple model with a large sample; $m = k = 5$, $n = 10{,}000$

(iii) a sophisticated model with a small sample; $m = k = 30$, $n = 400$

(iv) a sophisticated model with a large sample; $m = k = 30$, $n = 10{,}000$

Our experiments on the LM statistic over 2000 iterations (available upon request) confirms well-known statistical facts that the distribution moves to the right where the critical values increase as the degrees of freedom increase. But the shapes of empirical distributions do not change under different degrees of freedoms. That is, the sample size does not change the shape of the empirical distribution.

In the second stage regression of the LM test, a residual obtained from the first stage, u_t, is regressed on all the $X_{j,t}$'s and the $Z_{j,t}$'s. We total the number of statistically significant irrelevant variables as $Z_{j,t}$'s in each second stage regression and Figure 1 provides their frequency tables over 2000 iterations. We can conclude that the sample size does not have a significant effect on the number of included irrelevant variables. The simple model specifications ($m = k = 5$) include a roughly 20% chance of including irrelevant variables in an incorrect way, regardless of the sample size. In contrast, the sophisticated model's specifications ($m = k = 30$) have at least one irrelevant variable chosen incorrectly with an approximately 60% chance. This problem does not change with the sample size, and the maximum percentages are roughly the same regardless of the sample sizes or whether the irrelevant variables are included or not.[2]

Interestingly, Figure 1 indicates the increased difficulty with modelling on a larger scale. Thus, we consider modelling strategies that allow the use of large scaled data in the regression. The data are generated with the same process as before, $Y_t = \sum_{j=1}^{k} X_{j,t} + \varepsilon_t$, and then two different models are estimated.

$$y_t = \hat{\beta}_0 + \hat{\beta}_1 x_{1t} + \cdots + \hat{\beta}_k x_{kt} + \hat{\gamma}_1 z_{1t} + \cdots + \hat{\gamma}_m z_m \tag{3.1}$$

$$y_t = \hat{\beta}_0 + \hat{\beta}_1 x_{1t} + \cdots + \hat{\beta}_k x_{kt} \tag{3.2}$$

Figure 2 provides simulated R^2's over 2000 iterations with several notable findings (shown only for model 3.1). First, R^2 is quite high in both estimated models (bigger than 0.9). Second, R^2 for the model (3.1) is slightly higher than, but not equal to, the R^2 in the model (3.2). Thus, adding even irrelevant variables increases the mean and median R^2 value slightly but not

[2]The results are available upon request.

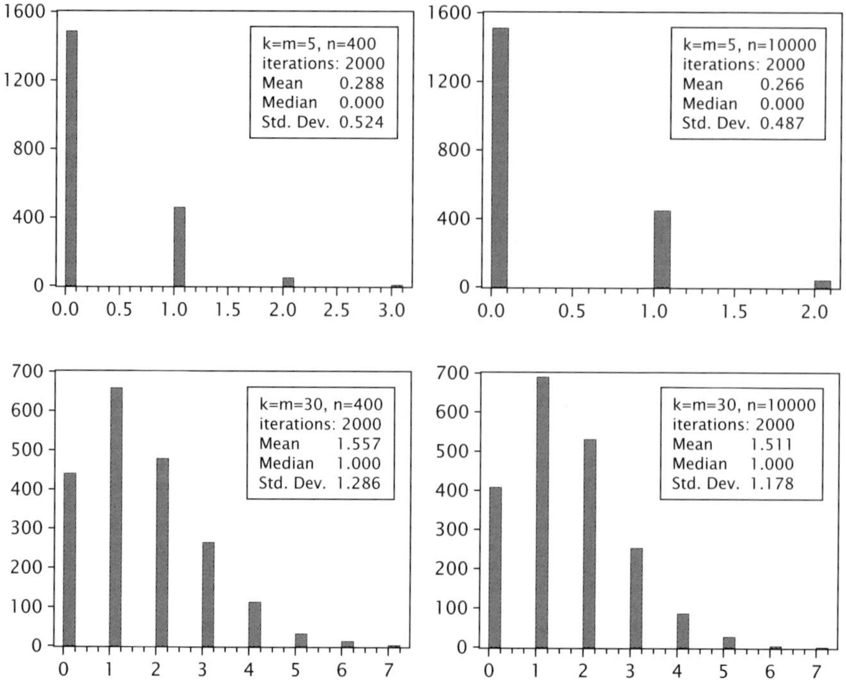

Figure 1. The number of statistically significant irrelevant variables (with 2000 iterations). The vertical-axis indicates the frequency out of 2000 simulations and the horizontal-axis represents the number of irrelevant variables identified.

significantly, which reflects the theoretical fact that the R^2 never decreases when any variable is added to a regression. Third, even though the mean and median for R^2 are similar as the sample size increases, the standard deviations decrease as $n \to \infty$ in both models.[3]

In both regressions, all relevant variables $X_{j,t}$'s are found to be statistically significant by rejecting the null hypothesis of H_0: $\beta_j = 0$, $j = 1, \ldots, k$. Also, we test H_0: $\gamma_i = 0$ for $i = 1, \ldots, m$. The simulation results (not shown here) replicate those of Figure 1. That is, simple model specifications include irrelevant variables with a 20% chance of occurrence while sophisticated model specifications occur with an approximately 60% chance. Also, we test H_0: $\beta_j = 1$, for $j = 1, \ldots, k$. The frequency patterns in dropping statistically insignificant relevant variables, are quite similar in both small and large data sets. When $m = k = 5$, approximately 20% of equations have one wrong term. In contrast, when $m = k = 30$, approximately 55% of equations have at least one incorrect term. We calculate the number of significant variables as k

[3]The Durbin Watson statistics (not shown here) do not indicate any serious serial correlations in the residual terms with large samples, despite the fact that the Durbin Watson statistics are biased toward negative correlations with small samples in both simple and sophisticated models.

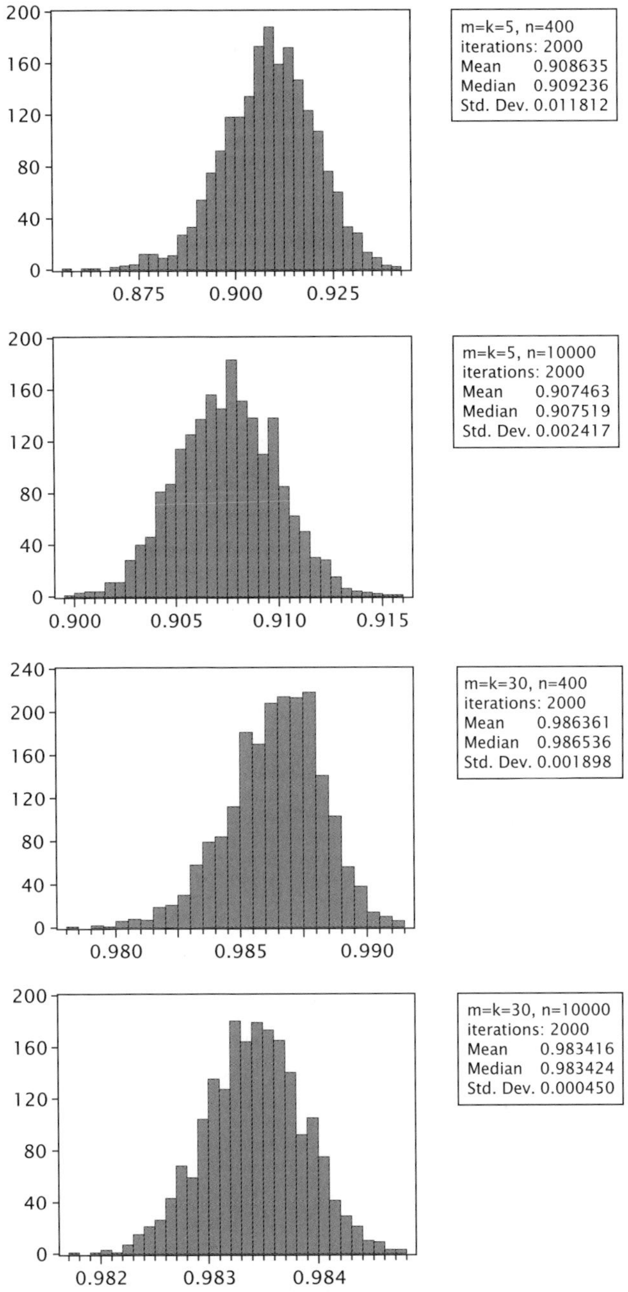

Figure 2. The frequency tables: R^2's from the estimated model (3.1) with 2000 iterations. The vertical-axis indicates the frequency out of 2000 simulations and the horizontal-axis represents R^2.

minus the number of statistically insignificant relevant variables $X_{j,t}$'s *plus* the number of statistically significant irrelevant variables $Z_{j,t}$'s.[4] Figure 3 indicates when $m = k = 5$ (that is at most 10 variables), the numbers of statistically significant variables are distributed between 1 to 8. In large scaled models (when $m = k = 30$), only 22 to 36 variables are significant. Each of the diagrams is symmetric, and the patterns do not change with the size of the sample. In terms of misspecification using the techniques discussed here, the amount of data available appears to have very little impact.

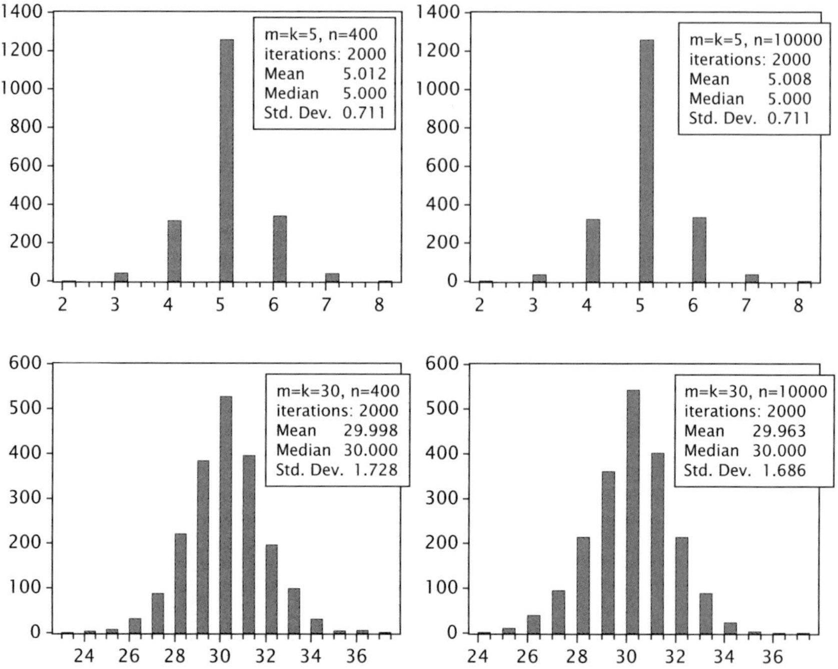

Figure 3. The frequency tables: the number of statistically significant variables with 2000 iterations

4 Time series models

In the typical textbook analysis of the standard regression model (2.1), the basic form of the model is chosen at the start of the analysis and is maintained throughout. For example, in (2.1) the values of k and m which are the numbers of included and possibly excluded variables are unchanged as the sample size n increases. This is quite unrealistic, as most researchers would

[4]We refer to the number of statistically insignificant relevant variables as some $X_{j,t}$'s which cannot reject H_0: $\hat{\beta}_j = 1$, for $j = 1, \dots, k$, and we refer to the number of statistically significant irrelevant variables as some $Z_{j,t}$ which cannot reject H_0: $\hat{\gamma}_i = 0$, for $i = 1, \dots, m$.

consider exploring further possibilities, different types of model and formulations when the amount of data is not a limitation and when computing is fast, cheap and plentiful. There should be explorations about what variables belong in the basic, starting k terms in the regression and how many extra variables to include in the expanded m set. Will it matter if these variables are almost collinear, such as alternative definitions of unemployment or GNP?

When considering a fairly simple time series model the question that will naturally arise is whether or not the parameters are constant over time or change in some simple way. There can be structural breaks in the system, changes in laws or institutions or just gradual developments in tastes or economic behavior. When a known break occurs, it can be specifically introduced into the constant and by multiplying some parameters. A more general approach is to allow parameters to change over time using a regime-switching format such as Hamilton (1989) or the more flexible form based on the Kalman filter and a state-space representation (Harvey 1989). These parameter-changing models will be often found to fit the data better, but are frequently difficult to explain based on our knowledge of the economy.[5]

It may be possible with a large sample to obtain data for an 'implied experiment', in which most of the sample respond correctly to a question about the value of an important economic variable such as the short-term interest rate, whereas a small percentage believe that this rate is something different. For example, if the short-term interest rate is currently 5% but 10% of the sample thinks that it is 7% (assuming rationality), the analyst can reach conclusions about the effects on various parts of the economy from a rise in interest rates. Naturally, it will be important to see if the forecasts made by such implied experiments in the past were supported by actual observations on the economy.

It is an observed property of many macro and financial series that they have to be differenced to become stationary. For this reason they are called integrated of order one, denoted I(1), and a stationary series is denoted I(0). It is possible that a linear combination of I(1) series is I(0), and this is called cointegration. When a group of series is cointegrated, they must be generated by a particular multivariate set of equations known as the 'error-correction system'.

The large sample situation adds little here as the various important tests are stated in an asymptotic form. For example, the first test for I(1) for Y_t, by Dickey and Fuller (1979), consists of forming the regression

$$Y_t - Y_{t-1} = c + bY_{t-1} + e_t \tag{4.1}$$

[5]In recent years large samples have been frequently encountered in cross-section studies, sometimes with many explanatory variables but often producing 'dry-sticks' with quite low R^2 values. Of course with cross-section data there is no question of having time-varying parameters, the parameters could vary across regions but this would be picked up with region-specific dummies being included in the explanatory variables.

and then testing the null of $b = 0$ against $b < 0$.[6] Then, we turn to cointegration in the bivariate case with two I(1) variables, X_t and Y_t, to find the linear combination $X_t + bY_t$. I(0) is well known to be "super-efficient", so with a large sample any group of cointegrations should be estimated very well.[7] The error-correction model will be like the regression models discussed above in Section 2, with little or no uncertainty around the estimated parameter values, unless many lags of the explanatory variables are considered to be required or if time-varying parameters are implemented. It seems that most of the practical problems that arise with analysis based on standard size samples will not be present with large samples. However, the usual problems of economic interpretation of the results will certainly remain.

5 Modelling strategies

The more data availability with fewer computing limitations suggests that modelling should explore more diverse specifications and that the restrictions we have suffered under in the past should be forgotten. While it is certainly correct that we can consider many models, there are too many options to accurately consider all the possibilities. Therefore, it is important to specify quite clearly what the objectives of the modelling process are before widening our search. Some of the common objectives are:

(a) asking if a variable is really "explanatory", so that it is potentially useful as an indicator of some kind

(b) estimating a parameter that has some economic importance

(c) building a model useful for forecasting

(d) building a policy model

Some of these objectives are easy to evaluate while others are much less so. It will no longer be relevant to only think in terms of the linear regression model considered in Section 2. Rather than just considering the mean of Y_t conditional on the X_t's, it will now be necessary to consider the whole distribution of Y_t conditional on the X_t's. This makes the modelling process not only more difficult, but more exciting. It is clear that if the tails of the distribution are of particular interest, then a great deal of data may be required to get a satisfactory estimate, although we are not sure how well developed a class of estimates relevant for the quantiles is for multi-dimensional distributions.

---

[6]Wooldridge, page 609, gives the asymptotic critical values for significance levels of 1% to 10%, which are the values most used in practice. On page 612 Wooldridge gives the corresponding values for the test when it includes a linear trend.

[7]If the number of cointegrations is small compared to the number of variables involved, then again the cointegrations should be easy to identify and estimate. The actual cointegrations cannot be identified, only the linear constraints within which they lie.

Classes of non-linear terms for explanatory variables may be considered such as the neural network models. Although, our impression is that the linear regression with time-varying parameters is a better alternative. Taking a non-linear transformation of the dependent variable, such as squaring, taking the absolute value or the logarithm or the Box–Cox transform is essentially changing the objective of the modelling exercise. It can be done, but there should be a good reason for it.

The concept known as Granger causality asks the question: if Y_t is forecast using a set of explanatory variables X_{t-j} where X_t should be a vector, can Y_t be better forecast by X_{t-j} and Z_{t-j}? ($j > 0$ in all cases). If the answer is positive, then Z Granger-causes Y with respect to X.[8] Having lots of data allows a variety of different types of model to be considered and therefore a deeper analysis attempted. When testing for this causality, the test is better if X_t, the vector of other explanatory variables, is as large as possible. With large data sets we should not have to worry about spurious fits by 'explanatory' variables and so the forecasting test should perform correctly. The test should be in distribution, but the standard methods will only consider mean or variance.

The area of economics that has made possibly the greatest increase in attention to size in the last decade is panel data in the fields of finance, marketing, and sections of micro-economics. If we describe the size of a panel in term of $[N, T]$, where N is the number of cross-section units and T the number of time terms, then traditionally N was rather large, in the several K range but T was very small, say just 5 or 6. However, in recent years panels can be both N and T in the thousands.[9]

When T was a very small number, panel analysis would make a "poolability" assumption which stated that every unit in the N-dimension (state, region, company, person etc) would obey a model having exactly the same dynamics. Since there has been very little time data available, this assumption was usually difficult to disprove even though it seemed unlikely to be correct. Eventually, data with large enough T became available and the poolability assumption was tested and often rejected (Jeon 2005).

It is clear that some sensible, parsimonious model needs to be considered and the one that is conceptually the most obvious is a factor model. If a relatively few common factors could be determined to explain the majority of the relationship between the N dependent variables, then each variable could be lagged on several of its own lags plus some lags of the common

[8] It should be noted that the definition is about forecasting and not about the quality of fit of a model, so the comments about forecast evaluation in the previous paragraph continue to hold.

[9] Just for purposes of consideration, suppose that $N = 10\text{K}$ and $T = 1\text{K}$, so that we have ten thousand long time series to analyse, given a late 20th century viewpoint. The natural model to think about would be the Vector Autoregressive (VAR), and a fairly modest number of lags would be $q = 10$, for instance. The lag parameter matrix would contain N^2 terms, i.e. 100M. With 10 lags this gives a total number of 1B terms to be estimated, which is not only possibly too many to actually perform the estimation but is way too many to try to interpret.

factor. Methods to discover the common factors need to be determined, but a sensible start has been proposed by Vahid (1999), for example.

6 Conclusion

Having more data does not necessarily make things easier for the empirical economist or econometrician. As pointed out in G2, we can now consider a wider variety of specifications, discover more subtle effects, distinguish between close specifications, obtain better estimates of parameters, do better out-of-sample evaluation, and attempt types of analysis not previously possible.

However, we have not made any attempt to survey all of the results that are available in this area, as that would be a daunting task.[10] Without constraints on data or computing, there is no reason to stay with a single model specification. In many situations, it is helpful to have several alternative models to consider. We call this 'thick modelling' as compared to 'thin modelling' when there is a single model (Granger and Jeon 2004). With lots of data and a specific goodness of fit measure for a model such as a loss function or the likelihood, some models will appear to be clearly inferior to others and should be discarded. If a sufficiently rich variety of models are considered, there should remain several of similar quality that will make up the thick set. Decision makers seem to find it helpful to have results from several models to compare rather than just a single number, when making their decisions.

Large data sets will be encountered with greater probability into the future. This means we should be prepared to re-write the textbooks, alter our basic courses and become mentally prepared for what should be an exciting period.

References

Dickey, D. A. and Fuller, W. A. (1979). Distribution of the estimators for autoregressive time series with a unit root. *Journal of the American Statistical Association*, 74, 427–431.

Granger, C. W. J. (1998). Extracting information from mega-panels and high frequency data. *Statistica Neerlandica*, 52, 258–272.

Granger, C. W. J. (2003). Some methodological questions arising from large data sets. In *Computer-Aided Econometrics*. Edited by D. E. Giles. Marcel Decker, Inc. Pp. 1–9.

Granger, C. W. J. and Jeon, Y. (2004). Thick modeling. *Economic Modelling*, 21, 323–343.

Granger, C. W. J. and Hendry, D. (2005). A dialog concerning a new instrument for econometric modeling. *Econometric Theory*, forthcoming.

Hamilton, J. D. (1989). A new approach to the economic analysis of nonstationary time series and the business cycle. *Econometrica*, 57, 357–384.

Harvey, A. (1989). *Forecasting, Structural Time Series Models and the Kalman Filter.* Cambridge University Press.

[10] David Hendry's automatic modelling procedure PC-GIVE has been tried with large data sets and found to work well (Granger and Hendry 2005).

Jeon, Y. (2005). Information advantages from modelling state-level coincident indexes. Central Michigan University Working Paper.

Vahid, F. (1999). Partial pooling: a possible answer to 'To pool or not to pool'. In *Cointegration, Causality, and Forecasting.* Edited by R. F. Engle and H. White. Oxford University Press. Pp. 410–428.

Wooldridge, J. M. (2003). *Introductory Econometrics* (2nd ed.). Cincinnati, Ohio: South-Western College Publishing.

CLIVE W. J. GRANGER
Department of Economics, University of California
San Diego, La Jolla, CA 92093-0508
cgranger@ucsd.edu
http://weber.ucsd.edu/~cgranger/

YONGIL JEON
Department of Economics
Central Michigan University, Mount Pleasant, MI 48859
yjeon@mail.cmich.edu

Festschrift for Tarmo Pukkila on his 60th Birthday
Eds. E. P. Liski, J. Isotalo, J. Niemelä, S. Puntanen, and G. P. H. Styan

Univ. of Tampere, 2006, ISBN 978-951-44-6620-5, pages 115–125

Copula models for estimating outstanding claim provisions

TÕNU KOLLO & GAIDA PETTERE

Abstract. The bivariate distribution of two variables is modelled using copulas. The two variables of interest are the claim size and the time from the moment when claim occurred to the moment when the payment out has been made. Approximations to the distributions of both variables have been found as well as the bivariate distribution modelled using Archimedean copulas. Data examined come from a Latvian insurance company. A method for estimating outstanding claim provisions is suggested. The results are illustrated by graphs and tables.

2000 MSC codes: 62E17, 62H12.

Key words and phrases: Archimedean copula; Claim distribution; Clayton copula; Frank copula; Gumbel copula; Outstanding claim provisions.

1 Introduction

The authors have been inspired by the track of interests of Professor Tarmo Pukkila – from multivariate statistical methods to insurance mathematics. The paper can be considered as a tiny attempt in this direction. There has been growing interest to the modelling of financial and actuarial data by copulas in recent years (see Cherubini et al. (2004), Clemen and Reilly (1999), Klugman and Parsa (1999), for example). In insurance mathematics Archimedean copulas have become a common tool since Frees and Valdes (1998). Usually claim size and expenses allocated to each claim have been the two variables of interest in copula models. We accentuate to the claim size and its development in time. The variable "development factor" measures time from the moment when claim occurred to the moment when the company pays out the sum. These two variables form the basis for estimating outstanding claim provisions. As the variables are correlated we need to take into account their joint distribution in the modelling process. The analysis is based on claims of a Latvian insurance company. In Section 2 we give a short summary of necessary notions and notation from the copula theory. Archimedean copulas are of the main interest. In Section 3 we describe the data: correlation coefficients between the variables are found and basic characteristics of the marginal distributions given. When finding approximations to the distributions of the random variables of interest the least squares method was used. In Section 4 several copula models for the joint distribution are examined and goodness-of-fit tests applied. Three classes of Archimedean copulas (Clayton, Frank and Gumbel) form the set of used models. Finally we describe the estimation of outstanding claim provisions on the basis of the found models. All the calculations have been made using MathCad and Microsoft Excel software.

2 Notions and results from the copula theory

Copulas have become an intensively used method in modelling of financial data in recent years. Frees and Valdes (1998), Durrleman et al. (2000), Lindskog (2000), Rank (2000), Cherubini and Luciano (2001), Jouanin et al. (2001), Roncalli (2001), de Matteis (2001), Embrechts et al. (2003), Luciano and Marena (2003) are referred to here from the long list of existing studies. For additional references Cherubini et al. (2004) can be recommended. Our intension is to use bivariate copulas to model a bivariate random vector.

Bivariate copula is the joint distribution function of two uniformly distributed random variables:

$$C(u,v) = P(U \leq u, V \leq v),$$

where $U, V \sim U(0,1)$. Let X and Y be two random variables with distribution functions F and G respectively. As $F(X)$ and $G(Y)$ are uniformly distributed, we may take $F(X) = U$, $G(Y) = V$ and get the copula in the following form

$$\begin{aligned} C(F(x), G(y)) &= P(F(X) \leq F(x), G(Y) \leq G(y)) \\ &= P(X \leq x, Y \leq y) = F_{X,Y}(x,y). \end{aligned}$$

This means we have been able to present the joint distribution function of X and Y as a copula. Our aim is to find the best Archimedean copula. Bivariate Archimedean copulas are attractive in two reasons. Firstly, Archimedean copulas are characterized by one scalar parameter, which can be presented through a rank correlation coefficient (Spearman or Kendall) between the two variables. Secondly, due to Genest and Rivest (1993) an algorithm is available to check the fit of the obtained model with the data using univariate Kolmogorov-Smirnov test-statistic (see also Genest et al. 1995). Necessary notions and notation are given below.

Definition 1. If the copula $C(u,v)$ can be presented of the form

$$C(u,v) = \varphi^{-1}(\varphi(u) + \varphi(v)) \tag{1}$$

for a continuous strictly decreasing function φ from $[0,1]$ to $[0,\infty)$ with $\varphi(1) = 0$, we call the copula Archimedean. The function φ in (1) is called the generator of the copula.

Detailed list of different classes of Archimedean copulas can be found in Nelsen (1999), pp. 94–97, their properties and fitting problems are carefully studied in the thesis de Matteis (2001), for example.

There exist several classes of Archimedean copulas, which are of particular interest in financial applications. Some important classes are presented in the following Table 1 (Nelsen 1999; Frees and Valdes 1998).

Table 1. Archimedean copulas.

Family	Generator φ	Copula $C(u,v)$
Independent	$-\ln t$	uv
Clayton	$(t^{-\theta}-1)/\theta, \quad \theta > 0$	$(u^{-\theta}+v^{-\theta}-1)^{-1/\theta}$
Gumbel	$(-\ln t)^{\theta}, \quad \theta \geq 1$	$\exp\{-[(-\ln u)^{\theta}+(-\ln v)^{\theta}]^{1/\theta}\}$
Frank	$-\ln \frac{e^{-\theta t}-1}{e^{-\theta}-1}, \quad 0 < \lvert\theta\rvert < \infty$	$-\frac{1}{\theta}\ln\left(1+\frac{(e^{-\theta u}-1)(e^{-\theta v}-1)}{e^{-\theta}-1}\right)$

Family	Kendall's τ	Spearman's ρ
Independent	0	0
Clayton	$\theta/(\theta+2)$	complicated
Gumbel	$1-\theta^{-1}$	no explicit form
Frank	$1-\frac{4}{\theta}[D_1(-\theta)-1]$	$1-\frac{12}{\theta}[D_2(-\theta)-D_1(-\theta)]$

In Table 1 D_1 and D_2 denote the Debye functions defined as

$$D_k(x) = \frac{k}{x^k}\int_0^x \frac{t^k}{e^t-1}\,dt, \qquad k = 1,2.$$

For negative arguments we have (Frees and Valdes 1998):

$$D_k(-x) = D_k(x) + \frac{kx}{k+1}.$$

The procedure suggested by Genest and Rivest (1993) to identify an Archimedean copula defined by a generator φ is based on the following argument. From bivariate data (x_i, y_i), $i = 1,\ldots,n$ we construct values of a univariate pseudovariable Z:

$$z_i = \frac{\#\{(x_j,y_j) : x_j < x_i,\ y_j < y_i\}}{n-1}, \qquad i = 1,\ldots,n. \tag{2}$$

In Genest and Rivest (1993) it is proved that $F_Z(x) = K_{\varphi}(x)$, where

$$K_{\varphi}(x) = x - \frac{\varphi(x)}{\varphi'(x)} \tag{3}$$

with $\varphi'(x)$ being the derivative of $\varphi(x)$.

Now the standard procedure of Kolmogorov-Smirnov criteria can be used to compare empirical distribution function $F_n(x)$ of z_i and $K_{\varphi}(x)$.

3 Data description

The data under consideration consists of 1123 claims. The claim size is measured in Latvian currency, LVL. Basic characteristics of the claim size are presented in the following Table 2.

Table 2. Characteristics of claim size.

Mean	319.61	Kurtosis	86.43
Standard Error	19.31	Skewness	8.22
Median	172.15	Range	9000
Mode	0	Minimum	0
Standard Deviation	647.75	Maximum	9000
Sample Variance	419577.04	Sum	358916.93
		Sample size	1123

As one can see from Table 2, the distribution is heavily skewed. Skewness measure β_1 is 8.22 and the sample mean is almost twice bigger than sample median: while the sample mean equals 319.61 LVL, the sample median is only 172.15 LVL. The empirical distribution was modelled by four distributions: Pareto, Γ-distribution, lognormal, and Wald (inverse Gaussian) distribution. From these four classes of distributions only lognormal and Wald distributions gave satisfactory models. The lognormal distribution was used in the following parameterization: random variable X is lognormally distributed with parameters μ and σ, if $\ln X = Y \sim N(\mu, \sigma)$, where $EY = \mu$ and $DY = \sigma^2$. The best fitting lognormal density is sketched in Figure 1.

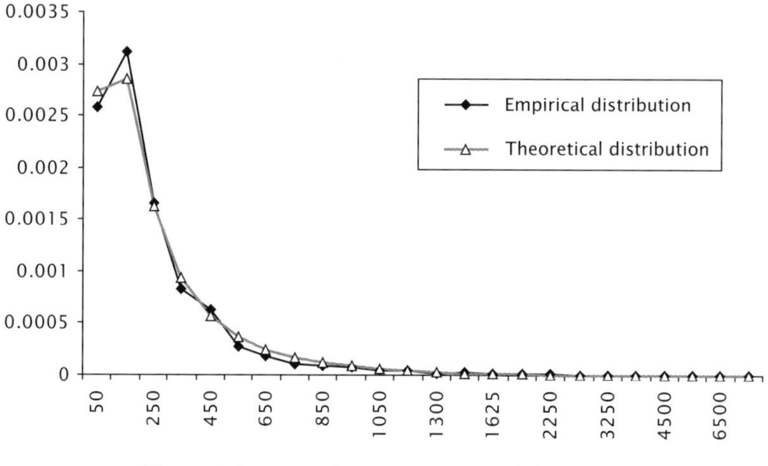

Figure 1. Lognormal approximation of claim size

The best fit was obtained with the lognormal distribution with parameters $\mu = 5.16$, $\sigma = 0.92$. The Kolmogorov-Smirnov two-sided test-statistic $K_n =$

0.016 which allows us to accept the model at the significance level $\alpha = 0.05$ (critical value equals 0.0406).

Consider now modelling of the development factor. Range of values of this variable runs from 0 to 1100 days (about three years). Basic characteristics of the variable are presented in Table 3.

Table 3. Characteristics of the development factor.

Mean	80.64	Kurtosis	12.89
Standard Error	3.82	Skewness	3.38
Median	34	Range	872
Mode	13	Minimum	1
Standard Deviation	128.00	Maximum	873
Sample Variance	16383.96	Sum	90562
		Sample size	1123

Again we have extremely skewed distribution with the sample mean being much bigger than median. The same time skewness measure β_1 equals 3.38. Lognormal distribution does not give us the best model this time. The two-sided Kolmogorov-Smirnov statistic $K_n = 0.0476$ for the best fitting distribution with parameters $\mu = 3.65$ and $\sigma = 1.02$ (critical value equals 0.0406 at the 5% significance level). The approximation is sketched in Figure 2.

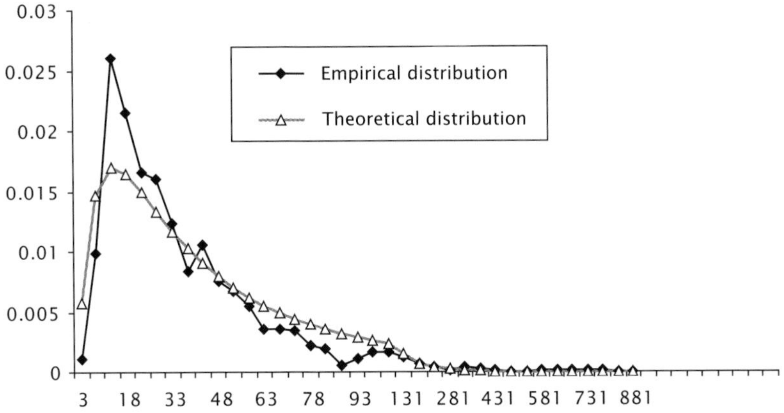

Figure 2. Approximation of development factor with lognormal distribution.

Wald distribution gives better fit with the data. Random variable X has Wald distribution with parameters μ and λ, if its density function is of the form (Balakrishnan and Nevzorov 2003):

$$f_X(x) = \sqrt{\frac{\lambda}{2\pi x^3}} \exp\left\{-\frac{\lambda}{2\mu^2 x}(x-\mu)^2\right\}, \qquad \lambda, \mu > 0, \quad x > 0.$$

The distribution function of the Wald distribution can be presented through the standard normal distribution:

$$F_X(x) = \Phi\left(\sqrt{\frac{\lambda}{x}}\left(\frac{x}{\mu} - 1\right)\right) + e^{2\lambda/\mu}\Phi\left(-\sqrt{\frac{\lambda}{x}}\left(\frac{x}{\mu} + 1\right)\right).$$

The best fit was obtained by the distribution with the parameter values $\mu = 62.94$ and $\lambda = 40.06$, sketched in Figure 3. Kolmogorov–Smirnov test-statistic $K_n = 0.034$ for this distribution.

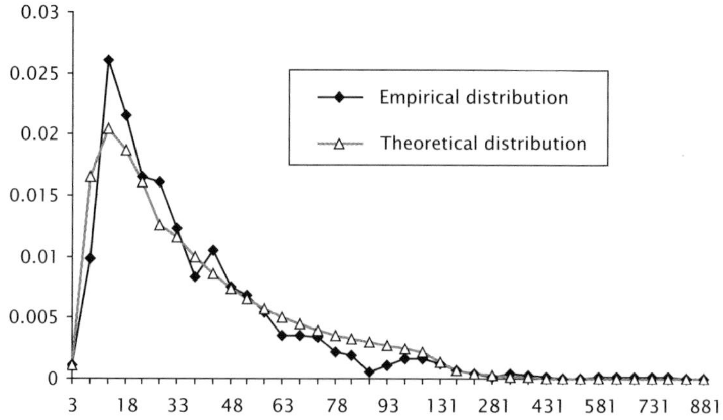

Figure 3. Approximation of development factor with Wald distribution.

Correlation between these two variables is not high and in insurance practice varies for different samples from 0.15 to 0.3. In our case the sample linear correlation coefficient equals 0.18. For our sample size 1123 this correlation appears to be significant. Spearman and Kendall rank correlation coefficients are close to the linear one.

4 Copula models

We are going to present results of modelling of the bivariate distribution of the two variables of interest: the claim size and the development factor. After studies of several possibilities (Gaussian copula, HTR copula, the copulas from Table 1 and several others) we examined more carefully three classes of Archimedean copulas with the distribution functions $K_\varphi(x, \theta)$ presented in Table 4.

As can be seen from Table 1, the parameter θ could be determined by the Kendall rank correlation coefficient τ. Because of extremely skewed marginal distributions and discrete nature of the second variable "development factor", the sample estimate of τ is not reliable and varies from sample to sample. Therefore we decided to use the least squares method to find the best model.

Table 4. Distribution functions $K_\varphi(x,\theta)$ for used copulas.

Copula	$K_\varphi(x,\theta)$
Clayton	$x - \frac{x^{\theta+1} - x}{\theta}$
Gumbel	$x - x\frac{\ln x}{\theta}$
Frank	$x - \frac{1}{\theta}\ln\left(\frac{e^{-\theta x} - 1}{e^{-\theta} - 1}\right)(e^{\theta x} - 1)$

The parameter θ was estimated by the least squares method by minimizing the function

$$\Psi(\theta) = \sum_{i=1}^{m} (K_\varphi(x,\theta) - F_n(x))^2,$$

where $m = 100$ and $F_n(x)$ is the empirical distribution function for Z. Some experiments were carried out with different values of m and it appeared that from $m = 100$ the results of approximation became stable already.

At the next step we compared the values of the function $\Psi(\theta)$ and the values of the function

$$LM(\theta) = \max|K_\varphi(x,\theta) - F_n(x)|$$

for chosen copulas with estimated value of the parameter θ. The results of comparison are presented in Table 5.

Table 5. Values of parameters and functions used for fitting Archimedean copulas.

Copula	θ	$\Psi(\theta)$	$LM(\theta)$
Clayton	0.075	0.037	0.036
Gumbel	0.400	0.022	0.032
Frank	1.060	0.016	0.032

Fitting of the obtained Archimedean copulas was tested by the Kolmogorov-Smirnov test again which was applied to pseudovalues, defined by (2) in Section 2. As one can see from Table 5, the values of $LM(\theta)$ for all copulas are less than the 5% critical value of the Kolmogorov-Smirnov statistic which equals 0.0406.

Comparison of theoretical functions $K_\varphi(x,\theta)$ and the empirical distribution function $F_n(x)$ for Z are shown in Figures 4, 5 and 6.

From Table 5 and Figures 4, 5 and 6 one can see that all the found models give good fit with the data. On the basis of the values of functions $\Psi(\theta)$ and $LM(\theta)$ (Table 5) one should prefer Gumbel or Frank copula.

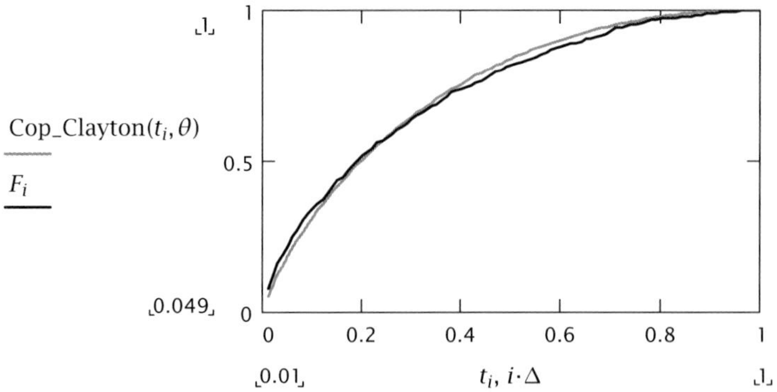

Figure 4. Approximation with Clayton copula.

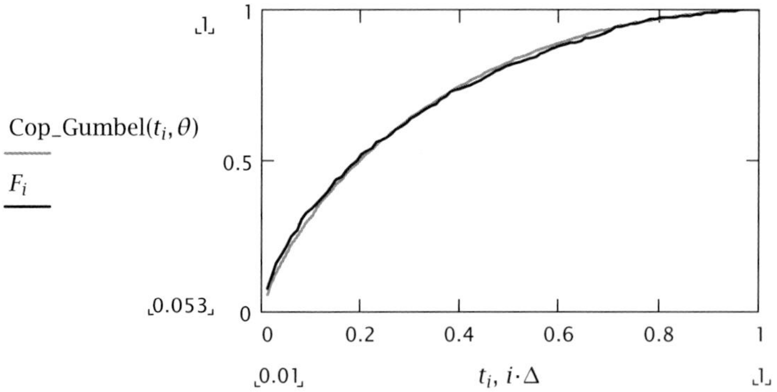

Figure 5. Approximation with Gumbel copula.

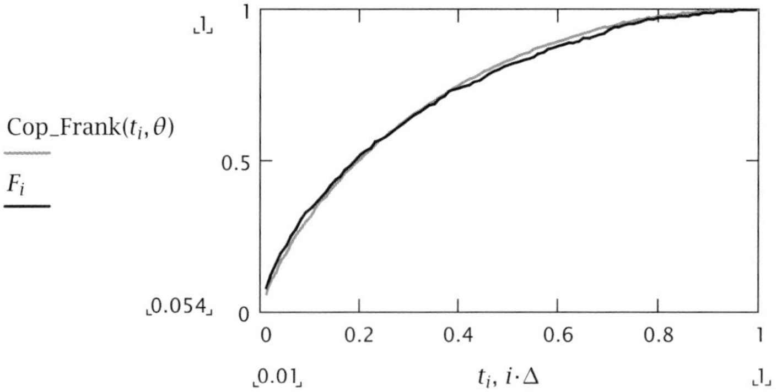

Figure 6. Approximation with Frank copula.

At the next step we shall analyse behaviour of the models in a simulation experiment. We simulate repeatedly data from the copula models and calculate each time values of the two functions:

$$\Delta = \sum_{i,j=1}^{k} ((fs)_{ij} - (fr)_{ij})^2$$

and

$$J = \max_{i,j} |(fs)_{ij} - (fr)_{ij}|$$

where $(fs)_{ij}$ and $(fr)_{ij}$ are the relative frequencies of simulated points and original data respectively in ij-th cell, and k is the number of classes into which ranges of both variables are divided. Simulation was carried out in two cases: when both marginals were lognormally distributed and secondly, when the claim size had lognormal distribution and the development factor followed the Wald distribution. After that the basic characteristics (mean, standard deviation, skewness, kurtosis etc.) of the empirical distributions of Δ and J were found for different number of classes k in both cases. All the three copula models performed well. When comparing the two models with different marginal distributions we could conclude that the case with lognormally distributed claim size and Wald distributed development factor could be preferred as in this case the standard deviation was smaller for all models as well as the maximum difference between initial and simulated data sets. The same time there is no reason to give clear preference to one of the three acceptable models. We only point out two possible advantages of the Frank copula: the parameter range is wider than for other models what can be an advantage in the cases when the value of θ is close to the limiting value, and secondly, both rank correlation coefficients (Kendall and Spearman) can be used in calculations.

In insurance business not all claims are known from the moment when they occur. All not known claims are splitted into two categories: RBNS claims (Reported But Not Settled) and IBNR claims (Incurred But Not Reported). Much attention has been paid in literature to the problem of estimating future claim amounts and their development in time. One way of solving the problem is to use a copula model of the joint distribution for claim size and its development factor. The joint distribution is needed because of correlatedness of the two variables. At the first step we shall find by simulation from the copula model average outstanding claim amount in each development day. At the second step we estimate the distribution of the number of claims reported during development time. It came out that lognormal distribution is a good model for this random variable. Combining these two random variables and taking into account the total number of claims we can estimate outstanding claim provisions for our portfolio.

Acknowledgements

Tõnu Kollo is grateful for support from the Estonian Research Foundation through the grant 5686.

References

Balakrishnan, N. and Nevzorov, V. B. (2003). *A Primer on Statistical Distributions*. New York: John Wiley.

Cherubini, U. and Luciano, E. (2001). Value at risk trade-off and capital allocation with copulas. *Economic Notes*, 30, 235–256.

Cherubini, U., Luciano, E., and Vecchiato, W. (2004). *Copula Methods in Finance*. Chichester: John Wiley.

Clemen, R. T. and Reilly, T. (1999). Correlations and copulas for decision and risk analysis. *Management Science*, 45, 208–224.

Durrleman, V., Nikeghbali, A., and Roncalli, T. (2000). Which copula is the right one? Working paper, Groupe de Recherche Operationelle, Credit Lyonnais.

Embrechts, P., Lindskog, F., and McNeil, A. (2003). Modelling dependence with copulas and applications to risk management. In *Handbook of Heavy Tailed Distributions in Finance*. Ed. E. Rachev. Amsterdam: Elsevier/North-Holland pp. 329–384.

Frees, E. W. and Valdez, E. A. (1998). Understanding relationships using copulas. *North American Actuarial Journal*, 2, 1–25.

Genest, C. and Rivest, L. P. (1993). Statistical inference procedures for bivariate Archimedean copulas. *Journal of the American Statistical Association*, 88, 1034–1043.

Genest, C., Ghoudi, K., and Rivest, L. P. (1995). A semiparametric estimation procedure of dependence parameters in multivariate families of distributions. *Biometrika*, 82, 543–552.

Jouanin, J. F., Riboulet, G., and Roncalli, T. (2001). Modelling dependence for credit derivatives with copulas. Working paper, Groupe de Recherche Operationelle, Credit Lyonnais.

Klugman, S. A., Parsa, R. (1999). Fitting bivariate loss distributions with copulas. *Insurance: Mathematics and Economics*, 24, 139–148.

Lindskog, F. (2000). Modelling dependence with copulas. Master Thesis, MS-2000-06, Department of Mathematics, Royal Institute of Technology, Stockholm.

Luciano, E. and Marena, M. (2003). Copulae as a new tool in financial modelling. *Operational Research: An International Journal*, 2, 139–155.

de Matteis R. (2001). Fitting copulas to data. Diploma Thesis, Institute of Mathematics, University of Zurich.

Nelsen, R. B. (1999). *An Introduction to Copulas*. New York: Springer-Verlag.

Rank, J. (2000). Copulas in financial risk management. Diploma Thesis in Mathematical Finance, University of Oxford.

Roncalli, T. (2001). Copulas: A tool for dependence in finance. Working paper, Groupe de Recherche Operationelle, Credit Lyonnais.

TÕNU KOLLO
University of Tartu, J. Liivi Street 2, Tartu 50409, Estonia
Tonu.Kollo@ut.ee
http://bronti.ms.ut.ee/english/

Gaida Pettere
Riga Technical University, Kalku Street 1, Riga LV 1658, Latvia
gaida@latnet.lv
http://www.ditf.rtu.lv/IMK/main.asp?lang=eng&id=website/people/docents/pattere.asp

Festschrift for Tarmo Pukkila on his 60th Birthday
Eds. E. P. Liski, J. Isotalo, J. Niemelä, S. Puntanen, and G. P. H. Styan

Univ. of Tampere, 2006, ISBN 978-951-44-6620-5, pages 127–144

Dealing with serial correlation in regression

SERGIO G. KOREISHA & YUE FANG

Abstract. In this article we show how a misspecified, albeit adequate, representation of the form of the autocorrelation can be used to estimate and forecast regression models that suffer from serial correlation. We will present not only distributional properties of these estimators, but will also demonstrate by means of exhaustive Monte Carlo experiments how effective the proposed methods are for finite samples.

Key words and phrases: Autocorrelation; Autoregressive moving average; Consistency; Estimation; Generalized least squares; Model identification; Relative predictive efficiency.

1 Introduction

It is well known that ordinary least squares (OLS) yield unbiased, but inefficient estimates for parameters in regression models with serially correlated error structures, and that these OLS regression estimates have larger sampling variances than those obtained from procedures such as generalized least squares (GLS) that deal explicitly with the autocorrelation of the residuals. Furthermore, that forecasts generated from such models can be seriously inefficient, not just because of the inefficiency of the parameter estimates themselves, but also because the error between the fitted and actual value in the last observation is apt to persist into the future.

Since Cochrane and Orcutt (1949) and Durbin and Watson (1950) developed an approximate transformation to deal with and to test for autoregressive disturbances of order 1, a great deal of research has been conducted to alleviate the problems mentioned above. A close examination of this literature (see Hildreth (1986) and Choudhury et al. (1999) for chronologies of major developments in this area), however, indicates that a vast preponderance of the studies conducted over the last five decades assume that the error covariance matrix Ω from the regression model,

$$Y = X\beta + \varepsilon \tag{1}$$

where Y is a $(T \times 1)$ vector of observations on a dependent variable, X is a $(T \times k)$ design matrix and ε is a random vector with $E(\varepsilon) = 0$ and $E(\varepsilon'\varepsilon) =$

$\sigma^2\Omega = \{\gamma(i-j)\}_{i,j=1}^{T}$, is either known or can be estimated consistently from data. Very few studies considered the properties of estimators when the structure of Ω was incorrectly identified or when its parameters were inefficiently estimated. Moreover, of the few studies that considered these issues (noticeably Amemiya (1973) and Engle (1974)) most dealt with or depended on asymptotic results which can often be at odds with results obtained from sample sizes generally available to model builders.

In this article, based on our past and current research, we will show how to deal effectively with serial correlation in regression models using misspecified, albeit adequate, representations of the form of the autocorrelation. After discussing the challenges associated with identifying the form of the serial correlation based on finite samples (Section 2), we will present in Section 3 some theoretical properties of incorrect GLS (IGLS) estimates, i.e., GLS estimators based on a wrongly identified Ω, and compare their finite-sample efficiencies vis-à-vis ordinary and generalized least squares. In Section 4 we will also show that for finite samples IGLS corrections based on AR($\tilde{p}$) approximations (IGLS-AR($\tilde{p}$)) for ARMA serial correlations can yield as good, and more often, better forecasts than generated from OLS, or from GLS using the correct form of the serial autocorrelation structure. In Section 5 we will discuss a new two-step procedure for generating forecasts for regression models with serial correlation based exclusively on ordinary least squares (2SOLS) estimation that compares very favorably with GLS-type procedures. This new approach is simple, and can be readily operationalized in any computer system, even desktops without any programming effort. It does not require the use of nonlinear search algorithms nor inversion of large matrices such as generalized least squares. Moreover, as will be demonstrated the method is robust to different serial correlation error structures. Finally in Section 6 we offer some concluding remarks.

We will assume that the serially correlated disturbances ε in (1) follow an autoregressive moving average (ARMA) process (Box and Jenkins 1976):

$$\Phi(B)\varepsilon_t = \Theta(B)a_t, \tag{2}$$

where $\Phi(B)$ and $\Theta(B)$ are finite polynomials of orders p and q respectively in the back shift operator B, i.e., $\Phi(B) = 1 - \sum_{i=1}^{p} \phi_i B^i$ and $\Theta(B) = 1 - \sum_{i=1}^{q} \theta_i B^i$. $\{a_t\}$ is a Gaussian white noise process with variance σ_a^2. We say that process (2) is both stationary and invertible if the roots of the characteristic equations $\Phi(B) = 0$ and $\Theta(B) = 0$ are outside the unit circle. Stationary and invertible ARMA(p, q) models can also be expressed as either infinite autoregressions, $\Pi(B)\varepsilon_t = a_t$ or infinite moving averages, $\varepsilon_t = \psi(B)a_t$. In practice, however, such representations may be approximated by processes of relatively low order because the coefficients in $\Pi(B)$ and $\Psi(B)$ may be effectively zero beyond some finite lag.

Throughout this article we will deal with the estimator of the linear regression model specified by (1) and (2),

$$\hat{\beta} = (X'\Xi^{-1}X)^{-1}X'\Xi^{-1}Y. \tag{3}$$

Setting $\Xi = I$ in (3) defines the ordinary least squares estimator, $\hat{\beta}_{\text{OLS}}$; if $\Xi = \Omega$, then (3) yields the well-known Aitken estimator, $\hat{\beta}_{\text{GLS}}$. If the structure of Ω is known, but its elements have to be estimated, i.e., $\Xi = \hat{\Omega}$, then we will refer to (3) as estimated GLS and denote it as $\hat{\beta}_{\text{EGLS}}$. We will refer to (3) as the incorrect GLS, $\hat{\beta}_{\text{IGLS}}$, if $\Xi = \Sigma \neq \Omega$, and as estimated incorrect GLS, $\hat{\beta}_{\text{EIGLS}}$, if $\Xi = \hat{\Sigma}$, e.g., $\hat{\beta}_{\text{EIGLS-AR}(\tilde{p})}$ is the IGLS estimate based on an AR($\tilde{p}$) correction.

2 The identification of serially correlated disturbances

In this section using a small simulation study we demonstrate how difficult it is to construct the structure of the covariance matrix Ω when GLS is used to estimate the regression model with autocorrelated disturbances. The challenges of identifying the true correlation structures of disturbances have also been studied by Walker (1967), Kadiyala (1970), and King (1983) among others. Walker and King discussed the practical difficulties of testing for AR(1) against MA(1) disturbances. Kadiyala has shown that the null hypothesis that ε follows $N(0, \Omega_0)$ cannot be tested against the alternative hypothesis that ε follows $N(0, \Omega_1)$ under certain conditions on Ω_i ($i = 0, 1$) and the design matrix X. The test aside from a scalar factor may have the same distribution for both the null and the alternative hypotheses. Moreover, as pointed out by Thursby (1987), if the regression suffers from omitted variables, then it may not be possible to identify the form of the autocorrelation present in the regression model.

For sample sizes generally available to model builders "correct" identification of ARMA(p, q) process associated with the serially correlated disturbances can be quite illusive. Using the SAS pseudo-random number generator RANNOR, we generated, for sample sizes of 50, 100, and 200 observations, 1,000 realizations for 3 stationary and invertible Gaussian ARMA(1, 1) disturbance structures. Then, we created the regression model

$$y_t = 2.0 + 0.5x_t + \varepsilon_t, \tag{4}$$

where the generating process for the exogenous variable x_t followed an AR(1) process, $(1 - \eta B)x_t = v_t$, with $v_t \sim N(0, 1)$, and $E(\varepsilon_t, v_s) = 0$, $\forall t \neq s$, and $\eta = \{0, 0.5, 0.9, 1.0\}$. Table 1 contains the frequency distribution of identified error structures selected automatically using the Akaike information criterion (AIC) and the Schwartz's Bayesian information criterion (BIC) from the OLS residuals.

As can be seen, correct identification of the simulated order of the ARMA structure governing the estimated residuals is at best tenuous. The identification performance of BIC improves substantially as the sample size increases,

Table 1. Frequency distribution of identified structures from autocorrelated disturbances.

		Simulated Disturbance ARMA(1, 1) with $T = 50$											
		$(\phi_1, \theta_1) = (0.8, 0.5)$				$(\phi_1, \theta_1) = (0.8, -0.7)$				$(\phi_1, \theta_1) = (-0.8, 0.7)$			
		$\eta = 0.0$	0.5	0.9	1.0	$\eta = 0.0$	0.5	0.9	1.0	$\eta = 0.0$	0.5	0.9	1.0
AIC	White Noise	5.0	7.6	5.2	8.0	0.0	0.0	0.0	0.0	0.0	0.0	0.0	0.0
	MA(1)	0.0	0.0	0.0	0.0	0.0	0.0	0.0	0.0	0.0	0.0	0.0	0.0
	AR(1)	27.4	23.2	30.4	26.0	4.4	2.4	0.0	0.0	12.4	1.6	0.0	0.4
	ARMA(1, 1)	2.8	3.2	1.4	1.8	2.4	2.8	1.2	1.8	20.2	17.8	21.4	9.4
	ARMA(1, 2)	0.6	0.4	0.0	0.6	0.8	0.6	0.0	2.6	2.6	2.2	3.2	9.0
	ARMA(2, 1)	37.4	42.8	36.2	41.0	71.4	76.2	72.8	47.8	37.8	54.4	47.4	44.8
	ARMA(2, 2)	26.8	22.8	26.8	22.6	21.0	21.4	22.6	47.8	27.0	24.0	28.0	36.4
BIC	White Noise	47.2	49.0	55.6	52.6	1.2	1.0	3.0	0.0	0.2	0.2	1.6	0.0
	MA(1)	0.0	0.0	0.0	0.0	0.0	0.0	0.0	0.0	0.0	0.0	0.0	0.0
	AR(1)	30.4	28	24.2	32.2	22.6	8.4	4.4	0.6	29.0	11.0	8.2	0.4
	ARMA(1, 1)	7.2	6.4	3.2	2.6	40.0	33.2	48.6	21.8	48.8	49.4	62.2	37.4
	ARMA(1, 2)	1.8	1.4	1.0	0.6	1.2	1.0	0.0	6.2	3.8	2.2	2.0	12.8
	ARMA(2, 1)	9.8	11.8	12.2	8.4	31.4	40.6	36.2	41.8	13.6	30.0	18.0	33.6
	ARMA(2, 2)	3.6	3.4	3.8	3.6	3.6	5.8	7.8	29.6	4.6	7.2	8.0	15.8
		$T = 100$											
AIC	White Noise	1.6	1.8	3.4	1.0	0.0	0.0	0.0	0.0	0.0	0.0	0.0	0.0
	MA(1)	0.0	0.0	0.0	0.0	0.0	0.0	0.0	0.0	0.0	0.0	0.0	0.0
	AR(1)	17.0	14.6	16.6	7.6	0.2	0.2	0.0	0.0	0.2	0.4	0.0	0.0
	ARMA(1, 1)	3.4	3.2	2.0	4.8	2.0	4.2	4.4	3.0	14.4	15.8	8.0	8.6
	ARMA(1, 2)	0.2	0.2	1.2	0.0	0.0	0.0	0.0	0.4	1.2	2.2	0.0	1.0
	ARMA(2, 1)	58.0	59.4	56.4	54.6	77.6	77.2	68.6	62.2	71.8	65.2	67.2	75.2
	ARMA(2, 2)	19.8	20.8	20.4	32.0	20.2	18.4	27.0	34.4	12.4	16.4	24.8	15.2
BIC	White Noise	25.4	27.4	29.2	14.8	0.0	0.0	0.0	0.0	0.0	0.0	0.0	0.0
	MA(1)	0.0	0.0	0.0	0.0	0.0	0.0	0.0	0.0	0.0	0.0	0.0	0.0
	AR(1)	36.8	36.2	40.2	25.2	2.8	2.0	0.0	0.0	2.6	3.4	0.0	0.0
	ARMA(1, 1)	22.2	19.6	15.6	27.0	63.0	72.6	57.2	55.6	74.8	72.4	71.0	62.8
	ARMA(1, 2)	1.0	0.6	0.0	1.8	0.6	0.4	0.0	1.2	0.4	0.8	1.4	1.4
	ARMA(2, 1)	13.4	13.8	12.0	23.8	30.4	23.2	38.2	32.0	21.6	22.2	26.2	32.4
	ARMA(2, 2)	1.2	2.4	3.0	7.4	3.2	1.8	4.6	11.2	0.6	1.2	1.4	3.4
		$T = 200$											
AIC	White Noise	0.2	0.2	0.0	0.2	0.0	0.0	0.0	0.0	0.0	0.0	0.0	0.0
	MA(1)	0.0	0.0	0.0	0.0	0.0	0.0	0.0	0.0	0.0	0.0	0.0	0.0
	AR(1)	3.2	2.2	6.4	4.8	0.0	0.0	0.0	0.0	0.2	0.0	0.0	0.0
	ARMA(1, 1)	5.6	7.6	7.6	6.0	3.8	2.6	5.6	5.8	5.6	9.6	10.2	8.4
	ARMA(1, 2)	0.4	0.4	0.0	0.0	0.0	0.0	0.0	0.0	0.6	0.6	0.0	0.4
	ARMA(2, 1)	72.4	72.2	69.4	67.8	76.4	76.2	67.4	75.2	83.8	78.6	64.8	64.4
	ARMA(2, 2)	18.2	17.4	16.6	21.2	19.8	21.2	27.0	19.0	9.8	11.2	25.0	26.8
BIC	White Noise	7.6	6.8	12.4	12.8	0.0	0.0	0.0	0.0	0.0	0.0	0.0	0.0
	MA(1)	0.0	0.0	0.0	0.0	0.0	0.0	0.0	0.0	0.0	0.0	0.0	0.0
	AR(1)	25.2	23.4	22.6	30.6	0.4	0.4	0.0	0.0	0.8	0.2	0.0	0.0
	ARMA(1, 1)	51.4	52.6	49.0	42.4	78.8	74.6	57.2	77.2	82.2	80.8	73.4	71.6
	ARMA(1, 2)	0.6	0.4	0.0	0.2	0.2	0.2	0.0	0.0	0.2	0.6	1.2	0.2
	ARMA(2, 1)	14.0	15.6	14.2	13.0	19.4	22.6	38.2	20.6	16.4	17.8	19.0	19.4
	ARMA(2, 2)	1.2	1.2	1.8	1.0	1.2	2.2	4.6	2.2	0.4	0.6	6.2	8.8

but it is relatively inadequate, varying from nearly 50% when the sample size $T = 50$ to 80% when T reaches 200. AIC, as also noted in other studies, severely overestimates the order of the process, and at least for the three parameterizations reported here its performance does not improve when sample size increases.

3 Generalized least squares with misspecified serial correlation structure

Koreisha and Fang (2001) established the conditions for IGLS to yield unbiased and consistent regression estimators. Using an adaptation of GLS results in Schmidt (1976) they showed that:

Theorem 1. *If X is nonstochastic and the regressors (columns of X) are linearly independent, then*

(a) *$\hat{\beta}_{\text{IGLS}}$ is unbiased, and if $\lim_{T\to\infty} T^{-1}X'\Xi^{-1}X$ is finite and nonsingular, then $\hat{\beta}_{\text{IGLS}}$ is consistent.*

(b) *if $\text{plim}_{T\to\infty} T^{-1}X'\hat{\Xi}^{-1}\hat{\Omega}^{-1}\hat{\Xi}^{-1}X$ is finite and nonsingular and $\text{plim}_{T\to\infty}$ $T^{-1}X'\hat{\Xi}^{-1}\hat{\Omega}^{-1}\Lambda\varepsilon = 0$, where Λ is a non-singular unitary matrix such that $\Lambda'\Lambda = \Xi^{-1}$, then $\hat{\beta}_{\text{EIGLS}}$ is consistent.*

Moreover, if the transformed regressors, ΛX, are sufficiently well behaved (as specified below) and the off-diagonal terms in $\Lambda^{-1}\Omega\Lambda^{-1}$ diminish sufficiently rapidly, then $\hat{\beta}_{\text{EIGLS}}$ is asymptotically normally distributed (Fang and Koreisha 2005).

Theorem 2. *Let $Z = \Lambda X = \{z_{i,j}\}$ and $\varepsilon^* = \Lambda\varepsilon$. Under the following assumptions:*

(a) $\lim_{T\to\infty} S_{iT}^{*2} = \infty$ *for all i, where* $S_{iT}^{*2} = \sum_{t=1}^{T} z_{i,t}^2$.

(b) $\lim_{T\to\infty}(z_{i,T}^2/S_{iT}^{*2}) = 0$ *for all i.*

(c) $\lim_{T\to\infty}(\sum_{t=1}^{T-l} z_{i,t}z_{j,t+l}/S_{iT}^{*}S_{jT}^{*}) = \rho_{ij}^{*}(l)$ *exists for all i and j.*

(d) *Let $R^*(l) = \{\rho_{ij}^{*}(l)\}$; then $R^*(0)$ is non-singular.*

(e) *$\varepsilon_t^* = \psi^*(B)a_t^*$, where a_t^*'s are independent with zero mean and constant variance σ^2. $\psi^*(.)$ is absolutely summable. The distribution function of ε_t^*, $F_t^*(v)$, satisfies*

$$\sup_{t=1,2,\ldots} \int_{|v|>c} v^2\, dF_t^*(v) \to 0$$

as $c \to \infty$ for all $t = 0, \pm1, \pm2, \ldots$.

then

$$\sqrt{T}(\hat{\beta}_{\text{EIGLS}} - \beta) \quad \text{converges to} \quad N(0, V_{\Xi}),$$

where

$$V_{\Xi} = \lim_{T\to\infty}[\sigma^2(X'\Xi^{-1}X)^{-1}X'\Xi^{-1}\Omega\Xi^{-1}X(X'\Xi^{-1}X)^{-1}].$$

Koreisha and Fang (2001) also established theoretical efficiency bounds for IGLS relative to GLS and OLS for finite samples assuming that X was non-stochastic. To gain some idea of the magnitude of those bounds let us consider the case for which there is only one exogenous variable in the regression model and the intercept is set to zero. In this simple case their theorems lead to the following corollaries.

Corollary 1. *Let* ν_1 *and* ν_T *be the smallest and the largest eigenvalues of* $\Lambda\Omega\Lambda'$, *with* Λ *satisfying* $\Lambda'\Lambda = \Xi^{-1}$, *then*

$$1 \le \frac{\text{cov}(\hat{\beta}_{\text{IGLS}})}{\text{cov}(\hat{\beta}_{\text{GLS}})} \le \mathcal{M}_U, \tag{5}$$

where $\mathcal{M}_U \equiv (\nu_1 + \nu_T)^2/(4\nu_1\nu_T)$.

Corollary 2. *Let* λ_1 *and* λ_T *be the smallest and the largest eigenvalues of* Ω, *and let* ν_1 *and* ν_T *be the smallest and the largest eigenvalues of* $\Lambda\Omega\Lambda'$, *with* Λ *satisfying* $\Lambda'\Lambda = \Xi^{-1}$, *then*

$$\mathcal{M}_L \le \frac{\text{cov}(\hat{\beta}_{\text{IGLS}})}{\text{cov}(\hat{\beta}_{\text{OLS}})} \le \mathcal{M}_U, \tag{6}$$

where $\mathcal{M}_U$ *is given in Corollary 1 and* $\mathcal{M}_L \equiv 4\lambda_1\lambda_T/(\lambda_1 + \lambda_T)^2$.

In Table 2 we present the limits ($\mathcal{M}_U$ and $\mathcal{M}_L$) for the relative efficiency of IGLS-AR($\tilde{p}$), $\tilde{p} = \{1, 4, 7\}$ vis-à-vis OLS and GLS when the disturbance term of the regression model follows an MA(1) process with $|\theta_1|$ ranging 0.3 to 0.9 for $T = 50$. Also included in the table are the corresponding eigenvalues λ_1, λ_T and ν_1, ν_T.[1]

As can be seen, $\mathcal{M}_U$ and $\mathcal{M}_L$ do not depend on the sign of the MA coefficient θ_1. When $|\theta_1|$ is small, both ν_1 and ν_T are close to 1 and so is $\mathcal{M}_U$, implying that the efficiency loss in using IGLS relative to GLS is small. As $|\theta_1|$ increases, the difference between ν_1 and ν_T increases, thus, forcing $\mathcal{M}_U$ to increase away from 1, indicating that the loss of efficiency in using IGLS relative to GLS can be substantial for some design matrices X. This loss of efficiency, however, decreases substantially as the order of the AR($\tilde{p}$) process used to represent the MA(1) simulated disturbance structure increases. On the other hand, $\mathcal{M}_L$ is less than 1 for all values of θ and orders $\tilde{p}$ studied, indicating that OLS can be considerably less efficient than IGLS. Although theoretically the upper bound for the relative efficiency of IGLS vis-à-vis OLS

[1] They concentrated on only AR($\tilde{p}$) GLS corrections for disturbances generated by mixed ARMA(p, q) processes. This type of correction is probably the most widely used one by practitioners, at least based on textbook coverage, and one which has been implemented on many commonly employed statistical packages such as SAS and Splus. Its origin can be traced all the way back to Cochrane and Orcutt (1949) when they developed a simple transformation for OLS estimation of linear models with an AR(1) disturbance term.

Table 2. Bounds for the relative efficiency of IGLS-AR($\tilde{p}$) vis-à-vis OLS and GLS when the serially correlated disturbance follows an MA(1) process.

$\tilde{p}$		$\lvert\theta_1\rvert = 0.3$	$\lvert\theta_1\rvert = 0.5$	$\lvert\theta_1\rvert = 0.7$	$\lvert\theta_1\rvert = 0.9$
1	$\mathcal{M}_U$	1.0325	1.2795	1.7580	10.7587
	ν_1	0.8361	0.6036	0.6036	0.2315
	ν_T	1.1965	1.6628	2.9123	9.4921
4	$\mathcal{M}_U$	1.0000	1.0037	1.1110	3.7109
	ν_1	0.9953	0.9415	0.7233	0.2988
	ν_T	1.0047	1.0624	1.3917	3.8138
7	$\mathcal{M}_U$	1.0000	1.0001	1.0114	1.8710
	ν_1	0.9999	0.9928	0.8995	0.4566
	ν_T	1.0001	1.0072	1.1133	2.4179
1, 4, 7	$\mathcal{M}_L$	0.6981	0.3624	0.1204	0.0148
	λ_1	0.6454	0.5560	0.5160	0.5019
	λ_T	2.2193	4.9624	16.0987	134.9336

can be greater than 1, based on our simulation results, the efficiency in estimating the slope of a regression model with one exogenous variable using EIGLS-AR($\tilde{p}$) procedures is always superior to OLS.

Since the EIGLS-AR($\tilde{p}$) estimator is a special case of EIGLS from Theorem 2, we know that it also converges to a normal distribution as $T \to \infty$. Note that the limiting distribution of EIGLS-AR($\tilde{p}$) depends, in general, on Ξ, and on $\tilde{p}$ in particularly. If $\tilde{p}$ is allowed to go to infinity at an appropriate rate of T, then it can be shown (Fang and Koreisha 2005) that its limiting distribution is the same as that of the GLS.

Theorem 3. *Under the following assumptions:*

(a) $\lim_{T\to\infty} S_{iT}^2 = \infty$ *for all* i, *where* $S_{iT}^2 = \sum_{t=1}^{T} x_{i,t}^2$.

(b) $\lim_{T\to\infty}(x_{i,T}^2/S_{iT}^2) = 0$ *for all* i.

(c) $\lim_{T\to\infty}(\sum_{t=1}^{T-l} x_{i,t}x_{j,t+l}/S_{iT}S_{jT}) = \rho_{ij}(l)$ *exists for all* i *and* j.

(d) *Let* $R(l) = \{\rho_{ij}(l)\}$; *then* $R(0)$ *is non-singular.*

(e) *Let* $\Pi(B)\varepsilon_t = a_t$. *There exist constants* $\varrho \in (0,1)$ *and* $C > 0$, *such that*

$$\max\{|\pi_m|\} \le C\varrho^m \qquad \text{for all } m \ge 0,$$

then

$$\sqrt{T}(\hat{\beta}_{\text{EIGLS-AR}(\tilde{p})} - \beta) \quad \text{converges to} \quad N(0, V),$$

as $T \to \infty$ *and* $\tilde{p} \to \infty$ *such that* $\varrho^{\tilde{p}} T \to 0$, *where*

$$V = \lim_{T\to\infty} [\sigma^2(X'\Omega^{-1}X)^{-1}].$$

It should be noted that the assumption (e) is satisfied by a wide range of time series including the stationary and invertible ARMA processes (Brockwell and Davis 1991). The condition that $\varrho^{\tilde{p}} T \to 0$ is less restrictive than the typical time series convergent rates such as $\tilde{p} = O(T^{\lambda})$ for some positive λ (Berk 1974; Bhansali 1978) and $\tilde{p} = O\{(\ln T)^{\alpha}\}$ for $\alpha > 0$ (Hannan et al. 1980; Saikkonen 1986).

To evaluate the finite sample quality of the regression estimates obtained from EIGLS procedures, an exhaustive simulation study was conducted. For sample sizes of 50, 100, and 200 observations 1,000 realizations were generated for each of a variety of stationary and invertible Gaussian ARMA(p, q) structures with varying parameter values as the residuals for the regression model with one exogenous variable generated by an AR(1) process discussed in Section 2. The parameter values for the residual ARMA structures were chosen to not only conform with other previously published studies such as Glasbey (1982), Pukkila et al. (1990), Zinde-Walsh and Galbraith (1991), and Koreisha and Fang (1999), but also to provide a representative set of examples of possible autocorrelated error structures in regression models. Although the Monte Carlo experiment involved tens of thousands of trials, for brevity, we will report just a small subset of the simulations we performed preferring to focus only on the main findings of their study.

Table 3, for example, contrasts the efficiency of the GLS estimates relative to that of OLS in terms of mean squared error (MSE), $\hat{\varsigma}_{\beta_i} \equiv \sum(\hat{\beta}_{i,\text{GLS}} - \beta_i)^2 / \sum(\hat{\beta}_{i,\text{OLS}} - \beta_i)^2$ where $i = 0, 1$, for 5 GLS estimates: the GLS based on the correct residual model structures and known ARMA coefficients (denoted as GLS); the GLS based on the correct residual model structures but with estimated ARMA coefficients (denoted as EGLS); the GLS based on AR(1) correction with an estimated AR coefficient (denoted as EIGLS-AR(1)), and two other EIGLS-AR$(\tilde{p})$ estimates with lags $\tilde{p}$ equal to the closest integer part of $\sqrt{T}/2$ and $\sqrt{T}$,[2] respectively. A ratio less than 1 indicates that the GLS estimates are more efficient than OLS.

Based on these types of results Koreisha and Fang (2001) were able to show that with few exceptions[3] regardless of sample size for all model structures and parameterizations the efficiency in estimating the parameters of the regression model was higher for the GLS procedures including those based on incorrectly identified error structures (IGLS) than for OLS when the exogenous variable was stationary. The relative efficiency gain of GLS and IGLS over OLS in estimating the regression parameters, as would be expected, depended not only on the ARMA(p, q) error structure, but also on the magnitude of the parameters themselves. For error structures that were not close to white noise GLS and IGLS efficiencies were very often more

---

[2] Since $\tilde{p} = O(\sqrt{T})$ satisfies $\varrho^{\tilde{p}} T \to 0$, the convergence rate of $\tilde{p}$ in Theorem 3 is also met.

[3] In a few cases when the sample size was small or the order of the autoregression correction was set equal to 1, the efficiency in estimating the intercept term was higher for OLS than GLS or IGLS.

Table 3. Relative estimation efficiency for selected ARMA(p, q) error processes.

T	GLS Type	$(\phi_1, \theta_1) = (-0.8, 0.7)$					
		$\eta = 0.0$		$\eta = 0.5$		$\eta = 1.0$	
		$\hat{\varsigma}_{\beta_0}$	$\hat{\varsigma}_{\beta_1}$	$\hat{\varsigma}_{\beta_0}$	$\hat{\varsigma}_{\beta_1}$	$\hat{\varsigma}_{\beta_0}$	$\hat{\varsigma}_{\beta_1}$
50	GLS	0.4374	0.0236	0.4038	0.0194	0.3082	0.0513
	EGLS	0.4566	0.0387	0.4264	0.0283	0.318	0.0542
	EIGLS-AR(1)	0.4884	0.0676	0.45	0.0449	0.343	0.07
	EIGLS-AR(4)	0.4694	0.0491	0.4484	0.0401	0.3275	0.0605
	EIGLS-AR(7)	0.4801	0.0627	0.4743	0.0493	0.3555	0.0689
100	GLS	0.2976	0.0214	0.3318	0.0275	0.396	0.1029
	EGLS	0.31	0.0304	0.3428	0.0335	0.3967	0.1049
	EIGLS-AR(1)	0.3435	0.0611	0.3761	0.0621	0.4474	0.1465
	EIGLS-AR(5)	0.3157	0.0377	0.3526	0.0429	0.4032	0.1119
	EIGLS-AR(10)	0.325	0.0428	0.3584	0.0486	0.405	0.115
200	GLS	0.3707	0.023	0.3593	0.0255	0.5203	0.2039
	EGLS	0.373	0.0266	0.362	0.0288	0.5198	0.2041
	EIGLS-AR(1)	0.4016	0.0631	0.3897	0.0593	0.5532	0.24
	EIGLS-AR(7)	0.3777	0.0295	0.3684	0.0337	0.5232	0.2077
	EIGLS-AR(14)	0.3836	0.0354	0.3745	0.0391	0.5266	0.2097
		$(\phi_1, \theta_1, \theta_2) = (0.6, -0.5, -0.9)$					
50	GLS	0.9073	0.0607	0.9061	0.0393	0.8763	0.1021
	EGLS	0.912	0.0851	0.9168	0.0669	0.8908	0.1763
	EIGLS-AR(1)	0.9486	0.1	0.9478	0.1114	0.9373	0.3043
	EIGLS-AR(4)	0.9609	0.1081	0.9633	0.0859	0.9554	0.3187
	EIGLS-AR(7)	0.9893	0.1123	0.9996	0.1017	0.9982	0.3383
100	GLS	0.9477	0.0288	0.9438	0.0272	0.9237	0.1372
	EGLS	0.9505	0.0432	0.9488	0.0455	0.9288	0.1895
	EIGLS-AR(1)	0.9727	0.1174	0.9693	0.1194	0.9453	0.4692
	EIGLS-AR(5)	0.9549	0.0718	0.9542	0.0753	0.9391	0.3314
	EIGLS-AR(10)	0.9649	0.0677	0.9668	0.0727	0.9531	0.3226
200	GLS	0.9793	0.0201	0.9748	0.0162	0.7649	0.198
	EGLS	0.982	0.0326	0.978	0.0277	0.7753	0.2397
	EIGLS-AR(1)	0.9961	0.1328	0.9919	0.113	0.9164	0.7444
	EIGLS-AR(7)	0.9824	0.0681	0.9789	0.0578	0.8553	0.4917
	EIGLS-AR(14)	0.9853	0.0612	0.9823	0.0517	0.8558	0.4632
		$(\phi_1, \phi_2, \theta_1) = (-0.5, -0.9, 0.6)$					
50	GLS	0.2598	0.044	0.2654	0.029	0.284	0.0713
	EGLS	0.2599	0.0445	0.2654	0.0291	0.2841	0.0714
	EIGLS-AR(1)	0.6428	0.7521	0.6424	0.4493	0.6271	0.3402
	EIGLS-AR(4)	0.2652	0.0735	0.2714	0.0451	0.3588	0.1986
	EIGLS-AR(7)	0.2653	0.0913	0.2773	0.0579	0.2952	0.1045
100	GLS	0.3097	0.027	0.3219	0.0242	0.227	0.0571
	EGLS	0.31	0.0271	0.3221	0.0242	0.2273	0.0574
	EIGLS-AR(1)	0.682	0.6807	0.6165	0.4519	0.6466	0.4972
	EIGLS-AR(5)	0.3235	0.0399	0.3337	0.034	0.2279	0.0597
	EIGLS-AR(10)	0.3336	0.1241	0.344	0.042	0.2734	0.0691
200	GLS	0.3793	0.0172	0.2845	0.0138	0.354	0.1086
	EGLS	0.3794	0.0172	0.2846	0.0138	0.3541	0.1087
	EIGLS-AR(1)	0.8201	0.7495	0.6533	0.4632	0.5641	0.4209
	EIGLS-AR(7)	0.3832	0.022	0.2906	0.0184	0.3535	0.1087
	EIGLS-AR(14)	0.39	0.027	0.2973	0.0226	0.358	0.1144

than an order of magnitude higher than OLS. Moreover, the differences in the relative efficiency of EIGLS vis-à-vis true GLS and EGLS in estimating regression parameters were not very large. In fact, when the error structure was assumed to follow an AR(p) model with $\tilde{p} = [\sqrt{T}/2]$ the relative efficiency of EIGLS was comparable to that of EGLS regardless of sample size. For non-stationary exogenous variables gains in efficiency of GLS and IGLS over OLS are less than those of corresponding stationary cases.[4]

4 Forecasting with serially correlated regression models

Fang and Koreisha (2004) established the form of the IGLS-AR($\tilde{p}$) predictor and its predictive mean square error when β and Ω were estimated from data. Moreover, they obtained the form of the asymptotic predictive mean squares error (APMSE) of the estimated predictor $\hat{y}^*$ for EGLS, EIGLS-AR($\tilde{p}$), OLS, and the conditions for which

$$\text{APMSE}(\hat{y}^*_{\text{EGLS}}) \leq \text{APMSE}(\hat{y}^*_{\text{EIGLS-AR}(\tilde{p})}) \leq \text{APMSE}(\hat{y}^*_{\text{OLS}}). \tag{7}$$

In addition they showed that

Theorem 4. *If future values of the exogenous variables are known and both β and Ω are estimated consistently, then*

$$\begin{aligned}\lim_{h\to\infty} \text{APMSE}[\hat{y}^*_{\text{EGLS}}(T+h)] &= \lim_{h\to\infty} \text{APMSE}[\hat{y}^*_{\text{EIGLS-AR}(\tilde{p})}(T+h)] \\ &= \lim_{h\to\infty} \text{APMSE}[\hat{y}^*_{\text{OLS}}(T+h)],\end{aligned}$$

where $\hat{y}^*_{\text{EGLS}}(T+h)$, $\hat{y}^*_{\text{EIGLS-AR}(\tilde{p})}(T+h)$, and $\hat{y}^*_{\text{OLS}}(T+h)$ are predictors of y_{T+h} at time T based on EGLS, EIGLS-AR($\tilde{p}$), *and* OLS *estimates, respectively.*

To evaluate the forecast performance of IGLS methods for finite samples they conducted a large simulation study similar to those described in Section 3. For each trial realization, however, ten additional observations were generated so they could be used as the basis for the evaluation of the forecasts. The relative predictive efficiencies among estimation methods based on mean squared error,

$$\hat{\xi}_{i/j}(T+h) \equiv E(\hat{y}^*_{(i)}(T+h) - y_{T+h})^2 / E(\hat{y}^*_{(j)}(T+h) - y_{T+h})^2,$$
$$i, j = \{\text{OLS}, \text{EGLS}, \text{EIGLS-AR}(\tilde{p})\}, \quad \text{and} \quad i \neq j, \tag{8}$$

where $\hat{y}^*_{(m)}(T+h)$ represents the forecasted value based on method m at the time $T+h$, y_{T+h} is the actual generated value at $T+h$, was calculated for four forecast horizons, $h = \{1, 2, 5, 10\}$.

[4]These results are in general agreement with Krämer (1986) asymptotic results showing that when ε_t is an AR(p) process and x_t follows an integrated process, OLS and GLS are asymptotically equivalent.

Table 4 presents the relative predictive mean squares errors efficiencies for five serial autocorrelation correction methods for a few selected autocorrelation structures. Based on these types of results Fang and Koreisha (2004) showed that regardless of sample size for practically all model structures and parameterizations, the predictive efficiency of estimated GLS, including those based on incorrectly identified error structures (AR($\tilde{p}$)), was higher than for OLS for short and medium term horizons ($h \leq 5$). The degree of improvement in relative predictive efficiencies, however, depended on the structure of the serial correlation. The improvement in the relative predictive efficiency, in general, ranged from nearly zero to more than an order of magnitude.

Moreover, the differences in predictive efficiencies between EGLS and EIGLS-AR($\tilde{p}$) with few exceptions was not very large. In fact when the error structure was modeled as an AR($\tilde{p}$) process with $\tilde{p} = [\sqrt{T}/2]$ the forecast performance of this correction was quite comparable to that of EGLS regardless of the actual simulated serial correlation structure, sample size, and stationarity condition of the exogenous variable. When $\tilde{p} = [\sqrt{T}/2]$, it was very infrequent for values for $\hat{\xi}_{\frac{\text{EIGLS-AR}(\tilde{p})}{\text{EGLS}}}(T+h)$ to be greater than 1.06. For the vast majority of the error structures, $1.01 \leq \hat{\xi}_{\frac{\text{EIGLS-AR}(\tilde{p})}{\text{EGLS}}}(T+h) \leq 1.05$ when $\tilde{p} = [\sqrt{T}/2]$. In many cases the differences in efficiencies could not be distinguished from sampling variation.

Furthermore, consistent with Theorem 4 as h increased, the differences in predictive efficiencies decreased among all methods.

5 Two-step forecasting procedures based on OLS

Suppose the serial correlation of the regression model,

$$y_t = \beta_0 + \sum_{i=1}^{k} \beta_i x_{i,t} + \varepsilon_t, \tag{9}$$

for which we are interested in generating forecasts follows a stationary and invertible ARMA process.

The new two-step forecasting procedure consists in first obtaining OLS estimates for the residual series $\hat{\varepsilon}_t$ of the regression model (9). Then, assuming that the form of the ARMA serial correlation can be approximated by an AR($\tilde{p}$) process (Box and Jenkins 1976; Koreisha and Fang 2001), an augmented regression model that includes $\tilde{p}$ additional first-step residual variables,

$$y_t = \beta_0 + \sum_{i=1}^{k} \beta_i x_{i,t} + \sum_{j=1}^{\tilde{p}} \gamma_j \hat{\varepsilon}_{t-j} + u_t \tag{10}$$

is estimated using OLS yielding new 2SOLS-lagged residuals (2SOLS-LR($\tilde{p}$)) estimates for β_i, namely $\hat{\beta}_i^{\text{2SOLS-LR}}$.

Table 4. Relative predictive efficiencies of EIGLS-AR correction associated with selected ARMA(p, q) error processes.

T	$\tilde{p}$	h	$(\phi_1, \theta_1) = (-0.8, 0.7)$								
			$\eta = 0.0$			$\eta = 0.5$			$\eta = 1.0$		
			PMSE (EIGLS)	$\hat{\xi}_{\frac{EIGLS}{EGLS}}$	$\hat{\xi}_{\frac{EIGLS}{OLS}}$	PMSE (EIGLS)	$\hat{\xi}_{\frac{EIGLS}{EGLS}}$	$\hat{\xi}_{\frac{EIGLS}{OLS}}$	PMSE (EIGLS)	$\hat{\xi}_{\frac{EIGLS}{EGLS}}$	$\hat{\xi}_{\frac{EIGLS}{OLS}}$
50	1	1	1.458	1.187	0.193	1.662	1.535	0.244	1.604	1.273	0.205
		2	3.708	1.086	0.532	3.766	1.068	0.562	3.561	1.041	0.575
		5	7.976	1.136	1.031	6.898	1.068	0.912	6.845	1.075	0.955
		10	8.592	1.206	1.123	8.135	1.095	1.099	8.265	1.222	1.114
	4	1	1.235	1.006	0.163	1.154	1.066	0.170	1.286	1.021	0.164
		2	3.679	1.078	0.528	3.615	1.026	0.540	3.629	0.959	0.586
		5	7.151	1.018	0.924	6.761	1.047	0.894	6.487	1.019	0.905
		10	7.317	1.027	0.956	7.469	1.005	1.009	6.658	0.984	0.898
	7	1	1.265	1.030	0.167	1.264	1.167	0.186	1.495	1.187	0.191
		2	3.928	1.151	0.563	3.693	1.048	0.551	3.965	1.048	0.641
		5	6.964	0.991	0.900	7.264	1.124	0.960	6.891	1.082	0.961
		10	8.577	1.203	1.121	7.626	1.027	1.030	8.499	1.256	1.146
100	1	1	1.623	1.448	0.211	1.496	1.375	0.197	1.255	1.201	0.185
		2	4.059	1.261	0.543	3.642	1.105	0.510	3.236	1.139	0.468
		5	6.748	1.031	0.911	6.964	1.088	0.886	6.506	1.131	0.901
		10	6.989	0.990	1.049	7.481	1.084	0.981	7.882	1.182	1.145
	5	1	1.165	1.039	0.151	1.083	0.995	0.143	1.088	1.041	0.160
		2	3.280	1.019	0.439	3.349	1.016	0.469	3.295	1.058	0.477
		5	6.743	1.031	0.910	6.452	1.008	0.821	6.608	1.047	0.915
		10	7.146	1.012	1.032	7.221	1.046	0.947	6.717	1.007	0.976
	10	1	1.194	1.065	0.155	1.065	0.979	0.149	1.231	1.178	0.181
		2	4.023	1.249	0.538	3.207	0.973	0.499	3.435	1.103	0.497
		5	7.423	1.135	1.002	6.735	1.052	0.857	6.695	1.061	0.927
		10	8.474	1.200	1.247	7.997	1.158	1.049	7.211	1.082	1.048
200	1	1	1.593	1.536	0.222	1.370	1.377	0.190	1.451	1.386	0.181
		2	4.104	1.268	0.577	3.394	1.187	0.474	3.580	1.175	0.478
		5	6.974	1.101	0.935	6.878	1.217	1.011	6.386	1.126	0.858
		10	8.207	1.173	1.059	7.217	1.032	1.016	7.713	1.201	1.002
	7	1	1.057	1.019	0.147	1.003	1.008	0.139	1.099	1.050	0.137
		2	3.205	0.990	0.451	3.006	1.052	0.420	3.194	1.048	0.426
		5	6.299	0.994	0.845	5.827	1.031	0.857	6.593	1.059	0.886
		10	7.126	1.019	0.920	7.052	1.008	0.992	6.688	1.041	0.869
	14	1	1.074	1.036	0.149	1.105	1.110	0.153	1.17	1.117	0.146
		2	3.342	1.033	0.470	3.211	1.123	0.448	3.703	1.215	0.494
		5	7.047	1.112	0.945	6.213	1.099	0.913	6.396	1.128	0.859
		10	8.009	1.145	1.034	8.315	1.189	1.170	8.278	1.289	1.075
			$(\phi_1, \theta_1, \theta_2) = (0.6, -0.5, -0.9)$								
100	5	1	1.354	1.040	0.229	1.395	1.013	0.224	1.403	1.043	0.240
		2	4.118	1.028	0.724	4.177	1.016	0.632	3.911	0.998	0.663
		5	4.864	1.062	0.810	4.855	1.010	0.743	4.561	1.027	0.733
		10	5.857	1.011	1.002	5.695	1.093	0.969	5.912	1.097	0.974

Continued on facing page

Table 4. Continued.

T	$\tilde{p}$	h	$(\phi_1, \phi_2, \theta_1) = (-0.5, -0.9, 0.6)$								
			$\eta = 0.0$			$\eta = 0.5$			$\eta = 1.0$		
			PMSE (EIGLS)	$\hat{\xi}_{\frac{\text{EIGLS}}{\text{EGLS}}}$	$\hat{\xi}_{\frac{\text{EIGLS}}{\text{OLS}}}$	PMSE (EIGLS)	$\hat{\xi}_{\frac{\text{EIGLS}}{\text{EGLS}}}$	$\hat{\xi}_{\frac{\text{EIGLS}}{\text{OLS}}}$	PMSE (EIGLS)	$\hat{\xi}_{\frac{\text{EIGLS}}{\text{EGLS}}}$	$\hat{\xi}_{\frac{\text{EIGLS}}{\text{OLS}}}$
100	5	1	1.089	1.002	0.116	1.104	0.999	0.112	1.068	1.022	0.116
		2	2.321	1.055	0.244	2.220	1.002	0.206	2.306	0.997	0.250
		5	4.018	1.053	0.427	3.947	0.999	0.366	3.890	1.003	0.442
		10	6.552	1.075	0.719	6.864	1.002	0.733	6.557	1.002	0.700

PMSE: prediction mean squared error.
EIGLS is based on AR($\tilde{p}$) correction (i.e., EIGLS-AR($\tilde{p}$)).

The rationale for using (10) is based on the fact that any stationary and invertible ARMA(p, q) model can be expressed as an infinite autoregression, $\varepsilon_t = \Pi(B)\varepsilon_t + a_t$, where $\Pi(B) = \sum_{i=1}^{\infty} \pi_i B^i$. Hence the serially correlated regression model (9) can be rewritten as

$$y_t = \beta_0 + \sum_{i=1}^{k} \beta_i x_{i,t} + \Pi(B)\varepsilon_t + a_t. \tag{11}$$

Since the coefficients in $\Pi(B)$ may be effectively zero beyond[5] some finite lag, the infinite autoregressive representation may be approximated by a process of relatively low order.

It can be shown that the 2SOLS-LR($\tilde{p}$) estimates based on (10) are asymptotically unbiased and consistent if the lag parameter $\tilde{p}$ is sufficiently large (Koreisha and Fang 2005). Furthermore, the 2SOLS estimates are asymptotically normal with a variance that is dependent on $\tilde{p}$.[6]

It should be noted that this procedure could be allowed to iterate until convergence based on some criterion such as MSE is established. In this study we will only present the results associated with the first iteration. This is because in preliminary trials we did not observe much difference in the regression estimates after a few iterations.

[5] In Theorem 3 we have shown that if $\tilde{p} = O(\varrho^{\tilde{p}} T)$ then $\hat{\beta}_{\text{EIGLS-AR}(\tilde{p})}$ will have the same limiting distribution as GLS. Through extensive experimentation Poskitt and Salau (1995) in demonstrating asymptotic equivalency of the Koreisha and Pukkila (1990) generalized least squares estimation procedure for univariate and vector ARMA processes vis-à-vis Gaussian estimation procedures, have shown that for sample sizes similar to the ones used in our study, $\tilde{p}$ must be less than or equal to $(\ln T)^{1.8}$. Pukkila, Koreisha, and Kallinen (1990) have also provided some basis for fixing $\tilde{p}$ at $kT^{1/2}$, where k ranged from 0.5 to 1.5.

[6] These properties are relatively straightforward to obtain when the true regression residuals follow a purely autoregressive process (see, for example, Wickens 1969). However, when the residuals contain moving-average terms some technical difficulties arise in the calculation of the inverse of the covariance matrix which can be overcome by conducting the analysis in the frequency domain similar to Amemiya (1973).

Based on the thus derived $\hat{\beta}_i^{\text{2SOLS-LR}}$ as well as $\hat{\gamma}_j$ from (10), the h-step ahead forecasts at time t can be constructed by sequentially generating future estimates for $\hat{\varepsilon}_{T+h}$ from

$$\hat{\varepsilon}_{T+h} = \sum_{j=1}^{\tilde{p}} \hat{\gamma}_j \hat{\varepsilon}_{T+h-j},$$

thus yielding the forecasts for y_{T+h}, namely,

$$\hat{y}_{T+h}^{\text{2SOLS-LR}} = \hat{\beta}_0^{\text{2SOLS-LR}} + \sum_{i=1}^{k} \hat{\beta}_i^{\text{2SOLS-LR}} x_{i,T+h} + \hat{\varepsilon}_{T+h}. \tag{12}$$

Another equivalent way to generate forecasts from serially correlated regression models is through the use of lagged dependent $\{y_{t-j}\}$ and explanatory $\{x_{t-j}\}$ variables instead of estimated lagged residuals $\{\hat{\varepsilon}_{t-j}\}$.

Assuming again that ε_t can be approximated by an AR($\tilde{p}$) process, then (9) can be reexpressed as

$$y_t = \beta_0 + \sum_{i=1}^{k} \beta_i x_{i,t} + \sum_{j=1}^{\tilde{p}} \pi_j \varepsilon_{t-j} + u_t. \tag{13}$$

Thus, since

$$\varepsilon_{t-j} = y_{t-j} - \Big(\beta_0 + \sum_{i=1}^{k} \beta_i x_{i,t-j}\Big),$$

(13) can be rewritten as,

$$y_t = \beta_0 + \sum_{j=1}^{\tilde{p}} \pi_j y_{t-j} + \sum_{i=1}^{k} \beta_i \Big(x_{i,t} - \sum_{j=1}^{\tilde{p}} \pi_j x_{i,t-j}\Big) + w_t. \tag{14}$$

Note, however, that because the coefficients associated with $x_{i,t-j}$ are restricted to be the product of the coefficients of y_{t-j} and $x_{i,t}$, one has to use nonlinear procedures (which often are not available in statistical packages, even SAS which only permits linear restrictions) to estimate (14).

It should be clear that (14) is mathematically equivalent to (10). The difference between the two 2SOLS methods hinges on how the regression coefficients are obtained. The forecast performance of these two linear approaches are very comparable, thus, for the sake of brevity, and also because of the simplicity and ease for which the 2SOLS-LR procedure can be adapted to any commercially available statistical software package, we will only highlight the performance comparisons between the 2SOLS-LR approach and other more efficient nonlinear procedures such as generalized least squares.

From Table 5 which contrasts selected predictive relative mean squares error efficiencies among 2SOLS-LR($\tilde{p}$) and other EGLS procedures and more

Table 5. Relative predictive efficiencies of 2SOLS-LR correction associated with selected ARMA(p, q) error processes.

T	h	ARMA(1, 1) with $(\phi_1, \theta_1) = (-0.8, 0.7)$											
		$\eta = 0.0$				$\eta = 0.5$				$\eta = 0.9$			
		PMSE 2SOLS	$\hat{\xi}_{\frac{2SOLS}{EGLS}}$	$\hat{\xi}_{\frac{2SOLS}{EIGLS}}$	$\hat{\xi}_{\frac{2SOLS}{OLS}}$	PMSE 2SOLS	$\hat{\xi}_{\frac{2SOLS}{EGLS}}$	$\hat{\xi}_{\frac{2SOLS}{EIGLS}}$	$\hat{\xi}_{\frac{2SOLS}{OLS}}$	PMSE 2SOLS	$\hat{\xi}_{\frac{2SOLS}{EGLS}}$	$\hat{\xi}_{\frac{2SOLS}{EIGLS}}$	$\hat{\xi}_{\frac{2SOLS}{OLS}}$
50	1	1.255	1.022	1.016	0.166	1.181	1.090	1.023	0.174	1.313	1.005	1.005	0.174
	2	3.802	1.114	1.033	0.545	3.840	1.089	1.062	0.573	3.766	1.024	1.011	0.548
	5	7.081	1.008	0.990	0.915	6.670	1.033	0.987	0.882	6.661	0.999	0.988	0.937
	10	7.342	1.030	1.003	0.959	7.459	1.004	0.999	1.008	7.326	1.016	1.008	1.001
100	1	1.270	1.133	1.090	0.165	1.148	1.055	1.060	0.152	1.313	1.026	1.016	0.174
	2	3.624	1.125	1.105	0.485	3.590	1.090	1.072	0.502	3.766	1.043	1.024	0.548
	5	6.484	0.991	0.962	0.875	6.537	1.021	1.013	0.832	6.661	1.059	1.050	0.937
	10	7.186	1.018	1.006	1.058	7.205	1.044	0.998	0.945	7.329	0.996	0.988	1.001
200	1	1.066	1.028	1.009	0.148	1.071	1.076	1.068	0.149	1.215	1.079	1.047	0.167
	2	3.363	1.039	1.049	0.473	3.179	1.112	1.058	0.444	3.775	1.070	1.059	0.533
	5	6.554	1.035	1.040	0.879	6.076	1.075	1.043	0.893	6.485	1.017	1.010	0.904
	10	7.155	1.023	1.004	0.924	7.152	1.023	1.014	1.006	7.197	1.018	1.003	0.999
		ARMA(1, 2) with $(\phi_1, \theta_1, \theta_2) = (0.6, -0.5, -0.9)$											
100	1	1.454	1.117	1.074	0.246	1.557	1.131	1.116	0.250	1.445	1.183	1.154	0.250
	2	4.072	1.017	0.989	0.716	4.173	1.015	0.999	0.632	2.864	1.007	0.993	0.478
	5	5.026	1.097	1.033	0.837	4.978	1.036	1.025	0.762	6.673	0.999	1.008	1.028
	10	6.265	1.081	1.070	1.072	5.773	1.108	1.014	0.983	6.949	1.004	1.006	1.015
		ARMA(2, 1) with $(\phi_1, \phi_2, \theta_1) = (-0.5, -0.9, 0.6)$											
50	1	1.445	1.082	1.087	0.143	1.270	1.016	1.023	0.143	1.504	1.076	1.091	0.169
	2	2.839	1.103	1.108	0.291	2.540	1.165	1.067	0.256	2.637	1.014	1.008	0.266
	5	4.416	1.101	1.040	0.457	4.369	1.037	1.044	0.494	4.410	1.102	1.067	0.455
	10	7.196	1.055	0.996	0.753	6.893	1.001	1.010	0.773	6.970	1.019	0.971	0.752
100	1	1.167	1.074	1.072	0.125	1.199	1.085	1.086	0.121	1.176	1.120	1.075	0.120
	2	2.417	1.098	1.041	0.254	2.385	1.076	1.074	0.222	2.442	1.059	1.048	0.264
	5	3.940	1.032	0.981	0.419	4.045	1.024	1.025	0.375	4.006	1.015	0.995	0.432
	10	6.768	1.110	1.033	0.743	6.736	0.983	0.981	0.719	6.684	1.073	1.043	0.686
200	1	1.096	1.092	1.100	0.113	1.012	1.005	1.008	0.096	1.056	1.065	1.016	0.118
	2	2.267	0.990	0.996	0.240	2.172	1.078	1.078	0.217	2.544	1.060	1.009	0.284
	5	3.780	1.054	0.980	0.410	3.816	1.000	1.001	0.365	3.876	1.001	1.003	0.434
	10	6.259	1.086	1.013	0.712	6.262	0.957	0.964	0.689	7.254	1.021	1.013	0.782

PMSE: prediction mean squared error.
EIGLS is based on an AR($\tilde{p}$) correction.
2SOLS is based on 2SOLS-LR approach.
The order $\tilde{p}$ of the AR correction for EIGLS and 2SOLS is set at $[\sqrt{T}/2]$ for all cases.

extensive simulation results found in Koreisha and Fang (2005) it can be also concluded that for short and medium term horizons ($h \leq 5$) the predictive efficiency of the 2SOLS-LR($\tilde{p}$) method is higher than those obtained from OLS. As noted earlier the degree of improvement in the predictive relative efficiency is dependent on the structures of the serial correlation, ranging from nearly zero to more than an order of magnitude.

Moreover, the predictive efficiency of the 2SOLS-LR method is very comparable to that of IGLS based on AR($\tilde{p}$) corrections with $\tilde{p} = [\sqrt{T}/2]$ which as shown previously is very similar to EGLS, i.e. with known Ω. This suggests that for predictive purposes there is not much to be gained in trying to identifying the correct order and form of the serial correlation or in using more intricate estimation methods such as generalized least squares or maximum likelihood procedures which often require inversion of large matrices. For longer horizons OLS yields forecasts that are as efficient as those generated by 2SOLS-LR and GLS approaches.

6 Concluding remarks

In this article we have shown both asymptotically and for finite samples that IGLS procedures based on AR($\tilde{p}$) representations for the serial correlation can be used effectively to construct regression models with autocorrelation. Consequently, there is not much to be gained in trying to identify the correct order and form of the serial autocorrelation. For short to medium term horizons we have also demonstrated that simple procedures based OLS can generate forecasts that are comparable to those generated by GLS procedures, for which Ω is known. For longer horizons OLS yields forecasts that are as efficient as those generated by methods that try to correct for the serial correlation.

References

Amemiya, T. (1973). Generalized least squares with an estimated autocovariance matrix. *Econometrica*, 41, 723–732.

Berk, K. N. (1974). Consistent autoregressive spectral estimates. *Annals of Statistics*, 2, 489–502.

Bhansali, R. J. (1978). Linear prediction by autoregressive model fitting in the time domain. *Annals of Statistics*, 6, 224–231.

Box, G. and Jenkins G. (1976). *Time Series Analysis: Forecasting and Control*, 2nd ed. San Francisco: Holden-Day.

Brockwell, P. and Davis R. (1991). *Time Series: Theory and Methods*, 2nd ed. New York: Springer-Verlag.

Choudhury, A., Hubata R., and Louis R. (1999). Understanding time-series regression estimators. *The American Statistician*, 53, 342–348.

Cochrane, D. and Orcutt G. (1949). Application of least squares regression to relationships containing autocorrelated error terms. *Journal of American Statistical Association*, 44, 32–61.

Durbin, J. and Watson G. (1950). Testing for serial correction in least squares regression. *Biometrika*, 37, 409–428.

Engle, R. (1974). Specification of the disturbance for efficient estimation. *Econometrica*, 42, 135–146.

Fang, Y. and Koreisha, S. (2004). Forecasting with serially correlated regression models. *Journal of Statistical Computation and Simulation*, 74, 625–649.

Fang, Y. and Koreisha, S. (2005). Distributional Properties of Misspecified GLS Estimators in Regressions with Autocorrelation. Working paper. University of Oregon.

Glasbey, C. A. (1982). A generalization of partial autocorrelation useful in identifying ARMA models. *Technometrics*, 24, 223–228.

Hannan, E. J., Dunsmuir, A., and Deistler, M. (1980). Estimation of vector ARMAX models. *Journal of Multivariate Analysis*, 10, 275–295.

Hildreth, C. (1986). *Lecture Notes in Economics and Mathematical Systems 271: The Cowles Commission in Chicago, 1939–1955*. New York: Springer-Verlag.

Kadiyala, K. (1970). Testing for the independence of regression disturbances. *Econometrica*, 38, 97–117.

King, M. (1983). Testing for autoregressive against moving average errors in the linear regression model. *Journal of Econometrics*, 21, 35–51.

Koreisha, S. and Fang, Y. (1999). The impact of measurement errors on ARMA prediction. *Journal of Forecasting*, 18, 95–110.

Koreisha, S. and Fang, Y. (2001). Generalized least squares with misspecified serial correlation structures. *Journal of the Royal Statistical Society, Series B*, 63, 515–531.

Koreisha, S. and Fang, Y. (2005). Using Least Squares to Generate Forecasts in Regression Models with Autocorrelated Disturbances. Working paper. University of Oregon.

Koreisha, S. and Pukkila, T. (1990). A generalized least squares approach for estimation of autoregressive moving average models. *Journal of Time Series Analysis*, 11, 139–151.

Krämer, W. (1986). Least squares regression when the independend variable follows an ARIMA process. *Journal of the American Statistical Association*, 81, 150–154.

Poskitt, D. and Salau, M. (1995). On the relationship between generalized least squares and Gaussian estimation of vector ARMA models. *Journal of Time Series Analysis*, 16, 617–645.

Pukkila, T., Koreisha S., and Kallinen A. (1990). The identification of ARMA models. *Biometrika*, 77, 537–549.

Saikkonen, P. (1986). Asymptotic properties of some preliminary estimators for autoregressive moving average time series models. *Journal of Time Series Analysis*, 7, 133–155.

Schmidt, P. (1976). *Econometrics*. New York: Marcel Dekker.

Thursby, J. (1987). OLS or GLS in the presence of specification error? *Journal of Econometrics*, 35, 359–374.

Walker, A. (1967). Some tests of separate families of hypotheses in time series analysis. *Biometrika*, 54, 39–68.

Wickens, M. (1969). The consistency and efficiency of generalized least squares in simultaneous equation systems with autocorrelated errors. *Econometrica*, 37, 651–659.

Zinde-Walsh, V. and Galbraith J. (1991). Estimation of a linear regression model with stationary ARMA(p, q) errors. *Journal of Econometrics*, 47, 333–357.

SERGIO G. KOREISHA
Lundquist College of Business, University of Oregon,
Eugene, Oregon 97403, USA
sergiok@lcbmail.uoregon.edu
http://darkwing.uoregon.edu/~sergiok/skres.html

Yue Fang
Lundquist College of Business, University of Oregon,
Eugene, Oregon 97403, USA
yfang@lcbmail.uoregon.edu
http://darkwing.uoregon.edu/~yfang/

Festschrift for Tarmo Pukkila on his 60th Birthday
Eds. E. P. Liski, J. Isotalo, J. Niemelä, S. Puntanen, and G. P. H. Styan
© Dept. of Mathematics, Statistics and Philosophy,
Univ. of Tampere, 2006, ISBN 978-951-44-6620-5, pages 145–157

Statistical applications in Finnish pension insurance

LASSE A. KOSKINEN

Abstract. This paper surveys two statistical applications in Finnish pension insurance where advanced computational models and simulations are being used. The first application deals with system level aspects and the second one with the company level. At the beginning of 2005, the statutory earnings-related pension scheme of Finland underwent the largest reform in its history. In the reform the uncertainties of the future demographics were taken into account by statistical methods. Here we survey the reform from this point of view. Second, a quite different application is related to investment management of the funds of Finnish pension insurance companies. Here a stochastic programming model for the asset liability management of a typical Finnish pension insurance company is reviewed.

1 Introduction

Risk is the potential harm that may arise from some present process or from some future event. The estimation of risk is usually based on two elements: (i) the probability of the event occurring on the basis of expert knowledge and observed data, and (ii) the value of the consequence of the event given that it has occurred. Insurance is a form of risk management primarily used to hedge against the risk of potential financial loss. On the other hand statistics is the discipline concerned with the study of variability, with the study of uncertainty and with the decision-making in the face of uncertainty. Thus, statistics is especially crucial in insurance and statistical methods have played in a natural way a key role in the development of the insurance industry.

The objective of this paper is to review certain published applications of statistics in the context of Finnish pension insurance. We give a survey of some demographic and investment applications in which statistics has an important impact. Although relative simple mathematical methods have traditionally been used to assess demographic trends and asset liability management in pension insurance, use of modern statistical methods offers significant advantages for forecasting the future, and for assessing the uncertainty.

The Finnish earnings-related pension scheme aims to provide retirement income sufficient to cover consumption comparable to levels enjoyed during working years and to current workers' consumption. It covers risks related to old age, disability, long-term unemployment of aging workers, and death of family earners. The scheme is statutory by law but largely run by private pension companies and funds (there is also large local government and a state pension fund). The amount of funds only affects contributions. When a person receives a pension his/her funds are used to pay that part of the pension benefit that was prefunded. The rest comes from the PAYG part, the so-called pooled component in the contribution rate paid by working people.

Pension companies and funds have collected substantial wealth to smooth the contribution increases due to forecasted population aging in the future. Funding is collective but based on individual pension rights. Individual pension benefits do not depend on the existence or yield of funds (at least in the short run). A detailed description of the system can be found in Hietaniemi and Vidlund (2003). The Finnish pension system was reformed in 2005. The reform is evaluated e.g. in Lassila and Valkonen (2005).

A statistical decision is essential for effective development planning, policy formulation, action program and monitoring of the progress made in pension insurance. It is fundamental for informed decision-making by its institutions as well as individuals. In pension insurance a vital topic, where statistics plays a central role, is demographics (the study of the size, distribution, structure and growth of populations). In recent years, several methodologies for measuring demographic risks have been introduced that demonstrate the benefits of using statistical models. For example, sustainability of the pension system and intergenerational fiscal equity under population aging are problems where understanding the nature of population forecasts and their uncertainty is needed (see e.g. Auerbach and Lee (2001)).

The actuarial profession all over Europe highlights the need to allow for uncertainty in future mortality as it unveils sharp improvement in pensioner mortality figures. During the past two decades alternative methods for producing stochastic forecasts have been proposed. All approaches share the following structure: (i) the vital processes are viewed as realizations of stochastic processes, and (ii) once the parameters of the processes have been specified, sample paths for future population age-groups are stochastically simulated (see e.g. Alho and Spencer (2005)). Combining stochastic population simulations with economic models provides a new way to analyze the sustainability of pension systems. Here the statistical applications for addressing these kinds of issues in the Finnish pension system are reviewed.

Another central issue in pension insurance is asset liability management (ALM). Few problems are as important and complex to insurance companies and funds than the management of their assets in such a way that their liabilities can be covered. The assets must be invested over time to achieve favorable returns subject to various uncertainties, constraints (policy and regulatory), taxes and liability commitments. This subject shows the importance of a broad mathematical viewpoint in solving concrete problems.

An expansive set of statistical and computational methods has proved to be very useful in the ALM context. For instance, stochastic programming is an efficient approach in designing effective strategies in the wealth management of pension companies and funds in practice (see e.g. Ziemba and Mulvey (2001)). This is due to its ability to cope with the dynamics and complex constraint structures. This paper describes a stochastic programming model application for the asset liability management of a Finnish pension insurance company.

2 Demographic uncertainty and the pension system

"In fact, we believe that by integrating modern statistical tools into a standard economic model we have been able to provide a better analytical framework for assessing the economic effects of demographic risks. This integration has been computationally demanding, and the obvious challenge of including risk assessments in households' and firms' decision making in this setup has been left for future studies." Alho, Jensen, Lassila, and Valkonen (2005).

2.1 Stochastic population forecasts

Population aging is generated by two distinct demographic processes that demand two different policy responses. The first process is fertility decline. In Finland the peak of the baby boom was relatively early, around 1947. The size of the 1947 cohort is about 40 percent larger than the 1972 cohort. There is little one can do about the cause of this extra financial burden: the fertility decline is a historical fact. The only option is that members of the baby-boom generation have to pay some part of their pensions themselves by saving for their own retirement. This pre-funding mechanism is the natural policy reaction to the smaller cohort size of the baby-bust generation.

The second process underlying population aging is the increase in longevity. An increasing life span creates no problems if everything in an economy adapts in proportion, especially the economically active life span. This, however, does not happen automatically, since many rules and regulations are fixed and respond slowly to demographic changes. Longevity only creates a financing problem for pensions if the retirement age does not move in proportion to longevity.

Demographic projections are always uncertain, and erroneous projections can lead to misleading or even wrong policy decisions. Conducted research has increased understanding of demographic processes but unfortunately this has not improved forecast accuracy (see e.g. Alho and Spencer (2005)). Therefore, good policies should be robust against forecasting errors.

A traditional way of handling uncertainty is to present alternative scenarios in addition to a benchmark projection. The problem is that, a priori, it is hard to determine what aspects of future demographics should be varied and by how much. In some cases, the use of scenarios can even be harmful, if they give a false impression that all relevant contingencies have been covered. In practice experts have often underestimated future uncertainty when they have used the scenario technique.

Another way is to create scenarios so that explicit probabilities can be attached to them. A third alternative is to take the uncertainty explicitly into account by presenting stochastic population projections. One can then analyze the effects of a given policy under a realistic range of different population paths. Scenarios still remain as an important way to compare policy actions because of their simplicity.

An important advantage with stochastic population projections is that they lead naturally to formulating policies so that they state what action will be taken under a large number of possible states of the world that cover a realistic range of demographic developments. A very illustrative comparison (see Table 1) of traditional and stochastic population forecasting methods is made in Ahn et al. (2006).

In the following applications the used computational tools are "Program for Error Propagation (PEP)" (see e.g. Alho (1998)) and "Overlapping Generations Model for Finnish Economy (FOG)" (see. e.g. Lassila and Valkonen (2003)). In PEP the parameters of the stochastic process are specified to match the error of the past forecasts. They can be taken from time-series or they can be based on judgment. FOG is an Auerbach-Kotlikoff type, perfect foresight numerical overlapping generations model. It is adjusted to imitate the Finnish economy by a process of calibration.

2.2 Adjustment factor for mortality change

An increase in life expectancy can put a strain on the finances of a pension system as explained above. In a pay-as-you-go system this may mean increasing the contribution levels of current workers. In a funded system, the development of life expectancy must be anticipated in setting the contributions of the future retirees. In Finland, the earnings-related pension scheme is partially prefunded, so both aspects are relevant.

In anticipation of future gains in life expectancy, a law has been passed in Finland in 2003 that automatically adjusts pensions if life expectancy changes. The aim of the legislation is to preserve the net present value of future pensions. Thus, the adjustment factor shifts part of the risk from future workers to retirees and makes pension benefits more actuarially fair in the intergenerational sense. The essential source of uncertainty concerning the future values of the adjustment factor comes from the fact that future mortality rates are unknown.

Table 1. Conventional and stochastic population forecasts: pros and cons (Ahn et al. 2006).

	Conventional Population Forecast	Stochastic Population Forecast
Transparency	Involves addition, subtraction and multiplication only. The results may be checked by direct inspection, and understood based on modest education.	Forecasts are carried out by simulation. Checking is more complex. Understanding the results requires more education (including probabilities and statistics).
Simplicity of presentation	Middle scenario may be sufficient to convey the main message. Alternative calculations may be provided, with one leading to a higher population, another leading to a lower population etc. These can be printed back-to-back in a book. Results for aggregated age-groups are produced by addition.	A full predictive distribution is approximated via computer simulation. Still, it may not be necessary to display more than the point forecast for a lay audience. Prediction intervals can be published for individual ages, but to produce intervals for aggregates a database of simulated values must (and can) be accessed.
Ease of preparation	Only a point forecast needs to be specified.	In addition, the specification of variances and correlations is required.
Interpretation and logical coherence of intervals	High and low intervals are (usually) interpreted as providing a "plausible range". But, there is no way to guarantee the comparability of the ranges for different ages, different sexes, different forecast years, etc. The results for different demographic functionals are necessarily incoherent.	Intervals with desired probability content for the size of any population aggregate and for the size of any demographic functional (such as age ratios) at any future time can be provided.
Ability to handle uncertainty	Cannot handle uncertainty in a coherent and interpretable manner.	Uncertainty is handled in a coherent and interpretable manner.
Use of past data	Only trend estimates can be used. Judgment is necessary for questions like which models and which data periods to use. Knowledge of intermediate correlations (i.e., different from ± 1) across demographic variables cannot be used.	Can utilize information on varying trends, lack of fit, changes of volatility etc. The uncertainty related to the choice of models and data periods can be incorporated statistically. Knowledge of intermediate correlations can be incorporated.
Conditional forecasts and scenarios	Can represent scenarios that correspond, e.g., to assumed effects of policy interventions or exogenous factors.	Can, in addition, incorporate information about the uncertainty concerning the effects of interventions or exogenous factors.
Sensitivity analysis	Can vary values of fertility, mortality or migration to see what the effect is.	Can, in addition, vary second moments.
Ease of computation	A large number of computer programs are available. There is extensive experience of their use. Results are obtained in seconds.	Several computer programs are available, but with differing capabilities. There is experience of their use from the past 10–15 years only. Results are obtained in minutes.

From 2010 onwards, benefits will be indexed by life expectancy (see e.g. Lindell (2004)). The aim of the adjustment factor is to adjust benefit levels so that the present value of the benefits does not increase when life expectancy is increasing. Beginning with the cohort of 1948, the starting level of the old-age pension of each cohort entering retirement is multiplied by this factor. The factor then remains constant during retirement for this cohort. The factor is computed as the annuity value of a Euro for a person aged 62 years in this person's retirement year relative to the annuity value for a person who is aged 62 in the year 2009.

As the development of future mortality is uncertain, it is of interest to consider the level of uncertainty one can expect in future life expectancy and in net present values. Alho (2003) has provided a stochastic analysis of the life expectancy adjustment factor in Finland. His calculations use simple trend extrapolation methods. The main result is a predictive distribution for the adjustment factor that reflects the past uncertainty of such trend forecasts, with little or no subjective input. The distribution indicates that by the year 2050 Finland can expect an adjustment factor of 0.87. The width of an 80 per cent prediction interval is 20 percentage points, if past volatility of mortality is used as a guide. Thus, the likely reduction of future pensions is remarkable as well as its uncertainty.

These results are valuable in two types of decisions. First, the working-age people may prepare better for their own retirement. Second, predictive distributions are needed for the economic analysis of retirement decisions, so that the risk aversion of future retirees can properly be accounted for.

2.3 Sustainability of the pension system

Combining stochastic population simulations with economic models provides a new way to think about the sustainability of the pension system. Stochastic population simulations produce a wide range of possible outcomes. In some, the pension system may seem sustainable, in others it may be considered unsustainable, depending on how the strain is felt by the contributors or by the pensioners. Both qualitative and quantitative insights can be obtained on how demographic risks can be shifted in time or between groups in society.

Alho et al. (2005) discuss a mechanism of pension pension indexation schemes that tries to alleviate the effect of unexpected changes in fertility in Finland. Their analytical apparatus comprises four building blocks, namely (i) the stochastic forecasting method; (ii) the pension system; (iii) multivariate assessment criteria, needed as indicators of the degree of success in achieving the objective of reducing the variability caused by uncertain demographics; and (iv) an economic simulation model, to help quantifying how alternative demographic trajectories and pension indexation schemes impact on economic outcomes and intergenerational welfare.

First, by adopting the technique of stochastic forecasting, Alho et al. (2005)

have acknowledged the empirical finding that the level of uncertainty in demographic forecasts is typically much higher than expected. Second, by adopting a numerical general equilibrium model with overlapping generations, they have been able to illustrate some important economic outcomes of demographic uncertainty.

In more concrete terms the results show that rather than average wage-bill indexation, the total wage-bill indexation effectively serves to lower the sensitivity of pension contributions to demographic uncertainty. It does so at the cost of transferring demographic risks to pensioners, but, according to the authors' interpretation, without endangering the basic subsistence function of the pensions. There is an ex ante trade-off between contribution rate variability and replacement rate variability, the former declining and the latter increasing with the degree of wage-bill indexation. One way of limiting the possible negative effects of the reformed indexation rule to the replacement rate is to announce to the worker well in advance the likely pension level and to accrue a higher pension by retiring later.

3 Investment management for a pension insurance company

"Some of the most critical parameters in the model, namely drift rates and certain long-term equilibrium values, are taken user-specified instead of relying completely on statistical information. This is essential when the available data displays drifts or other characteristics that are believed to change in the future." Koivu, Pennanen, and Ranne (2005).

3.1 Stochastic programming and investment decision

In investment practice, most decision problems involve factors whose values are unknown at the time a decision has to be made (the future returns on some of the available assets are unknown) but whose values significantly affect the outcome. Stochastic programming is a method that helps finding optimal investment strategies in that kind of situation. The investment problem can be formulated as an optimization problem where the uncertainty and dynamics of investment instruments are explicitly taken into account while trying to find a decision strategy that is optimal with respect to given constraints (e.g. regulation) and objective function. The uncertain factors are modeled as random variables.

In static problems, the outcome only depends on investment decisions made at the present time, but in dynamic problems, the outcome is significantly affected also by decisions made at later decision stages where more information may be available. Investment problems become dynamic as soon as one has the option to update the investment portfolio within the planning period. Optimal portfolio updates will depend on the information revealed by the time of the update. The relevant information would be earlier investment returns (since they determine the amount of wealth that can be invested) as well as any other available information that could affect the future distribution of the returns.

The advantage of stochastic programming over more traditional approaches (e.g. stochastic optimal control and dynamic programming) is its wider applicability. Stochastic programming is based on well-developed techniques of mathematical programming, where optimal solutions are sought numerically. These techniques apply to far more general models than stochastic control or dynamic programming. Of course, this flexibility has been obtained at the cost of a more complex system.

Many real-life investment decision strategies are best modeled as infinite-dimensional stochastic programs where the uncertainty is described by general stochastic processes (instead of finite scenario trees). This approach has several advantages: First, it allows one to use well-developed statistical (econometric) models in describing the uncertainty. Second, it allows for rigorous analysis of the problem and solution schemes (see http://hkkk.fi/~systems/sp/). A general introduction to stochastic programming and review of software packages is available at the official stochastic programming (The Committee of Stochastic Programming) site: www.stoprog.org.

Formulation of a stochastic optimization problem starts with specifying the decision stages, decision variables, uncertain factors, objective function and constraints. The approach consists of formulating the model and then solving it. The process can be broken down into four phases:

A. Modeling the problem:

 1. Modeling the decision problem as an optimization problem;
 2. Modeling the stochastic factors;

B. Solving the model:

 3. Discretization of the optimization problem;
 4. Numerical solution of the discretized problem.

Evaluation of the solution may suggest improvements to phases 1–4, so that one ends up passing through these steps more than once. Statistical methods are mainly needed in phases 1 and 2.

The probability measure can represent the subjective views of the decision maker. It should not be a mere description of historical data but a model of the future development of the uncertain factors in the decision problem. One can find well-developed and analyzed techniques in the vast literature on statistical modeling, e.g. econometrics and financial modeling.

Ideally, the modeling of the uncertainty should be independent of the solution phase, but when the discretization of a stochastic programming model is done by computers, one needs a parametric description of the stochastic process in terms of a finite number of parameters. For instance conditional Gaussian processes cover a wide variety of econometric models studied in the literature.

3.2 Asset liability management of a Finnish pension insurance company

Finnish pension insurance companies manage massive investment funds, and they face a larger number of retiring policyholders during the years 2010–2030 because of the baby-boom and longer life span. An application of stochastic programming to the asset liability management of a typical Finnish pension insurance company has been reported in Hilli et al. (2006) and Koivu, Pennanen, and Ranne (2005). In Finland similar models have been implemented and used at least for one pension company and several pension funds. The model addresses a long-term dynamic investment problem where the aim is to cover the uncertain future liabilities with dynamic investment strategies. Mortality is an important factor but it has not been dealt with stochastically.

The assets are considered as the aggregate investment classes of cash, bonds, stocks, property and loans to policyholders. In addition to investment decisions, their model looks for optimal bonus payments and it takes explicitly into account various portfolio and transaction restrictions as well as some legal restrictions coming from the intricate pension system in Finland. The legal restrictions form a unique part of the model not present in earlier applications of stochastic programming.

Koivu, Pennanen, and Ranne (2005) pay particular attention to describing the uncertain factors in the model which include investment returns, cash-flows, and the technical reserves used in the definition of the statutory restrictions. This is important since the solution of a stochastic programming model usually depends heavily on the underlying model for the stochastic factors.

There are several constraints stemming from the regulations of the Finnish pension system. The objective of Hilli et al. (2006) is to optimize the development of the company's solvency situation as described by the Ministry of Social Affairs and Health as well as the amount of bonuses paid to policyholders. The resulting model imitates a typical Finnish pension insurance company. The parts of the model are briefly described in the following.

1. *Stochastic factors.* The duration of the liabilities is usually very long (over 20 years), which calls for realistic models for long-term scenarios of investment returns and liability flows. Such models form the basis for pension companies' asset and liability management. The stochastic factors in the optimization model are first expressed in terms of seven economic variables, namely short-term interest rate, long-term bond yield, stock price index, dividend index, property price index, rental index and wage index.

Hilli et al. (2006) use the stochastic model for assets and liabilities developed in Koivu, Pennanen, and Ranne (2005) where a vector equilibrium correction model which, in addition to short-term dynamics, takes into account long term equilibrium relations between certain economic factors.

2. *The optimization model.* The model is a multistage stochastic program where a sequence of decisions (asset allocations etc.) is interlaced with a sequence of observations of random variables (asset returns etc.). At each stage, decisions are made based on the information revealed up to that point, so the decision variables at one stage are functions of the random variables observed up to that stage. The decision variables characterize the asset management strategy as well as the company's solvency situation and the bonus strategy.

3. *Statutory restrictions.* The statutory restrictions (Solvency Capital, Solvency Limit, Upper Bound for Bonuses) for Finnish pension insurance companies are quite strict, and they form a unique part of our stochastic programming model. Besides imposing constraints on the decision variables, these rules form the basis for defining the objective function in our model. A fundamental restriction is that the assets of a company must always cover its technical reserves, which corresponds to the present value of future pension expenditure discounted with the so-called "technical interest rate". The difference of assets and the technical reserves is called the solvency capital. If at any time it becomes negative, the company is declared bankrupt.

4. *Objective function.* There are many possibilities for measuring the performance of a company. Natural candidates would be expected utility of wealth or solvency capital under various utility functions. Here a utility function takes explicitly into account the unique features of the Finnish pension system. Five different shortfall penalty coefficients were used. The problem is to maximize the objective function over all the decision variables and subject to all constraints.

Comparisons with fixed-mix and portfolio insurance strategies

The stochastic programming model was tested against static fixed-mix and dynamic portfolio insurance strategies. Fixed-mix strategies are simple decision rules that always rebalance the investment portfolio to maintain fixed asset proportions. Portfolio insurance strategies are based on the constant proportion portfolio insurance framework, where the proportion of risky assets is kept as a constant multiple of the difference between the portfolio value and a protective floor. If the portfolio value hits or falls below the floor, all the funds are invested in less risky assets.

A portfolio insurance strategy seems appropriate for a pension insurance company because it allocates more wealth to risky assets, stocks when the company's solvency ratio improves and reduces the stock market exposure when the company approaches insolvency. Fixed-mix and portfolio insurance are by no means realistic models for the behavior of a real pension insurance company. However, they are often used for various simulation purposes in practice, which motivates their use as benchmarks.

The out-of-sample testing procedure recommended e.g. by Tillinghast - Towers Perrin was used. In the test, Hilli et al. (2006) evaluated the performance of each strategy over 325 randomly simulated scenarios of stochastic parameters over 20 years. Portfolio rebalancing was made every year.

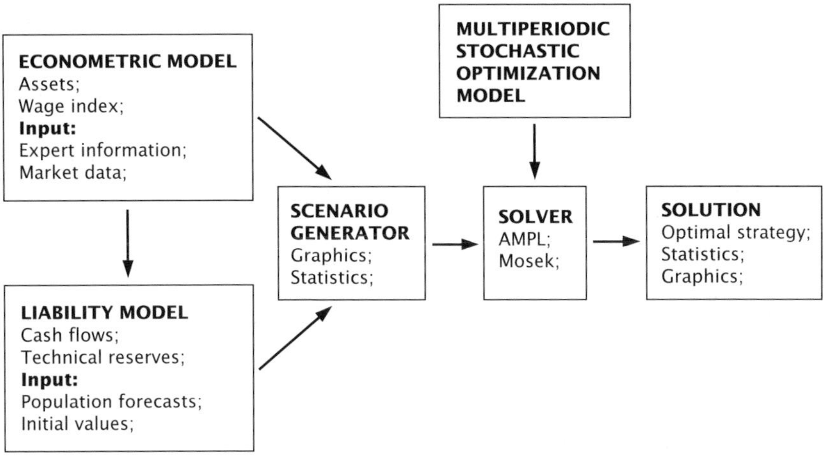

Figure 1. In the stochastic optimization system the model and data from scenario generator are processed in AMPL modeling language and fed to Mosek, which is an interior-point solver for convex programs (convex approximations were made).

Considering the main risk of the company, bankruptcy, and the level of average solvency capital, the stochastic programming strategies clearly dominate both the fixed-mix and portfolio insurance strategies, even though the probability of bankruptcy was not explicitly minimized. In the long run the stochastic programming strategy produces superior returns compared to the portfolio insurance and fixed-mix strategy, without increasing the company's bankruptcy risk.

4 Discussion

In Western countries pension systems must be adjusted to the rapidly changing demography in the near future. Another level of challenge is the need of insurance company modeling and fast transforming of information into useful knowledge and effective investment decisions. In order to meet the challenges, data intensive computational models and simulations are being used more and more frequently in the insurance sector. This development is desirable but we like to stress that scenarios and stochastic simulations complement each other and they should not be seen as alternative tools.

Accurate forecasting will be a critical capability that enables effective planning of operations. With an assessment of the predictive distribution, insurance experts can distinguish unlikely alternatives from probable ones, and if the forecast is very uncertain, flexible adaptive strategies can be sought. The presented applications bridge nicely the gap between theory and practice in this area.

The surveyed applications are examples of the use of simulation methods for forecasting, control and planning purposes. In these examples some emphasis is being placed on the tandem use of judgmental and statistical models. A judgmental forecast is used as input information to stochastic formulation. The practical usefulness of the models is advanced by combining ideas from these two modeling approaches.

Sources of forecast errors can be classified e.g. into six categories:

1. Model mis-specification (model error);
2. Errors in parameter estimates;
3. Errors in expert judgment;
4. Random variation inherited in the stochastic (even correct) model;
5. Erroneous or missing data;
6. Human errors.

Alho and Spencer (2005) have carefully studied categories 1–4 in the demographic context.

Model mis-specifiation is a central component of forecast error, but rarely discussed in statistical literature. Here surveyed demographic applications emphasis that aspect. We believe that model mis-specification is also a very important factor in the ALM applications since the result usually depends heavily on the underlying model for the stochastic factors. We think that a promising direction in this area is to stress more of that point. In practical applications human errors and data problems might be the most serious issues. This is a challenge to both the applications surveyed here.

Of course, there remain many important areas utilizing statistical methods in Finnish pension insurance that are not presented in this article.

Acknowledgements

I would like to express my gratitude to Jukka Lassila, Teemu Pennanen and Tarmo Valkonen for helpful comments and the material they provided.

References

Ahn, M., Alho, J., Bruecker, H., Cruijsen, H., Laakso, S., Lassila, J. (Coordinator), Morkuniene, A., Määttänen, N., and Valkonen, T. (2006). The use of demographic trends and long-term population projections in public policy planning at EU, national, regional and local level - Summary, conclusions and recommendations. *Studies on policy implications of demographic changes in the enlarged EU.* http://europa.eu.int/comm/employment_social/social_situation/studies_en.htm.

Alho, J. (1998). A stochastic forecast of the population of Finland. *Reviews*, 1998/4. Statistics Finland.

Alho, J. (2002). The population of Finland in 2050 and beyond. ETLA, Discussion Papers No. 826, Helsinki.

Alho, J. (2003). Predictive distribution of adjustment for life expectancy change. Finnish Centre for Pensions, Working Papers 3, Helsinki.

Alho, J. and Spencer, B. (2005). *Statistical Demography and Forecasting.* New York: Springer Verlag.

Alho, J.M., Jensen, S.E.H., Lassila, J., and Valkonen, T. (2005). Controlling the effects of demographic risks: The role of pension indexation schemes. *Journal of Pension Economics and Finance*, 4, 139-153.

Auerbach, A.J. and Kotlikoff, L.J. (1987). *Dynamic Fiscal Policy.* Cambridge, UK: Cambridge University Press.

Auerbach, A. and Lee, R. (2001). *Demographic Change and Fiscal Policy.* Cambridge, UK: Cambridge University Press.

Hietaniemi, M. and Vidlund, M. (eds.) (2003). The Finnish Pension System. The Finnish Centre for Pensions (http://www.etk.fi).

Hilli, P., Koivu, M., Pennanen, T., and Ranne, A. (2006). A stochastic programming model for asset and liability management of a Finnish pension company. *Annals of Operations Research*, to appear.

Koivu, M., Pennanen, T., and Ranne, A. (2005). Modeling assets and liabilities of a Finnish pension company: a VEqC approach. *Scandinavian Actuarial Journal*, 2005, 46-76.

Lassila, J. and Valkonen, T. (2003). Ageing, demographic risks and pension reform. In *Pension Reform: Redistribution and Risk.* Ed. M. Weale. NIESR, Occasional paper, No. 56.

Lassila, J. and Valkonen, T. (2005). The Finnish pension reform of 2005. ETLA, Discussion papers No. 1000, Helsinki.

Lindell, K. (2004). Life expectancy increases - what will happen to retirement age? Finnish Centre for Pensions, Working Papers 6, Helsinki.

Ziemba, W. and Mulvey, J. (eds.) (2001). *Worldwide asset and liability modelling.* Cambridge, UK: Cambridge University Press.

LASSE A. KOSKINEN
Insurance Supervisory Authority of Finland
lasse.koskinen@vakuutusvalvonta.fi

Festschrift for Tarmo Pukkila on his 60th Birthday
Eds. E. P. Liski, J. Isotalo, J. Niemelä, S. Puntanen, and G. P. H. Styan

Univ. of Tampere, 2006, ISBN 978-951-44-6620-5, pages 159–172

Normalized ML and the MDL principle for variable selection in linear regression

ERKKI P. LISKI

Abstract. *The Normalized Maximum Likelihood* formulation of the *the stochastic complexity* (Rissanen 1996) contains a component that may be interpreted as the parametric complexity of the model class. The stochastic complexity for the data, relative to a class of suggested models, serves as a criterion for model selection. We compare the performance of the NML selection criterion with the traditional fixed penalty criteria like *AIC* and *BIC* in simple Gaussian linear regression. As opposed to traditional fixed penalty criteria, the NML criteria have dimensionality penalties that depend on the data.

2000 MSC codes: 62B10, 62J05, 62F99.

Key words and phrases: Stochastic complexity; Parametric complexity; Fixed penalty criteria; Adaptive selection.

1 Introduction

Suppose that the response variable $\boldsymbol{y}$ and the potential explanatory variables $\boldsymbol{x}_1, \dots, \boldsymbol{x}_K$ are vectors of n observations. Often there is uncertainty about which explanatory variables to use. Such a situation typically prevails when K is large and many of the variables $\boldsymbol{x}_1, \dots, \boldsymbol{x}_K$ are thought to be irrelevant. The problem of variable selection arises when one wants to decide which variables to include in the model. Let the variable γ index all the 2^K subsets of explanatory variables $\boldsymbol{x}_1, \dots, \boldsymbol{x}_K$. We fit the normal linear model

$$\boldsymbol{y} = \boldsymbol{X}_\gamma \boldsymbol{\beta}_\gamma + \boldsymbol{\epsilon}, \tag{1}$$

where $\boldsymbol{X}_\gamma$ is an $n \times k$ regression matrix whose columns correspond to the γth subset of size k, $\boldsymbol{\beta}_\gamma$ is the $k \times 1$ vector of unknown regression coefficients of the variables in the γth subset and $\boldsymbol{\epsilon}$ follows the normal distribution $N_n(\mathbf{0}, \sigma^2 \boldsymbol{I})$.

The response data $\boldsymbol{y}$ are modelled with the normal density functions

$$f(\boldsymbol{y};\boldsymbol{\beta}_\gamma,\sigma^2) = \frac{1}{(2\pi\sigma^2)^{n/2}}\exp\Big(-\frac{1}{2\sigma^2}\|\boldsymbol{y}-\boldsymbol{X}_\gamma\boldsymbol{\beta}_\gamma\|^2\Big), \tag{2}$$

where $\|\cdot\|$ denotes the Euclidean norm of a vector.

The likelihood function L for a given observed vector $\boldsymbol{y}$ is defined as

$$L(\boldsymbol{\beta}_\gamma,\sigma^2;\boldsymbol{y}) = f(\boldsymbol{y};\boldsymbol{\beta}_\gamma,\sigma^2),$$

where $\boldsymbol{\beta}_\gamma \in \mathbb{R}^k$ and $\sigma^2 \in \mathbb{R}^+$. Then the maximum likelihood (ML) estimates of $\boldsymbol{\beta}_\gamma$ and σ^2 are

$$\hat{\boldsymbol{\beta}}_\gamma = (\boldsymbol{X}_\gamma'\boldsymbol{X}_\gamma)^{-1}\boldsymbol{X}_\gamma'\boldsymbol{y}$$

and

$$\hat{\sigma}_\gamma^2 = RSS_\gamma / n,$$

where

$$RSS_\gamma = \|\boldsymbol{y}-\boldsymbol{X}_\gamma\hat{\boldsymbol{\beta}}_\gamma\|^2 \tag{3}$$

is the residual sum of squares corresponding to the model γ. We will assume that $\boldsymbol{X}_\gamma$ is of full rank.

2 Stochastic complexity and the MDL principle

Consider the normalized maximum likelihood (NML) function (Rissanen 1996; Barron, Rissanen, and Yu 1998)

$$\hat{f}(\boldsymbol{y};\gamma) = \frac{f(\boldsymbol{y};\hat{\boldsymbol{\theta}}_\gamma(\boldsymbol{y}))}{C(\gamma)}, \tag{4}$$

where $\hat{\boldsymbol{\theta}}_\gamma = (\hat{\boldsymbol{\beta}}',\hat{\sigma}_\gamma^2)'$ and

$$C(\gamma) = \int f(\boldsymbol{y};\hat{\boldsymbol{\theta}}_\gamma(\boldsymbol{y}))\,\mathrm{d}\boldsymbol{y} \tag{5}$$

is the normalizing constant. Thus $\hat{f}(\boldsymbol{y};\gamma)$ is a density function, provided that $C(\gamma)$ is bounded. Rissanen (1996) considers the NML function in the context of coding and modelling theory and takes

$$-\log\hat{f}(\boldsymbol{y};\gamma) = -\log f(\boldsymbol{y};\hat{\boldsymbol{\theta}}_\gamma(\boldsymbol{y})) + \log C(\gamma) \tag{6}$$

as the "shortest code length" for the data $\boldsymbol{y}$ that can be obtained with the model γ and calls it *the stochastic complexity* of $\boldsymbol{y}$, given γ. The last term in the equation (6) is called *the parametric complexity*.

Here we consider the model classes

$$\mathcal{M}_\gamma = \{\, f(\boldsymbol{y};\boldsymbol{\beta}_\gamma,\sigma^2) : \gamma \in \{1,\dots,2^K\}\,\}$$

defined by the 2^K subsets of explanatory variables and the normal densities (2). The aim of variable selection is to find the optimal value of index γ. It is clear that the NML function (4) attains its maximum and the "code length" (6) its minimum for the same value of γ. According to *the MDL* (Minimum Description Length) *principle* we seek to find the index value $\gamma = \hat{\gamma}$ that minimizes the stochastic complexity:

$$-\log \hat{f}(\boldsymbol{y};\hat{\gamma}) = \min_{\gamma}\{-\log f(\boldsymbol{y};\hat{\boldsymbol{\theta}}_{\gamma}(\boldsymbol{y})) + \log C(\gamma)\}.$$

Since $\hat{\gamma}$ maximizes (4), we can call it the NML estimate of γ within the model class $\mathcal{M}_{\gamma}$.

For the normal distribution (2), however, the NML function is undefined, since the normalizing constant $C(\gamma)$ is not bounded. One approach to this problem is to constrain the data space properly (Rissanen 2000). For the constrained data space the stochastic complexity $C(\gamma)$ is bounded, but then it will depend on certain hyperparameters.

3 NML selection criterion when σ^2 is known

We suppose now that σ^2 in (2) is known. Since the following development will be for a fixed γ, we may drop the subindex γ for a while without loss of clarity. Here $\boldsymbol{X}$ is an $n \times k$ matrix and $\boldsymbol{\beta}$ a $k \times 1$ vector with $k \le K$. As we will see soon, the normalizing constant

$$C = \int f(\boldsymbol{y};\hat{\boldsymbol{\beta}}(\boldsymbol{y}))\,\mathrm{d}\boldsymbol{y}$$

is not bounded for the normal distribution (2).

Following the approach suggested by Rissanen (2000), we constrain the data to those $\boldsymbol{y}$ for which the fitted values $\hat{\boldsymbol{y}} = \boldsymbol{X}\hat{\boldsymbol{\beta}}$ lie on the set

$$\mathcal{Y}(R) = \{\,\boldsymbol{y} : \|\hat{\boldsymbol{y}}\|^2 \le nR\,\}, \tag{7}$$

where R is a positive constant. Then (See Appendix (40))

$$C(R) = \int_{\mathcal{Y}(R)} f(\boldsymbol{y};\hat{\boldsymbol{\beta}})\,\mathrm{d}\boldsymbol{y} = \left(\frac{nR}{2\sigma^2}\right)^{k/2} \Big/ \Gamma\left(\frac{k}{2}+1\right). \tag{8}$$

It is now clear that $C(R) \to \infty$, when $R \to \infty$.

Maximized NML Function. The hyper-parameter R can estimated by maximizing the NML function

$$\hat{f}(\boldsymbol{y};R) = \frac{f(\boldsymbol{y};\hat{\boldsymbol{\beta}})}{C(R)} \tag{9}$$

with respect to R. Substituting

$$\hat{R} = \|\hat{\boldsymbol{y}}\|^2/n \tag{10}$$

into (9) in place of R yields the maximized NML function mNML

$$\hat{f}(\boldsymbol{y};\hat{R}) = \frac{f(\boldsymbol{y};\hat{\boldsymbol{\beta}})}{C(\hat{R})}, \tag{11}$$

where

$$f(\boldsymbol{y};\hat{\boldsymbol{\beta}}) = (2\pi\sigma^2)^{-n/2}\exp\left(-\frac{RSS}{2\sigma^2}\right)$$

and

$$C(\hat{R}) = \frac{\|\hat{\boldsymbol{y}}\|^k}{(2\sigma^2)^{k/2}\Gamma(k/2+1)}.$$

Also the mNML function can be considered as a model selection criterion: Select the model which maximizes the mNML function. This kind of criterion was briefly discussed by Hansen and Yu (2001). However, the the mNML function (11) is not a density function for $\boldsymbol{y}$. Therefore Rissanen (2000) suggested the same normalization process for (11) as for the ML function in (4).

Normalized mNML Function. To keep the normalizing constant of the mNML function finite, the data $\boldsymbol{y}$ are constrained such that the fitted values $\hat{\boldsymbol{y}}$ lie in the set

$$\mathcal{Y}(R_1,R_2) = \{\,\boldsymbol{y} : nR_1 \le \|\hat{\boldsymbol{y}}\|^2 \le nR_2\,\}, \tag{12}$$

where $0 < R_1 < R_2$. The normalizing constant for the mNML function (11) can be written as (see Appendix (42))

$$C(R_1,R_2) = \int_{\mathcal{Y}(R_1,R_2)} \hat{f}(\boldsymbol{y};\hat{R})\,\mathrm{d}\boldsymbol{y} = \frac{k}{2}\log\frac{R_2}{R_1}. \tag{13}$$

Now the normalized mNML function

$$\hat{f}(\boldsymbol{y};\gamma) = \frac{\hat{f}(\boldsymbol{y};\hat{R}_\gamma)}{C(R_1,R_2)} \tag{14}$$

is defined for every model γ. Using the results (11) and (13) one obtains

$$-2\log\hat{f}(\boldsymbol{y};\gamma) = \frac{RSS_\gamma}{\sigma^2} + k\log\hat{R}_\gamma - k\log\left(\frac{2\sigma^2}{n}\right) - 2\log\Gamma\left(\frac{k}{2}\right) + n\log(2\pi\sigma^2) + 2\log\log\frac{R_1}{R_2}, \tag{15}$$

the stochastic complexity of $\boldsymbol{y}$ (multiplied by 2), given γ. The variable selection criterion is now to find the model $\hat{\gamma}$ which minimizes the stochastic complexity of $\boldsymbol{y}$ within the model class $\mathcal{M}_\gamma$.

NML Criterion. Note that the last two terms in (15) do not depend on γ or the number of parameters k. Hence these terms can be omitted from the criterion function. The residual sum of squares can be written as

$$RSS_\gamma = \|\boldsymbol{y}\|^2 - \|\hat{\boldsymbol{y}}_\gamma\|^2. \tag{16}$$

By applying Stirling's approximation

$$\Gamma(x+1) \approx (2\pi)^{1/2}(x+1)^{1/2}e^{-x-1}$$

to Γ-function and omitting the terms that do not depend on γ or k, we obtain the NML criterion function of the form

$$NML(\gamma) = \frac{\|\boldsymbol{y}\|^2}{\sigma^2} + k\left(\log\frac{\|\hat{\boldsymbol{y}}_\gamma\|^2}{k\,\sigma^2} - \frac{\|\hat{\boldsymbol{y}}_\gamma\|^2}{k\,\sigma^2} + 1\right) + \log k. \tag{17}$$

Let $\mathcal{M}_\gamma(k)$ denote the set of models with k parameters. We see from (17) that the function $NML(\gamma)$ and

$$h(\|\hat{\boldsymbol{y}}_\gamma\|^2) = \log\frac{\|\hat{\boldsymbol{y}}_\gamma\|^2}{k\sigma^2} - \frac{\|\hat{\boldsymbol{y}}_\gamma\|^2}{k\sigma^2} + 1 \tag{18}$$

attain their minimum for the same model $\hat{\gamma}(k)$ within the model class $\mathcal{M}_\gamma(k)$.

Theorem 1. *The model $\hat{\gamma}$ that minimizes $NML(\gamma)$ is obtained either by minimizing or by maximizing the residual sum of squares RSS_γ for some $k = \hat{k}$, where $\hat{k}$ is the number of parameters in the model $\hat{\gamma}$.*

Proof. In view of (17) and (18), the functions $NML(\gamma)$ and $h(\|\hat{\boldsymbol{y}}_\gamma\|^2)$ have their minimum at the same $\gamma(k) = \hat{\gamma}(k)$ within the model class $\mathcal{M}_\gamma(k)$. The function $h(\|\hat{\boldsymbol{y}}_\gamma\|^2)$ is strictly concave. It is decreasing within $\mathcal{M}_\gamma(k)$ when

$$\|\hat{\boldsymbol{y}}_\gamma\|^2 \geq k\sigma^2, \tag{19}$$

otherwise it is increasing. Then, among the k parameter models $\mathcal{M}_\gamma(k)$ satisfying (19), $h(\|\hat{\boldsymbol{y}}_\gamma\|^2)$ has the minimum exactly when $\|\hat{\boldsymbol{y}}_\gamma\|^2$ has the maximum. Since by (16)

$$\min_\gamma RSS_\gamma = \|\boldsymbol{y}\|^2 - \max_\gamma \|\hat{\boldsymbol{y}}_\gamma\|^2,$$

$h(\|\hat{\boldsymbol{y}}_\gamma\|^2)$ and RSS_γ have their minimum for the same $\gamma(k) = \hat{\gamma}(k)$ within $\mathcal{M}_\gamma(k)$.

On the other hand, $h(\|\hat{\boldsymbol{y}}_\gamma\|^2)$ is increasing within $\mathcal{M}_\gamma(k)$ for models γ that do not satisfy (19). Hence $h(\|\hat{\boldsymbol{y}}_\gamma\|^2)$ and $\|\hat{\boldsymbol{y}}_\gamma\|^2$ have their minimum at the same value of $\gamma(k) = \hat{\gamma}(k)$ within $\mathcal{M}_\gamma(k)$. But by (16) $\|\hat{\boldsymbol{y}}_\gamma\|^2$ has the minimum exactly when RSS_γ has the maximum.

Consequently, if $\hat{\gamma}(k)$ minimizes $h(\|\hat{\boldsymbol{y}}_\gamma\|^2)$ within $\mathcal{M}_\gamma(k)$, then $\hat{\gamma}(k)$ either minimizes or maximizes RSS_γ within $\mathcal{M}_\gamma(k)$. Now clearly

$$\min_\gamma NML(\gamma) = \min_{0<k\leq n} NML[\hat{\gamma}(k)],$$

which yields the desired conclusion. □

It may happen by Theorem 1 that $\hat{y}(k)$ minimizes the criterion (17) but $RSS_{\hat{y}(k)} \geq RSS_{y(k)}$ holds for all y within $\mathcal{M}_y(k)$. Then $\hat{y}(k)$ is the worst fitting model in the class $\mathcal{M}_y(k)$. Such a situation may arise when $\|\hat{\boldsymbol{y}}_y\|^2 < k\sigma^2$.

4 Traditional fixed penalty criteria and NML

For the variable selection problem in the normal linear model, the selection criteria like *AIC*, C_p, *BIC* and *RIC* have fixed dimensionality penalties. The *Akaike information criterion* (Akaike 1973; Burnham and Anderson 2002) is defined by

$$AIC(y) = -2\log f(\boldsymbol{y};\hat{\boldsymbol{\theta}}_y(\boldsymbol{y})) + 2k, \tag{20}$$

where k is the dimension of the parameter vector $\boldsymbol{\theta}_y$. In the case of the normal regression model (1) *AIC* can be written

$$AIC(y) = n\log RSS_y + 2k, \tag{21}$$

where constants not affecting model selection are omitted. The *Bayesian information criterion* for model (1) is

$$BIC(y) = n\log RSS_y + k\log n. \tag{22}$$

BIC was introduced by Schwarz (1978), and independently by Rissanen (1978) as an implementation of the MDL principle.

4.1 Orthonormal regression with σ^2 known

To make the conclusions more transparent, we suppose that the variance σ^2 is known and the K explanatory variables are orthonormal such that $\boldsymbol{X}'\boldsymbol{X} = \boldsymbol{I}_K$. The residual sum of squares RSS_y for fitting a k-dimensional submodel with orthonormal regression matrix $\boldsymbol{X}_y$ is by (16)

$$RSS_y = \|\boldsymbol{y}\|^2 - \|\hat{\boldsymbol{\beta}}_y\|^2 = \|\boldsymbol{y}\|^2 - \sum_{j=1}^{k}\hat{\beta}_j^2, \tag{23}$$

where k is the number of parameters. Since the regression variables are orthonormal, the estimated regression coefficients are not changed if variables are added or deleted from the model.

Fixed Penalty Criteria. Now by (21) *AIC* has the form

$$AIC(y) = \frac{RSS_y}{\sigma^2} + 2k = \frac{\|\boldsymbol{y}\|^2}{\sigma^2} - \sum_{j=1}^{k}\left(\frac{\hat{\beta}_j^2}{\sigma^2} - 2\right), \tag{24}$$

where the second equality follows from (23). In general, the fixed penalty criteria are of the form

$$FPC(y) = \frac{\|\boldsymbol{y}\|^2}{\sigma^2} - \sum_{j=1}^{k}\left(\frac{\hat{\beta}_j^2}{\sigma^2} - d\right), \tag{25}$$

where d is a fixed threshold. Choosing $d = \log n$ in (25) yields the *BIC*-criterion.

Fitting the full model with all variables gives K estimated regression coefficients $\hat{\beta}_1, \ldots, \hat{\beta}_K$. It is clear from (24) that minimizing *AIC* is equivalent to including into the model all the variables x_j, $1 \le k \le K$, whose coefficients $\hat{\beta}_j$ satisfy $\hat{\beta}_j^2/\sigma^2 > 2$. This type of selection rule has a connection with hypothesis testing. Actually, $|\hat{\beta}_j|/\sigma$ is the z-statistic for the testing problem

$$H_0\colon\ \beta_j = 0 \quad \text{vs.} \quad H_1\colon\ \beta_j \ne 0,$$

based on the observed z. The decision for accepting or rejecting H_0 is done at the significance level $\alpha = P(|z| \ge \sqrt{2}) \approx 0.157$. In the case when the coefficients are zero, the probability of choosing the correct model is $P(|z| < \sqrt{2})^K$ which for large values of K is close to zero. Minimising the *BIC*-criterion (22) is equivalent to including variables with $\hat{\beta}_j^2/\sigma^2 > \log n$, where now the threshold depends on n.

Foster and George (1994) introduced the *Risk Inflation Criterion* (*RIC*) which is obtained by choosing $d = 2\log K$ in (25). Although *RIC* was initially motivated by minimax considerations, later George and Foster (2000) motivated *RIC* by its relationship to the expected size of the largest z-statistic (or t-statistic) under the null model. When $\boldsymbol{X}$ is orthonormal and $\beta_1 = \cdots \beta_K = 0$, it can be shown that

$$E[\max(z_1^2, \ldots, z_K^2)] \approx 2\log K$$

for large K, where $z_j^2 = \hat{\beta}_j^2/\sigma^2$, $1 \le j \le K$. *RIC* essentially selects only those variables whose squared z-statistic exceeds the expectation of the maximum under the null model. This optimal bound was also discovered independently by Donoho and Johnstone (1994) in the wavelet regression context.

Mallows (1973) recommended a measure of predictive accuracy of a model, which is well known as Mallows' C_p. In the orthogonal setup C_p can be written as (Seber and Lee 2003, p. 406)

$$C_p(y) = AIC(y) - n. \tag{26}$$

Thus Mallows' C_p and *AIC* are equivalent variable selection criteria for orthonormal regression. However, Mallows (1973) specifically warned against using straightforwardly minimum C_p rule as a variable selection criterion.

Many other criteria corresponding to different choices of d in (25) have been proposed in the literature, e.g. Burnham and Anderson (2002) and McQuarrie and Tsai (1998). One of the drawbacks of using fixed threshold criteria like (25) is that models of a particular size are favored. Small d favors large models and large d favors small models. *RIC*, for example, does well when there are only few large coefficients and the others are close to zero. To choose an optimal value of a threshold d we should know the number of useful predictors in advance!

NML Criterion. For orthonormal regression with $X_\gamma' X_\gamma = I_k$ the *NML* criterion (17) can be written by (18) and (23) as

$$NML(\gamma) = \frac{\|\boldsymbol{y}\|^2}{\sigma^2} - kh(\|\hat{\boldsymbol{\beta}}_\gamma\|^2) + \log k. \tag{27}$$

Fitting the model with all K variables yields K estimated coefficients $\hat{\beta}_1, \ldots, \hat{\beta}_K$. We order these estimates and write them as $\hat{\beta}_{(j)}$, $1 \leq j \leq K$, where $\hat{\beta}^2_{(1)} \geq \cdots \geq \hat{\beta}^2_{(K)}$. Then clearly

$$\sum_{j=1}^{k} \hat{\beta}^2_{(j)} \geq \|\hat{\boldsymbol{\beta}}_\gamma\|^2 \geq \sum_{j=1}^{k} \hat{\beta}^2_{(K-k+j)} \tag{28}$$

for all models γ with k parameters. Now the following corollary is an immediate consequence of Theorem 1

Corollary 1. *For orthonormal regression matrices the model $\hat{\gamma}$ that minimizes the NML criterion* (27) *is given either by the k largest or k smallest coefficients in absolute value for some $k = \hat{k}$.*

4.2 A simulation experiment

To illustrate the performance of the *NML* criterion compared with that of fixed penalty criteria, a simple simulation experiment was carried out. We set $\boldsymbol{X} = \boldsymbol{I}_K$ in (1), reducing the model to $\boldsymbol{y} = \boldsymbol{\beta} + \boldsymbol{\epsilon}$. Note that now $K = n$. Here the variable selection problem becomes one of identifying the nonzero components of a multivariate normal mean.

To simulate a value of $\boldsymbol{y}$, we first fix a value of $k \leq K$, and then we generate the first k components of $\boldsymbol{\beta}$ such that $\beta_1, \ldots, \beta_k \sim N(0, c)$ independently, where c is a given constant. The components $\beta_{k+1}, \ldots, \beta_K$ are set to zero. We get a value of $\boldsymbol{y}$ by adding $\boldsymbol{\epsilon} \sim N_K(\boldsymbol{0}, I)$ to $\boldsymbol{\beta}$. Then each selection criterion *AIC*, *BIC*, *RIC* and *NML* is applied to $\boldsymbol{y}$, and the loss

$$L(\boldsymbol{\beta}, \hat{\boldsymbol{\beta}}_{\hat{\gamma}}) = \|\hat{\boldsymbol{\beta}}_{\hat{\gamma}} - \boldsymbol{\beta}\|^2 \tag{29}$$

was evaluated using the least squares estimate $\hat{\boldsymbol{\beta}}_{\hat{\gamma}}$ under the selected model $\hat{\gamma}$. Note that $\hat{\beta}_i = y_i$ when $\hat{\gamma}$ includes the ith variable, and otherwise $\hat{\beta}_i = 0$.

We fixed $n = K = 1000$, $c = 5$ and repeated the simulation 2000 times for $k = 0, 10, 25, 50, 100, 200, 300, 500, 750$ and 1000. For each model size k, the loss for each selection procedure was averaged over 2000 repetitions. If we know the correct model γ with size k, then the loss (29) follows the χ^2-distribution with k degrees of freedom. Thus the expected loss of this "oracle" criterion is k.

Figure 1 presents the simulation results. The performance of each fixed penalty criterion *AIC*, *BIC* and *RIC* deteriorates linearly as k increases. The large penalty value of *RIC* yields a very good performance when k is small, but then deteriorates very rapidly when k increases. *AIC* does very well for large k but not for small or medium k. The performance of *BIC* is good over a wide range of model sizes, but not for very large models. Finally, the performance of *NML* deviates strikingly from that of fixed penalty criteria. *NML* seems to emulate adaptively the performance of the best fixed penalty criterion for each k.

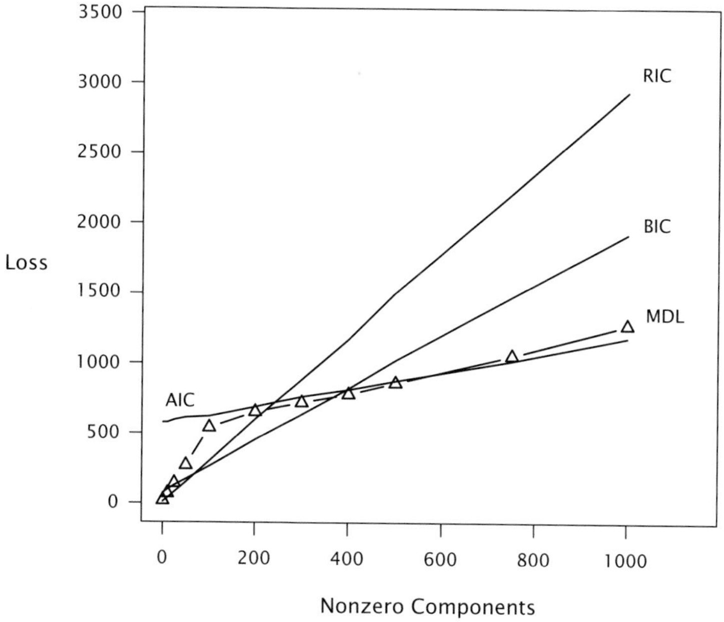

Figure 1. The average loss of the selection procedures when the number of nonzero components are $k = 0, 10, 25, 50, 100, 200, 300, 500, 750, 1000$.

5 NML criterion when σ^2 is unknown

When σ^2 is unknown, the maximum of the likelihood function is

$$L(\hat{\boldsymbol{\theta}}; \boldsymbol{y}) = (2\pi\hat{\sigma}^2 e)^{-n/2}. \tag{30}$$

Since here again the normalizing constant (5) is not bounded, Rissanen (2000) normalized the ML function (30) over the constrained data space

$$\mathcal{Y}(\sigma_0^2, R) = \{\, \boldsymbol{y} : \|\hat{\boldsymbol{y}}\|^2 \le nR,\ \hat{\sigma}^2 \ge \sigma_0^2 \,\}, \tag{31}$$

where $\sigma_0^2 > 0$ and $R > 0$ are given constants. Then the NML density for $\boldsymbol{y}$ under the constraints (31) will be

$$\hat{f}(\boldsymbol{y}; \tau_0, R) = \frac{(2\pi\hat{\sigma}_{\hat{y}}^2(\boldsymbol{y})e)^{-n/2}}{C(\sigma_0^2, R)}, \tag{32}$$

where the normalization constant $C(\sigma_0^2, R)$ depends on two hyperparameters.

To get rid of these hyperparameters Rissanen (2000) applied another level of normalization. The idea is to treat these hyperparameters R and σ_0^2 as the parameters $\boldsymbol{\beta}$ and σ^2. Maximizing the function (32) with respect of R and σ^2 yields their estimates $\hat{R}_\gamma = \|\hat{\boldsymbol{y}}_\gamma\|^2/n$ and $\hat{\sigma}_0^2 = \hat{\sigma}_\gamma^2$. The maximized NML function mNML is obtained by substituting these estimates into (32) in place of σ_0^2 and R. Then the function mNML is normalized. In this second stage normalization the data space is constrained such that

$$\mathcal{Y} = \{\, \boldsymbol{y} : nR_1 \le \|\hat{\boldsymbol{y}}\|^2 \le nR_2,\ \sigma_1^2 \le \hat{\tau} \le \sigma_2^2 \,\}.$$

Finally, the normalized mNML function $\hat{f}(\boldsymbol{y};\gamma)$ is obtained. The negative logarithm of $\hat{f}(\boldsymbol{y};\gamma)$ multiplied by 2 is given by

$$-2\log\hat{f}(\boldsymbol{y};\gamma) = (n-k)\log\hat{\sigma}_\gamma^2 + k\log\hat{R}_\gamma - 2\log\Gamma\left(\frac{n-k}{2}\right) - 2\log\Gamma\left(\frac{k}{2}\right) + n\log(n\pi) + 2\log\left[\log\frac{\sigma_2^2}{\sigma_1^2}\log\frac{R_2}{R_1}\right],$$

where $\hat{R}_\gamma = \boldsymbol{y}'\boldsymbol{y} - RSS_\gamma$. The details of this derivation process can be found to within a small calculation error in Rissanen (2000), see also Rissanen (2005).

By applying Stirling's approximation to Γ-functions we get

$$-2\log\hat{f}(\boldsymbol{y};\gamma) = (n-k)\log\frac{\hat{\sigma}_\gamma^2}{n-k} + k\log\frac{\hat{R}_\gamma}{k} + \log[k(n-k)] + c, \tag{33}$$

where the constant c does not depend on k or $\boldsymbol{y}$. By denoting

$$S_\gamma^2 = \frac{RSS_\gamma}{n-k} \quad \text{and} \quad F_\gamma = \frac{\boldsymbol{y}'\boldsymbol{y} - RSS_\gamma}{kS_\gamma^2}$$

we can write (33) as

$$-2\log\hat{f}(\boldsymbol{y};\gamma) = n\log S_\gamma^2 + k\log F_\gamma + \log[k(n-k)] + c_1,$$

where the constant c_1 has no effect on model selection. Here F_γ is the usual F-statistics for testing the hypothesis that each element of $\boldsymbol{\beta}$ is zero and S_γ^2 is an unbiased estimate of σ^2. Then *NML* criterion takes the form

$$NML(\gamma) = n\log S_\gamma^2 + k\log F_\gamma + \log[k(n-k)]. \tag{34}$$

From (21) and (22) it is easy to see that *AIC* and *BIC* order models of the same dimension according to *RSS*. So, holding k fixed, these criteria are increasing functions of *RSS*. Unlike these criteria, *NML* (34) applies an adaptively determined penalty on model size. We find that *NML* depends on the F-statistics so that models of "bad fit" receive a larger penalty. However, the most striking difference between *NML* and the criteria like *AIC* and *BIC* is that *NML* is not necessarily an increasing function of *RSS* when k is fixed.

To show this, we consider the *NML* criterion (34) as a function of RSS_γ. For a fixed k the function $NML(RSS_\gamma)$ is a strictly concave function of RSS_γ, and its first derivative is

$$NML'(RSS_\gamma) = \frac{n-k}{RSS_\gamma} - \frac{k}{\boldsymbol{y}'\boldsymbol{y} - RSS_\gamma}. \tag{35}$$

It follows from (35) that $NML(RSS_\gamma)$ is increasing if

$$\frac{\boldsymbol{y}'\boldsymbol{y} - RSS_\gamma}{kS^2} = F_\gamma \geq 1, \tag{36}$$

and decreasing if $F_\gamma \leq 1$.

Theorem 2. *The model* $\hat{\gamma}$ *that minimizes the NML criterion* (34) *is obtained either by minimizing or by maximizing* RSS_γ *for some* $k = \hat{k}$.

Proof. Let us first fix the number of parameters k and restrict ourselves to the model class $\mathcal{M}_\gamma(k)$. We consider first the models γ satisfying the condition (36). Since under (36) $NML(RSS_\gamma)$ is an increasing function of $RSS_\gamma \geq 0$, $NML(RSS_\gamma)$ and RSS_γ attain their minimum at the same $\gamma = \hat{\gamma}(k)$.

On the other hand, for models γ satisfying $F_\gamma \leq 1$, $NML(RSS_\gamma)$ is a decreasing function of RSS_γ within $\mathcal{M}_\gamma(k)$. Hence, the minimum of $NML(RSS_\gamma)$ and the maximum of RSS_γ are obtained at the same $\hat{\gamma} = \hat{\gamma}(k)$. Now clearly the model $\hat{\gamma}$ that minimizes $NML(\gamma)$ lies in $\mathcal{M}_\gamma(k)$ for some $k = \hat{k}$. This proves our assertion. □

Rissanen (2000) proved Theorem 2 for orthonormal regression. Since in the orthonormal regression by (28)

$$\min_\gamma RSS_\gamma = \|\boldsymbol{y}\|^2 - \sum_{j=1}^{k} \hat{\beta}^2_{(j)} \quad \text{and} \quad \max_\gamma RSS_\gamma = \|\boldsymbol{y}\|^2 - \sum_{j=1}^{k} \hat{\beta}^2_{(K-k+j)},$$

his result follows now directly from Theorem 2. Orthogonality of $\boldsymbol{X}$ makes the computation of the minimum and maximum of the residual sum of squares *RSS* feasible. In general, however, evaluating the minimum of $NML(\gamma)$ can be computationally very intensive.

Appendix

We posit the model (1) and denote $\boldsymbol{\theta} = (\boldsymbol{\beta}^{\mathrm{T}}, \sigma^2)$. The ML estimator $\hat{\boldsymbol{\theta}}$ of $\boldsymbol{\theta}$ is minimal sufficient for $\boldsymbol{\theta}$. Here the development will be for a fixed γ, and we drop the subindex γ in the formulas to follow. By sufficiency the density (2) can be written as

$$f(\boldsymbol{y}; \boldsymbol{\theta}) = f(\boldsymbol{y} \mid \hat{\boldsymbol{\theta}}) g(\hat{\boldsymbol{\theta}}; \boldsymbol{\theta}), \tag{37}$$

where the conditional density $f(\boldsymbol{y} \mid \hat{\boldsymbol{\theta}})$ does not depend on the unknown parameter vector $\boldsymbol{\theta}$.

It is known from standard distributional theory of linear regression (See e.g Seber and Lee 2003, p. 47) that the ML estimators $\hat{\boldsymbol{\beta}}$ and $\hat{\sigma}^2$ are independent, $\hat{\boldsymbol{\beta}}$ follows the normal distribution $N_k[\boldsymbol{\beta}, \sigma^2(\boldsymbol{X}^\top\boldsymbol{X})^{-1}]$ and $n\hat{\sigma}^2/\sigma^2$ has the χ^2-distribution with $n-k$ degrees of freedom. Then the densities of $\hat{\boldsymbol{\beta}}$ and $\hat{\sigma}^2$ are

$$g_1(\hat{\boldsymbol{\beta}}; \boldsymbol{\theta}) = \frac{|\boldsymbol{X}^\top\boldsymbol{X}|^{1/2}}{(2\pi\sigma^2)^{k/2}} \exp\left(-\frac{1}{2\sigma^2}\|\hat{\boldsymbol{y}} - \boldsymbol{X}\boldsymbol{\beta}\|^2\right) \tag{38}$$

and

$$g_2(\hat{\sigma}^2; \sigma^2) = \frac{n^{(n-k)/2}}{\Gamma(\frac{n-k}{2})2^{(n-k)/2}} \left(\frac{\hat{\sigma}^2}{\sigma^2}\right)^{(n-k)/2} \hat{\sigma}^{-2} \exp\left(-\frac{n\hat{\sigma}^2}{2\sigma^2}\right),$$

where $\hat{\boldsymbol{y}} = \boldsymbol{X}\hat{\boldsymbol{\beta}}$. Since $\hat{\boldsymbol{\beta}}$ and $\hat{\sigma}^2$ are independent

$$g(\hat{\boldsymbol{\theta}}; \boldsymbol{\theta}) = g_1(\hat{\boldsymbol{\beta}}; \boldsymbol{\theta}) g_2(\hat{\sigma}^2; \sigma^2). \tag{39}$$

When σ^2 is known, $\boldsymbol{\theta} = \boldsymbol{\beta}$ in (37) and $g = g_1$ is given by (38). Then the normalizing constant $C(R)$ in (8) can be written as

$$\int_{\mathcal{Y}(R)} f(\boldsymbol{y}; \hat{\boldsymbol{\beta}})\, \mathrm{d}\boldsymbol{y} = \int_{\mathcal{B}(R)} \left[\int_{\mathcal{Y}(\hat{\beta})} f(\boldsymbol{y} \mid \hat{\boldsymbol{\beta}})\, \mathrm{d}\boldsymbol{y}\right] g_1(\hat{\boldsymbol{\beta}}; \hat{\boldsymbol{\beta}})\, \mathrm{d}\hat{\boldsymbol{\beta}}, \tag{40}$$

where $\mathcal{B}(R) = \{\hat{\boldsymbol{\beta}} : \|\boldsymbol{X}\hat{\boldsymbol{\beta}}\|^2 \le nR\}$ is a k-dimensional ellipsoid. Integrating first the inner integral in (40) over $\mathcal{Y}(\hat{\boldsymbol{\beta}}) = \{\boldsymbol{y} : \hat{\boldsymbol{\beta}} = \hat{\boldsymbol{\beta}}(\boldsymbol{y})\}$ for a fixed $\hat{\boldsymbol{\beta}} = \hat{\boldsymbol{\beta}}(\boldsymbol{y})$ gives unity. Since

$$g_1(\hat{\boldsymbol{\beta}}; \hat{\boldsymbol{\beta}}) = \frac{|\boldsymbol{X}'\boldsymbol{X}|^{1/2}}{(2\pi\sigma^2)^{k/2}}$$

and

$$V(R) = \int_{\mathcal{B}(R)} \mathrm{d}\hat{\boldsymbol{\beta}} = \frac{(n\pi)^{k/2}}{\Gamma(\frac{k}{2}+1)|\boldsymbol{X}'\boldsymbol{X}|^{1/2}} R^{k/2} = V_k R^{k/2} \tag{41}$$

is the volume of the ellipsoid $\mathcal{B}(R)$ (Cramér, p. 120), the result (8) follows. By sufficiency factorization (37) the normalization constant for the mNML function (11) can be calculated as

$$\begin{aligned} C(R_1, R_2) &= \int_{\mathcal{Y}(R_1,R_2)} \hat{f}(\boldsymbol{y}; \hat{R})\, \mathrm{d}\boldsymbol{y} = \int_{\mathcal{Y}(R_1,R_2)} \frac{f(\boldsymbol{y} \mid \hat{\boldsymbol{\beta}}) g(\hat{\boldsymbol{\beta}}; \hat{\boldsymbol{\beta}})}{C(\hat{R})} \\ &= \int_{\mathcal{B}(R_1,R_2)} \frac{g(\hat{\boldsymbol{\beta}}; \hat{\boldsymbol{\beta}})}{C(\hat{R})} \left[\int_{\mathcal{Y}(\hat{\beta})} f(\boldsymbol{y} \mid \hat{\boldsymbol{\beta}})\, \mathrm{d}\boldsymbol{y}\right] \mathrm{d}\hat{\boldsymbol{\beta}} = \frac{k}{2}\log\frac{R_2}{R_1}, \end{aligned} \tag{42}$$

where

$$\mathcal{B}(R_1, R_2) = \{\hat{\boldsymbol{\beta}} : nR_1 \le \|\boldsymbol{X}\hat{\boldsymbol{\beta}}\|^2 \le nR_2\}.$$

Again the integral (42) is evaluated by integrating first the inner integral over its range while keeping $\hat{\boldsymbol{\beta}}(\boldsymbol{y}) = \hat{\boldsymbol{\beta}}$ at fixed values, which gives unity. Since by (41) the volume element $\mathrm{d}V = \frac{k}{2} V_k \hat{R}^{k/2-1}\,\mathrm{d}\hat{R}$, the outer integral in (42) can be computed by the formula

$$\int_{\mathcal{B}(R_1,R_2)} \frac{g(\hat{\boldsymbol{\beta}};\hat{\boldsymbol{\beta}})}{C(\hat{R})}\,\mathrm{d}\hat{\boldsymbol{\beta}} = \frac{k}{2}\int_{R_1}^{R_2} \hat{R}^{-1}\,\mathrm{d}\hat{R}.$$

References

Akaike, H. (1973). Information theory as an extension of the maximum likelihood principle. Pages 267–281 in B.N. Petrov and F. Csaki, (eds.) *Second International Symposium on Information Theory*. Akademiai Kiado, Budapest.

Barron, A.R., Rissanen, J., and Yu, B. (1998). The MDL principle in modeling and coding. *Special Issue of Information Theory to Commemorate 50 Years of Information Theory*, 44, 2743–2760.

Burnham, K.P. and Anderson D.R. (2002). *Model Selection and Multi-model Inference.* New York: Springer-Verlag.

Cramér, H. (1946). *Mathematical Methods of Statistics.* Princeton: Princeton University Press.

Donoho, D.L. and Johnstone, I.M. (1994). Ideal spatial adaptation by wavelet shrinkage. *Biometrika*, 81, 425–456.

Foster, D.P. and George, E.I. (1994). The risk inflation criterion for multiple regression. *The Annals of Statistics*, 4, 1947–1975.

George, E.I. and Foster, D.P. (2000). Calibration and empirical Bayes variable selection. *Biometrika*, 87, 731–747.

Hansen, A.J. and Yu, B. (2001). Model selection and the principle of minimum description length. *Journal of the American Statistical Association*, 96, 746–774.

McQuarrie, A.D.R. and Tsai, C-L. (1998). *Regression and time series model selection.* Singapore: World Scientific Publishing Company.

Mallows, C.L. (1973). Some comments on C_p. *Technometrics*, 15, 661–675.

Rissanen, J. (1978). Modeling by shortest data description. *Automatica*, 14, No. 1, 465–471.

Rissanen, J. (1996). Fisher information and stochastic complexity. *IEEE Transactions on Information Theory*, IT-42, No. 1, 40–47.

Rissanen, J. (2000). MDL denoising. *IEEE Transactions on Information Theory*, IT-46, No. 1, 2537–2543.

Rissanen, J. (2005). Complexity and Information in Modeling. Chapter IV in *Computability, Complexity and Constructivity in Economic Analysisi.* Ed. K. Vela Velupillai. Oxford: Blackwell Publishing.

Schwarz, G. (1978). Estimating the dimension of a model. *Annals of Statistics*, 6, 461–464.

Seber, G.A.F. and Lee, A.J. (2003). *Linear Regression Analysis*, 2nd ed. New York: Wiley.

ERKKI P. LISKI
Department of Mathematics, Statistics and Philosophy
FI-33014 University of Tampere, Finland
Erkki.Liski@uta.fi
http://www.uta.fi/~epl/

Festschrift for Tarmo Pukkila on his 60th Birthday
Eds. E. P. Liski, J. Isotalo, J. Niemelä, S. Puntanen, and G. P. H. Styan

Univ. of Tampere, 2006, ISBN 978-951-44-6620-5, pages 173–181

Exhibiting latent linear associations in large datasets

THOMAS MATHEW & KENNETH NORDSTRÖM

Abstract. A methodology is developed for assessing the latent linear associations that may exist among a given set of variables. Towards this, a linear transformation of the original variables is constructed so as to maximize the canonical correlations among the transformed variables. The transformation is explicitly characterized, along with the attainable maxima of the canonical correlations. Associated inference problems are also discussed.

2000 MSC codes: 62H20.

Key words and phrases: Canonical correlations; Kantorovich inequality.

1 Introduction

In many areas of science such as the atmospheric, earth, and space sciences, classical linear multivariate methods continue to be extensively applied. As in many other areas of scientific enquiry today, very large datasets tend to be the norm in these areas, and methods such as principal component analysis and canonical correlation analysis are frequently employed both as exploratory tools for the general purpose of dimension reduction and as part of the statistical analysis itself. While much of the more recent (and potentially useful) statistical methodology is currently prohibitively computationally intensive when dealing with such large datasets, the classical linear multivariate methods rely essentially only on standard eigenroutines for which very fast and parallelizable algorithms are readily available.

In this paper a method is proposed which aims at revealing the latent strong linear associations that often exist among variables in such large datasets. The specific goal is the construction of a transformation of the original variables which would somehow capture the maximal achievable internal linear associations as measured by canonical correlations, and which could be used e.g. for the purpose of dimension reduction.

To this end a general result on the maximization of canonical correlations of transformed variables is derived (Theorem). This result gives attainable upper bounds on the canonical correlations, together with an explicit construction of maximizing transformations. This suggests a conceptually simple and computationally feasible method wherein the raw variables are rotated so as to sequentially maximize the individual canonical correlations between the components of a partition of the rotated variables. Depending on the relative magnitudes of the eigenvalues of the covariance matrix, the rotated variables may display strong linear associations which would remain altogether unnoticed in terms of the original variables.

The present setting differs from the traditional one where canonical correlation analysis is applied in that no prespecified grouping of the variables is involved. Indeed, whereas canonical correlations are traditionally employed to measure (linearly) the cohesion between two sets of random variables, the variables are here treated symmetrically as in principal component analysis.

The idea of transforming the variables to maximize some measure of dependence is, of course, not new; see, e.g., Breiman and Friedman (1985) and the references on maximal correlation therein. However, as in the ACE algorithm of Breiman and Friedman, such methods typically involve a natural splitting of the variables into two sets, with corresponding separate maximizing variable transformations. A notable exception is Koyak (1987), who considers nonlinear transformations of a random vector to measure the internal dependence among its components.

On the other hand, transformations of variables may, of course, be undertaken for other purposes as well. For example, Cox and Wermuth (1996, Section 8.2) consider transformations of the response variables so as to achieve a specified structure of conditional independence which would be appealing on subject-matter grounds.

The paper is structured as follows. In Section 2 the problem of maximizing the canonical correlations of transformed variables is addressed from a technical point of view, with proof deferred to the Appendix. The statistical implications in terms of a method for discovering latent linear associations, together with the corresponding inference considerations for assessing their strength, are outlined in Section 3.

2 Maximizing canonical correlations of transformed variables

Let X be a p-dimensional random vector with positive definite covariance matrix Σ, and let A be a $p \times p$ matrix partitioned as $A = (A_1, A_2)$, where A_1 and A_2 are, respectively, of size $p \times k$ and $p \times (p-k)$. Assume without loss of generality that $k \leq p/2$, and let $\rho_i = \rho_i(A_1'X, A_2'X)$ denote the ith canonical correlation between $A_1'X$ and $A_2'X$, with $\rho_1 \geq \cdots \geq \rho_k$.

If A is allowed to be an arbitrary nonsingular matrix, it is not difficult to verify that each $\rho_i(A_1'X, A_2'X)$ can be made arbitrarily close to one by choosing A suitably. In fact, the supremum of $\rho_i(A_1'X, A_2'X)$ over nonsingular A is one, and is attained at a singular A. This degeneracy can, however, be avoided by choosing $A = (A_1, A_2)$ nonsingular and satisfying $A_1'A_2 = 0$. With such a choice it is, furthermore, enough to consider orthogonal matrices only. Indeed, define $B = (B_1, B_2) = [A_1(A_1'A_1)^{-1/2}, A_2(A_2'A_2)^{-1/2}]$, and note that B is orthogonal. The eigenvalues of $(B_1'\Sigma B_1)^{-1}B_1'\Sigma B_2(B_2'\Sigma B_2)^{-1}(B_2'\Sigma B_1)$ are now the same as those of $(A_1'\Sigma A_1)^{-1}A_1'\Sigma A_2(A_2'\Sigma A_2)^{-1}(A_2'\Sigma A_1)$, and the square roots of the latter are the canonical correlations between $A_1'X$ and $A_2'X$. Hence, as long as the natural condition $A_1'A_2 = 0$ is imposed, it is enough to consider orthogonal matrices A in order to maximize the canonical correlations $\rho_1, \ldots, \rho_k$.

On the other hand, under the condition $A_1'A_2 = 0$ one obtains

$$\begin{aligned}(A_1'\Sigma A_1)^{-1}&A_1'\Sigma A_2(A_2'\Sigma A_2)^{-1}(A_2'\Sigma A_1)\\ &= (A_1'\Sigma A_1)^{-1}A_1'\{\Sigma - A_1(A_1'\Sigma^{-1}A_1)^{-1}A_1'\}A_1\\ &= I_k - (A_1'\Sigma A_1)^{-1}(A_1'\Sigma^{-1}A_1)^{-1}, \qquad (1)\end{aligned}$$

so that the canonical correlations are maximized when A_1 is chosen to maximize the eigenvalues of $f(A_1) = (A_1'\Sigma A_1)(A_1'\Sigma^{-1}A_1)$.

The following result provides attainable bounds on the ρ_i's, together with an explicit expression for the maximizing transformations.

Theorem. *Let X be a p-dimensional random vector with positive definite covariance matrix $\Sigma = R\Lambda R'$, where $\Lambda = \mathrm{diag}(\lambda_1, \ldots, \lambda_p)$, $\lambda_1 \geq \cdots \geq \lambda_p$, are the eigenvalues of Σ and the columns $r_1, \ldots, r_p$ of R are corresponding orthonormal eigenvectors. For an orthogonal $p \times p$ matrix A partitioned as $A = (A_1, A_2)$, where A_1 is $p \times k$, A_2 is $p \times (p-k)$ and $k \leq p/2$, let $\rho_i(A_1'X, A_2'X)$, $i = 1, \ldots, k$, denote the canonical correlations between $A_1'X$ and $A_2'X$. Subject to the condition that the first $i-1$ canonical correlations have achieved their maxima, the maximum of $\rho_i(A_1'X, A_2'X)$ over all orthogonal $p \times p$ matrices A is given by $(\lambda_i - \lambda_{p-i+1})/(\lambda_i + \lambda_{p-i+1})$, $i = 1, \ldots, k$, and the maxima are attained at $A^* = (A_1^*, A_2^*)$, where $A_1^* = (a_1^*, \ldots, a_k^*)$, $a_i^* = (r_i \pm r_{p-i+1})/\sqrt{2}$, $i = 1, \ldots, k$, and A_2^* is any matrix such that A^* is orthogonal.*

Proof. See the Appendix.

Eaton (1976) has shown that

$$\rho_1^2(A_1'X, A_2'X) \leq \frac{(\lambda_1 - \lambda_p)^2}{(\lambda_1 + \lambda_p)^2},$$

making also the remark that $\rho_2^2(A_1'X, A_2'X)$ can be larger than $(\lambda_2 - \lambda_{p-1})^2/(\lambda_2 + \lambda_{p-1})^2$. This does not contradict our result, since we are maximizing $\rho_2^2(A_1'X, A_2'X)$ subject to the condition that $A = (A_1, A_2)$ provides the maximum value of $\rho_1^2(A_1'X, A_2'X)$. Without this condition, $\rho_2^2(A_1'X, A_2'X)$ can indeed be larger than $(\lambda_2 - \lambda_{p-1})^2/(\lambda_2 + \lambda_{p-1})^2$.

For a given grouping of X into k and $p-k$ ($k \leq p/2$) variables $X^{(1)}$ and $X^{(2)}$, respectively, several measures of (linear) association between $X^{(1)}$ and

$X^{(2)}$ have been proposed in the literature. Essentially, these quantities involve functions such as various means and products of the components of the vector $(\varrho_1^2, \dots, \varrho_k^2)$ of squared canonical correlations between $X^{(1)}$ and $X^{(2)}$ which is a natural maximal invariant for this problem. For example, Jupp and Mardia (1980) propose $\sum_{i=1}^k \varrho_i^2$ as a general correlation coefficient, measuring linear association between $X^{(1)}$ and $X^{(2)}$ also when the variables describe directional data. For general discussions of measures of association and further references, see, e.g., Anderson (1984, Section 9.8) or Mardia et al. (1979, Section 6.5).

For $f(A_1) = (A_1'\Sigma A_1)(A_1'\Sigma^{-1}A_1)$, Bloomfield and Watson (1975) and Knott (1975) have established an inequality for the determinant $|f(A_1)|$, and Khatri and Rao (1981) have established a corresponding inequality for the trace $\operatorname{tr} f(A_1)$. For a detailed review of such results, we refer to Drury et al. (2002, Section 5).

3 A method for discovering latent linear associations

3.1 General description

As explained in the introduction, our goal is a method by which one could easily discover the latent strong linear associations that typically exist among variables in large datasets. To be attractive and of practical use in areas such as oceanography, meteorology, astronomy, geosciences and other areas where the datasets tend to be very large, the method should be computationally feasible and preferably conceptually simple. To this end, the Theorem suggests, indeed, directly the following procedure.

Given p random variables $X = (X_1, \dots, X_p)'$ with covariance matrix Σ, one computes an eigenvalue decomposition $\Sigma = R\Lambda R'$, with eigenvalues $\Lambda = \operatorname{diag}(\lambda_1, \dots, \lambda_p)$ arranged in decreasing order $\lambda_1 \geq \cdots \geq \lambda_p$, and corresponding eigenvectors $r_1, \dots, r_p$. From this one computes the quantities

$$\xi_i = \xi_i(\Lambda) = \frac{\lambda_i - \lambda_{p-i+1}}{\lambda_i + \lambda_{p-i+1}}, \qquad i = 1, \dots, k, \quad k \leq [p/2],$$

where $[p/2]$ is $p/2$ or $(p-1)/2$, as p is even or odd, respectively. In view of our Theorem, the quantities ξ_i are natural measures of the strength of latent linear association that exists among the components of X. If, say, the s largest of the ξ_i's are close to 1, one concludes that there must exist s latent near linear dependencies among the components of X. On the other hand, if the λ_i's are nearly equal to begin with, the ξ_i's will be comparatively small. Therefore strong linear associations can be expected only when the λ_i's are rather unequal. This is not surprising, of course, since if the λ_i's are all equal, Σ will be a multiple of the identity matrix, as will be the covariance matrix of $A'X$ for any orthogonal matrix A.

From the Theorem and the discussion preceding it, it follows that a transformation A^* which maximizes the canonical correlations sequentially can always be taken to be orthogonal. Hence the transformed random vector $X^* = A^{*\prime}X$ is simply a rotation of X. As is plain from Theorem, there is a natural non-uniqueness to this problem, for A_1^* can be chosen in 2^k ways, after which A_2^* is chosen to make A^* orthogonal. Choosing, for example, $a_i^* = (r_i + r_{p-i+1})/\sqrt{2}$ as the ith column of A_1^*, the transformed variable $X_i^* = a_i^{*\prime}X$ exhibits the ith largest achievable canonical correlation $\mathrm{corr}(X_i^*, Y_i^*) = \xi_i(\Lambda)$ with the correspondingly transformed variable $Y_i^* = (r_i - r_{p-i+1})'X/\sqrt{2}$, $i = 1, \ldots, k$.

The above procedure is computationally rather attractive in that all the needed computations are obtainable as simple by-products from standard eigenroutines. Also, the maximizing transformations do not depend on the number of canonical correlations k to be studied, as is clear from the Theorem. Both aspects are in marked contrast with the approach of Koyak (1987), who suggests measuring the internal dependence among the components of a random vector by transforming nonlinearly each coordinate in order to maximize the largest partial sums of the eigenvalues of the correlation matrix of the transformed variables. In this case the optimal transformation typically depends on the number of terms included in the partial sum, and deriving the transformation leads to a substantial non-standard optimization problem. On the other hand, Koyak's approach is rather different from ours, aiming at a multivariate analog of maximal correlation. On the methodological map, our procedure uses a standard multivariate tool, canonical correlation analysis, but in an "unsupervised" setting, contrary to normal usage.

3.2 Inference considerations

In practice the covariance matrix Σ will, of course, be unknown, and one must consider the sample version of the problem. Therefore interest focuses on inference for the quantities $\xi_i(\Lambda)$, based on the corresponding sample quantities

$$\xi_i(U) = \frac{u_i - u_{p-i+1}}{u_i + u_{p-i+1}}, \qquad i = 1, \ldots, k,$$

computed from the sample covariance matrix $S = PUP'$. Of particular interest are (lower) confidence intervals for the $\xi_i(\Lambda)$'s.

Using standard results on the asymptotic distribution of the eigenvalues of S given, for example, in Anderson (1984, Chapter 13), one obtains directly large-sample confidence intervals for the $\xi_i(\Lambda)$'s. Indeed, assuming a sample of n observations from a p-variate normal distribution with unknown mean and covariance matrix Σ with distinct eigenvalues $\lambda_1 > \cdots > \lambda_p$, and letting

$$u = (u_1, \ldots, u_p)' \quad \text{and} \quad \lambda = (\lambda_1, \ldots, \lambda_p)'$$

(with $u_1 \geq \cdots \geq u_p$), the limiting distribution of $\sqrt{n-1}(u - \lambda)$ is p-variate normal with mean zero and covariance matrix $\text{diag}(2\lambda_1^2, \ldots, 2\lambda_p^2)$; see Theorem 13.5.1 in Anderson (1984). From this it follows directly that

$$\sqrt{n-1}(\xi_i(U) - \xi_i(\Lambda)) \sim N\left(0, \frac{16\lambda_i^2\lambda_{p-i+1}^2}{(\lambda_i + \lambda_{p-i+1})^4}\right),$$

asymptotically. The variance in the above asymptotic distribution can be consistently estimated by $16u_i^2u_{p-i+1}^2/(u_i + u_{p-i+1})^4$, yielding

$$\xi_i(\Lambda) \geq \xi_i(U) - \frac{z_{(1-\alpha)}}{\sqrt{n-1}} \frac{4u_iu_{p-i+1}}{(u_i + u_{p-i+1})^2}, \tag{2}$$

as a large-sample $100(1-\alpha)\%$ lower confidence interval for $\xi_i(\Lambda)$, where $z_{(1-\alpha)}$ is the $100(1-\alpha)$th percentile of the standard normal distribution.

Appendix. Proof of theorem

In view of (1), a matrix A_1 satisfying $A_1'A_1 = I_k$ must be chosen that will sequentially maximize the individual eigenvalues of $f(A_1) = (A_1'\Sigma A_1)(A_1'\Sigma^{-1}A_1)$. In other words, one must choose a class of matrices A_1 that will maximize the largest eigenvalue of $f(A_1)$ and, within this class, one must pick a subclass of matrices that will maximize the second largest eigenvalue of $f(A_1)$, and so on.

Let l_1 be a normalized eigenvector of $f(A_1)$ corresponding to its largest eigenvalue, say δ_1. Then $A_1'\Sigma^{-1}A_1l_1 = \delta_1(A_1'\Sigma A_1)^{-1}l_1$, implying

$$\delta_1 = \frac{l_1'A_1'\Sigma^{-1}A_1l_1}{l_1'(A_1'\Sigma A_1)^{-1}l_1}. \tag{A.1}$$

The maximum eigenvalue of $f(A_1)$ is thus obtained by maximizing (A.1) with respect to unit vectors l_1. Let $L = (l_1, L_1)$ be an orthogonal matrix. Then $l_1'A_1'\Sigma^{-1}A_1l_1 = (L'A_1'\Sigma^{-1}A_1L)_{11}$ and

$$l_1'(A_1'\Sigma A_1)^{-1}l_1 = \{L'(A_1'\Sigma A_1)^{-1}L\}_{11} = \{(L'A_1'\Sigma A_1L)^{-1}\}_{11},$$

where the subscripts indicate the respective first diagonal elements. Let $A_1L = H = (h_1, H_1)$. Then H is a $p \times k$ matrix satisfying $H'H = I_k$, and it follows from (A.1) and the arguments above that

$$\delta_1 = \frac{(H'\Sigma^{-1}H)_{11}}{\{(H'\Sigma H)^{-1}\}_{11}} = \frac{h_1'\Sigma^{-1}h_1}{\{h_1'\Sigma h_1 - h_1'\Sigma H_1(H_1'\Sigma H_1)^{-1}H_1'\Sigma h_1\}^{-1}}. \tag{A.2}$$

In view of (A.2), it is seen that maximizing (A.1) with respect to l_1 is equivalent to maximizing

$$h_1'\Sigma^{-1}h_1 \times \{h_1'\Sigma h_1 - h_1'\Sigma H_1(H_1'\Sigma H_1)^{-1}H_1'\Sigma h_1\} \tag{A.3}$$

with respect to $H = (h_1, H_1)$ satisfying $H'H = I_k$. Clearly, the maximum of (A.3) is obtained if $f(h_1) = h_1'\Sigma h_1 h_1'\Sigma^{-1}h_1$ is maximized over unit vectors h_1, and H_1 satisfies

$$h_1'H_1 = 0, \qquad h_1'\Sigma H_1 = 0, \qquad \text{and} \qquad H_1'H_1 = I_{k-1}. \tag{A.4}$$

By the well-known Kantorovich inequality

$$\max_{\|h_1\|=1} f(h_1) \leq \frac{(\lambda_1 + \lambda_p)^2}{4\lambda_1\lambda_p},$$

and the maximum is attained at

$$h_1 = \frac{r_1 + r_p}{\sqrt{2}}. \tag{A.5}$$

Observe that h_1 is not unique: $h_1 = (r_1 - r_p)/\sqrt{2}$ yields also the maximum of $f(h_1)$. Observe also that if λ_1 or λ_p (or both) have multiplicity greater than one, non-uniqueness of h_1 results also from the non-uniqueness of the corresponding eigenvectors. The arguments that follow remain valid whatever h_1 is used for achieving the maximum of $f(h_1)$. Hence assume in the sequel that h_1 is as given in (A.5).

We proceed to characterize the matrices H_1 satisfying conditions (A.4). Throughout the rest of the proof, let

$$R = (r_1, R_1, r_p) \qquad \text{and} \qquad \Lambda = \operatorname{diag}(\lambda_1, \Lambda_1, \lambda_p). \tag{A.6}$$

Defining $\tilde{R} = (R_1, (r_1 - r_p)/\sqrt{2})$ yields a matrix satisfying $\tilde{R}'\tilde{R} = I_{p-1}$ whose columns are all orthogonal to h_1. The condition $h_1'H_1 = 0$ implies that $H_1 = \tilde{R}\tilde{K}$ for some matrix $\tilde{K}$, and since $\Sigma h_1 = (\lambda_1 r_1 + \lambda_p r_p)/\sqrt{2}$, it follows that

$$h_1'\Sigma H_1 = \frac{1}{\sqrt{2}}(\lambda_1 r_1 + \lambda_p r_p)'\tilde{R}\tilde{K} = \frac{1}{\sqrt{2}}\left(0, \frac{\lambda_1 - \lambda_p}{\sqrt{2}}\right)\tilde{K}.$$

Hence $h_1'\Sigma H_1$ can be zero only if $\lambda_1 = \lambda_p$, or if the last row of $\tilde{K}$ is zero. On the other hand, if $\lambda_1 = \lambda_p$ all the eigenvalues of Σ are equal and Σ is a multiple of the identity matrix (in which case the theorem is trivially valid). Therefore one can assume that $\lambda_1 \neq \lambda_p$ and conclude that the last row of $\tilde{K}$ must be zero. But then $H_1 = R_1 K_1$ for a matrix K_1, and since $R_1'R_1 = I_{p-2}$ and $H_1'H_1 = I_{k-1}$, the matrix K_1 must satisfy $K_1'K_1 = I_{k-1}$.

Subject to the condition $H'H = I_k$, the largest eigenvalue of $f(H) = (H'\Sigma H)(H'\Sigma^{-1}H)$ is thus a maximum when $H = (h_1, H_1)$, where h_1 is as given in (A.5) and $H_1 = R_1 K_1$ for some matrix K_1, with R_1 defined in (A.6) and K_1 satisfying $K_1'K_1 = I_{k-1}$.

In order to maximize the second largest eigenvalue of $f(H)$, subject to the condition that the largest one has already been maximized, observe first that

$$f(H) = \operatorname{diag}\left(\frac{(\lambda_1 + \lambda_p)^2}{4\lambda_1\lambda_p}, f(R_1 K_1)\right).$$

Therefore the largest eigenvalue of $f(R_1K_1) = (K_1'R_1'\Sigma R_1K_1)(K_1'R_1'\Sigma^{-1}R_1K_1)$ is to be maximized, subject to the condition $K_1'K_1 = I_{k-1}$. On the other hand,

$$R_1'\Sigma R_1 = \Lambda_1 \quad \text{and} \quad R_1'\Sigma^{-1}R_1 = \Lambda_1^{-1},$$

and hence one must maximize the largest eigenvalue of $(K_1'\Lambda_1K_1)(K_1'\Lambda_1^{-1}K_1)$, with K_1 satisfying $K_1'K_1 = I_{k-1}$. As Λ_1 is a diagonal matrix of order $p-2$, the standard unit vectors in R^{p-2}, say $e_1, \ldots, e_{p-2}$, form an orthonormal set of eigenvectors of Λ_1. Arguing as before one concludes that, subject to the condition $K_1'K_1 = I_{k-1}$, the largest eigenvalue of $(K_1'\Lambda_1K_1)(K_1'\Lambda_1^{-1}K_1)$ achieves a maximum value of $(\lambda_2 + \lambda_{p-1})^2/(4\lambda_2\lambda_{p-1})$ when

$$K_1 = (k_2, K_2), \qquad k_2 = \frac{e_1 + e_{p-2}}{\sqrt{2}},$$

and K_2 satisfies

$$k_2'K_2 = 0, \qquad k_2'\Lambda_1K_2 = 0, \qquad \text{and} \qquad K_2'K_2 = I_{k-2}.$$

Since $H = (h_1, H_1)$ and $H_1 = R_1K_1$, the second column h_2 of H is given by

$$h_2 = R_1k_2 = \frac{r_2 + r_{p-1}}{\sqrt{2}}.$$

Continuing in this manner, the eigenvalues of $f(H)$ are maximized sequentially.

The maxima of the canonical correlations can now be obtained using (1). For example, the largest squared canonical correlation $\rho_1^2(A_1'X, A_2'X)$ has the upper bound

$$1 - \frac{4\lambda_1\lambda_p}{(\lambda_1 + \lambda_p)^2} = \frac{(\lambda_1 - \lambda_p)^2}{(\lambda_1 + \lambda_p)^2},$$

and if A_1 and A_2 are such that this bound is attained, then $\rho_2^2(A_1'X, A_2'X)$ has the upper bound $(\lambda_2 - \lambda_{p-1})^2/(\lambda_2 + \lambda_{p-1})^2$, and so on. From the proof of the theorem it is clear that the maxima are indeed attained when $A = A^* = (A_1^*, A_2^*)$, as specified in the theorem. This completes the proof of the Theorem.

Acknowledgement

We are grateful to a reviewer for drawing our attention to the review paper by Drury et al. (2002), which led to the detection of an inaccuracy in the manuscript version of this paper.

References

Anderson, T.W. (1984). *Introduction to Multivariate Statistical Analysis* (2nd ed). New York: John Wiley.

Bloomfield, P. and Watson, G. S. (1975). The inefficiency of least squares. *Biometrika*, 62, 121–128.

Breiman, L. and Friedman, J. H. (1985). Estimating optimal transformations for multiple regression and correlation (with discussion). *Journal of the American Statistical Association*, 80, 580–619.

Cox, D. R. and Wermuth, N. (1996). *Multivariate Dependencies*. London: Chapman and Hall.

Drury, S. W., Liu, S., Lu, C.-Y., Puntanen, S., and Styan, G. P. H. (2002). Some comments on several matrix inequalities with applications to canonical correlations: Historical background and recent developments. *Sankhyā, Series A*, 64, 453–507.

Eaton, M. L. (1976). A maximization problem and its applications to canonical correlation. *Journal of Multivariate Analysis*, 6, 422–425.

Jupp, P. E. and Mardia, K. V. (1980). A general correlation coefficient for directional data and related regression problems. *Biometrika*, 67, 163–173.

Khatri, C. G. and Rao, C. R. (1981). Some extentions of Kantorovich inequality and statistical applications. *Journal of Multivariate Analysis*, 44, 91–102.

Knott, M. (1975). On the minimum efficiency of least squares. *Biometrika*, 62, 129–132.

Koyak, R. A. (1987). On measuring internal dependence in a set of random variables. *Annals of Statistics*, 15, 1215–1228.

Mardia, K. V., Kent, J. T., and Bibby, J. M. (1979). *Multivariate Analysis*. London: Academic Press.

THOMAS MATHEW
Department of Mathematics and Statistics
University of Maryland, Baltimore County
Baltimore, MD 21250, USA
mathew@math.umbc.edu
http://www.math.umbc.edu/~mathew/

KENNETH NORDSTRÖM
Department of Mathematical Sciences
University of Oulu
FI-90014, Oulu, Finland
Kenneth.Nordstrom@oulu.fi
http://stat.oulu.fi/nordstrom/

Festschrift for Tarmo Pukkila on his 60th Birthday
Eds. E. P. Liski, J. Isotalo, J. Niemelä, S. Puntanen, and G. P. H. Styan
© Dept. of Mathematics, Statistics and Philosophy,
Univ. of Tampere, 2006, ISBN 978-951-44-6620-5, pages 183–190

Bounds for the Perron root using the sum of entries of matrix powers

JORMA K. MERIKOSKI & ARI VIRTANEN

Abstract. Let $\mathbf{A} = (a_{ik})$ be a nonnegative square matrix with Perron root $r(\mathbf{A})$. We survey and pursue further the question of finding bounds for $r(\mathbf{A})$ using the sum of entries of powers of $\mathbf{A}$ and $G(\mathbf{A}) = (\sqrt{a_{ik}a_{ki}})$ respectively. We encounter three open problems.

2000 MSC codes: 15A18, 15A42, 15A48.

Key words and phrases: Eigenvalue; Perron root; Matrix power.

1 Introduction

Throughout, we let $\mathbf{A} = (a_{ik})$ denote an $n \times n$ (elementwise) nonnegative matrix ($n \geq 2$). We call $\mathbf{A}$ *reducible* if there exists a permutation matrix $\mathbf{P}$ such that $\mathbf{P}^{\mathsf{T}}\mathbf{A}\mathbf{P}$ can be partitioned as

$$\mathbf{P}^{\mathsf{T}}\mathbf{A}\mathbf{P} = \begin{pmatrix} \mathbf{B} & \mathbf{C} \\ \mathbf{O} & \mathbf{D} \end{pmatrix},$$

where $\mathbf{B}$ and $\mathbf{D}$ are square matrices. Otherwise we call $\mathbf{A}$ *irreducible.*

The Perron–Frobenius theorem, see, e.g., Bapat and Raghavan (1997, Theorem 1.4.4), Horn and Johnson (1985, Theorem 8.4.4), Minc (1988, Section 1.4), states that if $\mathbf{A}$ is irreducible, then it has a real and positive eigenvalue, which is greater than or equal to the absolute value of any other eigenvalue. This eigenvalue, called the *Perron root* of $\mathbf{A}$, and denoted by $r(\mathbf{A})$, is algebraically and geometrically simple and has a positive eigenvector.

If $\mathbf{A}$ is reducible, then its Perron root has a nonnegative eigenvector.

Bounds for the Perron root are widely studied. For "classical" bounds, see, e.g., Marcus and Minc (1992) and Minc (1988). The sum of entries of $\mathbf{A}$, denoted by $\operatorname{su}\mathbf{A}$, has a role in some bounds. Namely, if $\mathbf{A}$ is symmetric, then $\operatorname{su}\mathbf{A}$ appears in the lower bound given by the Rayleigh quotient of $\mathbf{A}$ with respect to the vector whose all entries are equal to one. As to upper bounds, $\operatorname{su}\mathbf{A}$ itself is such a bound, since it is a submultiplicative matrix norm.

A natural attempt to improve a given bound (but making it more complex) is to apply it to $\mathbf{A}^2$ (or $\mathbf{A}^3$, etc.) and to take the square (or cubic, etc.) root. This process will lead us to study certain sequences whose m'th term involves $\operatorname{su}\mathbf{A}^m$.

We will first in Section 2 present relevant properties of the *geometric symmetrization* of $\mathbf{A}$, defined by

$$G(\mathbf{A}) = (\sqrt{a_{ik}a_{ki}}\,).$$

Next, we will study lower bounds in Section 3, and thereafter upper bounds in Section 4. The results rise some further questions, which we will finally discuss in Section 5.

2 Geometric symmetrization

The geometric symmetrization of $\mathbf{A}$ satisfies

$$r(G(\mathbf{A})) \le r(\mathbf{A}), \tag{1}$$

which is a special case of

$$r(\mathbf{A}_1^{(t)} \circ \mathbf{A}_2^{(1-t)}) \le r(\mathbf{A}_1)^t\, r(\mathbf{A}_2)^{1-t},$$

see, e.g., Bapat and Raghavan (1997, Theorem 3.3.4), Horn and Johnson (1991, Theorem 5.7.7). Here $\mathbf{A}_1$ and $\mathbf{A}_2$ are nonnegative $n \times n$ matrices, $0 \le t \le 1$, $\circ$ denotes the entrywise product, and a bracketed exponent denotes the entrywise power.

If $\mathbf{A}$ is primitive (i.e., $\mathbf{A}^q$ is positive for some positive integer q), then denoting

$$\rho_m = r\big(G(\mathbf{A}^m)\big)^{1/m},$$

we have

$$\lim_{m\to\infty} \rho_m = r(\mathbf{A}) \tag{2}$$

(Kolotilina 1993, Corollary 4).

We show that (2) holds generally if and only if $n = 2$.

For $n = 2$, we see easily that $r(G(\mathbf{A})) = r(\mathbf{A})$, and so, for all positive integers m,

$$\rho_m = r(\mathbf{A}^m)^{1/m} = r(\mathbf{A}).$$

For $n = 3$, consider

$$\mathbf{A} = \begin{pmatrix} 0 & 1 & 0 \\ 0 & 0 & 1 \\ 1 & 0 & 0 \end{pmatrix}; \tag{3}$$

then $\rho(\mathbf{A}) = 1$. Now

$$\mathbf{A}^m = \mathbf{A} \qquad \text{if } m \equiv 1 \pmod 3,$$

$$\mathbf{A}^m = \begin{pmatrix} 0 & 0 & 1 \\ 1 & 0 & 0 \\ 0 & 1 & 0 \end{pmatrix} \qquad \text{if } m \equiv 2 \pmod 3,$$

and

$$\mathbf{A}^m = \mathbf{I} \qquad \text{if } m \equiv 0 \pmod 3.$$

Therefore

$$G(\mathbf{A}) = G(\mathbf{A}^2) = G(\mathbf{A}^4) = G(\mathbf{A}^5) = \cdots = \mathbf{O}$$

but

$$G(\mathbf{A}^3) = G(\mathbf{A}^6) = G(\mathbf{A}^9) = \cdots = \mathbf{I}.$$

Hence $\rho_1 = \rho_2 = \rho_4 = \rho_5 = \cdots = 0$ but $\rho_3 = \rho_6 = \rho_9 = \cdots = 1$, contradicting (2).

For $n \geq 4$, the matrix whose left upper submatrix is (3) and the other entries are zero, provides a counterexample.

Szyld (1992, Theorem 2.2) proved that $\rho_1 \leq \rho_2 \leq \rho_4 \leq \rho_{16} \leq \cdots \leq r(\mathbf{A})$. According to Tasçi and Kirkland (1998, p. 23), it is not difficult to show that $\lim_{p\to\infty} \rho_{2^p} = r(\mathbf{A})$. However, (3) provides a counterexample to this claim and also shows that the sequence (ρ_m) is not necessarily increasing and not necessarily convergent.

Kolotilina (1993, Corollary 4) proved that the sequence (ρ_m) always has a subsequence converging to $r(\mathbf{A})$.

3 Lower bounds

Throughout, let $\mathbf{B}$ be an $n \times n$ matrix. If it is symmetric with largest eigenvalue $\lambda(\mathbf{B})$ and $\mathbf{0} \neq \mathbf{x} \in \mathbb{C}^n$, then, see, e.g., Horn and Johnson (1985, Theorem 4.2.2),

$$\frac{\mathbf{x}^*\mathbf{B}\mathbf{x}}{\mathbf{x}^*\mathbf{x}} \leq \lambda(\mathbf{B}).$$

In particular, choosing $\mathbf{x}$ to be the vector of ones, we have

$$\frac{\operatorname{su}\mathbf{B}}{n} \leq \lambda(\mathbf{B}),$$

and so, by (1),

$$\frac{\operatorname{su}G(\mathbf{A})}{n} \leq \lambda(G(\mathbf{A})) = r(G(\mathbf{A})) \leq r(\mathbf{A}).$$

Kolotilina (1993, Theorem 4) found better (but more complex) lower bounds

$$\frac{\operatorname{su}G(\mathbf{A})}{n} \leq \left(\frac{\operatorname{su}G(\mathbf{A}^2)}{n}\right)^{1/2} \leq \cdots \leq \left(\frac{\operatorname{su}G(\mathbf{A}^{2^p})}{n}\right)^{1/2^p} \leq \cdots \leq r(\mathbf{A}). \tag{4}$$

The whole sequence

$$l_m = \left(\frac{\operatorname{su} G(\mathbf{A}^m)}{n}\right)^{1/m}$$

is not necessarily increasing even if $\mathbf{A}$ is symmetric. For a counterexample (Laakso 1999, p. 52), let

$$\mathbf{A} = \begin{pmatrix} 1 & 2 \\ 2 & 0 \end{pmatrix}.$$

Then $x_2 = 2.5495$ but $x_3 = 2.5458$.

If $\mathbf{A}$ is (symmetric and) nonnegative definite, then (l_m) is increasing, see London (1966, p. 518). For some further developments, see Kankaanpää and Merikoski (1985, Theorem 6).

The counterexample (3) shows that $\lim_{m\to\infty} l_m = r(\mathbf{A})$ does not necessarily hold. (In fact, it shows that even $\lim_{p\to\infty} l_{2^p} = r(\mathbf{A})$ does not necessarily hold.) However, Kolotilina (1993, Theorem 4) proved that if $\mathbf{A}$ is irreducible, then the sequence (l_m) has a subsequence converging to $r(\mathbf{A})$. The question of the existence of such a sequence in the reducible case remains open. Since $\lim_{m\to\infty} n^{1/m} = 1$, all this can be said also about the sequence $v_m = (\operatorname{su} G(\mathbf{A}^m))^{1/m}$. We will come back to this sequence in Section 5.

4 Upper bounds

Denote by $\rho(\mathbf{B})$ the spectral radius of $\mathbf{B}$. Since $\operatorname{su}|\mathbf{B}|$ is a submultiplicative matrix norm ($|.|$ is understood entrywise), we have

$$\rho(\mathbf{B}) \le \operatorname{su}|\mathbf{B}|,$$

see, e.g., Horn and Johnson (1985, Theorem 5.6.9), and so

$$r(\mathbf{A}) \le \operatorname{su}\mathbf{A}. \tag{5}$$

An elementary and well-known way to find better (but more complex) upper bounds is to note that $r(\mathbf{A}^m) = r(\mathbf{A})^m$ and $\operatorname{su}\mathbf{A}^m \le (\operatorname{su}\mathbf{A})^m$ for all positive integers m. Therefore,

$$r(\mathbf{A}) \le \cdots \le (\operatorname{su}\mathbf{A}^{2^p})^{1/2^p} \le \cdots \le (\operatorname{su}\mathbf{A}^2)^{1/2} \le \operatorname{su}\mathbf{A}. \tag{6}$$

We show that, for $n \ge 3$, the sequence

$$u_m = (\operatorname{su}\mathbf{A}^m)^{1/m}$$

is not necessarily decreasing even if $\mathbf{A}$ is symmetric. Consider

$$\mathbf{A} = \begin{pmatrix} 0 & \dots & 0 & 1 \\ \vdots & \ddots & \vdots & \vdots \\ 0 & \dots & 0 & 1 \\ 1 & \dots & 1 & 0 \end{pmatrix}$$

(Merikoski 1984, p. 181; Laakso 1999, p. 55). Then

$$\mathbf{A}^{2p-1} = \begin{pmatrix} 0 & \cdots & 0 & (n-1)^{p-1} \\ \vdots & \ddots & \vdots & \vdots \\ 0 & \cdots & 0 & (n-1)^{p-1} \\ (n-1)^{p-1} & \cdots & (n-1)^{p-1} & 0 \end{pmatrix}$$

and

$$\mathbf{A}^{2p} = \begin{pmatrix} (n-1)^{p-1} & \cdots & (n-1)^{p-1} & 0 \\ \vdots & \ddots & \vdots & \vdots \\ (n-1)^{p-1} & \cdots & (n-1)^{p-1} & 0 \\ 0 & \cdots & 0 & (n-1)^{p} \end{pmatrix},$$

and so

$$\operatorname{su}\mathbf{A}^{2p-1} = 2(n-1)^p, \qquad \operatorname{su}\mathbf{A}^{2p} = n(n-1)^p.$$

It is easy to see that $u_{p-1} < u_p$ if p is sufficiently large. It is also easy to see that $u_3 < u_4$ if and only if $n \geq 14$.

The question of the validity of

$$u_3 \geq u_4, \tag{7}$$

for $3 \leq n \leq 13$, remains open.

We prove (7) for $n = 2$. Let

$$\mathbf{A} = \begin{pmatrix} a & b \\ c & d \end{pmatrix}.$$

An equivalent claim is

$$(\operatorname{su}\mathbf{A}^3)^4 \geq (\operatorname{su}\mathbf{A}^4)^3. \tag{8}$$

A brute computation shows that

$$(\operatorname{su}\mathbf{A}^3)^4 - (\operatorname{su}\mathbf{A}^4)^3 = 2b^5c^5(c^2 - bc + b^2) + 3a^3d^6(a^3 - ad^2 + d^3) + 3a^6d^3(a^3 - a^2d + d^3) + e,$$

where e is a sum of many nonnegative terms. Since

$$bc \leq \frac{b^2 + c^2}{2} \leq b^2 + c^2,$$

$$ad^2 = add = (a^3d^3d^3)^{1/3} \leq \frac{a^3 + 2d^3}{3} \leq a^3 + d^3,$$

and, similarly, $a^2d \leq a^3 + d^3$, then (8) follows.

The inequality

$$u_2 \geq u_3 \tag{9}$$

does not hold generally for $n = 2$, as we see by the counterexample

$$\mathbf{A} = \begin{pmatrix} 0 & 1 \\ 6 & 0 \end{pmatrix}$$

(Laakso 1999, p. 56). Then $u_2 = 3.464$ but $u_3 = 3.476$. But if

$$\mathbf{A} = \begin{pmatrix} a & b \\ b & d \end{pmatrix},$$

then

$$(\mathrm{su}\,\mathbf{A}^2)^3 - (\mathrm{su}\,\mathbf{A}^3)^2 = 2a^2d^2(a^2 - ad + d^2) + \text{nonnegative terms} \geq 0,$$

and so (9) holds for $n = 2$ if $\mathbf{A}$ is symmetric. The question whether the whole sequence (u_m) is decreasing in this case remains open.

The norm property, see, e.g., Horn and Johnson (1985, Corollary 5.6.14), of $\mathrm{su}\,\mathbf{A}$ implies that

$$\lim_{m\to\infty} u_m = r(\mathbf{A}).$$

5 Further questions

In the view of (2), (4) and (6), we ask, whether

$$r(\mathbf{A}) \leq \cdots \leq \left(\mathrm{su}\,G(\mathbf{A}^{2^p})\right)^{1/2^p} \leq \cdots \leq \left(\mathrm{su}\,G(\mathbf{A}^2)\right)^{1/2} \leq \mathrm{su}\,G(\mathbf{A}) \tag{10}$$

holds. The counterexample (3) shows that the answer is negative if $n \geq 3$. A weaker question is to ask, whether the subsequence (v_{2^p}) of the sequence $v_m = (\mathrm{su}\,G(\mathbf{A}^m))^{1/m}$ is decreasing. For a counterexample, let

$$\mathbf{A} = \begin{pmatrix} 1 & 101 & 1 \\ 1 & 1 & 101 \\ 101 & 1 & 1 \end{pmatrix}.$$

Then $v_2 = 96.15$ but $v_1 = 63.30$. However, the counterexamples are very rare. Our computer experiments with millions of matrices did not reveal any counterexample.

We prove (10) for $n = 2$. To show that the sequence (v_{2^p}) is decreasing, it is enough to show that $v_2 \leq v_1$; i.e.,

$$\left(\mathrm{su}\,G(\mathbf{A}^2)\right)^{1/2} \leq \mathrm{su}\,G(\mathbf{A}). \tag{11}$$

If

$$\mathbf{A} = \begin{pmatrix} a & b \\ c & d \end{pmatrix},$$

then

$$\mathbf{A}^2 = \begin{pmatrix} a^2 + bc & ab + bd \\ ac + cd & bc + d^2 \end{pmatrix},$$

and further

$$\begin{aligned} \operatorname{su} G(\mathbf{A}^2) &= a^2 + 2bc + d^2 + 2\sqrt{(ab+bd)(ac+cd)} \\ &= a^2 + 2bc + d^2 + 2\sqrt{a^2bc + 2abcd + 2d^2bc} \\ &= a^2 + 2bc + d^2 + 2(a+d)\sqrt{bc} \end{aligned}$$

and

$$\begin{aligned} (\operatorname{su} G(\mathbf{A}))^2 &= (a + 2\sqrt{bc} + d)^2 \\ &= a^2 + 4bc + d^2 + 4a\sqrt{bc} + 4d\sqrt{bc} + 2ad \\ &= a^2 + 2bc + d^2 + 2(a+d)\sqrt{bc} + 2[ad + (a+d)\sqrt{bc} + bc]. \end{aligned}$$

Hence (11) follows. Therefore (v_{2^p}) is decreasing and, since $r(G(\mathbf{A})) = r(\mathbf{A})$, we have (10).

Somewhat related to (11), the inequality

$$\operatorname{su} G(\mathbf{A}^2) \geq \operatorname{su}(G(\mathbf{A})^2)$$

is generally valid (Kolotilina 1993, Remark 4).

References

Bapat, R. B. and Raghavan, T. E. S. (1997), *Nonnegative Matrices and Applications.* Cambridge University Press.

Horn, R. A. and Johnson, C. R. (1985). *Matrix Analysis.* Cambridge University Press.

Horn, R. A. and Johnson, C. R. (1991). *Topics in Matrix Analysis.* Cambridge University Press.

Kankaanpää, H. and Merikoski, J. K. (1985). Two inequalities for the sum of elements of a matrix. *Linear and Multilinear Algebra*, 18, 9–22.

Kolotilina, L. Ju. (1993). Lower bounds for the Perron root of a nonegative matrix. *Linear Algebra and its Applications*, 180, 133–151.

Laakso, V. (1999). Matriisin potenssin alkioiden summa. Licentiate's thesis, University of Tampere.

London, D. (1966). Inequalities in quadratic forms. *Duke Mathematical Journal*, 33, 511–522.

Marcus, M. and Minc, H. (1992). *A Survey of Matrix Theory and Matrix Inequalities.* Dover Publications.

Merikoski, J. K. (1984). On the trace and the sum of elements of a matrix. *Linear Algebra and its Applications*, 60, 177–185.

Minc, H. (1988). *Nonnegative Matrices.* John Wiley & Sons.

Szyld, D. B. (1992). A sequence of lower bounds for the spectral radius of nonnegative matrices. *Linear Algebra and its Applications*, 174, 239–242.

Tasçi, D. and Kirkland, S. (1998). A sequence of upper bounds for the Perron root on a nonnegative matrix. *Linear Algebra and its Applications*, 273, 23-28.

Jorma K. Merikoski
Department of Mathematics, Statistics and Philosophy
FI-33014 University of Tampere, Finland
jorma.merikoski@uta.fi
http://mtl.uta.fi/~jkm/

Ari Virtanen
Department of Mathematics, Statistics and Philosophy
FI-33014 University of Tampere, Finland
ari.virtanen@uta.fi

Festschrift for Tarmo Pukkila on his 60th Birthday
Eds. E. P. Liski, J. Isotalo, J. Niemelä, S. Puntanen, and G. P. H. Styan
© Dept. of Mathematics, Statistics and Philosophy,
Univ. of Tampere, 2006, ISBN 978-951-44-6620-5, pages 191–204

Logarithmic mean for several arguments

Seppo Mustonen

Abstract. The logarithmic mean is generalized for n positive arguments x_1, ..., x_n by examining series expansions of typical mean numbers in case $n = 2$. The generalized logarithmic mean defined as a series expansion can then be presented also in closed form which proves to be the $(n-1)$th divided difference (multiplied by $(n-1)!$) of values $f(u_1), \ldots, f(u_n)$ where $f(u_i) = e^{u_i} = x_i$, $i = 1, \ldots, n$. Various properties of this generalization are studied and an efficient recursive algorithm for computing it is presented.

Key words and phrases: Logarithmic mean; Series expansions; Divided differences.

1 Introduction

Some statisticians and mathematicians have proposed generalizations of the logarithmic mean for n arguments ($n > 2$), see Dodd (1941) and Pittenger (1985).

The generalization presented in this paper differs from the earlier suggestions and has its origin in an unpublished manuscript of the author (Mustonen 1976). This manuscript based on a research made in early 70's is referred to in the paper of Törnqvist et al. (1985). It essentially described a generalization in cases $n = 3, 4$ and provided a suggestion for a general form which will be derived in this paper.

The logarithmic mean $L(x_1, x_2)$ for two arguments $x_1 > 0$, $x_2 > 0$ is defined by

$$L(x_1, x_2) = \frac{x_1 - x_2}{\log(x_1/x_2)} \quad \text{for } x_1 \neq x_2 \qquad \text{and} \qquad L(x_1, x_1) = x_1. \tag{1}$$

Obviously Leo Törnqvist was the first to advance the “log-mean” concept in his fundamental research work related to price indexes (Törnqvist 1935). Yrjö Vartia then implemented the logarithmic mean in his log-change index numbers (Vartia 1976).

In Törnqvist et al. (1985) the log-change $\log(x_2/x_1)$ is suggested to be used instead of the common relative change $(x_2 - x_1)/x_1$ as an indicator of relative change for several theoretical and practical reasons. It is connected to the logarithmic mean simply by

$$\log(x_2/x_1) = \frac{x_1 - x_2}{L(x_1, x_2)}. \tag{2}$$

Among other things it will be shown that a corresponding formula is valid in the generalized case.

2 Generalization

The starting point for the generalization is the observation that $L(x_1, x_2)$ is found to be related to the arithmetic mean $A(x_1, x_2) = (x_1 + x_2)/2$ and the geometric mean $G(x_1, x_2) = \sqrt{x_1 x_2}$ by using suitable series expansions for each of them.

By denoting

$$x_1 = \exp u_1, \qquad x_2 = \exp u_2$$

the following expansions based on

$$\exp u = 1 + u + u^2/2! + u^3/3! + \cdots$$

are immediately obtained:

$$\begin{aligned}
A(x_1, x_2) &= 1 + (u_1 + u_2)/2 + (u_1^2 + u_2^2)/(2 \cdot 2!) + (u_1^3 + u_2^3)/(2 \cdot 3!) + \cdots, \\
G(x_1, x_2) &= \sqrt{e^{u_1} e^{u_2}} = \exp[(u_1 + u_2)/2] \\
&= 1 + (u_1 + u_2)/2 + (u_1 + u_2)^2/(2^2 \cdot 2!) \\
&\qquad + (u_1 + u_2)^3/(2^3 \cdot 3!) + \cdots \\
&= 1 + (u_1 + u_2)/2 + (u_1^2 + 2u_1u_2 + u_2^2)/(2^2 \cdot 2!) \\
&\qquad + (u_1^3 + 3u_1^2u_2 + 3u_1u_2^2 + u_2^3)/(2^3 \cdot 3!) + \cdots, \\
L(x_1, x_2) &= (e^{u_1} - e^{u_2})/(u_1 - u_2) \\
&= 1 + (u_1 + u_2)/2 + (u_1^2 + u_1u_2 + u_2^2)/(3 \cdot 2!) \\
&\qquad + (u_1^3 + u_1^2u_2 + u_1u_2^2 + u_2^3)/(4 \cdot 3!) + \cdots.
\end{aligned}$$

The expansions are identical up to the first degree. In the term of degree $m > 1$ the essential factor is a symmetric homogeneous polynomial of the form

$$B_m u_1^m + B_{m-1} u_1^{m-1} u_2 + B_{m-2} u_1^{m-2} u_2^2 + \cdots + B_0 u_2^m$$

divided by the sum of its coefficients $B_m, B_{m-1}, \ldots, B_0$. These coefficients characterize each of the means completely.

In the arithmetic mean we have

$$B_0 = B_1 = 1 \quad \text{and} \quad B_2 = \cdots = B_{m-1} = 0.$$

In the geometric mean they are binomial coefficients

$$B_i = C(m, i), \qquad i = 0, 1, \ldots, m$$

and in the logarithmic mean all coefficients equal to 1:

$$B_i = 1, \qquad i = 0, 1, \ldots, m.$$

The coefficients of the logarithmic mean arise from division

$$(u_1^{m+1} - u_2^{m+1})/(u_1 - u_2)$$

which symmetrizes its structure. Also other means (like harmonic and moment means) have similar expansions but their B coefficients are more complicated. The logarithmic mean has the most balanced B structure.

On the basis of this fact it was natural to generalize L in such a way that it keeps this simple structure. Thus the logarithmic mean for n observations

$$x_i = \exp u_i, \qquad i = 1, 2, \ldots, n$$

is defined by

$$\begin{aligned} L(x_1, x_2, \ldots, x_n) \\ &= 1 + (u_1 + u_2 + \cdots + u_n)/n \\ &+ \frac{u_1^2 + u_1 u_2 + \cdots + u_1 u_n + u_2^2 + u_2 u_3 + \cdots + u_n^2}{C(n+1, 2) \cdot 2!} + \cdots \\ &+ \frac{u_1^m + u_1^{m-1} u_2 + \cdots + u_n^m}{C(n+m-1, m) \cdot m!} + \cdots . \end{aligned} \tag{3}$$

In this series expansion the polynomial in the term of degree m has the form

$$P(n, m) = \sum_{\substack{i_1 + i_2 + \cdots + i_n = m \\ i_1 \geq 0, i_2 \geq 0, \ldots, i_n \geq 0}} u_1^{i_1} u_2^{i_2} \cdots u_n^{i_n}$$

and so the all B coefficients are equal to 1. They have divisors $C(n+m-1, m)$ corresponding to the number of summands.

In my earlier study (Mustonen 1976) I succeeded in transforming this expansion to a closed form

$$L(x_1, x_2, \ldots, x_n) = (n-1)! \sum_{i=1}^{n} \frac{x_i}{\prod\limits_{\substack{j=1 \\ j \neq i}}^{n} \log(x_i / x_j)} \tag{4}$$

when all the x's are mutually different positive numbers. In fact, I was then able to prove (4) in cases $n = 3, 4$ and the general form was only a natural conjecture. I lost my interest in further studies since the formula is numerically very unstable for large n values. It is better to use the series expansion (3) in practice. However, in theoretical considerations (4) is important.

3 Derivation of the formula (4)

Polynomials $P(n,m)$ can be represented in a recursive form according to decreasing powers of the last u as

$$\begin{aligned} P(n,m) = \quad & u_n^m \\ & + u_n^{m-1} P(n-1,1) \\ & + u_n^{m-2} P(n-1,2) + \cdots \\ & + u_n^1 P(n-1,m-1) \\ & + u_n^0 P(n-1,m) \end{aligned} \tag{5}$$

with side conditions $P(n,1) = u_1 + u_2 + \cdots + u_n$, $P(1,m) = u_1^m$.

If all x's (and therefore also u's) are mutually different, it is fundamental to notice that polynomials $P(n,m)$ can be represented by another way by using expressions

$$Q(n,m) = \sum_{i=1}^{n} \frac{u_i^m}{U_i}, \qquad m = 0,1,2,\ldots \tag{6}$$

where

$$U_i = \prod_{\substack{j=1 \\ j \neq i}}^{n} (u_i - u_j), \qquad i = 1,2,\ldots,n. \tag{7}$$

The following identities are valid and will be proved in the next chapter.

$$Q(n,m) = 0 \quad \text{for } m = 0,1,2,\ldots,n-2, \tag{8}$$

$$Q(n,n-1) = 1, \tag{9}$$

$$Q(n,m) = P(n,m-n+1) \quad \text{for } m = n,n+1,n+2,\ldots. \tag{10}$$

By means of these identities the formula (4) can be derived from the definition (3) as follows:

$$\begin{aligned} L(x_1,x_2,\ldots,x_n) &= 1 + P(n,1)/n + P(n,2)/[C(n+1,2)\cdot 2!] + \cdots \\ &\quad + P(n,m)/[C(n+m-1,m)\cdot m!] + \cdots \\ &= 1 + (n-1)! \sum_{m=1}^{\infty} \frac{P(n,m)}{(n+m-1)!} \\ &= 1 + (n-1)! \sum_{m=1}^{\infty} \frac{Q(n,n+m-1)}{(n+m-1)!} \qquad \text{from (10)} \\ &= 1 + (n-1)! \sum_{k=n}^{\infty} \frac{Q(n,k)}{k!} \\ &= (n-1)! \sum_{k=n-1}^{\infty} \frac{Q(n,k)}{k!} \qquad \text{from (9)} \end{aligned}$$

$$= (n-1)! \sum_{k=0}^{\infty} \frac{Q(n,k)}{k!} \qquad \text{from (8)}$$

$$= (n-1)! \sum_{k=0}^{\infty} \frac{\sum_{i=1}^{n} u_i^k / U_i}{k!} \qquad \text{from (6)}$$

$$= (n-1)! \sum_{i=1}^{n} \frac{\sum_{k=0}^{\infty} u_i^k / k!}{U_i}$$

$$= (n-1)! \sum_{i=1}^{n} \frac{\exp u_i}{\prod_{\substack{j=1 \\ j \neq i}}^{n} (u_i - u_j)} \qquad \text{from (7)}$$

which is identical with (4) since $u_i = \log x_i$, $i = 1, 2, \ldots, n$.

4 Proof of identities (8), (9), (10)

It can be seen immediately that the identities are valid for $n = 2$. In this case

$$Q(2,k) = \frac{u_1^k}{u_1 - u_2} + \frac{u_2^k}{u_2 - u_1} = \frac{u_1^k - u_2^k}{u_1 - u_2}, \qquad k = 0, 1, 2, \ldots$$

and thus

$$Q(2,0) = 0, \qquad Q(2,1) = 1 \quad \text{and} \quad Q(2,k) = P(2, k-1) \ \text{for } k = 2, 3, \ldots.$$

The general proof is based on induction from $n-1$ to n. Thus by assuming that the identities are valid in case $n-1$ it will be shown that they are valid in case n, too.

By writing denominators u_i^m of (6) in the form $(u_i^m - u_n^m) + u_n^m$ and by splitting these terms and by dividing the first part by the last factor $u_i - u_n$ in divisor (7) we get a recursion formula

$$\begin{aligned} Q(n,m) = \quad & u_n^{m-1} Q(n-1, 0) \\ & + u_n^{m-2} Q(n-1, 1) + \cdots \\ & + u_n^0 Q(n-1, m-1) + u_n^m Q(n, 0), \qquad m = 1, 2, \ldots. \end{aligned} \tag{11}$$

Let us denote $Q(n,0) = f(u_1, u_2, \ldots, u_n)$ and study the function f with the inverse values of its arguments, i.e. the function $f(1/u_1, 1/u_2, \ldots, 1/u_n)$. Then the expressions $1/u_i - 1/u_j$ can be written in the form $(u_j - u_i)/(u_i u_j)$ and after simplification we get

$$f(1/u_1, 1/u_2, \ldots, 1/u_n) = (-1)^n u_1 u_2 \cdots u_n Q(n, n-2).$$

By applying the recursion formula (11) to the last factor and by observing that (8) is valid in case $n-1$, we see that only the last term in the recursion formula can be different from 0 and hence

$$f(1/u_1, 1/u_2, \ldots, 1/u_n) = (-1)^n u_1 u_2 \cdots u_n u_n^{n-2} f(u_1, u_2, \ldots, u_n).$$

Function $f(u_1, u_2, \ldots, u_n)$ is homogeneous and symmetric. If f were else than identically zero, it leads to a contradiction since the right side of the last equation could not be a symmetric function in cases $n > 2$. Thus $Q(n, 0) = 0$ for $n = 2, 3, \ldots$ and (8) has been proved in case $m = 0$.

Then in (11) the last term can be omitted and we have

$$\begin{aligned} Q(n,m) = \quad & u_n^{m-1} Q(n-1, 0) \\ & + u_n^{m-2} Q(n-1, 1) + \cdots \\ & + u_n^0 Q(n-1, m-1), \qquad m = 1, 2, \ldots . \end{aligned} \tag{12}$$

By the induction assumption this gives

$$\begin{aligned} Q(n,1) &= u_n^0 Q(n-1,0) = 0, \\ Q(n,2) &= u_n^1 Q(n-1,0) + u_n^0 Q(n-1,1) = 0, \\ &\vdots \\ Q(n,n-2) &= u_n^{n-3} Q(n-1,0) + \cdots + u_n^0 Q(n-1,n-3) = 0 \end{aligned}$$

and so (8) has been proved also for $m = 1, 2, \ldots, n-2$.

In case $m = n - 1$ (12) gives

$$Q(n, n-1) = u_n^0 Q(n-1, n-2) = 1$$

and (9) is valid.

In case $m = n$ (12) gives

$$\begin{aligned} Q(n,n) &= u_n^1 Q(n-1, n-2) + u_n^0 Q(n-1, n-1) \\ &= u_n + (u_1 + u_2 + \cdots + u_{n-1}) = u_1 + u_2 + \cdots + u_n \end{aligned}$$

and (10) is valid when $m = n$ and hence $Q(n,n) = P(n,1)$.

By these results the recursion formula (12) is reduced to the form

$$\begin{aligned} Q(n,m) = \quad & u_n^{m-n+1} \\ & + u_n^{m-n} Q(n-1, n-1) + \cdots \\ & + u_n^0 Q(n-1, m-1), \qquad m = n, n+1, \ldots . \end{aligned} \tag{13}$$

By using this formula and (10) for $n - 1$ we get

$$\begin{aligned} Q(n, n+1) &= u_n^2 + u_n^1 Q(n-1, n-1) + u_n^0 Q(n-1, n) \\ &= u_n^2 + u_n P(n-1, 1) + P(n-1, 2) \\ &= P(n, 2) \qquad \text{from (5)} \end{aligned}$$

which means that (10) is valid for $m = n + 1$ and $Q(n, n+1) = P(n, 2)$. Similarly, when $m > n$ we obtain by using (13) and (10) (the latter for $n - 1$)

$$\begin{aligned} Q(n,m) = \; & u_n^{m-n+1} \\ & + u_n^{m-n} P(n-1,1) \\ & + u_n^{m-n-1} P(n-1,2) + \cdots \\ & + u_n^0 P(n-1, m-n+1) = P(n, m-n+1) \qquad \text{from (5)} \end{aligned}$$

and this proves (10) in general.

5 Logarithmic mean and divided differences

Since I felt that identities (8) and (9) must be known in some other connections and, in particular, the denominators (7) are present also in the Lagrange's interpolation formula, I sent an inquiry about their origin to some of my colleagues in Finland.

Jorma Merikoski (University of Tampere) remarked immediately that in fact (8) and (9) are well-known identities when considering divided differences (in the Lagrangian interpolation scheme) for powers u^k, $k = 0, 1, \ldots, n-2$.

His note led me to find out that (4) is equal to the (only) $(n-1)$th order divided difference of function values $x_i = \exp u_i$, $i = 1, 2, \ldots, n$, multiplied by $(n-1)!$ (See e.g. Fröberg 1965, p. 148).

For example, in case $n = 3$ the divided differences are

u	$f(u)$	1st difference	2nd difference
u_1	$\exp u_1$		
		$\dfrac{\exp u_2 - \exp u_1}{u_2 - u_1}$	
u_2	$\exp u_2$		$\dfrac{\dfrac{\exp u_3 - \exp u_2}{u_3 - u_2} - \dfrac{\exp u_2 - \exp u_1}{u_2 - u_1}}{u_3 - u_2}$
		$\dfrac{\exp u_3 - \exp u_2}{u_3 - u_2}$	
u_3	$\exp u_3$		

and the second divided difference is equal to

$$\begin{aligned} & L(\exp u_1, \exp u_2, \exp u_3)/2 \\ & = \frac{\exp u_1}{(u_1 - u_2)(u_1 - u_3)} + \frac{\exp u_2}{(u_2 - u_1)(u_2 - u_3)} + \frac{\exp u_3}{(u_3 - u_1)(u_3 - u_2)}. \end{aligned}$$

This means that $L(x_1, \ldots, x_n)$ can be computed recursively according to the formula

$$L(x_1,\dots,x_n) = (n-1)\frac{L(x_2,\dots,x_n) - L(x_1,\dots,x_{n-1})}{\log(x_n/x_1)} \qquad \text{for } n = 2,3,\dots. \tag{14}$$

Since, according to the classical mean value theorem the $(n-1)$th divided difference $d(u_1,\dots,u_n)$ for function values $f(u_1)$, …, $f(u_n)$ (for a function f which is continuously differentiable $n-1$ times) can represented in the form (see Fröberg 1965, p. 148)

$$d(u_1,\dots,u_n) = \frac{f^{(n-1)}(\xi)}{(n-1)!}$$

where $\min(u_1,\dots,u_n) < \xi < \max(u_1,\dots,u_n)$ we have now $f(u) = \exp u$ with all derivatives identically equal to $f(u)$ and hence

$$L(x_1,\dots,x_n) = e^{\xi}.$$

Thus the logarithmic mean is directly related to a 'mean value' also in the sense of standard analysis for real functions.

6 Relative changes

By (14) the relative change $\log(x_n/x_1)$ can be written as

$$\log(x_n/x_1) = (n-1)\frac{L(x_2,\dots,x_n) - L(x_1,\dots,x_{n-1})}{L(x_1,\dots,x_n)}.$$

Since trivially

$$\frac{x_n}{x_1} = \frac{x_2}{x_1}\cdot\frac{x_3}{x_2}\cdot\ \dots\ \cdot\frac{x_n}{x_{n-1}},$$

we have

$$\frac{\sum_{i=1}^{n-1}\log(x_{i+1}/x_i)}{n-1} = \frac{L(x_2,\dots,x_n) - L(x_1,\dots,x_{n-1})}{L(x_1,\dots,x_n)},$$

i.e. the average of the log-changes in series of observations $x_1, x_2, \dots, x_n$ is equal to a natural generalization of the right-hand side in (2).

7 Logarithmic mean for exponentially growing data

Let us consider the data set

$$x_0,\ x_0c,\ x_0c^2,\ x_0c^3,\ \dots,\ x_0c^{n-1}.$$

In this case (4) can be written in the form

$$L(x_1,\dots,x_n) = \frac{(n-1)!\,x_0}{(\log c)^{n-1}}\sum_{i=1}^{n}\frac{c^{i-1}}{\prod_{\substack{j=1\\ j\neq i}}^{n}(i-j)}.$$

The divisors in the sum are of the form $(-1)^{n-i}(i-1)!(n-i)!$ and then according to the formula $C(m,k) = m!/[k!(m-k)!]$ for binomial coefficients we have

$$\begin{aligned} L(x_1,\dots,x_n) &= \frac{(n-1)!\,x_0}{(\log c)^{n-1}} \sum_{i=1}^{n} \frac{(-1)^{n-i}C(n-1,i-1)c^{i-1}}{(n-1)!} \\ &= \frac{(n-1)!\,x_0}{(\log c)^{n-1}} \cdot \frac{(c-1)^{n-1}}{(n-1)!} \qquad \text{(from binomial formula)} \\ &= x_0[(c-1)/\log c]^{n-1} \\ &= x_0 L(c,1)^{n-1}. \end{aligned}$$

Thus when the observations are growing by a constant factor $c > 1$, the logarithmic mean grows by a constant factor $L(c,1)$. Apparently the same result is obtained for $0 < c < 1$, too.

In fact, a corresponding result is valid for the geometric mean since we get immediately that

$$G(x_1,x_2,\dots,x_n) = x_0 G(c,1)^{n-1}$$

where $G(c,1) = \sqrt{c \cdot 1}$. It shows certain similarity between the geometric and logarithmic mean. However, when $c \neq 1$, it follows that $\lim_{n\to\infty} L/G = \infty$ since

$$L(c,1) > G(c,1). \tag{15}$$

Inequality (15) for $c > 1$ can be proved simply by studying the behaviour of the function $f(x) = \log x[L(x^2,1) - G(x^2,1)] = (x^2-1)/2 - x\log x$ for $x > 1$. Since

$$L(ax,ay) = aL(x,y) \quad \text{and} \quad G(ax,ay) = aG(x,y) \quad \text{for } a > 0, \tag{16}$$

it follows immediately that (15) is valid also for $0 < c < 1$. Hence (15) has been proved for all positive $c \neq 1$. Similarly the inequality $L(x,y) > G(x,y)$ for $x \neq y$ is proved by using (15) and (16). Of course, other general proofs are available, see e.g. Carlson (1972).

8 Computational aspects

In principle, the generalized logarithmic mean can be computed quickly from the closed form (4) but this fails numerically for $n > 14$ although double precision is used. The reason for this unpleasant phenomen is the fact that (4) is a sum of 'huge' alternating terms and the number of significant digits are soon lost. Furthermore (4) is not applicable at all when some x's are equal. Also the recursive formula (14) suffers for same reasons.

Hence the main method for computing logarithmic means in the statistical system Survo (Mustonen 1992, http://www.survo.fi) is based on the original definition i.e. the series expansion (3). For this task I have created a new Survo program module LOGMEAN.

When using the series expansion it is essential how the symmetric, homogeneous polynomials $P(m, n)$ are evaluated. It is done by using the recursive formula (5). To speed up the recursion process the LOGMEAN module saves all computed $P(n, m)$ values in a table. Thus in each recursive step it is checked whether the current $P(n, m)$ has been already calculated. By this technique cases where n is less than 10000 are calculated very rapidly but on current PC's also cases where n is much higher can be handled.

For example, for a data set 1, 2, 3, ..., n ($n = 200000$) LOGMEAN gives

$$L_n = 73578.65538616560 \quad \text{(logarithmic mean)}$$
$$G_n = 73578.47151997556 \quad \text{(geometric mean)}$$

and after doing the same when the last observation 200000 is omitted we get for $n = 200000$

$$L_n - L_{n-1} = 0.36788036154758 \qquad L_n/n = 0.36789327693083$$
$$G_n - G_{n-1} = 0.36788036060170 \qquad G_n/n = 0.36789235759988$$

On the basis of these calculations it is obvious that

$$\lim_{n\to\infty} (L_n - L_{n-1}) = \lim_{n\to\infty} (G_n - G_{n-1}) = 1/e = 0.367879\ldots$$

and also

$$\lim_{n\to\infty} (L_n/n) = \lim_{n\to\infty} (G_n/n) = 1/e.$$

For the geometric mean these results can be proved by Stirling's formula. The same is not yet proved for the logarithmic mean.

9 Concluding remarks

The generalization presented in this paper comes close to that of Pittenger (1985) in certain aspects. However, already numerical examples with $n = 3$ show that it these generalizations are not the same. Also in principle Pittenger's approach is different since he starts from the inverse of $L(x_1, x_2)$ and by following Carlson (1972) writes this inverse as a certain definite integral which is then extended into multivariable form and finally represented as a closed expression.

It is obvious that the generalized logarithmic mean as defined in this paper satisfies inequalities

$$G(x_1, \ldots, x_n) \le L(x_1, \ldots, x_n) \le A(x_1, \ldots, x_n) \tag{17}$$

but it has not been proved for $n > 2$. By comparing series expansions of the form (3) it may be possible to show even a stronger result that the inequalities are valid term by term, i.e.

$$\frac{(u_1 + \cdots + u_n)^m}{n^m} \le \frac{P(n,m)}{C(n+m-1,m)} \le \frac{u_1^m + \cdots + u_n^m}{n} \tag{18}$$

for $u_i \ge 0$, $i = 1, 2, \ldots, n$. Then (17) is also valid when any of the u's is < 0, i.e. any of the x's $\in (0,1)$, since for any of these means, say M, we have $M(ax_1, \ldots, ax_n) = aM(x_1, \ldots, x_n)$ for all $a > 0$.

The LOGMEAN program includes options for checking the validity of (17) and (18). In rather extensive numerical tests no violation against these conjectures have been found.

Appendix 1. Proof of (18) in case $n = 2$ (26 December 2002)

When $n = 2$ it is sufficient to study the case $u_1 = u$, $u_2 = 1$ and assume that $u > 1$. Then (18) can be written as

$$\frac{(u+1)^m}{2^m} \le \frac{u^{m+1} - 1}{(m+1)(u-1)} \le \frac{u^m + 1}{2} \tag{19}$$

The second part of this double inequality is equivalent to

$$2(u^{m+1} - 1) \le (m+1)(u-1)(u^m + 1)$$

or

$$f(u) = (m-1)u^{m+1} - (m+1)u^m + (m+1)u - (m-1) \ge 0. \tag{20}$$

By studying the first and second derivatives of $f(u)$ it can be easily seen that (20) holds.

The first part of the double inequality is equivalent to

$$(m+1)(u-1)(u+1)^m \le 2^m(u^{m+1} - 1)$$

or

$$g(u) = 2^m(u^{m+1} - 1) - (m+1)(u-1)(u+1)^m \ge 0. \tag{21}$$

It can be shown by induction that the kth derivative of $g(u)$ is

$$g^{(k)}(u) = \frac{(m+1)!}{(m-k+1)!}[2^m u^{m-k+1} - k(u+1)^{m-k+1} - (m-k+1)(u-1)(u+1)^{m-k}]$$

for $k \le m+1$ and $g^{(k)}(u) = 0$ for $k > m+1$. Especially when $u = 1$ we have

$$g^{(k)}(1) = \frac{(m+1)!}{(m-k+1)!} 2^{m-k+1}(2^{k-1} - k), \qquad k \le m+1.$$

Thus $g(u)$ and all its derivatives are non-negative for $u = 1$ and from the Taylor expansion of $g(u)$ we can deduce that (21) holds for all m.

Appendix 2. Proof of the first part of (18) (10 June 2003) by Jorma Merikoski

Let $u_1, \ldots, u_n \geq 0$. Their m'th "symmetric mean" (see e.g. Mitrinović 1970, p. 95) is defined by

$$s_m(u_1, \ldots, u_n) = C(n, m)^{-1} \sum_{1 \leq i_1 < \cdots < i_m \leq n} u_{i_1} \cdots u_{i_m}.$$

Allowing also equal i_k's, we meet the "generalized m'th symmetric mean" (see e.g. Mitrinović 1970, p. 105, note that $C(n + m - 1, m) = C(n + m - 1, n - 1)$), defined by

$$h_m(u_1, \ldots, u_n) = C(n + m - 1, m)^{-1} \sum_{i_1 + \cdots + i_n = m} u_1^{i_1} \cdots u_n^{i_n} \qquad (i_1, \ldots, i_n \geq 0),$$

which appears in the middle of (18). (Here we define $0^0 = 1$. In fact, the functions s_m and h_m should not be called means, since they are not homogenous and all their values are not between $\min_i u_i$ and $\max_i u_i$. Neither should h_m be called a generalization of s_m, since s_m is not obtained from h_m as a special case. The functions $s_m^{1/m}$ and $h_m^{1/m}$ are actual means.)

Fix $u_1, \ldots, u_n$. Neuman (1986, Corollary 3.2) proved that

$$k \leq m \Rightarrow h_k^{1/k} \leq h_m^{1/m}. \tag{22}$$

Putting $k = 1$ proves the first part of (18). The second part remains open.

DeTemple and Robertson (1979) gave an elementary proof of (22) for $n = 2$, but Neuman's proof for general n is not elementary, applying B-splines. The problem, whether the first part of (18) has an elementary proof, and the stronger problem, whether (22) has such a proof, remain also open.

Appendix 3. Alternative derivations of (4). Proofs of (17) (7 October 2003) by Jorma Merikoski

I noted only recently that alternative derivations of (4) and proofs of (17) appear in the literature.

Neuman (1994) defined (as a special case of Neuman 1994, Eq. (2.3))

$$L(x_1, \ldots, x_n) = \int_{E_{n-1}} \left(\exp \sum_{i=1}^{n} v_i \log x_i \right) dv, \tag{23}$$

where $v_1 + \cdots + v_n = 1$,

$$E_{n-1} = \{ (v_1, \ldots, v_{n-1}) \mid v_1, \ldots, v_{n-1} \geq 0,\ v_1 + \cdots + v_{n-1} \leq 1 \},$$

and $dv = dv_1 \cdots dv_{n-1}$. He (Neuman 1994, Theorem 1 and the last formula) proved (17) and reduced (23) into (4).

Pečarić and Šimić (1999) tied Neuman's approach to a wider context. They studied extensively various logarithmic and other means. As a special case (Pečarić and Šimić 1999, Remark 5.4), they obtained (4).

Xiao and Zhang (unaware of Neuman 1994) defined

$$L(x_1,\ldots,x_n) = \frac{(n-1)!}{V(\log x_1,\ldots,\log x_n)} \sum_{i=1}^{n} (-1)^{n+i} x_i V_i(\log x_1,\ldots,\log x_n), \tag{24}$$

where V denotes the Vandermonde determinant and V_i is obtained from it by omitting the last row and i'th column. Actually (24) equals (4). Also they proved (17).

Appendix 4. An update (17 November 2005) by Jorma Merikoski

Motivated by this paper, I [J. Ineq. Pure Appl. Math. 5 (2004), Article 65] surveyed and further developed its results. Neuman [SIAM J. Math. Anal. 19 (1988), 736–750] proved the second part of (18).

Acknowledgements

I would like to thank Yrjö Vartia for his inspiring interest in my attempts in this project from early 1970's and Jorma Merikoski for a valuable remark related to divided differences.

References

Carlson, B. C. (1972). The logarithmic mean. *American Mathematical Monthly*, 79, 615–618.

DeTemple, D. W. and Robertson, J. M. (1979). On generalized symmetric means of two variables. *Univerziteta u Beogradu. Publikacije Elektrotehnickog Fakulteta. Serija Matematika i Fizika*, No. 634-677, 236–238.

Dodd, E. L. (1941). Some generalizations of the logarithmic mean and of similar means of two variates which become indeterminate when the two variates are equal. *Annals of Mathematical Statistics*, 12, 422–428.

Fröberg, C.-E. (1965). *Introduction to numerical analysis.* Addison-Wesley.

Mitrinović, D. S. (1970). *Analytic Inequalities.* Springer.

Mustonen, S. (1976). A generalized logarithmic mean. Unpublished manuscript. University of Helsinki, Dept. of Statistics.

Mustonen, S. (1992). *Survo – An integrated environment for statistical computing and related areas.* Helsinki: Survo Systems.

Neuman, E. (1986). Inequalities involving generalized symmetric means. *Journal of Mathematical Analysis and Applications*, 120, 315–320.

Neuman, E. (1994). The weighted logarithmic mean. *Journal of Mathematical Analysis and Applications*, 188, 885–900.

Pečarić, J. and Šimić, V. (1999). Stolarsky-Tobey mean in n variables. *Mathematical Inequalities and Applications*, 2, 325–341.

Pittenger, A. O. (1985). The logarithmic mean in n variables. *American Mathematical Monthly*, 92, 99–104.

Törnqvist, L. (1935). A memorandum concerning the calculation of Bank of Finland consumption price index. (Swedish). Unpublished memo. Helsinki: Bank of Finland.

Törnqvist, L., Vartia, P., and Vartia, Y. O. (1985). How should relative changes be measured? *American Statistician*, 39, 43–46.

Vartia, Y. O. (1976). Ideal log-change index numbers. *Scandinavian Journal of Statistics*, 3, 121–126.

Xiao, Z-G. and Zhang, Z-H. (2003) The inequalities $G \leq L \leq I \leq A$ in n variables. *Journal of Inequalities in Pure and Applied Mathematics*, 4, Article 39.

SEPPO MUSTONEN
Department of Statistics, University of Helsinki, Finland
P. O. Box 54, Unioninkatu 37, FI-00014 University of Helsinki
seppo.mustonen@helsinki.fi
http://mathstat.helsinki.fi/henkilot/seppo.mustonen.en.html

The current version of this paper can be downloaded from http://www.survo.fi/papers/logmean.pdf.

Festschrift for Tarmo Pukkila on his 60th Birthday
Eds. E. P. Liski, J. Isotalo, J. Niemelä, S. Puntanen, and G. P. H. Styan

Univ. of Tampere, 2006, ISBN 978-951-44-6620-5, pages 205–216

On the reliability of performance rankings

LEIF NORDBERG

Abstract. During recent years it has become more and more popular to use so-called performance indicators to measure the effectiveness or productivity of organizations or even individuals like teachers or football players. The purpose of this paper is to discuss some possibilities to evaluate and measure the reliability of rankings based on indicators of this kind. As an illustration we discuss the reliability of a recent ranking of the faculties of social sciences in Finland according to their scientific productivity.

2000 MSC codes: 62J05, 62H12.

Key words and phrases: Performance indicators; Rank distributions; Measures of the reliability of rankings; Scientific productivity.

1 Introduction

It has become very popular to use so-called performance indicators to measure the effectiveness or productivity of organizations such as universities, schools and health centrals, or even of individuals such as university teachers or football players. In some cases, these indicators may even play a major role in the making of decisions about the public funding of the institutions concerned. They may also affect the public demand of the services provided by the units.

Often, at least in the media, the results of these studies are compressed into so-called "league tables", giving only the rankings of the units concerned according to some overall measure of effectiveness or performance. Even though this practice has already been seriously criticized (see e.g. Goldstein and Spiegelhalter 1996, and Andersson et al. 1998), it is becoming more, rather than less, popular among both administrators and the general public. This raises the question of how much information rankings of this kind really provide. The more the rankings are, implicitly or explicitly, used in making decisions affecting in one way or another the future of the ranked units, the more important it is to also evaluate both the validity and reliability of the rankings.

According to Goldstein and Spiegelhalter (1996) "a performance indicator is a summary statistical measure on an institution or system which is intended to be related to the 'quality' of its functioning". It is clear that it may be quite difficult both to define such a measure and to measure its value for the units concerned. Thus, if the aim is really to measure the performance of an institution or a system, it is not enough to measure just the "value of the output", as this in most cases is a function not only of the effectiveness of the organization but also depends heavily on the "quality of the input". For example, looking just at the results in examinations or on test scores does not give a correct picture of the effectiveness of schools if there are differences in the social background of the pupils or in other extra-institutional factors that also affect the results. Medical performance indicators may be heavily biased if they are not adjusted for initial disease severity and other risk factors. In this study we will, however, assume that the basic indicators used are reasonable and theoretically well-defined. Thus we concentrate on the reliability of performance indicators, and ranking based on them, when the observed values are probably affected by measurement errors.

Let us assume that we want to rank n units according to their values Ψ_1, $\Psi_2, \ldots, \Psi_n$ on some performance indicator Ψ.

By a rank vector we mean a vector $\mathbf{r}$ consisting of the ranks $r_1, r_2, \ldots,$ r_n given to the evaluated units, where "1" denotes the "best" and "n" the "worst". Obviously there are $n!$ possible rank vectors. We assume that Ψ is defined in such a way that "higher value" means "better performance". Consequently the unit with the highest Ψ_i is the best unit and thus its "true rank" is "1", the unit with second highest Ψ_i is the second best unit and its "true rank" is 2 and so on. To simplify, we ignore the possibility of tied ranks. Connected which each rank vector $\mathbf{r}$ is an ordering $\langle(\mathbf{r},1),(\mathbf{r},2),\ldots,(\mathbf{r},n)\rangle$ where $(\mathbf{r},1)$ denotes the unit with lowest rank and $(\mathbf{r},n)$ the unit with the highest rank according to $\mathbf{r}$. Thus $\mathbf{r}^{(t)}$ is the "true rank vector" if and only if

$$\Psi_{(\mathbf{r}^{(t)},1)} > \Psi_{(\mathbf{r}^{(t)},2)} > \cdots > \Psi_{(\mathbf{r}^{(t)},n)}.$$

Assume now that the true values of the performance indicator are unobservable and we have to base the ranking on some estimates $y_1, y_2, \ldots, y_n$ of them. The observed rank vector $\mathbf{r}^{(o)}$ is then defined by the condition

$$y_{(\mathbf{r}^{(o)},1)} > y_{(\mathbf{r}^{(o)},2)} > \cdots > y_{(\mathbf{r}^{(o)},n)}.$$

Of course, if the observed indicators are discrete, we may observe the same value for several units. This means that the connection between the observed indicator values and the ranking is no more unambiguous and we need some rule about how to handle possible ties.

What we are interested in is the "properties" of $\mathbf{r}^{(o)}$ as an estimate of $\mathbf{r}^{(t)}$. We may, for instance, ask if is possible to measure the "reliability" of the estimated rank vector in some simple way or if it is possible to construct a confidence interval for the true rank of a given unit.

Obviously, we have to start with a model of the measurement process. Thus, let us assume that the observed values of the indicator can be considered as independent stochastic variables with distributions depending on the true values of the indicator and some parameters Θ describing the measurement process, i.e.

$$y_i \sim f(\cdot\,; \Psi_i, \Theta), \qquad i = 1, 2, \ldots, n.$$

In a more general setting the observed values must be allowed to be correlated, but here we assume that the values are measured independently for each unit.

Some examples:

Example 1. We want to rank the researchers in a certain research organization according to their ability to produce scientific papers. As the indicator, we use the number of papers accepted for publication in scientific journals during a certain time period, a year for instance. A simple way to model the measurement process is to assume that the number of papers by person i accepted for publication can be considered as an observation from a Poisson distribution with parameter Ψ_i, the measure of "true scientific ability". Thus we have that

$$y_i \sim \text{Po}(\Psi_i), \qquad i = 1, 2, \ldots, n$$

and $E(y_i) = \text{Var}(y_i) = \Psi_i$. The higher the true value of the indicator, the more variable the observed value.

Example 2. We are interested in ranking university departments according to the probability that their students will get a degree within, say, five years. The probabilities are estimated by the proportion of new students starting their studies at the beginning of year t who finished their studies before the end of year $t + 4$. If we assume within-department homogeneity, i.e. that the probabilities are the same for all students within the same department, the number of "successes" can be considered as observations from a binomial distributions with parameters (Ψ_i, m_i), where Ψ_i denote the probability of getting a degree within five years and m_i is the number of new students year t within department i, $i = 1, 2, \ldots, n$. Thus the observed success rate y_i can be assumed to be approximately normally distributed with $E(y_i) = \Psi_i$ and $\text{Var}(y_i) = \Psi_i(1 - \Psi_i)/m_i$:

$$y_i \sim N(\Psi_i, \Psi_i(1 - \Psi_i)/m_i), \qquad i = 1, 2, \ldots, n$$

unless the numbers of new students are not too small. We note that the variability of the indicator depends on both the success rate and the number of students. For a discussion of the use of the same type of indicators for ranking hospitals, see Andersson et al. (1998).

Example 3. In order to rank universities according to their productivity, we compute a productivity index. The index is constructed as a weighted sum of several component indices. The true value of the index for unit i is thus

$$\Psi_i = w_{i1}\xi_{i1} + w_{i2}\xi_{i2} + \cdots + w_{ip}\xi_{ip}$$

where $\xi_{i1}, \xi_{i2}, \ldots, \xi_{ip}$ are the true values of p productivity indices and w_{i1}, $w_{i2}, \ldots$ are known weights. For several reasons, it may be very difficult or even impossible to measure the component indices exactly. Thus, the only way to calculate the index is to use estimates of the indices. We may, for example, assume that the vector $\mathbf{x}_i = [x_{i1}, x_{i2}, \ldots, x_{ip}]'$ of observed values (estimates) of the indices for unit i can be considered as an observation from a p-dimensional normal-distribution with expected value vector $\boldsymbol{\xi}_i = [\xi_{i1}, \xi_{i2}, \ldots, \xi_{ip}]$ and variance-covariance matrix Σ_i. Thus

$$\mathbf{x}_i \sim N(\xi_i, \Sigma_i), \qquad i = 1, 2, \ldots, n,$$

assuming that the measurement procedure is unbiased. If productivity for unit i is calculated as $y_i = \mathbf{w}_i'\mathbf{x}_i$, where $\mathbf{w}_i = [w_{i1}, w_{i2}, \ldots, w_{ip}]'$, then

$$y_i \sim N(\Psi_i, \mathbf{w}_i'\Sigma_i\mathbf{w}_i), \qquad i = 1, 2, \ldots, n.$$

2 The distribution of the rankings

In the following, we will assume that both the latent and observed indicators are continuous variables. Let $R = \{\mathbf{r}^{(j)}\}$ be the set of possible rankings and let $\langle(\mathbf{r}^{(j)}, 1), (\mathbf{r}^{(j)}, 2), \ldots, (\mathbf{r}^{(j)}, n)\rangle$ be the order vector corresponding to the rank vector $\mathbf{r}^{(j)}$. Then if $\mathbf{r}$ is the observed ranking

$$P(\mathbf{r} = \mathbf{r}^{(j)}) = P\big(y_{(\mathbf{r}^{(j)},1)} > y_{(\mathbf{r}^{(j)},2)} > \cdots > y_{(\mathbf{r}^{(j)},n)}\big), \qquad \mathbf{r}^{(j)} \in R.$$

For example, assuming $n = 4$

$$P(\mathbf{r} = [2, 3, 1, 4]) = P(y_3 > y_1 > y_2 > y_4).$$

Obviously, using the independence assumption

$$P(\mathbf{r} = \mathbf{r}^{(j)}) = \int\!\!\int_{y_{(\mathbf{r}^{(j)},1)} > y_{(\mathbf{r}^{(j)},2)} > \cdots > y_{(\mathbf{r}^{(j)},n)}} \cdots \int \prod_{k=1}^{n} [f(y_{(\mathbf{r}^{(j)},k)}; \Psi_{(\mathbf{r}^{(j)},k)}, \Theta)\, dy_{(\mathbf{r}^{(j)},k)}].$$

Thus, given the distributions of the observed indicators, it is at least in principle easy to calculate the probability of all the possible rankings. If numerical integration causes problems we can use simulations to estimate the probabilities. We may for instance be especially interested in the probability of getting very wrong rankings.

Example 4. For four evaluated units 1, 2, 3 and 4, let us assume that the observed indicators are independent and normally distributed with means 104, 103, 101, 100 and standard deviations 3, 2, 2, 1. Thus the "true" rank vector is $[1, 2, 3, 4]$. To estimate the probability distribution of the observed ranking we generated 10 000 observations from the corresponding four dimensional normal distribution. Using the results above, we found that the probability of getting the correct ranking was just c. 0.23. In Table 1, we give the (est.) marginal distributions for the ranking of the four units.

Table 1. The marginal distributions of the rankings.

Unit	$P(r_i = j),\ j = 1, 2, 3, 4$			
	1	2	3	4
1	0.57	0.24	0.11	0.08
2	0.34	0.44	0.16	0.06
3	0.08	0.24	0.38	0.30
4	0.00	0.08	0.35	0.57

We note, for example, that the probability of the correct ranking of a given unit varies between 0.38 and 0.57.

3 Measures of the reliability of ranking

a) Credibility intervals for ranks. Using the marginal distribution of the rank for unit i r_i, it is easy to find limits $r_{i,b}$ and $r_{i,u}$ such that $r_{i,b} - r_{i,u}$ is as small as possible under the condition

$$P(r_{i,b} \le r_i \le r_{i,u}) > 1 - \alpha,$$

where $100(1 - \alpha)\%$ is the chosen credibility level. In this way it is possible to calculate what may be called a credibility interval for the rank of each unit. These intervals may, in general, be quite wide.

b) Correlation with true ranking. The more the observed ranking correlates with the true ranking, the more reliable the ranking. Let $\mathbf{r}^{(t)}$ and $\mathbf{r}^{(o)}$ again denote the true and observed rankings and let $\rho(\mathbf{r}^{(t)}, \mathbf{r}^{(o)})$ be some measure of the correlation between the two rankings (for example Spearman's or Kendall's rank correlation coefficient), then

$$E(\rho(\mathbf{r}^{(t)}, \mathbf{r}^{(o)})) = \sum P(\mathbf{r}^{(o)} = \mathbf{r}^{(j)})\rho(\mathbf{r}^{(t)}, \mathbf{r}^{(j)}),$$

can be used as an index of the reliability of the ranking. If, as in real applications always is the case, the true ranking is unknown, we may measure the correlation with the observed ranking.

c) Mean expected deviation between observed and true rank. Using the marginal distributions we can for each unit calculate the expected value of the deviation between the observed rank and the true rank. Thus let $r_i^{(j)}$ denote the rank of unit i in ranking j and let $r_i^{(t)}$ be the corresponding true rank, then

$$\delta_i = E(|r_i^{(o)} - r_i^{(t)}|) = P(\mathbf{r}^{(o)} = \mathbf{r}^{(j)})|r_i^{(j)} - r_i^{(t)}|$$

is the expectation of the rank deviation. The mean value of the expected deviation over all units, i.e

$$\Delta = \sum \delta_j / n$$

measures the overall reliability of the ranking. This is the measure suggested in Andersson et al. (1998). Of course, to make the measure operational we must also in this case use the observed ranking as a proxy for the true ranking.

Example 4 (continued). From Table 1 it is easily seen that the 95% credibility intervals for the ranks are:

Unit 1: $(1,4)$, Unit 2: $(1,4)$, Unit 3: $(1,4)$, Unit 4: $(2,4)$.

Thus the reliability of rankings based on just one observation on the set of indicators is quite low. The expected value of Spearman's rank correlation is 0.63 and the mean value of the expectations of the rank deviations is 0.63.

These measures are not operational in practical work as we do not normally know the true values of the indicators and the true ranking. However, we can get estimates if it appears reasonable to approximate the distributions of the observed indicators by some known parametric distributions. Then we may, for instance, use the observed indicator values as proxies for their true values and try to make some kind of informed "guess-estimates" of their variances. In some cases, it may also be possible to use empirical Bayes methods to get more realistic estimates of the distributions of the indicators (see e.g. Andersson et al. 1998, for an example). Instead of trying to derive analytical solutions, it is also often more practical to base the calculations on simulations using some kind of bootstrap approach.

If we know the ranking of the units concerned but nothing else, it is impossible to say anything about the reliability of the ranking. However, if we know the rankings based on several independent observations of the observable indicators it may be possible, by making suitable assumptions about the distribution of the measurement errors, to get ML-estimates of the parameters of the distribution or some transformation of them. This is a problem that has been much discussed within the theory of so-called random utility models (see e.g. Train 2003). Then, given such estimates, we may again use simulation techniques to study the variability of the rankings.

4 Illustration

Neittaanmäki et al. (2005) examine the funding of the Finnish universities' graduate and post-graduate training and scientific research, and in particular the productivity of different disciplines and universities. One of the key indicators is the number of articles published in international peer-reviewed scientific journals in relation to the resources available, as measured by basic or total funding. As the authors point out, disciplines and universities differ with respect to their funding, training and publication profiles and traditions. To avoid problems associated with such heterogeneity, we will only discuss the reliability of the ranking of the faculties of social sciences in Finland. We will also restrict the analysis to just one component in the overall productivity index presented in the report, namely the share of scientific publications divided by the share of basic funding of research. Further, we will make the quite unrealistic but simplifying assumption that the costs are measured without errors and in a comparable way in all the units compared. In Table 2, we give the total number of publications, the mean number of professors and the share of total basic funding during the years 2000–2004 for all faculties of social sciences in Finland. We exclude the faculty of social sciences at the University of Lapland since, according to Neittaanmäki et al. (2005), the data for this quite small faculty are very unreliable.

Let us assume that the number of publications produced by a professor during a given time period can be thought of as a Poisson distributed stochastic variable whose parameter depends only on the faculty at which he/she works. Thus, if x_{ji} denotes the number of publications of professor j at faculty i we assume that

$$x_{ji} \sim \mathrm{Po}(x;\lambda_i) \qquad j = 1,2,\ldots,m_i, \quad i = 1,2,\ldots,n$$

where m_i denotes the (mean) number of professors at faculty i. The higher the value of λ_i the more "scientifically productive" is the faculty. In reality, there may be a lot of within faculty variation in the publication rates. However, in this illustration we will assume homogeneity within faculties.

A part or all of the papers published may have been written by researchers who are not professors. However, it is the professors' duty, apart from writing scientific articles, to provide other researchers with good work opportunities. A professor may achieve a good result either by writing a lot of papers by himself or by providing a good working milieu for others.

If we further assume that the professors work independently of each other, also the aggregated number of publications follow a Poisson distribution, i.e.

$$x_i = \sum_i x_{ji} \sim \mathrm{Po}(x; m_i\lambda_i).$$

When ranking faculties according to the effectiveness in writing papers, it seems more reasonable to use as a criterion not the number of actually

Table 2. Scientific productivity of the faculties of social sciences in Finland 2000–2004.

University	Publications[1]		Professors[2]		Share of costs[3]	Productivity index	Rank
	Number	% (a)	Number	%	% (b)	$100(a)/(b)$	
University of Helsinki	460	29.1	47.2	26.0	23.8	122	3
University of Joensuu	97	6.1	19.0	10.5	7.7	79	5
University of Jyväskylä	195	12.3	13.0	7.2	3.4	362	1
University of Kuopio	28	1.8	12.2	6.7	3.0	60	7
University of Tampere	380	24.0	48.4	26.7	35.9	67	6
University of Turku	244	15.4	19.0	10.5	15.7	98	4
University of Vaasa	17	1.1	6.4	3.5	2.4	46	8
Åbo Akademi University	160	10.1	16.2	8.9	8.1	125	2
Total	1581	100	181.4	100	100	100	

[1]Publications in international journal with referee procedure.
[2]Mean number of professors during 2000–2004.
[3]Funding from the Ministry of Education that has been allocated to research.
Source: Neittaanmäki et al. (2005), KOTA-database of Ministry of Education.

published papers but the expectation of the number of published papers. At least in Finland, where all the faculties are quite small, there may be a lot of uncontrollable stochastic factors affecting the number of really published papers, especially if the time period is short.

Thus, the true ranking is the ranking corresponding to the indicator values $\Theta_1, \Theta_2, \ldots, \Theta_n$, where

$$\Theta_i = \frac{m_i\lambda_i / \sum m_i\lambda_i}{c_i / \sum c_i},$$

and $c_1/\sum c_i, c_2/\sum c_i, \ldots, c_n/\sum c_i$ are the shares of basic funding. Given the funding shares and the number of professors, the reliability of the rankings depends on the variability of the observed number of publications. One way to study how much the ranking is affected by randomness is to generate observations from some approximations of the distributions of the x_j-values. The simplest option is to assume that the distribution of x_j can be approximated by the corresponding Poisson distribution with the parameter λ_i

estimated by

$$\hat{\lambda}_i = x_i/m_i, \qquad i = 1, 2, \ldots, n$$

as $E(\hat{\lambda}_i) = \lambda_i$. However, as the faculties vary a lot in size, one may also use more robust parametric empirical Bayes methods to approximate the distributions (see e.g. Carlin and Louis 1996). Following Gaver and O'Muircheartaigh (1987), let us assume that the variability in the publication rates can be described by interpreting them as independent realizations of a random variable λ with a given parametric density function $g(\ ;\Phi)$, where Φ is a vector of parameters. Mainly for mathematical simplicity, we will in this illustration assume that g can be approximated by a gamma distribution, which is the conjugate prior distribution associated with the Poisson distribution. Thus, we assume that the observed number of publications x_i at unit i has been generated by a two-stage process where

(i) $\lambda_i \sim G(\lambda; \alpha, \beta) = \dfrac{\alpha^\beta}{\Gamma(\beta)} \lambda^{(\beta-1)} e^{(-\alpha\lambda)}, \qquad \lambda > 0,$

(ii) $x_i \mid \lambda_i \sim \text{Po}(x; m_i\lambda_i) = \dfrac{(\lambda_i m_i)^x}{x!} e^{-\lambda_i m_i}, \qquad x = 0, 1, 2, \ldots$

As is well known, the posteriori distribution of λ_i, given x_i, is a gamma distribution with parameters $(\alpha + m_i, \beta + x_i)$ and the corresponding predictive distribution for x_j is a negative binomial distribution, i.e

$$x_i^{(\text{pred})} \mid \alpha, \beta, x_i, m_i \sim NB(x; \gamma_i, \delta_i) = \binom{\gamma_i + x - 1}{x} \delta_i^{\gamma_i} (1 - \delta_i)^x, \qquad x = 0, 1, 2, \ldots$$

where

$$\gamma_i = \beta + x_i \quad \text{and} \quad \delta_i = (\alpha + m_i)/(\alpha + 2m_i).$$

In order to use this distribution for simulations, we just need estimates of the parameters of the a priori distribution, i.e. of α and β. Following the suggestion in Gaver and O'Muircheartaigh (1987), we have used the crude moment-type estimators, even if more refined estimation methods exist.

From the assumption above, using the well known conditioning principle, it follows that

$$\begin{aligned} E(q_i) &= E(\lambda), \\ \text{Var}(q_i) &= E(\lambda)/m_i + \text{Var}(\lambda), \end{aligned}$$

where $q_i = x_i/m_i$, i.e. the publication rate per professor.

Further, as $\lambda \sim G(\alpha, \beta)$, which implies that $E(\lambda) = \beta/\alpha$ and $\text{Var}(\lambda) = \beta/\alpha^2$, we get the following moment estimators for α and β:

$$\hat{\alpha} = \frac{\bar{q}}{s_{\bar{q}}^2 - \bar{q}\frac{1}{n}\sum\frac{1}{m_i}}, \qquad \hat{\beta} = \frac{(\bar{q})^2}{s_{\bar{q}}^2 - \bar{q}\frac{1}{n}\sum\frac{1}{m_i}}$$

where $\bar{q}$ and a_q^2 denote the mean and variance of the observed publications rates. Taking the means in the posterior distributions as estimates of the publications rates, we get the following adjusted EB-estimates of the publication rates:

$$\hat{\lambda}_i = \frac{\hat{\beta} + x_i}{\hat{\alpha} + m_i}.$$

Further, for simulation purposes, we can approximate the distribution of the total number of publications of faculty i by a $NB(\hat{\beta} + x_i, (\hat{\alpha} + m_i)/(\hat{\alpha} + 2m_i))$-distribution. All the parameter estimates are given in Table 3.

Table 3. Publication rates and the parameters of the predictive distributions

University	Estimates of publications rates		Estimates of predictive distributions $[NB(\gamma_i, \delta_i)]$	
	Direct est.	EB-est.	$\hat{\gamma}_i$	$\hat{\delta}_i$
University of Helsinki	9.75	9.73	463.24	0.502
University of Joensuu	5.11	5.17	100.24	0.505
University of Jyväskylä	15.00	14.80	198.24	0.507
University of Kuopio	2.30	2.48	31.24	0.508
University of Tampere	7.85	7.85	383.24	0.502
University of Turku	12.84	12.75	247.24	0.505
University of Vaasa	2.66	2.98	20.24	0.515
Åbo Akademi University	9.88	9.84	163.24	0.506

To study the robustness of the ranking, we have generated 10 000 sets of numbers of publications for the faculties and for each set ranked the faculties according to the quotient of the share of publications and the share of costs. To avoid ties, we have added some random noise to the simulated numbers of publications. All simulations have been made with the gennbreg procedure in Stata v.8. Table 4 gives the simulated marginal distribution of the rank for each faculty, the corresponding credibility intervals and the mean of the deviations from the observed ranking. The ordering of the faculties is according to the observed ranking.

The mean of the mean rank deviations is 0.47. We note that there seem to be no doubt about the top rank of the University of Jyväskylä. For all other universities, there would in the light of this exercise be a lot of uncertainty about the correct rank. For instance, for the University of Turku all ranks between 2 and 6 seem quite possible. It is clear that this exercise is based on many, more or less unrealistic assumptions. The main purpose is also to just illustrate one way to analyse how reliable a given ranking might be. Note, however, that treating the ranking of universities as containing no uncertainty and no measurement error may be the most unrealistic assumption of all.

Table 4. The marginal distribution of the ranking, credibility intervals and mean rank deviation.

University	$P(r_i = j),\ j = 1, 2, \ldots, 8$								95% Credibility interval	Expected rank deviation
	1	2	3	4	5	6	7	8		
University of Jyväskylä	1.00	0.00	0.00	0.00	0.00	0.00	0.00	0.00	(1,1)	0.00
Åbo Akademi University	0.00	0.55	0.40	0.05	0.00	0.00	0.00	0.00	(2,4)	0.53
University of Helsinki	0.00	0.45	0.53	0.02	0.00	0.00	0.00	0.00	(2,3)	0.47
University of Turku	0.00	0.01	0.06	0.79	0.13	0.01	0.00	0.00	(3,5)	0.21
University of Joensuu	0.00	0.00	0.01	0.10	0.62	0.19	0.07	0.01	(4,7)	0.46
University of Tampere	0.00	0.00	0.00	0.00	0.09	0.53	0.34	0.04	(5,7)	0.51
University of Kuopio	0.00	0.00	0.00	0.01	0.03	0.06	0.19	0.71	(6,8)	0.79
University of Vaasa	0.00	0.00	0.00	0.00	0.02	0.06	0.16	0.76	(6,8)	0.8

5 Concluding remarks

The use of rankings to provide information about the quality, effectiveness etc. of units like for example universities, schools or hospitals seem to become more and more popular. What is more seldom discussed is the validity and reliability of this kind of information. It is of course very important that the performance indicators on which the rankings are based really measure the performance of the units concerned ("value added") and are not for example distorted by systematic differences in important characteristics of the "treatment units". In this paper we have, however, not discussed this so called cake-mix problem and the use of different adjustment techniques to solve it. Instead we have discussed some possibilities to analyze and measure the randomness in rankings caused by stochastic errors in the indicators on which the rankings are based. As always when presenting statistical estimates it would also in the case of rankings be important to provide some information about the reliability of the figures.

In order to be able to do this we need much more research about the properties of rankings distributions under varying assumptions about the distribution and other characteristics of the performance indicators. A formal framework for studying the overall robustness of rankings would be very useful. In lack of that, it is important to try to get decision makers and other consumers of rankings aware of the uncertainty of all rankings of this kind.

References

Andersson, J., Carling, K., and Mattson, S. (1998). Random ranking of hospitals is unsound. *Chance*, 11, 34-39.

Carlin, B. P. and Louis, T. A. (1996). *Bayes and Empirical Bayes Methods for Data Analysis*. London: Chapman & Hall.

Gaver, D. P. and O'Muircheartaigh, I. G. (1987). Robust empirical Bayes analyses of event rates. *Technometrics*, 29, 1-15.

Goldstein, H. and Spiegelhalter, D. J. (1996). Leeague tables and their limitations: Statistical issues in comparison of institutional performance (with discussion). *Journal of the Royal Statistical Society, Ser.A*, 159, 385-443.

Neittaanmäki, P., Neittaanmäki, R., and Tiihonen, T. (2005). Yliopistojen tutkintokoulutuksen ja tutkimuksen rahoitus ja tulokset vuosina 2000-2004. *Tutkimusselosteita 26.* Koulutuksen tutkimuslaitos, University of Jyväskylä.

Train, K. E. (2003). *Discrete Choice Methods with Simulation.* Cambridge: Cambridge University Press.

LEIF NORDBERG
Åbo Akademi University
Department of Economics and Statistics
FI-20500 Turku, Finland
leif.nordberg@abo.fi

Festschrift for Tarmo Pukkila on his 60th Birthday
Eds. E. P. Liski, J. Isotalo, J. Niemelä, S. Puntanen, and G. P. H. Styan

Univ. of Tampere, 2006, ISBN 978-951-44-6620-5, pages 217–231

On the efficiency of invariant multivariate sign and rank tests

KLAUS NORDHAUSEN HANNU OJA DAVID E. TYLER

Abstract. Invariant coordinate selection (ICS) is proposed in Oja and Tyler (2006) for constructing invariant multivariate sign and rank tests. The multivariate data vectors are first transformed to invariant coordinates, and univariate sign and rank tests are then applied to the components of the transformed vectors. In this paper, the powers of different versions of the one sample and two samples location tests are compared via simulation studies.

2000 MSC codes: 62H12, 62G10, 62G05.

Key words and phrases: Hodges Lehmann estimate; Kurtosis; M-estimate; Multivariate median; Transformation and retransformation technique; Wilcoxon test.

1 Introduction

The classical L_1 type univariate sign and rank methods, estimates and tests, have been extended quite recently to the multivariate case. Multivariate extensions of the concepts of sign and rank based on (i) the vector of marginal medians, (ii) the so called spatial median or vector median, and (iii) the affine equivariant Oja median (Oja 1983) have been developed in a series of papers with natural analogues of one-sample, two-sample and multisample sign and rank tests. See e.g. Puri and Sen (1971), Möttönen and Oja (1995), Oja (1999), and Oja and Randles (2004) and references therein. These multivariate location estimates and tests are robust and nonparametric competitors of the classical MANOVA inference methods.

Unfortunately, the tests based on marginal signs and ranks and those based on spatial signs and ranks are not invariant under affine transformations of the observation vectors. Chakraborty and Chaudhuri (1996, 1998) and Chakraborty et al. (1998) introduced and discussed the so called transformation and retransformation technique to circumvent the problem: The data vectors are first linearly transformed back to a new, invariant coordinate system, the tests and estimates are constructed for these new vectors of variables, and, finally, the estimates are linearly retransformed to the original coordinate system. In the one sample and several samples p-variate location problems, the transformation matrix was then based on p and $p+1$ original observation vectors, respectively.

Other nonparametric approaches for multivariate data analysis include the depth-based rank sum tests introduced by Liu and Singh (1993). The so called zonotopes and lift-zonotopes have been used to describe and investigate the properties of a multivariate distribution, see Mosler (2002). Randles (1989) developed an affine invariant sign test based on *interdirections*, and was followed by a series of papers introducing nonparametric sign and rank interdirection tests for multivariate one-sample and two-sample location problems. These tests are typically asymptotically equivalent with spatial sign and rank tests. Finally, in a series of papers, Hallin and Paindaveine constructed *optimal signed-rank tests* for the location and scatter problems in the elliptical model; see the seminal papers by Hallin and Paindaveine (2002, 2006).

In this paper, as proposed by Oja and Tyler (2006), two different scatter matrices are used to construct an invariant coordinate system. It is remarkable that, in the new coordinate system, the marginal variables are ordered according to their kurtosis. The multivariate variables are first transformed to invariant coordinates, and the univariate sign and rank tests are then applied to these transformed variables. Unlike most other invariant multivariate sign and rank methods, the resulting tests are distribution-free not only at elliptically symmetric models but rather at any symmetric model. The powers of different versions of the one sample and two samples location tests are compared via simulation studies.

Hence the structure of the paper is as follows. In Section 2 we introduce the basic notations and tools that are necessary to construct an invariant coordinate system and show its relationship with the kurtosis of the components. In Section 3 we point out different strategies to use univariate tests on the transformed data components to test the location problem in the one and two sample case. Section 4 gives results of a simulation study which compares the performance of the different strategies. The paper ends with a brief discussion in Section 5. For a complete discussion of this approach, see Oja and Tyler (2006).

2 Invariant coordinate selection (ICS)

2.1 Notations

Let $\boldsymbol{y}_1, \boldsymbol{y}_2, \ldots, \boldsymbol{y}_n$ be independent p-variate observations and write

$$\boldsymbol{Y} = (\boldsymbol{y}_1\ \boldsymbol{y}_2\ \ldots\ \boldsymbol{y}_n)$$

for the corresponding $p \times n$ *data matrix* in the one sample case. In the several samples case, write

$$\boldsymbol{Y} = (\boldsymbol{Y}_1\ \ldots\ \boldsymbol{Y}_c)$$

where $Y_1, \ldots, Y_c$ are independent random samples with sample sizes $n_1, \ldots, n_c$, $n = n_1 + \cdots + n_c$, from p-variate distributions. In this paper we consider the one sample and two samples multivariate location problems only.

It is often desirable to have statistical methods which are invariant or equivariant under *affine transformations* of the data matrix, i.e. under transformations of the form

$$\boldsymbol{y}_i \to \boldsymbol{A}\boldsymbol{y}_i + \boldsymbol{b}, \qquad i = 1, \ldots, n,$$

or equivalently

$$\boldsymbol{Y} \to \boldsymbol{A}\boldsymbol{Y} + \boldsymbol{b}\boldsymbol{1}',$$

where $\boldsymbol{A}$ is a full-rank $p \times p$ matrix and $\boldsymbol{b}$ is a p-vector. The vector $\boldsymbol{1}$ is a n-vector full of ones. Some interesting transformations are *orthogonal transformations* ($\boldsymbol{Y} \to \boldsymbol{U}\boldsymbol{Y}$ with $\boldsymbol{U}'\boldsymbol{U} = \boldsymbol{U}\boldsymbol{U}' = \boldsymbol{I}$), *sign-change transformations* ($\boldsymbol{Y} \to \boldsymbol{J}\boldsymbol{Y}$ where $\boldsymbol{J}$ is a $p \times p$ diagonal matrix with diagonal elements ± 1), and *permutations* ($\boldsymbol{Y} \to \boldsymbol{P}\boldsymbol{Y}$ where $\boldsymbol{P}$ is a $p \times p$ permutation matrix obtained by successively permuting the rows and/or columns of $\boldsymbol{I}$). Note that transformation $\boldsymbol{Y} \to \boldsymbol{Y}\boldsymbol{P}$ with a $n \times n$ permutation matrix $\boldsymbol{P}$ permutes the observations.

2.2 Location vector and scatter matrices

We start by defining what we mean by a *location statistic*, a *scatter statistic*, and a *scatter statistic with respect to the origin*:

Definition. (i) A p-vector valued statistic $\boldsymbol{T} = \boldsymbol{T}(\boldsymbol{Y})$ is called a *location statistic* if it is affine equivariant, that is,

$$\boldsymbol{T}(\boldsymbol{A}\boldsymbol{Y} + \boldsymbol{b}\boldsymbol{1}') = \boldsymbol{A}\boldsymbol{T}(\boldsymbol{Y}) + \boldsymbol{b}$$

for all full-rank $p \times p$-matrices $\boldsymbol{A}$ and for all p-vectors $\boldsymbol{b}$.

(ii) Second, $p \times p$ matrix $\boldsymbol{S} = \boldsymbol{S}(\boldsymbol{Y}) \geq 0$ is a *scatter statistic* if it is affine equivariant in the sense that

$$\boldsymbol{S}(\boldsymbol{A}\boldsymbol{Y} + \boldsymbol{b}\boldsymbol{1}') = \boldsymbol{A}\boldsymbol{S}(\boldsymbol{Y})\boldsymbol{A}'$$

for all full-rank $p \times p$-matrices $\boldsymbol{A}$ and for all p-vectors $\boldsymbol{b}$.

(iii) Third, a *scatter statistic with respect to the origin* is affine equivariant in the sense that

$$\boldsymbol{S}(\boldsymbol{A}\boldsymbol{Y}\boldsymbol{J}) = \boldsymbol{A}\boldsymbol{S}(\boldsymbol{Y})\boldsymbol{A}'$$

for all full-rank $p \times p$-matrices $\boldsymbol{A}$ and for all $n \times n$ sign change matrices $\boldsymbol{J}$.

If $\boldsymbol{Y}$ is a random sample, it is also natural to require that the statistics are invariant under permutations of the observations, that is,

$$\boldsymbol{T}(\boldsymbol{Y}\boldsymbol{P}) = \boldsymbol{T}(\boldsymbol{Y}) \quad \text{and} \quad \boldsymbol{S}(\boldsymbol{Y}\boldsymbol{P}) = \boldsymbol{S}(\boldsymbol{Y})$$

for all $n \times n$ permutation matrices $\boldsymbol{P}$.

In the semiparametric elliptic model, for example, the location statistic estimates the unknown center of symmetry $\boldsymbol{\mu}$ and the scatter statistic $\boldsymbol{S}(\boldsymbol{Y})$, possibly multiplied by a correction factor, is an estimate of the regular covariance matrix $\boldsymbol{\Sigma}$ if it exists. Different scatter statistics $\boldsymbol{S}_1, \boldsymbol{S}_2, \ldots$ then estimate the same population quantity but have different statistical properties (consistency, efficiency, robustness, computational convenience). In practice, one would choose the one that is most suitable for the problem at hand.

Different location and scatter statistics may also be used to construct skewness and kurtosis statistics; e.g. as in Kankainen et al. (2006),

$$\|\boldsymbol{T}_1 - \boldsymbol{T}_2\|_{\boldsymbol{S}}^2 \quad \text{and} \quad \|\boldsymbol{S}_1^{-1}\boldsymbol{S}_2 - \boldsymbol{I}\|^2$$

that is, the squared Mahalanobis distance between location statistics $\boldsymbol{T}_1$ and $\boldsymbol{T}_2$ and the squared matrix norm (Frobenius norm) of $\boldsymbol{S}_1^{-1}\boldsymbol{S}_2 - \boldsymbol{I}$ where $\boldsymbol{S}_1$ and $\boldsymbol{S}_2$ (again equipped with correction factors) are different consistent estimates of the regular covariance matrix at the normal model. In this paper we will use two different scatter statistics to transform the data to invariant coordinates. See Section 2.4.

2.3 M-estimates of location and scatter

One of the earliest robust estimates developed for multivariate data are the M-estimates of multivariate location and scatter (Maronna 1976). The pseudo maximum likelihood (ML) estimates, including the regular mean vector and covariance matrix among others, are members of this class. Many other classes of estimates, like the S-estimates, CM-estimates and MM-estimates may be seen as special cases of M-estimates with auxiliary scale (Tyler 2002). M-estimates of location and scatter (one version), $\boldsymbol{T} = \boldsymbol{T}(\boldsymbol{Y})$ and $\boldsymbol{S} = \boldsymbol{S}(\boldsymbol{Y})$, satisfy implicit equations

$$\boldsymbol{T} = [\text{ave}[w_1(r_i)]]^{-1}\,\text{ave}[w_1(r_i)\boldsymbol{y}_i]$$

and

$$\boldsymbol{S} = \text{ave}[w_2(r_i)(\boldsymbol{y}_i - \boldsymbol{T})(\boldsymbol{y}_i - \boldsymbol{T})']$$

for some suitably chosen weight functions $w_1(r)$ and $w_2(r)$. The scalar r_i is the Mahalanobis distance between $\boldsymbol{y}_i$ and $\boldsymbol{T} = \boldsymbol{T}(\boldsymbol{Y})$, that is, $r_i = \|\boldsymbol{y}_i - \boldsymbol{T}\|_{\boldsymbol{S}}$. Mean vector and covariance matrix are given by the choices $w_1(r) = w_2(r) = 1$.

If $\boldsymbol{T}_1 = \boldsymbol{T}_1(\boldsymbol{Y})$ and $\boldsymbol{S}_1 = \boldsymbol{S}_1(\boldsymbol{Y})$ are any affine equivariant location and scatter functionals then one-step M-functionals $\boldsymbol{T}_2 = \boldsymbol{T}_2(\boldsymbol{Y})$ and $\boldsymbol{S}_2 = \boldsymbol{S}_2(\boldsymbol{Y})$, starting from $\boldsymbol{T}_1$ and $\boldsymbol{S}_1$, are given by

$$\boldsymbol{T}_2 = [\text{ave}[w_1(r_i)]]^{-1}\,\text{ave}[w_1(r_i)\boldsymbol{y}_i]$$

and

$$S_2 = \text{ave}[w_2(r_i)(y_i - T_1)(y_i - T_1)']$$

where now $r_i = \|y_i - T_1\|_{S_1}$. It is easy to see that T_2 and S_2 are affine equivariant as well. Repeating this step until it converges yields a solution to the M-estimating equations with weight functions w_1 and w_2. If T_1 is the mean vector and S_1 is the covariance matrix, then

$$T_2 = \frac{1}{p}\text{ave}[r_i^2 y_i] \quad \text{and} \quad S_2 = \frac{1}{p+2}\text{ave}[r_i^2(y_i - \bar{y})(y_i - \bar{y})']$$

are one-step or reweighted M-estimates of location and scatter. Note that the scatter statistic $S_2 = S_2(Y)$ is a *scatter matrix estimate based on fourth moments.* It is consistent for the regular covariance matrix at the multinormal model.

2.4 Invariant coordinate selection

Scatter matrices are often used to standardize the data:

$$Y \to Z = [S(Y)]^{-1/2}Y.$$

Transformation matrix $[S(Y)]^{-1/2}$ thus yields the new coordinate system with uncorrelated components (in the sense of S). Unfortunately, this new coordinate system is not invariant under affine transformations; it is only true that

$$[S(AY)]^{-1/2}(AY) = U[S(Y)]^{-1/2}Y$$

with an orthogonal matrix U depending on Y, A and S.

Two different scatter functionals $S_1 = S_1(Y)$ and $S_2 = S_2(Y)$ may be used to find an invariant coordinate system as follows. For a more detailed discussion of the *invariant coordinate selection (ICS)*, see Oja and Tyler (2006). Starting with S_1 and S_2, define a $p \times p$ transformation matrix $B = B(Y)$ and a diagonal matrix $D = D(Y)$ by

$$S_2^{-1}S_1B' = B'D$$

that is, B gives the eigenvectors of $S_2^{-1}S_1$. The following result can then be shown to hold.

Result 1. The transformation $Y \to Z = B(Y)Y$ yields an *invariant coordinate system* in the sense that

$$B(AY)(AY) = JB(Y)Y$$

for some $p \times p$ sign change matrix J. Matrix B can be made unique by requiring that the element with largest absolute value in each row of B is positive.

2.5 Kurtosis and ICS

Let $\boldsymbol{B} = \boldsymbol{B}(\boldsymbol{Y})$ be the transformation matrix yielded by $\boldsymbol{S}_1$ and $\boldsymbol{S}_2$. Observe that the elements of $\boldsymbol{Z} = \boldsymbol{B}(\boldsymbol{Y})\boldsymbol{Y}$ are now standardized with respect to $\boldsymbol{S}_1$ and uncorrelated with respect to $\boldsymbol{S}_2$, that is,

$$\boldsymbol{S}_1(\boldsymbol{Z}) = \boldsymbol{I} \quad \text{and} \quad \boldsymbol{S}_2(\boldsymbol{Z}) = \boldsymbol{D}$$

where $\boldsymbol{D}$ is a diagonal matrix. The diagonal elements of $\boldsymbol{D}$ yield the kurtosis measures for the components. Therefore the components of $\boldsymbol{Z}$ are *ordered with respect to kurtosis.* Recall the discussion on kurtosis in Section 2.3.

In the simulations in this paper we use the invariant coordinate selection based on the regular covariance matrix $\boldsymbol{S}_1$ and the scatter matrix $\boldsymbol{S}_2$ based on the fourth moments. The jth diagonal element of matrix $\boldsymbol{D}$ is then

$$D_{jj} = \frac{1}{p+2}\,\text{ave}_i\{z_{ij}^2(z_{i1}^2 + \cdots + z_{ip}^2)\}, \qquad j = 1, \ldots, p.$$

Consider the case having some special interest in our simulations: Assume that $\boldsymbol{Y} = \{\boldsymbol{y}_1 \ \ldots \ \boldsymbol{y}_n\}$ is a random sample from a distribution which is a mixture of two multivariate normal distribution differing only in location: $\boldsymbol{y}_i$ has a $N_p(\boldsymbol{0}, \boldsymbol{I})$-distribution with probability $1 - \varepsilon$ and a $N_p(\Delta \boldsymbol{e}_p, \boldsymbol{I})$-distribution with probability ε ($\varepsilon \le 0.5$). (The last element in vector $\boldsymbol{e}_p$ is one, other elements are zero.) Then $\boldsymbol{S}_1(\boldsymbol{Y}) \to_P \boldsymbol{I}$ and $\boldsymbol{S}_2(\boldsymbol{Y}) \to_P \boldsymbol{D}$ where $\boldsymbol{D}$ is a diagonal matrix with $D_{11} = \cdots = D_{p-1,p-1} = 1$. The last diagonal element is $1 + b_2/(p+2)$ where b_2 is the *classical univariate kurtosis* measure for the last component. Note that the last component has the highest kurtosis for $\varepsilon < (3 + \sqrt{3})^{-1}$ and lowest kurtosis otherwise (compare Preston 1953). Also the amount of kurtosis strongly depends on the value of Δ; the greater Δ the larger is the absolute value of kurtosis. This behavior is visualized in Figures 1 and 2.

3 Invariant sign and rank tests

3.1 Marginal signs and ranks

Let $\boldsymbol{z}_i$, $i = 1, \ldots, n$, be the p-variate residuals in the multivariate location case, and consider the L_1 type criterion functions

$$\text{ave}_i\{|z_{i1}| + \cdots + |z_{ip}|\} \quad \text{and} \quad \text{ave}_{i,j}\{|z_{i1} - z_{j1}| + \cdots + |z_{ip} - z_{jp}|\}.$$

The resulting L_1 estimates are the vectors of marginal medians and marginal Hodges-Lehmann estimates. The corresponding score tests are based on the vectors of marginal (univariate) signs or marginal (univariate) ranks. See Puri and Sen (1971) for a complete discussion of this approach. The inference methods are invariant/equivariant under componentwise rescaling

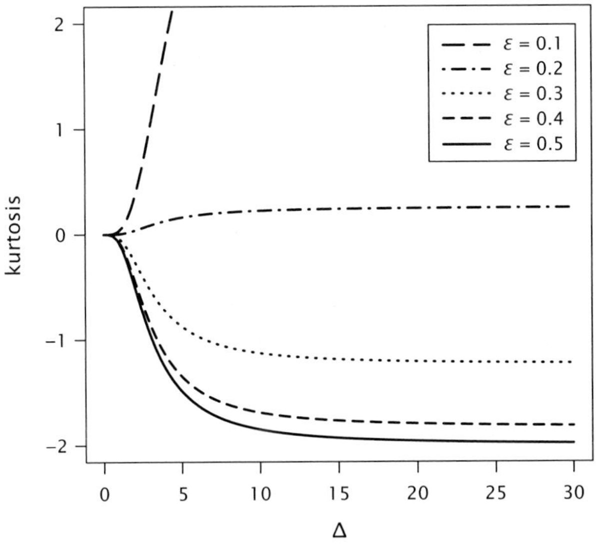

Figure 1. Kurtosis for a location mixture of normal distributions as a function of Δ for different ε.

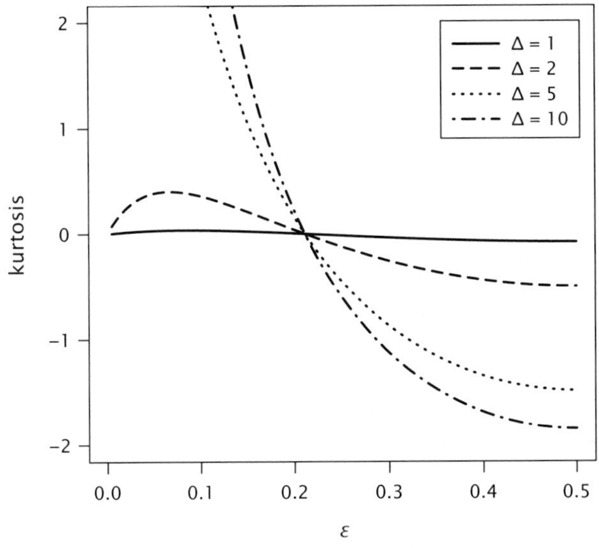

Figure 2. Kurtosis for a location mixture of normal distributions as a function of ε for different Δ.

but not orthogonally invariant/equivariant. The efficiencies do not exceed the univariate efficiencies and are quite low if the margins are highly correlated.

Invariant test versions can be obtained by first transforming the data to invariant coordinates. The use of the standardized data set $[\boldsymbol{S}(\boldsymbol{Y})]^{-1/2}\boldsymbol{Y}$ does not help as the standardization is not affine invariant. See Section 2.4. Chakraborty and Chaudhuri (1996, 1998) avoided the problem by using p observations with indices listed in $\alpha = (i_1, \dots, i_p)$, $1 \le i_1 < \cdots < i_p \le n$, to construct, in the one-sample location case, a transformation matrix $\boldsymbol{B}(\alpha) = (\boldsymbol{y}_{i_1}\ \boldsymbol{y}_{i_2}\ \dots\ \boldsymbol{y}_{i_p})^{-1}$. Now clearly $\boldsymbol{B}(\alpha)\boldsymbol{Y}$ is invariant under affine transformations $\boldsymbol{Y} \to \boldsymbol{A}\boldsymbol{Y}$ and the data set $\boldsymbol{B}(\alpha)\boldsymbol{Y}$ may then be used for invariant one-sample test construction. In the several sample case, they choose $\alpha = (i_1, \dots, i_{p+1})$, $1 \le i_1 < \cdots < i_{p+1} \le n$ and $\boldsymbol{B}(\alpha) = (\boldsymbol{y}_{i_1} - \boldsymbol{y}_{i_{p+1}}\ \boldsymbol{y}_{i_2} - \boldsymbol{y}_{i_{p+1}}\ \cdots\ \boldsymbol{y}_{i_p} - \boldsymbol{y}_{i_{p+1}})^{-1}$. This technique is then called the *transformation and re-transformation* (*TR*) *technique*. The problem naturally is how to choose α, that is, the coordinate system in an optimal adaptive way. Techniques proposed for choosing α tend to be computationally intensive since they require optimizing some criterion over all possible subsets of size $p + 1$ from the sample. In the following we use the computationally simple invariant coordinate selection method based on two scatter matrices $\boldsymbol{S}_1$ and $\boldsymbol{S}_2$.

3.2 One sample case

Let $\boldsymbol{Y} = (\boldsymbol{y}_1\ \dots\ \boldsymbol{y}_n)$ be a random sample from a p-variate continuous distribution symmetric around unknown $\boldsymbol{\mu}$. We wish to test the null hypothesis H_0: $\boldsymbol{\mu} = \boldsymbol{0}$ and estimate the unknown $\boldsymbol{\mu}$. For the test, let $\boldsymbol{S}_1$ and $\boldsymbol{S}_2$ be two scatter matrices with respect to the origin. Assume also that they are invariant under permutations to the observations. Then, for $k = 1, 2$,

$$\boldsymbol{S}_k(\boldsymbol{AYPJ}) = \boldsymbol{A}\boldsymbol{S}_k(\boldsymbol{Y})\boldsymbol{A}', \qquad \forall\, \boldsymbol{A}, \boldsymbol{P}, \boldsymbol{J},$$

and therefore

$$\boldsymbol{B}(\boldsymbol{YJP}) = \boldsymbol{B}(\boldsymbol{Y})$$

As, under the null hypothesis, $\boldsymbol{Y}$ is a random sample from distribution symmetric around the origin, it is also true that

$$\boldsymbol{Z}(\boldsymbol{Y}) \sim \boldsymbol{Z}(\boldsymbol{Y})\boldsymbol{JP}, \qquad \forall\, \boldsymbol{J}, \boldsymbol{P}.$$

Clearly $\boldsymbol{Z} = (\boldsymbol{z}_1\ \dots\ \boldsymbol{z}_n)$ is not a random sample any more. However, under the null hypothesis, the variables in $(\boldsymbol{z}_1, \dots, \boldsymbol{z}_n)$ are exchangeable.

Consider next the jth component of the $\boldsymbol{z}_i$ vectors, that is, the observations $(z_{j1}, \dots, z_{jn})$. Then, it is easy to see that

Result 2. Under the null hypothesis, the univariate *sign test statistic*

$$U_j = \sum_{i=1}^{n} I(z_{ji} > 0) \sim \mathrm{Bin}(n, 0.5).$$

Thus, for all $j = 1, \ldots, p$, U_j is an invariant distribution-free multivariate sign test statistic. Unfortunately, the p sign test statistics $U_1, \ldots, U_p$ are not mutually independent.

Let next R^+_{ji} be the rank of $|z_{ji}|$ among $|z_{j1}|, \ldots, |z_{jn}|$. The univariate *Wilcoxon signed-rank test statistic*

$$W_j = \sum_{i=1}^{n} \text{sgn}(z_{ji}) R^+_{ji}$$

is then distribution-free as well:

Result 3. Under the null hypothesis, the distribution of W_j is that of the one-sample Wilcoxon signed-rank test statistic.

The result easily follows from the facts that $\text{sgn}(z_{j1}), \ldots, \text{sgn}(z_{jn})$ are iid and independent of $(|z_{j1}|, \ldots, |z_{jn}|)$. Also, $|z_{j1}|, \ldots, |z_{jn}|$ are exchangeable.

All the test statistics $U_1, \ldots, U_p$ and $W_1, \ldots, W_p$ are thus distribution-free but dependent (the dependence structure depends on the background distribution). How then to choose U_j or W_j, or how to combine these statistics for the testing problem? One goal of the present paper then is to provide some insight into this rather complex question. As the components are ordered according to their kurtosis, and one expects to see a high absolute value of kurtosis in the direction of $\boldsymbol{\mu}$, often the last (or first) component is most powerful and contains the most information. This fact can be utilised when constructing the "overall" test statistic where one can choose between different strategies. For example one could use only the first or only the last component or those two components combined. One could also use a rule like use the $k \leq p$ components with the highest absolute value of kurtosis or one could simply use all components.

The corresponding *affine equivariant location estimates* are obtained as follows: Let $\boldsymbol{T}$ be the vector of marginal medians or the vector of marginal Hodges-Lehmann estimators. These estimates are not location statistics as they are not affine equivariant. Let $\boldsymbol{B} = \boldsymbol{B}(\boldsymbol{Y})$ be the transformation based on two scatter matrix estimates. Then multivariate affine equivariant *transformation-retransformation median* and *Hodges-Lehmann estimate* are obtained as

$$\tilde{\boldsymbol{T}}(\boldsymbol{Y}) = \boldsymbol{B}^{-1}\boldsymbol{T}(\boldsymbol{B}\boldsymbol{Y})$$

3.3 Two samples case

Let $\boldsymbol{Y} = (\boldsymbol{Y}_1\ \boldsymbol{Y}_2)$ where $\boldsymbol{Y}_1$ and $\boldsymbol{Y}_2$ are independent random samples of sizes n_1 and n_2, $n = n_1 + n_2$, from p-variate continuous distributions with cumulative density functions $F(\boldsymbol{y})$ and $F(\boldsymbol{y} - \boldsymbol{\mu})$, respectively. We wish to test the null hypothesis H_0: $\boldsymbol{\mu} = \boldsymbol{0}$ and estimate the unknown location shift $\boldsymbol{\mu}$. Let $\boldsymbol{S}_1 = \boldsymbol{S}_1(\boldsymbol{Y})$ and $\boldsymbol{S}_2 = \boldsymbol{S}_2(\boldsymbol{Y})$ be two scatter matrices *calculated from the combined data set and invariant under permutations to the observations.* This is to say that, for $k = 1, 2$,

$$S_k((AY + b1')P) = AS_k(Y)A', \qquad \forall\, A, b, P,$$

and $B(YP) = B(Y)$. Under the null hypothesis, the combined sample $Y = (Y_1 Y_2)$ is a random sample of size n, and

$$Z(Y) \sim Z(Y)P, \qquad \forall\, P.$$

Again, $Z = (z_1 \ \dots \ z_n)$ is not a random sample but, under the null hypothesis, the variables in $(z_1, \dots, z_n)$ are exchangeable.

Affine invariant distribution-free multivariate rank tests may be constructed as follows. Let now R_{ji} be the rank of z_{ji} among $z_{j1}, \dots, z_{jn}$. As $z_1, \dots, z_n$ are exchangeable,

Result 4. Under the null hypothesis the distribution of the univariate *Wilcoxon rank test statistic*

$$W_j = \sum_{i=n_1+1}^{n} R_{ji}$$

is that of regular two samples Wilcoxon test statistic with sample sizes n_1 and n_2.

General rank score test statistics $\sum_{i=n_1+1}^{n} a(R_{ji})$ may be constructed as well. The *two samples sign test statistic* (*Mood's test statistic*) is given by the choice $a(i) = 1(0)$ for $i > (\leq)(n + 1)/2$. All the test statistics $W_1, \dots, W_p$ are thus distribution-free but unfortunately dependent (the dependence structure depends on the background distribution). The question of which of those test statistics to use for the decision making allows the same strategies as in the one sample case.

Corresponding *affine equivariant multivariate shift estimates* are obtained as follows: Let T be the vector of marginal difference of the medians (Mood's test) or the vector of marginal two-sample Hodges-Lehmann shift estimators (Wilcoxon test). These estimates are not affine equivariant. Let $B = B(Y)$ be the transformation based on two scatter matrix estimates. Then multivariate affine equivariant *transformation retransformation* estimates are again obtained as

$$\tilde{T}(Y) = B^{-1}T(BY)$$

4 Simulation results

As mentioned in Section 3.2 and 3.3, several strategies are available for the decision making. We performed a simulation study to compare the following strategies in the one and two sample case:

(i) Using a componentwise sign test and signed rank test as described in Puri and Sen (1971) based on all p components, denoted as $U[1:p]$, respectively as $W[1:p]$.

(ii) Using the same componentwise sign test and signed rank test as before but only to combine the first and last component, denoted as $U[1,p]$, respectively as $W[1,p]$.

(iii) Using an exact sign test respectively a Wilcoxon signed rank test for the last component only, denoted as $U[p]$, respectively as $W[p]$.

for different sample sizes and underlying distributions. As a reference test also Hotelling's T^2 for the original observations is included. We note that both the exact and asymptotic distributions for case (i) and (ii) are still open questions. To approximate their distributions we suggest using distributions analogous to the asymptotic distributions given by Puri and Sen (1971), and conjecture that these approximate distributions are asymptotically correct. A size simulation (not shown here) supports this conjecture.

All simulations are based on 5000 repetitions and were performed using R 2.2.0 (R Development Core Team 2005) at the level $\alpha = 0.05$. The critical values for the tests were based on the limiting null distributions.

Not shown in the following subsections are results for the strategy which uses only the component with the largest absolute value of the kurtosis since this strategy had in all settings in the one sample case always less power than strategy (iii) and in the two sample case it was less powerful or about equal when compared to strategy (iii).

4.1 One sample case

In this simulation we obtained the ICS with respect to the origin as described in Section 2.5 for data coming from a normal distribution and t_3 and t_{10} distributions for different dimensions and sample sizes.

A size simulation (not shown here) yielded for all tests the designated level except for $U[p]$ which was always smaller than 0.05 due to the discreteness of the test statistic and for Hotelling's T^2 for heavy tailed distributions and small sample sizes.

To compare the power of the different strategies the location parameter of the distributions were set to $\boldsymbol{\mu}_0 = (\Delta, 0, \dots, 0)'$ and Δ in such a way chosen, that given the dimension p and the sample size n the power of Hotelling's T^2 is 0.5 under normality. This means

$$P[F(p, n-p, \delta) > F_\alpha(p, n-p)] = 0.5$$

where $F(p, n-p, \delta)$ is a random variable having a noncentral F distribution with degrees of freedom p and $n-p$ and noncentrality parameter $\delta = \frac{1}{n}\Delta^2$ and $F_\alpha(p, n-p)$ is the $1-\alpha$ quantile of $F(p, n-p) = F(p, n-p, 0)$. This gives in our case a range for Δ from 0.159 to 0.471.

The simulation results provided in Table 1 show that there is a lot of information in the last component, however the power of the strategies increases with the number of components they are based on and strategy (iii) can therefore not compete with strategy (i). Especially the signed rank test $W[1\!:\!p]$ can be seen as a serious competitor to Hotelling's T^2 since it is almost as efficient as Hotelling's T^2 under normality and more efficient for heavier tails.

Table 1. Simulated power in the one sample case in number of rejections per 1000 cases.

				sign tests			signed rank tests		
Dist.	p	n	T^2	$U[1\!:\!p]$	$U[1,p]$	$U[p]$	$W[1\!:\!p]$	$W[1,p]$	$W[p]$
normal	2	50	499	340	340	208	472	472	323
		200	502	333	333	220	479	479	327
	5	50	500	281	180	122	441	257	203
		200	508	319	197	137	472	283	213
	10	50	507	204	124	89	385	168	159
		200	503	288	140	104	458	195	152
t_{10}	2	50	415	317	317	194	417	417	309
		200	413	324	324	213	429	429	298
	5	50	405	256	180	138	387	235	211
		200	414	301	195	139	419	255	193
	10	50	427	191	124	92	334	166	158
		200	409	283	138	101	417	185	147
t_3	2	50	261	286	286	180	334	334	257
		200	221	281	281	193	334	334	249
	5	50	244	237	169	117	299	200	182
		200	215	267	177	129	315	205	168
	10	50	270	173	130	95	267	155	149
		200	213	246	131	105	313	153	135

4.2 Two samples case

The setup for the two sample simulations are of a similar fashion as in the one sample case. The size simulation (also not shown here) gave similar results as in the one sample case, namely that the size of $U[p]$ was always smaller than 0.05 and also Hotelling's T^2 was smaller for heavier tails when the sample size was small.

The difference of the population locations $\boldsymbol{\mu}_0 = (\Delta, 0\ldots, 0)'$ was set also in such a way that under normality Hotelling's T^2 would achieve a power of

0.5. The corresponding value of Δ can then be computed via

$$P[F(p, n-p-1, \delta) > F_\alpha(p, n-p-1)] = 0.5$$

where the noncentrality parameter δ is given as $\delta = \frac{n_1 n_2}{n_1+n_2}\Delta^2$. This gives a range for Δ from 0.223 to 0.637.

Table 2 shows the results for the two sample power simulations where in two settings the two populations are of equal size and in one setting the mixture probability is $\varepsilon = 0.2$ (compare Section 2.5).

The same conclusions as for the one sample case apply basically also for the two sample case except one surprising occurrance for the rank test $W[1:p]$ where the power drops considerably when the dimension and the sample sizes of both populations are large.

Table 2. Simulated power in the two sample case in number of rejections per 1000 cases.

					sign tests			signed rank tests		
Dist.	p	n_1	n_2	T^2	$U[1:p]$	$U[1,p]$	$U[p]$	$W[1:p]$	$W[1,p]$	$W[p]$
normal	2	50	50	504	321	321	177	482	482	321
		200	50	494	326	326	205	477	477	332
		200	200	494	329	329	203	477	477	317
	5	50	50	504	307	201	117	475	278	210
		200	50	491	309	191	137	464	267	199
		200	200	507	316	203	130	482	292	211
	10	50	50	499	259	136	86	449	192	159
		200	50	484	282	144	99	443	198	154
		200	200	501	212	145	92	310	199	153
t_{10}	2	50	50	404	304	304	170	423	423	297
		200	50	405	310	310	214	418	418	307
		200	200	409	306	306	195	421	421	294
	5	50	50	402	277	182	114	409	252	207
		200	50	400	290	195	135	422	256	201
		200	200	393	290	191	121	405	255	194
	10	50	50	422	251	130	89	416	186	167
		200	50	414	293	142	97	421	179	146
		200	200	410	189	132	86	280	176	138
t_3	2	50	50	233	277	277	160	334	334	244
		200	50	219	278	278	179	330	330	239
		200	200	214	285	285	179	336	336	246
	5	50	50	233	249	177	102	320	221	175
		200	50	213	254	181	122	321	211	164
		200	200	194	268	174	110	318	210	152
	10	50	50	230	204	123	72	296	145	132
		200	50	209	241	136	99	306	152	126
		200	200	197	183	135	84	211	149	119

5 Final comments

This simulation study serves as an introduction to the use of two different scatter matrices to obtain an ICS where invariant sign and rank tests can be constructed. It is obvious that invariance of the test statistics is a worthwhile aim to pursuit and the ICS is a promising tool to achieve this goal and has for example compared to the TR technique the advantage that not p, respectively $p+1$, data points have to be singled out on which the transformation depends on. However for the ICS a choice of the two scatter matrices must be made and further research is necessary to compare the effect of different choices. For instance from a nonparametric point of view the assumption of fourth order moments as in this study is not fortunate. Also surprising for us was that contrary to the spatial sign test in the elliptical case for large n and p the efficiencies of the tests used here seem not to tend to 1 in the two sample case.

Another point to pursuit would be the efficiencies of the tests for different values of Δ which would occur for example if a larger power for Hotelling's T^2 would be required because then, as can be seen in Figure 1, the main direction of the data would become more distinct given in the two sample case that the mixing probability ε would be not too close to $1/(3+\sqrt{3})$.

Acknowledgements

The work of Dave Tyler was supported by the NSF Grant DMS-0305858. The work of Klaus Nordhausen and Hannu Oja was supported by grants from Academy of Finland.

References

Chakraborty, B. and Chaudhuri, P. (1996). On a transformation retransformation technique for constructing affine equivariant multivariate median. *Proceedings of American Mathematical Society*, 124, 1529–1537.

Chakraborty, B. and Chaudhuri, P. (1998). On an adaptive transformation retransformation affine equivariant estimate of multivariate location. *Journal of the Royal Statistical Society*, Series B, 60, 145–157.

Chakraborty, B., Chaudhuri, P., and Oja, H. (1998). Operating transformation retransformation on spatial median and angle test. *Statistica Sinica*, 8, 767–784.

Hallin, M. and Paindaveine, D. (2002). Optimal tests for multivariate location based on interdirections and pseudo-Mahalanobis ranks. *Annals of Statistics*, 30, 1103–1133.

Hallin, M. and Paindaveine, D. (2006). Optimal rank-based tests for sphericity. *Annals of Statistics*, to appear.

Kankainen, A., Taskinen, S., and Oja, H. (2006). Tests of multinormality based on location vectors and scatter matrices. Submitted.

Liu, R. Y. and Singh, K. (1993). A quality index based on data depth and multivariate rank tests. *Journal of the American Statistical Association*, 88, 252–260.

Maronna, R. A. (1976). Robust M-estimators of multivariate location and scatter. *Annals of Statistics*, 17, 1608–1630.

Mosler, K. (2002). *Multivariate Dispersion, Central Regions and Depth: The Lift Zonoid Approach*. Lecture Notes in Statistics, Vol. 165. New York: Springer.

Möttönen, J. and Oja, H. (1995). Multivariate spatial sign and rank methods. *Journal of Nonparametric Statistics*, 5, 201–213.

Oja, H. (1983). Descriptive statistics for multivariate distributions. *Statistics & Probability Letters*, 1, 327–332.

Oja, H. (1999). Affine invariant multivariate sign and rank tests and corresponding estimates: A review. *Scandinavian Journal of Statistics*, 26, 319–343.

Oja, H. and Randles, R. (2004). Multivariate nonparametric tests. *Statistical Science*, 19, 598–605.

Oja, H. and Tyler, D. E. (2006). Invariant multivariate sign and rank tests. *Manuscript in preparation*.

Preston, E. J. (1953). A graphical method for the analysis of statistical distributions into two normal components. *Biometrika*, 40, 460–464.

Puri, M. L. and Sen, P. K. (1971). *Nonparametric Methods in Multivariate Analysis*. New York: Wiley & Sons.

R Development Core Team (2005). *R: A language and environment for statistical computing*. R Foundation for Statistical Computing, Vienna, Austria. ISBN 3-900051-07-0, URL http://www.R-project.org.

Randles, R. H. (1989). A distribution-free multivariate sign test based on interdirections. *Journal of the American Statistical Association*, 84, 1045–1050.

Tyler, D. E. (2002). High breakdown point multivariate M-estimation. *Estadistica*, 52, 213–247.

Klaus Nordhausen
Tampere School of Public Health
FI-33014 University of Tampere, Finland
Klaus.Nordhausen@uta.fi
http://www.uta.fi/~klaus.nordhausen/

Hannu Oja
Tampere School of Public Health
FI-33014 University of Tampere, Finland
Hannu.Oja@uta.fi
http://www.uta.fi/~hannu.oja/

David E. Tyler
Department of Statistics
The State University of New Jersey
Piscataway NJ 08854, USA
dtyler@rci.rutgers.edu
http://www.rci.rutgers.edu/~dtyler/

Festschrift for Tarmo Pukkila on his 60th Birthday
Eds. E. P. Liski, J. Isotalo, J. Niemelä, S. Puntanen, and G. P. H. Styan
© Dept. of Mathematics, Statistics and Philosophy,
Univ. of Tampere, 2006, ISBN 978-951-44-6620-5, pages 233–242

Matrices and politics

MICHEL BALINSKI & FRIEDRICH PUKELSHEIM

Abstract. Biproportional apportionment methods provide a novel approach of translating electoral votes into parliamentary seats. A two-way proportionality is achieved, to districts relative to their populations, and to parties relative to their total votes. The methods apply when the electoral region is subdivided into several electoral districts, each with a prespecified "district magnitude," that is, the number of seats per district. The input data thus consists of a matrix with rows and columns corresponding to districts and parties, and entries to party votes in districts. A biproportional apportionment method converts the party votes into an apportionment matrix of corresponding seat-numbers such that, within a district, the sum of the seat-numbers matches the prespecified district magnitude, while within a party, the seat-numbers sum to the overall party seats that are proportional to the vote totals across the whole electoral region. The method had its world premiere in February 2006, with the election of the Zürich City Parliament.

2000 MSC codes: 65K05, 62P25.

Key words and phrases: Alternating scaling algorithm; Biproportional apportionment methods; Doubly stochastic matrices; Electoral systems of Belgium, Faroe Islands, France, Italy, Mexico, Switzerland, USA; Frequency tables with given marginals; Iterative proportional fitting procedure; Neues Zürcher Zuteilungsverfahren; Proportional representation; Theory of apportionment.

1 Introduction

A new technique for converting votes into seats is described for parliamentary systems where the whole electoral region is subdivided into various electoral districts. *Biproportional apportionment methods* achieve a two-way proportionality: to the populations of the districts, and to the parties' vote totals.

In Section 2 we illustrate the approach by means of the new Zürich apportionment procedure [Neues Zürcher Zuteilungsverfahren, NZZ]. The example constitutes the world premiere of the method, the election of the Zürich City Parliament on 12 February 2006. The use of biproportional apportionment methods will undoubtedly proliferate.

The new methods may be viewed as discrete counterparts of the continuous Iterative Proportional Fitting procedure for the adjustment of statistical tables to match prespecified marginals. However, there are vital differences. Section 3 reviews the pertinent literature, contrasting the continuous and discrete aspects of the problem.

2 The new Zürich apportionment procedure

A geographical subdivision of a large electoral region into several *electoral districts* is an ubiquitous tool for ensuring that electoral systems honor historically drawn political and administrative subdivisions. Many systems apportion the total number of seats well ahead of election day, in the middle of the legislative period say, on the grounds of population counts. Thus each district is assigned its *district magnitude*, the number of seats allocated to it. The methods to carry out apportionment are well understood, as expounded in the monograph of Balinski and Young (2001).

There are and have been some ten parties in Zürich. Formerly, parties presented lists of candidates in districts, and votes were converted into seats within each of them separately. However, due to population mobility some of the districts shrank to as few as two or three seats, making it impossible to meet the ideal of proportionality. In particular, some voters could justifiably complain that their votes counted for naught, and did! A citizen in a district with few seats who repeatedly voted for a party that received no seats in the district brought suit complaining that his vote counted for nothing, and won. This provided the impetus to amend the electoral law and to implement a biproportional system.

Biproportional apportionment methods originate with Balinski and Demange (1989a,b), and were explored further by Balinski and Rachev (1993, 1997). Balinski and Ramírez-González (1997, 1999a,b) pointed out that the then Mexican electoral system suffered from severe deficiencies that might be overcome by using a biproportional method. M. B. wrote a popular science article (Balinski 2002) outlining the idea of biproportional representation and how it could answer the implicit demands of the Mexican law. F. P. translated the article into German, when shortly afterwards Christian Schuhmacher from the Zürich Justice and Interior Department hit upon the Augsburg group in the Internet. Pukelsheim and Schuhmacher (2004) adopted Balinski's idea to the Zürich situation. The *new Zürich apportionment procedure* [Neues Zürcher Zuteilungsverfahren, NZZ] celebrated its debut performance with the Zürich City Parliament election on 12 February 2006.

The 2006 Zürich election data and apportionment are presented here. Eight of the competing parties had sufficient votes to participate in the apportionment process. The initial step, the *superapportionment*, allocates all 125 City Parliament seats among the parties proportionally to their vote totals in all districts, resulting in the *overall party seats*. The superapportionment

Table 1. Biproportional divisor method with standard rounding, Zürich City Parliament election of 12 February 2006.

		SP	SVP	FDP	Grüne	CVP	EVP	AL	SD	*City divisor*
Support size		23180	12633	10300	7501	5418	3088	2517	1692	*530*
		Biproportional apportionment, based on party ballot counts								
	125	*44*	*24*	*19*	*14*	*10*	*6*	*5*	*3*	*District divisor*
"1+2"	*12*	28518-4	15305-2	21833-3	12401-2	7318-1	2829-0	2413-0	1651-0	*7000*
"3"	*16*	45541-7	22060-3	10450-1	17319-3	8661-1	2816-0	7418-1	3173-0	*6900*
"4+5"	*13*	26673-5	8174-2	4536-1	10221-2	4099-1	1029-0	9086-2	1406-0	*5000*
"6"	*10*	24092-4	9676-1	10919-2	8420-1	4399-1	3422-1	2304-0	1106-0	*6600*
"7+8"	*17*	61738-5	27906-2	51252-5	25486-2	14223-1	10508-1	5483-1	2454-0	*11200*
"9"	*16*	42044-6	31559-4	12060-2	9154-1	11333-1	9841-1	2465-0	5333-1	*7580*
"10"	*12*	35259-4	19557-3	15267-2	9689-1	8347-1	4690-1	2539-0	1490-0	*7800*
"11"	*19*	56547-6	40144-4	19744-2	12559-1	14762-2	11998-2	3623-1	6226-1	*9000*
"12"	*10*	13215-3	10248-3	3066-1	2187-1	4941-1	0-0	429-0	2078-1	*4000*
Party divisor		*1.006*	*1.002*	*1.01*	*0.97*	*1*	*0.88*	*0.8*	*1*	

A table entry is of the form *p-s*, where *p* is the party ballot count in the district, and *s* is the seat-number apportioned to that party's list in the district. The party ballot count *p* is divided by the associated district and party divisors, and then rounded to obtain *s*. In district "1+2", party SP had $p = 28518$ ballots and was awarded $s = 4$ seats, since $p/(7000 \times 1.006) = 4.05 \searrow 4$. The divisors (right and bottom, in italics) are such that the district magnitudes and the overall party seats (left and top, in italics) are met exactly. The overall party seats result from the superapportionment based on the electorate support sizes.

responds to the recent constitutional order to assure that each person's vote counts. It no longer matters whether voters cast their ballots in districts that are large or small.

A peculiar feature of the Zürich electoral law is that each voter has as many ballots as are given by the district magnitude. Thus voters in district "1+2" command 12 ballots, in district "3" they have 16, etc. The counts of the ballots provide the raw data that are returned from the polling stations, called *party ballot counts* [Parteistimmen], as shown in the body of Table 1. For the aggregation across the whole electoral region, the districtwise party ballot counts are adjusted so that every person (as opposed to every ballot) has equal weight. Party ballot counts are divided by the district magnitude and rounded, yielding the *district support size* [Distriktwählerzahl] of a party. District support sizes are taken to be integer numbers, in order to support the interpretation that they designate the number of people in the district who back the party considered. The sum of the district support sizes, the overall *support size* [Wählerzahl], is the number of persons who back the party across the whole electoral region (in this case: the City of Zürich). The transition to overall support sizes adjusts for the different number of ballots in the districts, so that each voter contributes equally to the superapportionment.

In Table 1, the SP's district support size in district "1+2" is $28518/12 = 2376.5 \nearrow 2377$, while in district "3" it is $45541/16 = 2846.3 \searrow 2846$. The eight parties eligible to receive seats had overall support sizes of 23180 : 12633 : 10300 : 7501 : 5418 : 3088 : 2517 : 1692. Using the divisor method with standard rounding (often named after D. Webster or A. Sainte-Laguë), the superapportionment results in the overall party seats 44 : 24 : 19 : 14 : 10 : 6 : 5 : 3 (city divisor 530).

At the final step, the *biproportional divisor method with standard rounding* computes the *subapportionment*. It secures a two-way proportionality, verifying the prespecified district magnitudes as well as allocating all of the overall party seats. These restrictions form the left and top borders of Table 1, printed in italics. The body of the table displays the original party ballot counts. Two sets of divisors are needed, *district divisors* and *party divisors*, bordering Table 1 on the right and at the bottom. Every party ballot count is divided by the associated district divisor and the associated party divisor, and the resulting quotient is rounded in the standard way to obtain the seat-number. For instance, the SP in district "1+2" receives $28518/(7000 \cdot 1.006) = 4.05 \searrow 4$ seats. All party ballot counts in a given district are adjusted by the same (district) divisor, so that in effect they have simply been rescaled. Similarly, in all districts the party ballot counts of a given party are adjusted by the same (party) divisor, so they, too, are only rescaled. It may be proved that the resulting apportionment is unique (except possibly for ties).

Two-way proportionality is of interest in political systems beyond the one of Zürich. Bochsler (2005) studies its use for the election of the Swiss national parliament. Balinski (2004) discusses its application to elect France's representatives in the European Parliament. Biproportionality is a possible remedy to the corruptive effects of gerrymandering in the USA (Balinski 2006b), and in the current Italian electoral law it would remove "The Bug" described by Pennisi (2006). Legislative preparations to install a biproportional system are under way in the Faroe Islands (Zachariassen and Zachariasen 2005, 2006).

District and party divisors are the key quantities [Wahlschlüssel] of biproportional methods. They are not unique, since nothing is changed when the districts' divisors are multiplied by a scalar and the party divisors are divided by the same amount. Moreover, a slight variation does not matter as long as the resulting quotients round to the same integers. The divisors cannot be obtained from a closed formula, but must be determined algorithmically. The BAZI program, available at www.uni-augsburg.de/bazi, implements several approaches to finding them (Pukelsheim 2004, 2006). While BAZI now offers a selection of algorithms (Maier 2006), it originally started out with an Alternating Scaling algorithm that is similar to the Iterative Proportional Fitting procedure.

3 Biproportional apportionment and iterative proportional fitting

The breakthrough to a practically persuasive and theoretically convincing approach to the matrix biproportional apportionment problem is due to Balinski and coauthors (see Section 1). The starting point is an axiomatic theory of apportionment for vector problems developed by Balinski and Young (2001). A major result is that among all conceivable apportionment methods, *divisor methods* are the only acceptable ones. They are in one-to-one correspondence with rounding functions, that is, with the prescription of how to round a positive real number to one of its neighboring integers, in each closed interval $[n-1, n]$ $(n = 1, 2, \ldots)$ of the nonnegative half-line.

For vector problems, divisor methods determine a divisor (multiplier, scaling constant) so that when the input weights are scaled and rounded, using the rounding function that comes with the method, the resulting integers verify the prespecified side condition. The same approach works for matrix problems, except that now two *sets* of divisors are needed, row divisors and column divisors, and that an entry of the input weight matrix is scaled twice, by its row divisor and by its column divisor, before it is rounded to an integer. It is thus tempting to aim at a theory emphasizing the similarity of vector and matrix problems (Balinski 2006a).

Gaffke and Pukelsheim (2006a) formulate the matrix apportionment problem as an integer optimization problem, exhibiting the apportionment as the mode of a multinomial-type probability density function. This optimization approach is delineated already by Carnal (1993), for the specific divisor method with rounding down (T. Jefferson, V. D'Hondt, E. Hagenbach-Bischoff), referring to the electoral system for the Swiss Canton of Bern, see also Carnal and Riedwyl (1982). Once the primal optimization problem is set up, the row and column divisors then emerge as the values of the solution to an associated dual problem. This suggests a classification of algorithms as *primal algorithms*, or as *dual algorithms* (Gaffke and Pukelsheim 2006b).

From a statistical viewpoint, the biproportional apportionment problem is identical with the problem of adjusting a frequency table so as to meet prespecified row and column marginals. For a textbook example see Cochran (1977, page 124). The original paper on the statistical problem is Deming and Stephan (1940); the authors proposed what since has become known as the *Iterative Proportional Fitting* (IPF) procedure, but their convergence proof was flawed. Further research eventually established the conjectured convergence of the IPF procedure, see the encyclopedia article by Fienberg and Meyer (1983). In statistical jargon, the IPF procedure is sometimes called *raking* (Fagan and Greenberg 1987).

Besides statistics, Bacharach (1965, 1970) applies IPF to economic input-output analysis. Lamond and Stewart (1981) use it to solve transportation problems, and provide references from that field. In probability theory, the procedure has been used to convert a nonnegative matrix into a doubly stochastic matrix, by scaling rows and columns so that each of them sums to one. This problem generated a series of research papers, see Sinkhorn (1964, 1966, 1967, 1972), Sinkhorn and Knopp (1967), Marshall and Olkin (1968), Cottle, Duvali, and Zikan (1986), Khachiyan and Kalantari (1992).

However, IPF does not solve the problems of biproportional apportionment. It rescales a nonnegative matrix into another matrix with nonnegative *real* entries - not *integer* entries - that verify prespecified marginals. An iterative procedure, it stops when the side conditions are met to within a given error bound, so its solutions come with a disclaimer that, due to numerical inaccuracies, the marginal restrictions may not be met exactly, as in Bacharach (1970). The disclaimer is standard in statistical publications, when a frequency table is converted into percentages or tenths of a percent (Wainer 1998; Pukelsheim 1998). The disclaimer poses no problem as far as descriptive statistics or Bacharach's input-output analysis are concerned. It becomes problematic when stochastic matrices are generated where the probabilities must sum to one exactly, not just approximately. The disclaimer becomes definitely untenable in the context of apportioning the seats of a parliamentary body. It is unacceptable to leave a seat empty, or to create an extra seat, with the excuse that inaccuracies of the mathematical method cannot do better.

The IPF procedure is part of "continuous" mathematics, while biproportional apportionment belongs to "discrete" mathematics. Interestingly, this is an example where a presumably "soft science" such as political decision making insists on exact results, whereas a purportedly "exact science" such as calculus makes do with approximations.

A particular dual algorithm is alternating scaling (AS), a discrete variant of the (continuous) IPF procedure. While the IPF procedure is known to converge always, the AS algorithm may "stall", cycling from a solution that satisfies the row but not the column constraints to one that satisfies the column but not the row constraints, and back again. Extensive simulations suggest that this may happen only if there are sufficiently many ties in the solutions. For empirical election data, ties are extremely rare. Hence it is fair to say that the AS algorithm works fine, for all practical purposes. The reason is that empirical data usually are "well behaved" in that they are not only free of ties but determined by relatively large intervals of divisors. The BAZI program uses the AS algorithm because of its fast initial progress. The program safeguards against stalling by switching, if needed, to the "Tie-and-Transfer" algorithm of Balinski and Demange (1989b), as outlined by Maier (2006). Further algorithmic improvements are being investigated by Zachariasen (2006).

An entirely different approach to the biproportional problem has been proposed in the context of rounding census data. Called *controlled rounding* it may be interpreted as a generalization of the method of greatest remainders for vector rounding (often named after A. Hamilton, T. Hare / H. F. Niemeyer) to that of rounding matrices. Developed in a series of papers by Cox and coauthors (Cox and Ernst 1982; Causey, Cox, and Ernst 1985; Cox 1987, 2003; Cox and George 1989), it has been recommended for the Belgian electoral system (De Meur, Gassner, and Hubaut 1985; De Meur and Hubaut 1986; De Meur and Gassner 1987; Gassner 1988, 1989, 1991, 2000). It has severe drawbacks: it seriously distorts proportionality, and it lacks any axiomatic or theoretical justification.

Acknowledgement

F. P. would like to acknowledge the hospitality of the Laboratoire d'Économétrie, École Polytechnique, Paris, during a sabbatical visit 2005/6.

References

[See also the Proportional Representation literature list www.uni-augsburg.de/bazi/literature.html]

Bacharach, M. (1965). Estimating nonnegative matrices from marginal data. *International Economic Review (Osaka)*, 6, 294–310.

Bacharach, M. (1970). *Biproportional Matrices & Input-Output Change.* Cambridge, UK: Cambridge University Press.

Balinski, M. (2002). Une "dose" de proportionnelle: le système électoral mexicain. *Pour la Science*, April 2002, 58–59. [German: Verhältniswahlrecht häppchenweise: Wahlen in Mexiko. *Spektrum der Wissenschaft*, October 2002, 72–74.]

Balinski, M. (2004). *Le suffrage universel inachevé.* Paris: Editions Belin.

Balinski, M. (2006a). Apportionment: uni- and bi-dimensional. In *Mathematics and Democracy. Recent Advances in Voting Systems and Collective Choice.* Eds. B. Simeone and F. Pukelsheim. New York.

Balinski, M. (2006b). Fair majority voting (or How to eliminate gerrymandering). *American Mathematical Monthly*, forthcoming.

Balinski, M. and Demange, G. (1989a). An axiomatic approach to proportionality between matrices. *Mathematics of Operations Research*, 14, 700–719.

Balinski, M. and Demange, G. (1989b). Algorithms for proportional matrices in reals and integers. *Mathematical Programming*, 45, 193–210.

Balinski, M. and Rachev, S. T. (1993). Rounding proportions: rules of rounding. *Numerical Functional Analysis and Optimization*, 14, 475–501

Balinski, M. and Rachev, S. T. (1997). Rounding proportions: methods of rounding. *Mathematical Scientist*, 22, 1–26

Balinski, M. and Ramírez-González, V. (1997). Mexican electoral law: 1996 version. *Electoral Studies*, 16, 329–340.

Balinski, M. and Ramírez-González, V. (1999a). Mexico's 1997 apportionment defies its electoral law. *Electoral Studies*, 18, 117–124.

Balinski, M. and Ramírez-González, V. (1999b). Parametric methods of apportionment, rounding and production. *Mathematical Social Sciences*, 37, 107–122.

Balinski, M. and Young, H. P. (2001). *Fair Representation: Meeting the Ideal of One Man, One Vote. Second Edition.* Washington, DC: Brookings Institution Press.

Bochsler D. (2005). Biproportionale Wahlverfahren für den Schweizer Nationalrat. Online publication: www.opus-bayern.de/uni-augsburg/volltexte/2005/160

Carnal, H. (1993). Mathématiques et politique. *Elemente der Mathematik*, 48, 27–32.

Carnal, H. and Riedwyl, H. (1982). Wahlkreisverbandsarithmetik. Technischer Bericht No. 8, Institut für Mathematische Statistik und Versicherungslehre, Universität Bern.

Cochran, W. G. (1977). *Sampling techniques, Third Edition.* New York: Wiley.

Causey, B. D., Cox, L. H., and Ernst, L. R. (1985). Applications of transportation theory to statistical problems. *Journal of the American Statistical Association*, 80, 903–909.

Cottle, R. W., Duvali, S. G., and Zikan, K. (1986). A Lagrangian relaxation algorithm for the constrained matrix problem. *Naval Research Logistics Quarterly*, 33, 55–76.

Cox, L. H. (1987). A constructive procedure for unbiased controlled rounding. *Journal of the American Statistical Association*, 82, 520–524.

Cox, L. H. (2003). On properties of multi-dimensional statistical tables. *Journal of Statistical Planning and Inference*, 117, 251–273.

Cox, L. H. and Ernst, L. R. (1982). Controlled rounding. *Information Systems and Operational Research*, 20, 423–432.

Cox, L. H. and George, J. A. (1989). Controlled rounding for tables with subtotals. *Annals of Operations Research*, 20, 141–157.

De Meur, G. and Gassner, M. (1987). Problems of equity in political representation: what we want and why we can't. In *The Logic of Multiparty Systems.* Ed. M. J. Holler. Dordrecht: Martinus Nijhoff Publishers. Pp. 391–404.

De Meur, G. and Hubaut, X. (1986). Fair models of political fairness. *European Journal of Political Research*, 14, 239–252.

De Meur, G., Gassner, M., and Hubaut, X. (1985). A mathematical model for political bipolarization. *European Journal of Political Research*, 13, 409–420.

Deming, W. E. and Stephan, F. F. (1940). On a least squares adjustment of a sampling frequency table when the expected marginals totals are known. *Annals of Mathematical Statistics*, 11, 427–440.

Fagan, J. T. and Greenberg, B. V. (1987). Making tables additive in the presence of zeros. *American Journal of Mathematical and Management Sciences*, 7, 359–383.

Fienberg, S. S. and Meyer, M. M. (1983). Iterative proportional fitting. In *Encyclopedia of Statistical Sciences, Volume 4.* Ed. S. Kotz. New York: Wiley. Pp. 275–279.

Gaffke, N. and Pukelsheim, F. (2006a). Divisor methods for proportional representation systems: an optimization approach to vector and matrix problems. Submitted for publication.

Gaffke, N. and Pukelsheim, F. (2006b). Separable convex minimization in bounded integers under totally unimodular linear equations. Submitted for publication.

Gassner, M. (1988). Two-dimensional rounding for a quasi-proportional representation. *European Journal of Political Economy*, 4, 529–538.

Gassner, M. (1989). An impossibility theorem for fair bidimensional representation: towards a biproportional solution. In *Mathematical Psychology in Progress.* Ed. E. E. Roskam. Berlin: Springer. Pp. 345–365.

Gassner, M. (1991). A solution for two-dimensional proportional representation. *Journal of Theoretical Politics*, 3, 321–342.

Gassner, M. (2000). *Représentations parlementaires. Méthodes mathématiques biproportionnelles de Répartition des Sièges.* Éditions de l'Université de Bruxelles.

Khachiyan, L. and Kalantari, B. (1992). Diagonal matrix scaling and linear programming. *SIAM Journal on Optimization*, 2, 668–672.

Lamond, B. and Stewart, N.F. (1981). Bregman's balancing method. *Transportation Research Part B: Methodological*, 15, 239–248.

Maier, S. (2006). Algorithms for biproportional apportionment methods. In *Mathematics and Democracy. Recent Advances in Voting Systems and Collective Choice*. Eds. B. Simeone and F. Pukelsheim. New York.

Marshall, A.W. and Olkin, I. (1968). Scaling of matrices to achieve specified row and column sums. *Numerische Mathematik*, 12, 83–90.

Pennisi, A. (2006). When one plus one is not two: a flawed procedure for bi-proportional allocation in Italy. In *Mathematics and Democracy. Recent Advances in Voting Systems and Collective Choice*. Eds. B. Simeone and F. Pukelsheim. New York.

Pukelsheim, F. (1998). Rounding tables on my bicycle. *Chance* 11, 57–58.

Pukelsheim, F. (2004). BAZI: a Java programm for proportional representation. *Oberwolfach Reports*, 1, 735–737.

Pukelsheim, F. (2006). Current issues of apportionment methods. In *Mathematics and Democracy. Recent Advances in Voting Systems and Collective Choice*. Eds. B. Simeone and F. Pukelsheim. New York.

Pukelsheim, F. and Schuhmacher, C. (2004). Das neue Zürcher Zuteilungsverfahren für Parlamentswahlen. *Aktuelle Juristische Praxis – Pratique Juridique Actuelle*, 5, 505–522.

Sinkhorn, R. (1964). A relationship between arbitrary positive matrices and doubly stochastic matrices. *Annals of Mathematical Statistics*, 35, 876–879.

Sinkhorn, R. (1966). A relationship between arbitrary positive matrices and stochastic matrices. *Canadian Journal of Mathematics*, 18, 303–306.

Sinkhorn, R. (1967). Diagonal equivalence of matrices with prescribed row and column sums. *American Mathematical Monthly*, 74, 402–405.

Sinkhorn, R. (1972). Continuous dependence on A in the D_1AD_2 theorems. *Proceedings of the American Mathematical Society*, 32, 395–398.

Sinkhorn, R. and Knopp, P. (1967). Concerning nonnegative matrices and doubly stochastic matrices. *Pacific Journal of Mathematics*, 21, 343–348.

Wainer, H. (1998). Visual revelations: rounding tables. *Chance*, 11, 46–50.

Zachariasen, M. (2006). Algorithmic aspects of divisor-based biproportional rounding. Typescript.

Zachariassen, P. and Zachariasen, M. (2005). Frá atkvøðum til tingsessir. Samanbering av hættum til útrokning av tingmannabýti [Appendix: Seat distributions in the Faroe Parliament 1978–2004 according to 8 electoral formulae]. University of the Faroe Islands, Faculty of Science and Technology, Technical Report 2005:1.

Zachariassen, P. and Zachariasen, M. (2006). A comparison of electoral formulae for the Faroe Parliament (The Løgting). Typescript.

MICHEL BALINSKI
Laboratoire d'Économétrie, École polytechnique, 75005 Paris, France
Michel.Balinski@SHS.Polytechnique.Fr
http://ceco.polytechnique.fr/home/balinski

Friedrich Pukelsheim
Institut für Mathematik, Universität Augsburg, D-86135 Augsburg, Germany
Pukelsheim@Math.Uni-Augsburg.De
http://www.uni-augsburg.de/pukelsheim

Festschrift for Tarmo Pukkila on his 60th Birthday
Eds. E. P. Liski, J. Isotalo, J. Niemelä, S. Puntanen, and G. P. H. Styan

Univ. of Tampere, 2006, ISBN 978-951-44-6620-5, pages 243–259

On the role of the constant term in linear regression

JARKKO ISOTALO SIMO PUNTANEN GEORGE P. H. STYAN

Abstract. In this paper we comment on the role of the constant term in linear regression, with particular emphasis in teaching statistics. The constant term corresponds to a variable whose observed values are all identical and hence its variance is zero. Hence students might wonder if such a variable is indeed a proper variable. We go through some important geometric considerations and comment on various models and the role of the constant term therein. A numerical example run in the Survo computing environment, see e.g., Mustonen (2001), illustrates our comments.

2000 MSC codes: 62J05, 62H12, 62H20.

Key words and phrases: BLUE; Centering; Coefficient of determination; Collinearity; OLSE; Orthogonal projector; R-squared.

1 ...Life gets troublesome

Let us begin by quoting the following e-mail correspondence which took coded in LaTeX.)

```
Date: Wed, 15 May 1996
From: "Simo Puntanen" <sjp@uta.fi>
To: "David A. Belsley" <belsley@bc.edu>
Subject: high correlation
```

Dear Professor Belsley,

I'd like to bother you with the following simple question: on page 20 of your book, you say that "...a high correlation surely implies a low angle..."

I'm afraid that I have misunderstood something since it is easy to find an example where correlation is high but the angle is not low. Take $\mathbf{x} = (1, 1, 1.01)'$, $\mathbf{y} = (1, 0, -1)'$, and then $\text{cor}(x, y) = -.866$ but $\cos(x, y) = -.004$. Clearly I have missed something?

With best regards, Simo P.

```
Date: Wed, 15 May 1996 11:06:40 -0400 (EDT)
From: "David A. Belsley" <belsley@bc.edu>
```

Dear Simo P.,

Ah, you must be a mathematician or a statistician to think that $-.866$ is a high correlation. In the world of collinearity, that is pretty good; life doesn't get troublesome until the correlations are at least .96. And what I mean by a "high" correlation is really more like .99 or higher. You will note that this notion is made very clear as the monograph progresses.

Best wishes, David A. Belsley

```
Date: Wed, 15 May 1996 20:18:23 -0400 (EDT)
From: "David A. Belsley" <belsley@bc.edu>
```

Dear Simo P.,

I was entirely too quick and too flip in my previous answer to you. You are absolutely correct. It is quite possible for two variates to be perfectly correlated, yet also be orthogonal, i.e., perfectly conditioned. Your example comes very close. Letting $\mathbf{x} = (1, 1, \sqrt{2})'$ and $\mathbf{y} = (-1, -1, \sqrt{2})'$ comes right on the button. These have correlation 1 and cos 0.

I was also too quick in my book, giving away more than need be by following conventional wisdom, which, in this case, is wrong. It is indeed clear that correlation and conditioning are neither necessary nor sufficient to one another - which wonderfully strengthens my argument. For it is equally clear that two variates, such as exemplified above, do very well as regressands (without the constant term), even though they are perfectly correlated. [Note, however, that in situations like this, if you include the intercept (a column of 1s), the data become ill-conditioned and not suitable for regression.]

I thank you for pointing this out; strangely you are the first to do so. I know why I failed to pursue this issue further, because it was already clear that high correlation is not a suitable diagnostic for conditioning, and your example furthers this point.

Sincerely, David A. Belsley

2 Numerical illustration through Survo

The correspondence above is a lesson in itself. It illustrates how carefully we should proceed in the world of collinearity.

While teaching concepts related to regression and correlation, it is absolutely necessary to illustrate these concepts using geometric arguments. Students should realize that the sample correlation coefficient is the cosine between two specific vectors: these vectors are the centered values of corresponding variables. It is essential to observe that these vectors must be centered, or in geometric terms: the original vectors must be projected onto the plane which is orthogonal to the vector of ones; we denote this vector as $\mathbf{1}$ (or $\mathbf{1}_n$).

It is precisely due to this centering requirement that the concept of high correlation (absolute value) and high cosine (low angle) do not go hand-in-hand.

In his excellent book, Professor Belsley (1991, p. 20) has an illustrative example of the situation where the correlation is zero but the cosine is very close to 1. We go through this example using Survo, a statistical software developed by Professor Seppo Mustonen, see, e.g., Mustonen (2001). The calculations are shown in the example below.

The fundamental concept in Survo is the edit field. The user works with Survo by typing text in the edit field and by activating various commands and operations within the text; in the Example, these activated operations (except lines 11 and 12) are emphasized as a white text in a black background.

Between lines 20 and 24, we define a 3×2 matrix $\mathbf{B}$. Then, a 3×4 matrix $\mathbf{A}$ is created so that the first two columns of $\mathbf{A}$ comprise $\mathbf{B}$, while (in view of line 28) the last two columns of $\mathbf{A}$ include the values of variables U and V; they are functions of variables X and Y and a real number *eps*.

When line 36 is activated, the correlation matrix of all four variables will be calculated. We see at once that the correlation between U and V is zero. On line 45 we have calculated the cosines. In this situation $\cos(U,V)$ is extremely close to 1 (even though these variables are uncorrelated).

On line 54, the cosine $\cos(U,V)$ is expressed as a function of *eps*. We immediately confirm that $\cos(U,V)$ can go through all values when *eps* varies, but at the same time $\operatorname{cor}(U,V) = 0$ (except when $eps = 0$; then $\operatorname{cor} = 0/0$).

3 Introduction

The linear model that we are considering can be written as

$$\mathbf{y} = \mathbf{X}\boldsymbol{\beta} + \boldsymbol{\varepsilon} = \beta_0\mathbf{1} + \beta_1\mathbf{x}_1 + \cdots + \beta_k\mathbf{x}_k + \boldsymbol{\varepsilon}, \tag{3.1}$$

or in other notation, $\mathcal{M} = \{\mathbf{y}, \mathbf{X}\boldsymbol{\beta}, \sigma^2\mathbf{I}\}$, where $\mathrm{E}(\mathbf{y}) = \mathbf{X}\boldsymbol{\beta}$, $\mathrm{E}(\boldsymbol{\varepsilon}) = \mathbf{0}$, and $\operatorname{cov}(\mathbf{y}) = \operatorname{cov}(\boldsymbol{\varepsilon}) = \sigma^2\mathbf{I}$. Vector $\mathbf{y}$ is an $n \times 1$ observable random vector, $\boldsymbol{\varepsilon}$ is an $n \times 1$ random error vector, $\mathbf{X}$ is a known $n \times p$ model matrix, $\boldsymbol{\beta}$ is a $p \times 1$ vector of unknown parameters, and σ^2 is an unknown nonzero constant. By $\mathrm{E}(\cdot)$ and $\operatorname{cov}(\cdot)$ we denote the expectation vector and the covariance matrix, respectively.

We will use the symbols $\mathbf{A}'$, $\mathbf{A}^-$, $\mathbf{A}^+$, $\mathcal{C}(\mathbf{A})$, $\mathcal{C}(\mathbf{A})^\perp$ and $\mathrm{r}(\mathbf{A})$ to denote, respectively, the transpose, a generalized inverse, the Moore–Penrose inverse, the column space, the orthogonal complement of the column space, and the rank of the matrix $\mathbf{A}$. Furthermore we will write $\mathbf{P}_\mathbf{A} = \mathbf{A}\mathbf{A}^+ = \mathbf{A}(\mathbf{A}'\mathbf{A})^-\mathbf{A}'$ to denote the orthogonal projector (with respect to the standard inner product)

```
 -    - SURVO MM    Tue Mar 15 13:14:01 2006     C:\SP\D\    2000   100  0
 10 *
 11 * EXAMPLE:     Correlation is 0 BUT cosine is 0.999999999
 12 *              IN THE WORLD OF COLLINEARITY ...
 13 * Belsley (1991, p.20): Conditioning Diagnostics. Wiley.
 14 *   Let  X and Y be centered vectors such that X'Y = 0.
 15 *   Let us define variables U and V so that
 16 *   U=1+eps*X, V=1+eps*Y, where eps is a real number.
 17 *   (a) What is cor(U,V)?
 18 *           This is 0 for all nonzero eps, since cor(X, Y) = 0
 19 *   (b) What about cos(U,V)?
 20 *MATRIX B
 21 *///     X      Y
 22 *  1      1      1
 23 *  2     -1      1
 24 *  3      0     -2
 25 *
 26 *MAT A!=ZER(3,4)      / creates a 3 by 4 matrix (full of zeros)
 27 *MAT A(1:3,1:2)=B      / first two columns = B
 28 *MAT A(1:3,3:4)=CON(3,2)+eps*B / eps=0.001
 29 *MAT LOAD A                    / Last two cols are U and V
 30 *MATRIX A
 31 *///         X        Y        U        V
 32 *  1      1.00000  1.00000  1.00100  1.00100
 33 *  2     -1.00000  1.00000  0.99900  1.00100
 34 *  3      0.00000 -2.00000  1.00000  0.99800
 35 *
 36 *CORR A.MAT    / calculates the corr-mtx, saves it as CORR.M
 37 *MAT LOAD CORR.M
 38 *MATRIX CORR.M
 39 *///         X        Y        U        V
 40 *X        1.00000  0.00000  1.00000  0.00000
 41 *Y        0.00000  1.00000 -0.00000  1.00000
 42 *U        1.00000 -0.00000  1.00000 -0.00000
 43 *V        0.00000  1.00000 -0.00000  1.00000
 44 *
 45 *MAT COS!=(NRM(A))'*NRM(A)  / NRM scales the lengths
 46 *MAT LOAD COS               / of columns to 1
 47 *MATRIX COS
 48 *///          X         Y         U         V
 49 *X        1.000000  0.000000  0.000816  0.000000
 50 *Y        0.000000  1.000000  0.000000  0.001414
 51 *U        0.000816  0.000000  1.000000  0.999999
 52 *V        0.000000  0.001414  0.999999  1.000000
 53 *
 54 *GPLOT Y(eps)=n/SQRT((n+a*eps^2)*(n+b*eps^2))  / a=X'X b=Y'Y
```

cos(U, V) as a function of EPS, cor(U, V)=0

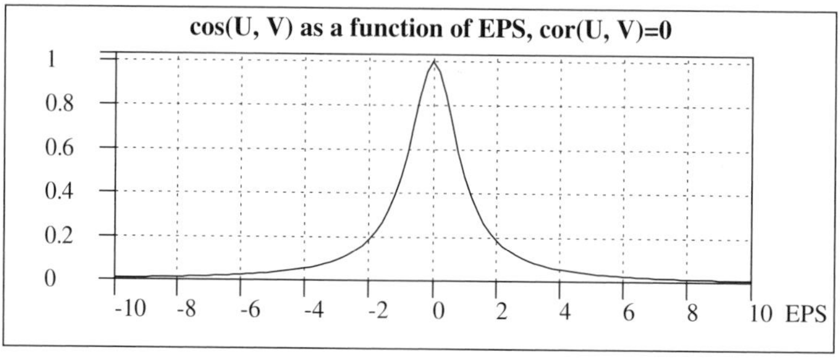

onto $\mathcal{C}(\mathbf{A})$. By $(\mathbf{A} : \mathbf{B})$ we denote the partitioned matrix with $\mathbf{A}$ and $\mathbf{B}$ as submatrices.

Our model matrix above is

$$\mathbf{X} = (\mathbf{1} : \mathbf{x}_1 : \ldots : \mathbf{x}_k) = (\mathbf{1} : \mathbf{X}_0), \qquad p = k + 1, \tag{3.2}$$

where $\mathbf{X}_0$ is an $n \times k$ matrix. Denoting $\mathbf{J} = \mathbf{P_1} = \frac{1}{n}\mathbf{1}\mathbf{1}'$ and $\mathbf{C} = \mathbf{I} - \mathbf{J}$, where $\mathbf{C}$ is a centering matrix, we get

$$\mathbf{T} = (\mathbf{X}_0 : \mathbf{y})'\mathbf{C}(\mathbf{X}_0 : \mathbf{y}) = \begin{pmatrix} \mathbf{X}_0'\mathbf{C}\mathbf{X}_0 & \mathbf{X}_0'\mathbf{C}\mathbf{y} \\ \mathbf{y}'\mathbf{C}\mathbf{X}_0 & \mathbf{y}'\mathbf{C}\mathbf{y} \end{pmatrix} = \begin{pmatrix} \mathbf{T}_1 & \mathbf{t}_2 \\ \mathbf{t}_2' & t_{yy} \end{pmatrix}, \tag{3.3}$$

and hence the sample covariance matrix and sample correlation matrix of variables $x_1, x_2, \ldots, x_k, y$ are

$$\mathbf{S} = \tfrac{1}{n-1}\mathbf{T} = \begin{pmatrix} \mathbf{S}_1 & \mathbf{s}_2 \\ \mathbf{s}_2' & s_y^2 \end{pmatrix}, \qquad \mathbf{R} = \begin{pmatrix} \mathbf{R}_1 & \mathbf{r}_2 \\ \mathbf{r}_2' & 1 \end{pmatrix}. \tag{3.4}$$

We will use the notation $\mathbf{H} = \mathbf{P_X}$ (= hat matrix), and $\mathbf{M} = \mathbf{I} - \mathbf{H}$, thereby obtaining the ordinary least squares (OLS) estimator of $\mathbf{X}\boldsymbol{\beta}$ as

$$\mathrm{OLSE}(\mathbf{X}\boldsymbol{\beta}) = \mathbf{X}\hat{\boldsymbol{\beta}} = \hat{\mathbf{y}} = \mathbf{H}\mathbf{y} = \mathbf{P_X}\mathbf{y}, \tag{3.5}$$

where $\hat{\boldsymbol{\beta}}$ is any solution to the normal equation $\mathbf{X}'\mathbf{X}\boldsymbol{\beta} = \mathbf{X}'\mathbf{y}$. The corresponding vector of residuals is

$$\mathrm{res}(\mathcal{M}) = \mathbf{e} = \mathbf{y} - \mathbf{X}\hat{\boldsymbol{\beta}} = \mathbf{y} - \mathbf{H}\mathbf{y} = \mathbf{M}\mathbf{y}. \tag{3.6}$$

One particular model deserves special attention: if the model matrix $\mathbf{X}$ has only one column and that column is $\mathbf{1}$, then we have the very simple basic model $\mathcal{M}_0 = \{\mathbf{y}, \mathbf{1}\beta_0, \sigma^2\mathbf{I}\}$. Under $\mathcal{M}_0$ we have $\mathrm{OLSE}(\mathbf{1}\beta_0 \mid \mathcal{M}_0) = \mathbf{J}\mathbf{y} = \bar{y}\mathbf{1}$, where $\bar{y} = \frac{1}{n}\sum_{i=1}^{n} y_i$; the residual vector is the centered $\mathbf{y}$:

$$\mathrm{res}(\mathcal{M}_0) = \mathbf{y} - \mathbf{J}\mathbf{y} = \mathbf{C}\mathbf{y} = \tilde{\mathbf{y}}. \tag{3.7}$$

The four orthogonal projectors

$$\mathbf{H} = \mathbf{P_X}, \qquad \mathbf{M} = \mathbf{P}_{\mathbf{X}^\perp} = \mathbf{I} - \mathbf{H}, \qquad \mathbf{J} = \mathbf{P_1}, \qquad \mathbf{C} = \mathbf{P}_{\mathbf{1}^\perp} = \mathbf{I} - \mathbf{J} \tag{3.8}$$

play crucial roles in many considerations related to linear regression.

As emphasized in Section 2, the sample correlation coefficient between variables x and y whose values are the elements of vectors $\mathbf{x}, \mathbf{y} \in \mathbb{R}^n$ is the cosine between the corresponding centered vectors:

$$\mathrm{cor_s}(x, y) = \mathrm{cor_d}(\mathbf{x}, \mathbf{y}) = \cos(\mathbf{C}\mathbf{x}, \mathbf{C}\mathbf{y}) = r_{xy} = \frac{\mathbf{x}'\mathbf{C}\mathbf{y}}{\sqrt{\mathbf{x}'\mathbf{C}\mathbf{x} \cdot \mathbf{y}'\mathbf{C}\mathbf{y}}}. \tag{3.9}$$

Note that the correlation $\mathrm{cor_s}(x, y)$ refers to a sample correlation coefficient when the arguments are the variables x and y, while in the correlation

$\operatorname{cor}_{\mathrm{d}}(\mathbf{x}, \mathbf{y})$ the arguments are the vectors (data) comprising the observed values of variables x and y.

Taking a look at the model matrix $\mathbf{X} = (\mathbf{1} : \mathbf{x}_1 : \ldots : \mathbf{x}_k)$, we see that the first column there looks just as any other column, but there is one big difference: all other variables represented in the model matrix $\mathbf{X}$ have a nonzero sample variance. (Of course we can request that there be no multiples of $\mathbf{1}$ in $\mathbf{X}_0$.) Belsley (1991, p. 196) writes:

> "Much confusion surrounding centering arises because of some commonly held misconceptions about the 'constant term'. This section [6.8] aims at several of these issues with the goal of showing that, for most of the part, despite much practice to the contrary, the constant is most reasonably viewed as just another element in a regression analysis that plays no role different from any other 'variate'."

We recall that variables (columns) $\mathbf{u}_1, \ldots, \mathbf{u}_m$ are said to be exactly collinear if one of the $\mathbf{u}_i$ is an exact linear combination of the others. This is exact collinearity, i.e., linear dependency, and by the term *collinearity* or *near dependency* we mean inexact collinear relations.

The book by Belsley (2001) offers a thorough discussion on the vector $\mathbf{1}$ and the collinearity. For example, Belsley (1991, p. 176) notes that "there is general tendency to confuse the two notions of collinearity and correlation, many practitioners thinking them to be the same." In this article, there is no space to consider such concepts, like condition number, in further detail and we refer to the interesting Chapter 6 in the book by Belsley (1991).

Inspired by Belsley's remarks, we now consider several features related to centering. Before that, we summarize (for clarity) our comments above and present three helpful lemmas that will be needed later on.

Proposition 1. *It is possible that*

(a) $\cos(\mathbf{x}, \mathbf{y})$ *is high, but* $\operatorname{cor}_{\mathrm{d}}(\mathbf{x}, \mathbf{y}) = 0$,

(b) $\cos(\mathbf{x}, \mathbf{y}) = 0$, *but* $\operatorname{cor}_{\mathrm{d}}(\mathbf{x}, \mathbf{y}) = 1$.

Moreover, let $\mathbf{x} \notin C(\mathbf{1})$ *and* $\mathbf{y} \notin C(\mathbf{1})$. *Then*

$$\operatorname{cor}_{\mathrm{d}}(\mathbf{x}, \mathbf{y}) = 0 \iff \mathbf{y} \in C(\mathbf{C}\mathbf{x})^{\perp} = C(\mathbf{1} : \mathbf{x})^{\perp} \oplus C(\mathbf{1}). \tag{3.10}$$

Lemma 1. *The orthogonal projector (with respect to the standard inner product) onto* $C(\mathbf{A} : \mathbf{B})$ *can be decomposed as* $\mathbf{P}_{(\mathbf{A}:\mathbf{B})} = \mathbf{P}_{\mathbf{A}} + \mathbf{P}_{(\mathbf{I}-\mathbf{P}_{\mathbf{A}})\mathbf{B}}$.

Lemma 2. *The rank of a partitioned matrix* $(\mathbf{A} : \mathbf{B})$ *can be expressed as*

$$\mathrm{r}(\mathbf{A} : \mathbf{B}) = \mathrm{r}(\mathbf{A}) + \mathrm{r}[(\mathbf{I} - \mathbf{P}_{\mathbf{A}})\mathbf{B}],$$

while the rank of the matrix product $\mathbf{AB}$ *is*

$$\mathrm{r}(\mathbf{AB}) = \mathrm{r}(\mathbf{A}) - \dim C(\mathbf{A}') \cap C(\mathbf{B}^{\perp}).$$

Lemma 3. *The following three statements are equivalent:*

(a) $\mathbf{P_A} - \mathbf{P_B}$ *is orthogonal projector,*

(b) $\mathbf{P_A P_B} = \mathbf{P_B P_A} = \mathbf{P_B}$,

(c) $C(\mathbf{B}) \subset C(\mathbf{A})$.

If any of the above conditions hold, then $\mathbf{P_A} - \mathbf{P_B} = \mathbf{P}_{C(\mathbf{A}) \cap C(\mathbf{B})^{\perp}}$.

For more about these three lemmas, see Marsaglia and Styan (1974) and Isotalo et al. (2005, Th. 1 and 4, Cor. 3.1).

4 Centered vector as a residual

Under $\mathcal{M}_0 = \{\mathbf{y}, \mathbf{1}\beta, \sigma^2\mathbf{I}\}$, the residual vector is the centered $\mathbf{y}$. What happens here is that we "eliminate" (we will return to this much-used phrase later on) the effect of the column vector of ones $\mathbf{1}$ from $\mathbf{y}$, and, what is left is just the residual which in this case is the centered $\mathbf{y}$, i.e., $\tilde{\mathbf{y}}$. Correspondingly, the centered $\mathbf{x}$ is the residual of $\mathbf{x}$ after the elimination of $\mathbf{1}$.

Consider two vectors $\mathbf{x}$ and $\mathbf{y}$ and the model $\mathcal{M}_{xy} = \{\mathbf{y}, \mathbf{x}\beta, \sigma^2\mathbf{I}\}$. A very natural measure for the "goodness" of this model would be

$$R^2_{xy} = \frac{\|\mathbf{P_x y}\|^2}{\|\mathbf{y}\|^2} = \frac{\|\hat{\mathbf{y}}\|^2}{\|\mathbf{y}\|^2} = \frac{\mathbf{y}' \cdot \mathbf{x}(\mathbf{x}'\mathbf{x})^{-1}\mathbf{x}' \cdot \mathbf{y}}{\mathbf{y}'\mathbf{y}} = \cos^2(\mathbf{x}, \mathbf{y}). \tag{4.1}$$

Note that the goodness measure above can also be expressed as

$$R^2_{xy} = \frac{\|[\mathbf{I} - (\mathbf{I} - \mathbf{P_x})]\mathbf{y}\|^2}{\|\mathbf{y}\|^2} = 1 - \frac{\|(\mathbf{I} - \mathbf{P_x})\mathbf{y}\|^2}{\|\mathbf{y}\|^2} = 1 - \frac{\mathrm{SSE}(\mathcal{M}_{xy})}{\|\mathbf{y}\|^2}, \tag{4.2}$$

where $\mathrm{SSE}(\mathcal{M}_{xy})$ refers to the sum of squares of errors under $\mathcal{M}_{xy}$.

The quantity R^2_{xy} defined here is now usually called the *coefficient of determination*, see Section 8 below. To distinguish between the situations of simple linear regression (one regressor) and multiple linear regression (more than one regressor), the terms *coefficient of simple determination* and *coefficient of multiple determination* have been used, respectively, see Puntanen and Styan (2006, page 6).

If we now eliminate the effect of $\mathbf{1}$ from $\mathbf{y}$ and $\mathbf{x}$, i.e., we center them, then we can consider the model $\mathcal{M}_{xy\cdot 1} = \{\tilde{\mathbf{y}}, \tilde{\mathbf{x}}\beta, \#\}$, where we have deliberately left the covariance matrix unnotated. Now a natural measure for the "goodness" of the model $\mathcal{M}_{xy\cdot 1}$ would be

$$R^2_{xy\cdot 1} = \frac{\|\mathbf{P}_{\tilde{\mathbf{x}}}\tilde{\mathbf{y}}\|^2}{\|\tilde{\mathbf{y}}\|^2} = \frac{\|\hat{\tilde{\mathbf{y}}}\|^2}{\|\tilde{\mathbf{y}}\|^2} = \frac{\tilde{\mathbf{y}}' \cdot \tilde{\mathbf{x}}(\tilde{\mathbf{x}}'\tilde{\mathbf{x}})^{-1}\tilde{\mathbf{x}}' \cdot \tilde{\mathbf{y}}}{\tilde{\mathbf{y}}'\tilde{\mathbf{y}}} = \cos^2(\tilde{\mathbf{x}}, \tilde{\mathbf{y}}). \tag{4.3}$$

Obviously $R^2_{xy\cdot 1} = \mathrm{cor_d}^2(\mathbf{x}, \mathbf{y}) = r^2_{xy}$, and hence we have shown that r^2_{xy} can be interpreted as a "measure of goodness" when $\mathbf{y}$ is regressed on $\mathbf{x}$ after the elimination of $\mathbf{1}$. We later discuss a more general corresponding situation. Note further that corresponding to (4.2), we have

$$R^2_{xy\cdot 1} = 1 - \frac{\|(\mathbf{I} - \mathbf{P}_{\tilde{\mathbf{x}}})\tilde{\mathbf{y}}\|^2}{\|\tilde{\mathbf{y}}\|^2} = 1 - \frac{\mathrm{SSE}(\mathcal{M}_{xy\cdot 1})}{\mathrm{SST}(\mathcal{M}_{xy\cdot 1})}, \tag{4.4}$$

where $\mathrm{SSE}(\mathcal{M}_{xy\cdot 1})$ refers to the sum of squares of errors under $\mathcal{M}_{xy\cdot 1}$ and $\mathrm{SST}(\mathcal{M}_{xy\cdot 1}) = \mathbf{y}'\mathbf{C}\mathbf{y}$.

5 OLSE of the constant term

In this section we simply introduce (in a handy way) the formula for the OLSE of the constant term. For that purpose we partition the model as

$$\mathbf{y} = \mathbf{X}\boldsymbol{\beta} + \boldsymbol{\varepsilon} = \beta_0\mathbf{1} + \mathbf{X}_0\boldsymbol{\beta}_{(2)} + \boldsymbol{\varepsilon}. \tag{5.1}$$

We recall that in the partitioned linear model $\mathcal{M}_{12}\colon \mathbf{y} = \mathbf{X}_1\boldsymbol{\beta}_1 + \mathbf{X}_2\boldsymbol{\beta}_2 + \boldsymbol{\varepsilon}$, we have (assuming $\mathbf{X}$ to have full column rank)

$$\hat{\boldsymbol{\beta}}_1(\mathcal{M}_{12}) = (\mathbf{X}_1'\mathbf{M}_2\mathbf{X}_1)^{-1}\mathbf{X}_1'\mathbf{M}_2\mathbf{y}, \qquad \hat{\boldsymbol{\beta}}_2(\mathcal{M}_{12}) = (\mathbf{X}_2'\mathbf{M}_1\mathbf{X}_2)^{-1}\mathbf{X}_2'\mathbf{M}_1\mathbf{y}, \tag{5.2}$$

where $\mathbf{M}_i = \mathbf{I} - \mathbf{P}_i$, $\mathbf{P}_i = \mathbf{P}_{\mathbf{X}_i}$. Putting $\mathbf{X}_1 = \mathbf{1}$, $\mathbf{X}_2 = \mathbf{X}_0$ yields

$$\hat{\beta}_0 = [\mathbf{1}'(\mathbf{I} - \mathbf{P}_{\mathbf{X}_0})\mathbf{1}]^{-1}\mathbf{1}'(\mathbf{I} - \mathbf{P}_{\mathbf{X}_0})\mathbf{y}, \tag{5.3a}$$

$$\hat{\boldsymbol{\beta}}_{(2)} = (\mathbf{X}_0'\mathbf{C}\mathbf{X}_0)^{-1}\mathbf{X}_0'\mathbf{C}\mathbf{y} = (\tilde{\mathbf{X}}_0'\tilde{\mathbf{X}}_0)^{-1}\tilde{\mathbf{X}}_0'\mathbf{y} = \mathbf{T}_1^{-1}\mathbf{t}_2 = \mathbf{S}_1^{-1}\mathbf{s}_2, \tag{5.3b}$$

where $\tilde{\mathbf{X}}_0$ refers to the centered $\mathbf{X}_0$.

Usually the intercept $\hat{\beta}_0$ is not expressed as in (5.3a); the most common expression is

$$\hat{\beta}_0 = \bar{y} - \bar{\mathbf{x}}'\hat{\boldsymbol{\beta}}_{(2)} = \bar{y} - (\bar{x}_1\hat{\beta}_1 + \cdots + \bar{x}_k\hat{\beta}_k), \tag{5.4}$$

where $\bar{\mathbf{x}} = \frac{1}{n}\mathbf{X}_0'\mathbf{1} = (\bar{x}_1, \dots, \bar{x}_k)'$. To confirm (5.4), we use Lemma 1 which gives the decomposition

$$\mathbf{P}_{(\mathbf{A}:\mathbf{B})} = \mathbf{P}_{\mathbf{A}} + \mathbf{P}_{(\mathbf{I}-\mathbf{P}_{\mathbf{A}})\mathbf{B}}. \tag{5.5}$$

Substituting $\mathbf{A} = \mathbf{1}$, $\mathbf{B} = \mathbf{X}_0$ into (5.5) yields

$$\begin{aligned} \mathbf{H}\mathbf{y} = \mathbf{X}\hat{\boldsymbol{\beta}} &= \mathbf{1}\hat{\beta}_0 + \mathbf{X}_0\hat{\boldsymbol{\beta}}_{(2)} \\ &= \mathbf{J}\mathbf{y} + \mathbf{C}\mathbf{X}_0(\mathbf{X}_0'\mathbf{C}\mathbf{X}_0)^{-1}\mathbf{X}_0'\mathbf{C}\mathbf{y} = \mathbf{J}\mathbf{y} + \mathbf{C}\mathbf{X}_0\hat{\boldsymbol{\beta}}_{(2)}, \end{aligned} \tag{5.6}$$

i.e., $\mathbf{1}\hat{\beta}_0 = \mathbf{J}\mathbf{y} - \mathbf{J}\mathbf{X}_0\hat{\boldsymbol{\beta}}_{(2)}$, from which (5.4) follows.

Note that from (5.3a) we can immediately conclude the following:

$$\hat{\beta}_0 = 0 \iff \mathcal{C}(\mathbf{X}_0 : \mathbf{y}) \subset \mathcal{C}(\mathbf{1})^{\perp} \quad \text{or} \quad \mathbf{y} \in \mathcal{C}(\mathbf{X}_0), \tag{5.7}$$

and

$$\operatorname{var}(\hat{\beta}_0) = \frac{\sigma^2}{\mathbf{y}'(\mathbf{I} - \mathbf{P}_{\mathbf{X}_0})\mathbf{y}}. \tag{5.8}$$

The result (5.8) implies, as shown (by other means) by Seber and Lee (2003, pp. 251–252, and Ex. 9d, No. 1), that the variance of $\hat{\beta}_0$ does not depend on the scale used to measure the variables in $\mathbf{X}_0$; changing the scale means the multiplication $\mathbf{X}_0\mathbf{D}$, where $\mathbf{D}$ is a positive definite diagonal matrix.

6 Does centering 'get rid' of the constant term?

Belsley (1991, p. 199) writes:

> "It is generally thought that centering 'gets rid' of the constant term. But this is not the case; centering merely redistributes the constant among all the variates so that it continues to be present, but not explicitly."

To see what is behind this remark, we will consider the following models:

$$\mathcal{M}_{12} = \{\mathbf{y}, (\mathbf{1} : \mathbf{X}_0)\boldsymbol{\beta}, \sigma^2\mathbf{I}\}, \qquad \mathcal{M}_{12\cdot 1} = \{\mathbf{C}\mathbf{y}, \mathbf{C}\mathbf{X}_0\boldsymbol{\beta}_{(2)}, \sigma^2\mathbf{C}\}, \tag{6.1a}$$

$$\mathcal{M}_{c} = \{\mathbf{y}, (\mathbf{1} : \mathbf{C}\mathbf{X}_0)\boldsymbol{\beta}, \sigma^2\mathbf{I}\}, \qquad \mathcal{M}_{r} = \{\mathbf{y}, \mathbf{C}\mathbf{X}_0\boldsymbol{\beta}_{(2)}, \sigma^2\mathbf{I}\}. \tag{6.1b}$$

The model $\mathcal{M}_{12}$ is the full model and all other models are various versions of it. In all these versions we have done something related to the constant term: we have centered something. The above models frequently appear in practice (and in teaching regression in statistics courses). We now review some properties of these models.

We first note that the above models are special versions of the following more general models:

$$\mathscr{M}_{12} = \{\mathbf{y}, \mathbf{X}_1\boldsymbol{\beta}_1 + \mathbf{X}_2\boldsymbol{\beta}_2, \mathbf{V}\}, \qquad \mathscr{M}_{12\cdot 1} = \{\mathbf{M}_1\mathbf{y}, \mathbf{M}_1\mathbf{X}_2\boldsymbol{\beta}_2, \mathbf{M}_1\mathbf{V}\mathbf{M}_1\}, \tag{6.2a}$$

$$\mathscr{M}_{c} = \{\mathbf{y}, (\mathbf{X}_1 : \mathbf{M}_1\mathbf{X}_2)\boldsymbol{\beta}, \mathbf{V}\}, \qquad \mathscr{M}_{r} = \{\mathbf{y}, \mathbf{M}_1\mathbf{X}_2\boldsymbol{\beta}_2, \mathbf{V}\}. \tag{6.2b}$$

These models have recently been studied, for example, by Bhimasankaram et al. (1998), Groß and Puntanen (2000), and Chu et al. (2004, 2005).

We call $\mathscr{M}_{12\cdot 1}$ a reduced model. It is obtained by premultiplying the full model equation

$$\mathbf{y} = \mathbf{X}_1\boldsymbol{\beta}_1 + \mathbf{X}_2\boldsymbol{\beta}_2 + \boldsymbol{\varepsilon} \tag{6.3}$$

by the orthogonal projector $\mathbf{M}_1$. In the reduced model, the response variable is the residual when $\mathbf{y}$ is explained by the variables represented by $\mathbf{X}_1$, and the explanatory variables are the residuals of the $\mathbf{X}_2$ "after elimination of $\mathbf{X}_1$". Therefore, in the case when $\mathbf{X}_2 = \mathbf{x}_k$, the (squared) multiple correlation coefficient in the corresponding reduced model is the (squared) partial correlation between $\mathbf{y}$ and $\mathbf{x}_k$ after the elimination of all other $\mathbf{x}$-variables. The plots of residuals $\mathbf{M}_1\mathbf{y}$ and $\mathbf{M}_1\mathbf{x}_k$ are called added variable plots.

Now, let us return to $\mathcal{M}$-models. We assume that $\mathbf{X}$ has full column rank and thereby that $\hat{\boldsymbol{\beta}}(\mathcal{M}_{12})$ is unique. In view of Lemma 1, we have

$$p = \mathrm{r}(\mathbf{X}) = \mathrm{r}(\mathbf{1} : \mathbf{X}_0) = \mathrm{r}(\mathbf{1} : \mathbf{C}\mathbf{X}_0) = 1 + \mathrm{r}(\mathbf{C}\mathbf{X}_0), \tag{6.4}$$

and hence $\mathrm{r}(\mathbf{X}) = p \implies \mathrm{r}(\mathbf{C}\mathbf{X}_0) = k = p - 1$, and so $\mathbf{C}\mathbf{X}_0$ has also full column rank and hence $\beta_{(2)}$ is estimable under $\mathcal{M}_c$, etc.

Taking a look at the four models in (6.1), we immediately observe an interesting feature which we may state as a Proposition:

Proposition 2. *Consider the models defined in* (6.1), *and let* $\mathbf{X}$ *have full column rank. Then* $\hat{\boldsymbol{\beta}}_{(2)}$ *is the same in each model, i.e.,*

$$\hat{\boldsymbol{\beta}}_{(2)}(\mathcal{M}_{12}) = \hat{\boldsymbol{\beta}}_{(2)}(\mathcal{M}_{12\cdot 1}) = \hat{\boldsymbol{\beta}}_{(2)}(\mathcal{M}_r) = \hat{\boldsymbol{\beta}}_{(2)}(\mathcal{M}_c). \tag{6.5}$$

Moreover, the residuals under the models $\mathcal{M}_{12}$, $\mathcal{M}_{12\cdot 1}$, *and* $\mathcal{M}_c$ *are identical.*

Proof. The first two equalities in (6.5) are obvious. Model $\mathcal{M}_c$ is a reparameterization of $\mathcal{M}_{12}$. This is seen from $(\mathbf{1} : \mathbf{C}\mathbf{X}_0) = (\mathbf{1} : \mathbf{X}_0)\mathbf{A}$, where

$$\mathbf{A} = \begin{pmatrix} 1 & -\mathbf{1}^{+}\mathbf{X}_0 \\ \mathbf{0} & \mathbf{I}_{k-1} \end{pmatrix} = \begin{pmatrix} 1 & -(\mathbf{1}'\mathbf{1})^{-1}\mathbf{1}'\mathbf{X}_0 \\ \mathbf{0} & \mathbf{I}_{k-1} \end{pmatrix} = \begin{pmatrix} 1 & -\bar{\mathbf{x}}' \\ \mathbf{0} & \mathbf{I}_{k-1} \end{pmatrix}. \tag{6.6}$$

It is easy to confirm that $\hat{\beta}_0(\mathcal{M}_c) = \bar{y}$ and $\hat{\boldsymbol{\beta}}_{(2)}(\mathcal{M}_c) = \hat{\boldsymbol{\beta}}_{(2)}(\mathcal{M}_{12})$. Since $\mathcal{C}(\mathbf{1} : \mathbf{C}\mathbf{X}_0) = \mathcal{C}(\mathbf{1} : \mathbf{X}_0)$, the residual vectors under $\mathcal{M}_c$ and $\mathcal{M}_{12}$ are identical:

$$\mathrm{res}(\mathcal{M}_c) = \mathrm{res}(\mathcal{M}_{12}) = \mathbf{y} - \mathbf{H}\mathbf{y} = \mathbf{M}\mathbf{y} = \mathbf{e}. \tag{6.7}$$

The residual vector under $\mathcal{M}_{12\cdot 1}$ becomes (in view of Lemma 1)

$$\mathrm{res}(\mathcal{M}_{12\cdot 1}) = \mathbf{C}\mathbf{y} - \mathbf{P}_{\mathbf{C}\mathbf{X}_0}\mathbf{C}\mathbf{y} = \mathbf{y} - (\mathbf{P}_{\mathbf{1}}\mathbf{y} + \mathbf{P}_{(\mathbf{I}-\mathbf{P}_{\mathbf{1}})\mathbf{X}_0}\mathbf{y}) = \mathbf{M}\mathbf{y}. \tag{6.8}$$

□

The first equality in (6.5) is known as (a special case of) the Frisch–Waugh–Lovell Theorem, see, e.g., Frisch and Waugh (1933) and Lovell (1963), and further extensions by Groß and Puntanen (2000, 2005).

Premultiplying the equation

$$\mathbf{y} = \beta_0\mathbf{1} + \mathbf{X}_0\boldsymbol{\beta}_{(2)} + \boldsymbol{\varepsilon} \tag{6.9}$$

with $\mathbf{J} = \mathbf{P}_{\mathbf{1}}$ shows that

$$\beta_0\mathbf{1} = \bar{y}\mathbf{1} - \mathbf{P}_{\mathbf{1}}\mathbf{X}_0\boldsymbol{\beta}_{(2)} - \bar{\varepsilon}\mathbf{1}. \tag{6.10}$$

If (6.9) is premultiplied with $\mathbf{C}$ we obtain the reduced model $\mathcal{M}_{12\cdot 1}$ which can be written as

$$\tilde{\mathbf{y}} = \tilde{\mathbf{X}}_0\boldsymbol{\beta}_{(2)} + \tilde{\boldsymbol{\varepsilon}}, \tag{6.11}$$

$$\mathbf{y} - \bar{y}\mathbf{1} = (\mathbf{X}_0 - \mathbf{P}_{\mathbf{1}}\mathbf{X}_0)\boldsymbol{\beta}_{(2)} + (\boldsymbol{\varepsilon} - \bar{\varepsilon}\mathbf{1}). \tag{6.12}$$

Belsley (1991, p. 199), referring to the above equations, observes that

"In the form (6.11), there appears to be no constant term, but in the more transparent form (6.12) we see through to the fact that the information in (6.10) is indeed present; it is just incorporated into the other variates - the constant term is still there."

Belsley (1991, p. 199) also remarks (and proves, somewhat tediously) that "**1** does not even play a unique role in such 'reductive' transformations of the regression, for we may similarly transform (6.9) with any of the explanatory variates $\mathbf{x}_i$". Indeed this is so, and the explanation is simply the Frisch–Waugh–Lovell Theorem, which is not referred to by Belsley.

It is worth noting that in the reduced model $\mathcal{M}_{12\cdot1}$, the covariance matrix $\sigma^2\mathbf{C}$ is singular. It is well known that a linear model with a singular covariance matrix requires specific attention.

We recall that a linear unbiased estimator $\mathbf{Gy}$ is the BLUE of an estimable parametric function $\mathbf{K}'\boldsymbol{\beta}$ if it has the smallest covariance matrix (in the Löwner sense) among all unbiased linear estimators of $\mathbf{K}'\boldsymbol{\beta}$.

It is well known that $\hat{\boldsymbol{\beta}}_{(2)}$ is the BLUE of $\boldsymbol{\beta}_{(2)}$ under $\mathcal{M}_{12}$. But we may wonder what is the BLUE of $\boldsymbol{\beta}_{(2)}$ under $\mathcal{M}_{12\cdot1}$, denoted as $\tilde{\boldsymbol{\beta}}_{(2)}(\mathcal{M}_{12\cdot1})$. "Luckily" it appears to be equal to the corresponding OLSE. To prove this, we can use, for example, the following general result: Under the general linear model $\{\mathbf{y}, \mathbf{X}\boldsymbol{\beta}, \mathbf{V}\}$, $\mathrm{OLSE}(\mathbf{X}\boldsymbol{\beta}) = \mathrm{BLUE}(\mathbf{X}\boldsymbol{\beta})$ if and only if

$$C(\mathbf{VX}) \subset C(\mathbf{X}), \tag{6.13}$$

see, e.g., Rao (1967), Zyskind (1967), and Puntanen and Styan (1989). Substituting (6.13) into the model $\mathcal{M}_{12\cdot1}$, we obtain the column space inclusion $C(\mathbf{C}\cdot\mathbf{CX}_0) \subset C(\mathbf{CX}_0)$, which clearly holds. Hence we may state the following proposition.

Proposition 3. *Let* $\mathbf{X}$ *have full column rank. Then*

$$\mathrm{OLSE}(\boldsymbol{\beta}_{(2)} \mid \mathcal{M}_{12\cdot1}) = \mathrm{BLUE}(\boldsymbol{\beta}_{(2)} \mid \mathcal{M}_{12\cdot1}). \tag{6.14}$$

The model $\mathcal{M}_r$ may seem to be obscure, but we note that Groß and Puntanen (2000, p. 133) "...rather like to think of model $\mathcal{M}_r$ as a source of estimators whose properties under the model $\mathcal{M}_{12}$ are investigated...".

7 Rank of the sample correlation matrix

Let the $n\times p$ model matrix $\mathbf{X}$ be partitioned as $\mathbf{X} = (\mathbf{1} : \mathbf{x}_1 : \ldots : \mathbf{x}_k) = (\mathbf{1} : \mathbf{X}_0)$, where $p = k+1$. The sample covariance and correlation matrices of x-variables are

$$\mathbf{S}_1 = \tfrac{1}{n-1}\mathbf{X}_0'\mathbf{C}\mathbf{X}_0 = \tfrac{1}{n-1}\mathbf{T}_1, \qquad \mathbf{R}_1 = [\mathrm{diag}(\mathbf{T}_1)]^{-\frac{1}{2}}\mathbf{T}_1[\mathrm{diag}(\mathbf{T}_1)]^{-\frac{1}{2}}. \tag{7.1}$$

We assume that all x-variables have nonzero variances, that is, $\mathbf{x}_i \notin C(\mathbf{1})$, $i = 1,\ldots,k$. Then Lemma 1 now immediately gives the following result where the vector $\mathbf{1}$ has a crucial role:

Proposition 4. *Assume that all x-variables have nonzero variances. Then the rank of the model matrix* $\mathbf{X} = (\mathbf{1} : \mathbf{X}_0)$ *can be expressed as*

$$\begin{aligned} \mathrm{r}(\mathbf{X}) &= 1 + \mathrm{r}(\mathbf{X}_0) - \dim \mathcal{C}(\mathbf{1}) \cap \mathcal{C}(\mathbf{X}_0) = 1 + \mathrm{r}(\mathbf{C}\mathbf{X}_0) \\ &= 1 + \mathrm{r}(\mathbf{T}_1) = 1 + \mathrm{r}(\mathbf{S}_1) = 1 + \mathrm{r}(\mathbf{R}_1), \end{aligned} \tag{7.2}$$

and moreover,

$$\det(\mathbf{R}_1) \neq 0 \iff \mathrm{r}(\mathbf{X}) = k+1 \iff \mathrm{r}(\mathbf{X}_0) = k \quad \textit{and} \quad \mathbf{1} \notin \mathcal{C}(\mathbf{X}_0). \tag{7.3}$$

It is noteworthy that $r_{ij} = 1$ for some $i \neq j \implies \det(\mathbf{R}_1) = 0$ (but not vice versa). It is also easy to conclude that the correlation matrix $\mathbf{R}_1$ is singular if and only if (at least) one column, $\mathbf{x}_k$ say (for notational simplicity), of $\mathbf{X}_0$, is a linear combination of vectors $\mathbf{1}, \mathbf{x}_1, \dots, \mathbf{x}_{k-1}$.

8 Coefficient of determination

A place where the constant vector plays a fundamental role is in the concept of the coefficient of determination (squared sample multiple correlation coefficient), denoted as $R^2 = R^2_{y\cdot\mathbf{x}}$, see also §4 above. Let us consider the model

$$\mathcal{M}_{12} = \{\mathbf{y}, \mathbf{X}\boldsymbol{\beta}, \sigma^2\mathbf{I}\} = \{\mathbf{y}, \mathbf{1}\beta_0 + \mathbf{X}_0\boldsymbol{\beta}_{(2)}, \sigma^2\mathbf{I}\}, \tag{8.1}$$

and denote

$$\mathrm{SST} = \sum_{i=1}^n (y_i - \bar{y})^2, \quad \mathrm{SSR} = \sum_{i=1}^n (\hat{y}_i - \bar{y})^2, \quad \mathrm{SSE} = \sum_{i=1}^n (y_i - \hat{y}_i)^2. \tag{8.2}$$

Then, according to many textbooks on regression, e.g., Seber and Lee (2003, § 4.4),

$$\mathrm{SST} = \mathrm{SSR} + \mathrm{SSE}, \tag{8.3}$$

and the coefficient of determination can be defined as

$$R^2 = \frac{\mathrm{SSR}}{\mathrm{SST}} = 1 - \frac{\mathrm{SSE}}{\mathrm{SST}}. \tag{8.4}$$

Some statisticians prefer to adjust R^2 by dividing numerator and denominator in $1 - R^2$ by the corresponding degrees of freedom:

$$R^2_{\mathrm{adj}} = 1 - \frac{\mathrm{SSE}\,/\,(n-p)}{\mathrm{SST}\,/\,(n-1)}. \tag{8.5}$$

This adjusted R^2_{adj}, which is also known as Fisher's A statistic, is used in subset selection, see, e.g., Miller (2002, page 161), Puntanen and Styan (2006, page 9).

Why is R^2 so popular? For an interesting discussion about the "hot air" in R^2, see, McGuirk and Driscoll (1995, 1996) and Lavergne (1996).

We take a quick look at the equality (8.3). In matrix terms, we can write

$$\mathrm{SST} = \|(\mathbf{I} - \mathbf{J})\mathbf{y}\|^2, \qquad \mathrm{SSR} = \|(\mathbf{H} - \mathbf{J})\mathbf{y}\|^2, \qquad \mathrm{SSE} = \|(\mathbf{I} - \mathbf{H})\mathbf{y}\|^2, \tag{8.6}$$

and we trivially have $(\mathbf{I} - \mathbf{J})\mathbf{y} = (\mathbf{H} - \mathbf{J})\mathbf{y} + (\mathbf{I} - \mathbf{H})\mathbf{y}$. However, the equation

$$\|(\mathbf{I} - \mathbf{J})\mathbf{y}\|^2 = \|(\mathbf{H} - \mathbf{J})\mathbf{y}\|^2 + \|(\mathbf{I} - \mathbf{H})\mathbf{y}\|^2 \tag{8.7}$$

holds if and only if $(\mathbf{H} - \mathbf{J})\mathbf{y}$ and $(\mathbf{I} - \mathbf{H})\mathbf{y}$ are orthogonal, i.e.,

$$\mathbf{y}'(\mathbf{H} - \mathbf{J})(\mathbf{I} - \mathbf{H})\mathbf{y} = \mathbf{y}'(\mathbf{JH} - \mathbf{J})\mathbf{y} = 0. \tag{8.8}$$

Now (8.8) holds (for all $\mathbf{y}$) if and only if $\mathbf{J} = \mathbf{JH}$, and thereby $\mathbf{J} = \mathbf{JH} = \mathbf{HJ}$. Lemma 3 immediately gives the following Proposition:

Proposition 5. *Consider the model* $\mathcal{M} = \{\mathbf{y}, \mathbf{X}\boldsymbol{\beta}, \sigma^2\mathbf{I}\}$. *Then the decomposition* $\mathrm{SST} = \mathrm{SSR} + \mathrm{SSE}$ *holds (for all* $\mathbf{y}$*) if and only if* $\mathbf{1} \in \mathcal{C}(\mathbf{X})$.

Note that for $\mathrm{SST} = \mathrm{SSR} + \mathrm{SSE}$ to hold, it is not necessary that the vector $\mathbf{1}$ be explicitly a column of $\mathbf{X}$; it is enough if $\mathbf{1} \in \mathcal{C}(\mathbf{X})$. In this situation, in view of Lemma 3, $\mathbf{H} - \mathbf{J}$ is an orthogonal projector:

$$\mathbf{H} - \mathbf{J} = \mathbf{P}_{\mathcal{C}(\mathbf{X}) \cap \mathcal{C}(\mathbf{1})^{\perp}} = \mathbf{P}_{\mathbf{CX}_0}. \tag{8.9}$$

When $\mathbf{1} \notin \mathcal{C}(\mathbf{X})$, it makes no sense to use (8.4) as a statistic to describe how well OLS fits the data. When $\mathbf{1} \notin \mathcal{C}(\mathbf{X})$, R^2 as defined in (8.4), can be even negative. In the no-intercept model, it is natural [see, e.g., Searle (1982, p. 379)] to consider the decomposition

$$\mathbf{y}'\mathbf{y} = \mathbf{y}'\mathbf{Hy} + \mathbf{y}'(\mathbf{I} - \mathbf{H})\mathbf{y}, \qquad \mathrm{SST}_* = \mathrm{SSR}_* + \mathrm{SSE}. \tag{8.10}$$

Then the coefficient of determination can be defined as

$$R_*^2 = \frac{\mathrm{SSR}_*}{\mathrm{SST}_*} = \frac{\mathbf{y}'\mathbf{Hy}}{\mathbf{y}'\mathbf{y}} = 1 - \frac{\mathrm{SSE}}{\mathbf{y}'\mathbf{y}} = \cos^2(\mathbf{y}, \mathbf{Hy}). \tag{8.11}$$

However, there are some disadvantages in (8.11) as pointed out by Weisberg (2005, p. 84): "The quantity in (8.11) is not invariant under location change, so, for example, if units are changed from Fahrenheit to Celsius, you will get different value for (8.11)." See also Puntanen and Styan (2006, page 15).

We may end up with R^2 via different routes. One very natural approach in which the vector $\mathbf{1}$ has an important role is to consider the simple basic model where the only explanatory variable is a constant: $\mathcal{M}_0 = \{\mathbf{y}, \mathbf{1}\beta_0, \sigma^2\mathbf{I}\}$. Under $\mathcal{M}_0$ we have $\mathrm{OLSE}(\mathbf{1}\beta_0) = \mathbf{Jy} = \bar{y}\mathbf{1}$, while the residual vector is the centered $\mathbf{y}$, that is, $\mathbf{Cy}$, and hence the residual sum of squares under $\mathcal{M}_0$ is

$$\mathrm{SSE}_0 = \mathbf{y}'(\mathbf{I} - \mathbf{J})\mathbf{y} = \mathbf{y}'\mathbf{Cy} = t_{yy} = \sum_{i=1}^{n}(y_i - \bar{y})^2 = \mathrm{SST}. \tag{8.12}$$

We may want to compare the full model $\mathcal{M}_{12}$ and the simple basic model $\mathcal{M}_0$ by means of residual sum of squares: how much benefit is gained in the residual sum of squares when also using x-variables as explanatory variables. The change in SSE when moving from $\mathcal{M}_0$ to $\mathcal{M}_{12}$ is

$$\mathrm{SSE}_0 - \mathrm{SSE} = \mathbf{y}'(\mathbf{I}-\mathbf{J})\mathbf{y} - \mathbf{y}'(\mathbf{I}-\mathbf{H})\mathbf{y} = \mathbf{y}'(\mathbf{H}-\mathbf{J})\mathbf{y} = \mathrm{SSR}, \tag{8.13}$$

which is called "sum of squares due to regression". The value of SSR tells the reduction in SSE when using $\mathcal{M}_{12}$ instead $\mathcal{M}_0$, but it is definitely more informative to study the *relative* reduction in SSE, that is, we have reasons to calculate the ratio

$$\frac{\mathrm{SSE}_0 - \mathrm{SSE}}{\mathrm{SSE}_0} = \frac{\mathrm{SST}-\mathrm{SSE}}{\mathrm{SST}} = \frac{\mathrm{SSR}}{\mathrm{SST}} = 1 - \frac{\mathrm{SSE}}{\mathrm{SST}} = R^2. \tag{8.14}$$

A fundamental property of R^2 defined above is that it equals the square of the multiple correlation coefficient between the $\mathbf{y}$ and $\mathbf{Hy}$. This is a well-known result but we state it here since it nicely illustrates the important role of $\mathbf{1}$.

Proposition 6. *Consider the model* $\mathcal{M} = \{\mathbf{y}, \mathbf{X}\boldsymbol{\beta}, \sigma^2\mathbf{I}\}$, *where* $\mathbf{1} \in \mathcal{C}(\mathbf{X})$ *and let* R^2 *be defined as in* (8.14). *Then*

$$R = \mathrm{cor_d}(\mathbf{y}, \mathbf{Hy}) = \cos[(\mathbf{I}-\mathbf{J})\mathbf{y}, (\mathbf{I}-\mathbf{J})\mathbf{Hy}] = \cos(\mathbf{Cy}, \mathbf{CHy}). \tag{8.15}$$

Proof. In view of $\mathbf{1} \in \mathcal{C}(\mathbf{X}) \iff \mathbf{H1} = \mathbf{1} \iff \mathbf{J} = \mathbf{HJ} = \mathbf{JH}$, we observe that $(\mathbf{I}-\mathbf{J})\mathbf{H} = \mathbf{H}-\mathbf{J}$. Hence our claim is

$$R = \mathrm{cor_d}(\mathbf{y}, \mathbf{Hy}) = \cos[\mathbf{Cy}, (\mathbf{H}-\mathbf{J})\mathbf{y}] := \frac{a}{\sqrt{b \cdot c}}, \tag{8.16}$$

which indeed is true since $a = \mathbf{y}'(\mathbf{I}-\mathbf{J})\mathbf{Hy} = \mathbf{y}'(\mathbf{H}-\mathbf{J})\mathbf{y}$, $b = \mathbf{y}'\mathbf{Cy}$, and $c = \mathbf{y}'(\mathbf{H}-\mathbf{J})\mathbf{y}$. □

The geometry behind decomposition SST = SSR + SSE is illustrated in Figure 1.

Note that if *all* variables $x_1, \dots, x_k, y$ are random variables with the covariance matrix

$$\mathrm{cov}\begin{pmatrix}\mathbf{x}\\ y\end{pmatrix} = \begin{pmatrix}\boldsymbol{\Sigma}_{11} & \boldsymbol{\sigma}_2\\ \boldsymbol{\sigma}_2' & \sigma_y^2\end{pmatrix}, \tag{8.17}$$

then the population multiple correlation (squared) is defined as

$$\mathcal{R}^2 = \max_{\mathbf{a}} \mathrm{cor}^2(y, \mathbf{a}'\mathbf{x}) = \frac{\boldsymbol{\sigma}_2'\boldsymbol{\Sigma}_{11}^{-1}\boldsymbol{\sigma}_2}{\sigma_y^2} = 1 - \frac{\sigma_y^2 - \boldsymbol{\sigma}_2'\boldsymbol{\Sigma}_{11}^{-1}\boldsymbol{\sigma}_2}{\sigma_y^2}. \tag{8.18}$$

It is worth emphasizing (see, e.g., Weisberg 2005, § 4.4), that when the x-variables are controllable, fixed, then R^2 is not to be considered as an estimate of something like $\mathcal{R}^2$: for a linear model where $\mathbf{X}$ is fixed, there exists no

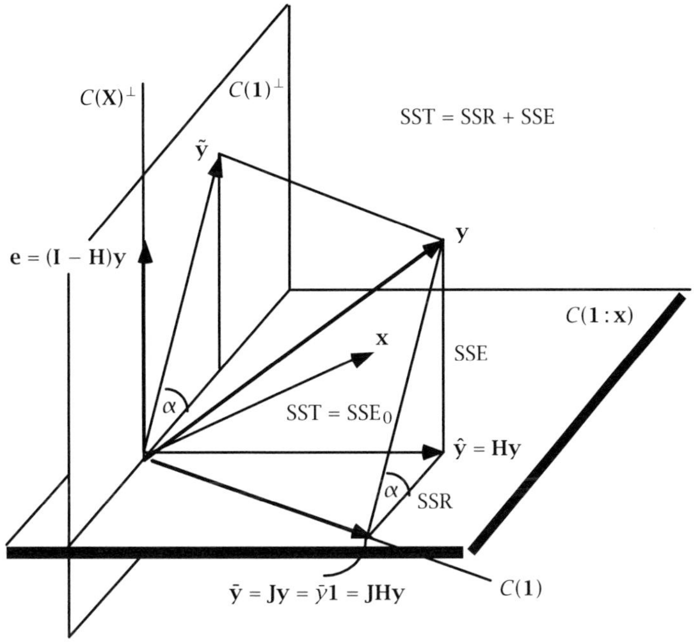

Figure 1. Illustration of SST = SSR + SSE.

such a parameter as $\mathcal{R}$. The sample value R^2 is merely a descriptive measure how well the OLS fits the data.

We complete this section by noting that in view of (3.3) and (8.9), we can express R^2, corresponding to (8.18), as

$$R^2 = \frac{\mathbf{y}'(\mathbf{H}-\mathbf{J})\mathbf{y}}{\mathbf{y}'(\mathbf{I}-\mathbf{J})\mathbf{y}} = \frac{\mathbf{t}_2'\mathbf{T}_1^{-1}\mathbf{t}_2}{t_{yy}}. \tag{8.19}$$

Acknowledgements

We wish to thank Professor Belsley for allowing us to publish the e-mail correspondence in the Section 1. The research of the third author was supported in part by the Natural Sciences and Engineering Research Council of Canada.

Noted added in proof

As we were reading the final page proofs of this paper we discovered the recent article by Friedman and Wall (2005), and the related Letter to the Editor by Christensen (2006), and reply by Friedman (2006). We plan to comment on this work in a further paper.

References

Belsley, D. A. (1991). *Conditioning Diagnostics: Collinearity and Weak Data in Regression.* New York: Wiley.

Bhimasankaram, P., Shah, K. R. and Saha Ray, R. (1998). On a singular partitioned linear model and some associated reduced models. *Journal of Combinatorics, Information & System Sciences*, 23, 415–421.

Christensen, R. (2006). Comment on Friedman and Wall (2005). Letter to the Editor. *The American Statistician*, 60, 101–102.

Chu, K. L., Isotalo, J., Puntanen, S. and Styan, G. P. H. (2004). On decomposing the Watson efficiency of ordinary least squares in a partitioned weakly singular linear model. *Sankhyā*, 66, 634–651.

Chu, K. L., Isotalo, J., Puntanen, S. and Styan, G. P. H. (2005). Some further results concerning the decomposition of the Watson efficiency in partitioned linear models. *Sankhyā*, 67, 74–89.

Friedman, L. (2006). Reply to Christensen (2006). Letter to the Editor. *The American Statistician*, 60, 102–103.

Friedman, L. and Wall, M. (2005). Graphical views of suppression and multicollinearity in multiple linear regression. *The American Statistician*, 59, 127–136.

Frisch, R. and Waugh, F. V. (1933). Partial time regressions as compared with individual trends. *Econometrica*, 1, 387–401.

Groß, J. and Puntanen, S. (2000). Estimation under a general partitioned linear model. *Linear Algebra and Its Applications*, 321, 131–144.

Groß, J. and Puntanen, S. (2005). Extensions of the Frisch–Waugh–Lovell Theorem. *Discussiones Mathematicae – Probability and Statistics*, 25, 39–49.

Isotalo, J., Puntanen, S. and Styan, G. P. H. (2005). Matrix tricks for linear statistical models: our personal Top Sixteen. Report A 363, Dept. of Mathematics, Statistics & Philosophy, University of Tampere.

Lavergne, P. (1996). The hot air in R^2: comment [on McQuirk and Driscoll (1995)]. *American Journal of Agricultural Economics*, 78, 712–714.

Lovell, M. C. (1963). Seasonal adjustment of economic time series and multiple regression analysis. *Journal of the American Statistical Association*, 58, 993–1010.

Marsaglia, G. and Styan, G. P. H. (1974). Equalities and inequalities for ranks of matrices. *Linear and Multilinear Algebra*, 2, 269–292.

McQuirk, A. and Driscoll, P. (1995). The hot air in R^2 and consistent measures of explained variation. *American Journal of Agricultural Economics*, 77, 319–328. [See also comment by Lavergne (1996) and Reply by McQuirk and Driscoll (1996).]

McQuirk, A. and Driscoll, P. (1996). The hot air in R^2: reply [to Lavergne (1996)]. *American Journal of Agricultural Economics*, 78, 715–717.

Mustonen, Seppo (2001). *SURVO MM: Computing Environment for Creative Processing of Text and Numerical Data.* http://www.survo.fi/english/index.html

Puntanen, S. and Styan, G. P. H. (1989). The equality of the ordinary least squares estimator and the best linear unbiased estimator. *The American Statistician*, 43, 153–164.

Puntanen, S. and Styan, G. P. H. (2006). Some easy matrix tricks useful in teaching linear statistical models, with some comments on subset selection criteria in multiple linear regression. Report 2006-04, Dept. of Mathematics and Statistics, McGill University.

Rao, C. R. (1967). Least squares theory using an estimated dispersion matrix and its application to measurement of signals. In *Proc. Fifth Berkeley Symposium on Mathematical Statistics and Probability: Berkeley, California, 1965/1966*, vol. 1. Eds. L. M. Le Cam and J. Neyman. Berkeley: Univ. of California Press, 355–372.

Searle, S. R. (1982). *Matrix Algebra Useful for Statistics.* New York: Wiley.

Seber, G. A. F. and Lee, A. J. (2003). *Linear Regression Analysis.* Second Edition. New York: Wiley.

Weisberg, S. (2005). *Applied Linear Regression.* Third Edition. New York: Wiley.

Zyskind, G. (1967). On canonical forms, non-negative covariance matrices and best and simple least squares linear estimators in linear models. *Annals of Mathematical Statistics*, 38, 1092–1109.

Jarkko Isotalo
Department of Mathematics, Statistics and Philosophy
FI-33014 University of Tampere, Finland
jarkko.isotalo@uta.fi

Simo Puntanen
Department of Mathematics, Statistics and Philosophy
FI-33014 University of Tampere, Finland
sjp@uta.fi
http://www.uta.fi/~sjp/

George P. H. Styan
Department of Mathematics and Statistics
McGill University, Burnside Hall Room 1005
805 rue Sherbrooke Street West
Montréal (Québec), Canada H3A 2K6
styan@math.mcgill.ca
http://www.math.mcgill.ca/styan/

Festschrift for Tarmo Pukkila on his 60th Birthday
Eds. E. P. Liski, J. Isotalo, J. Niemelä, S. Puntanen, and G. P. H. Styan

Univ. of Tampere, 2006, ISBN 978-951-44-6620-5, pages 261–284

On joint and separate history of probability, statistics and actuarial science

JUKKA RANTALA

Abstract. The article brings forward some highlights of the common history of probability, statistics and actuarial science and discusses the links of these three related sciences.

1 Introduction

When I more than 30 years ago was studying mathematics and statistics at the University of Tampere, I discovered in the library of the Statistical Department a book with the name "Risk Theory". The authors were Beard, Pentikäinen, and Pesonen. Inspired by both the name of the book and the fact that two of the authors were Finns, I began to read the book, but soon lost my interest. In those days I was more captivated by manipulation of formulas than by the practical approach used in the book. In addition, the application area, insurance, was totally unknown to me. Paradoxically, later in my career I got very much involved with insurance and insurance mathematics, Teivo Pentikäinen as my mentor.

The aim of this article is to discuss subjects and areas of common interest to actuarial science, probability theory and statistics. The fact that they have a lot in common can be seen just by glancing at the contents list of the Encyclopedia of Actuarial Science (2004). My approach is to write from an actuary's angle to statisticians and to try to illustrate shortly what has happened on the actuarial side of the field. On the other hand, I hope that actuaries possibly reading the article might get an inspiration to look more closely for additional opportunities the statistical methods could provide for their practical work. I believe that e.g. in Finland these opportunities have not been fully utilized, since the background of actuaries is usually in pure mathematics without much statistics in their syllabus. The same may concern actuaries in other countries too, perhaps with the exception that the mathematical education may have a smaller role than in Finland.

I apologize that the article is somewhat anecdotal. My excuse is that I am not a professional researcher and lack of time and space also have set their own limitations. I ask possible readers more interested in these issues to consult the references given at the end of the article.

As is well known, the development of probability theory started from studying certain problems of gambling. Insurance, on the other hand, is an organized way to mitigate financial consequences of risks. Daston (2005) expresses the connection and the difference between insurance and gambling in a nice way by saying that insurance and gambling are two institutionalized approaches to risk taking: gamblers pay to take unnecessary risks in hope of getting the prize and buyers of insurance pay to avoid the consequences of necessary risks.

The risks will occur with a certain probability. In insurance the assessment of these probabilities and the consequences of risks happening must mostly be based on what has been observed in the past. Hence collection of statistics and the use of statistical methods are of major importance for insurance. Statistics and probability theory are applied in many other areas too but mostly as an aid to develop the subject matter itself. Insurance is different, since in insurance the probability lies at the heart of the activity.

Many practical applications of actuarial science and insurance are based on innovations in statistics and probability theory. Many famous mathematicians and probabilists have contributed to insurance mathematics. Take names like Christiaan Huygens, Johann De Witt, Nicholas and Jakob Bernoulli and Leonhard Euler as examples. Many famous mathematicians also have made practical actuarial work. E.g. Gauss spent several years putting Göttingen University's widows' fund on a sound actuarial basis. On the other hand, actuarial innovations have given impetus to the development of statistics and probability. Some innovations have also been found parallel and independently without much influence from the other side.

In this article the origins of insurance and probability theory are first briefly discussed (Section 2). Then, Section 3 lists and describes some areas common to statistics and actuarial science. Finally, in Section 4, the role of actuarial science in the scientific community is discussed.

What is an actuary? The definition in the Glossary of International Association of Supervisors is the following: "an actuary is a professional trained in evaluating the financial implications of contingency events. Actuaries require an understanding of the stochastic nature of insurance and other financial services, the risks inherent in assets and the use of statistical models. In the context of insurance, these skills are, for example, often used in establishing premiums, technical provisions and capital levels."

Actuaries form a profession with requirements for qualification, standards of practice, compliance and disciplinary processes. The global number of qualified actuaries is around 35,000, which I guess is less than the number of statisticians. Actuarial science can be defined as a science concerned with the application of mathematical probability theory to problems of insurance and finance.

In most countries the insurers; in particular life insurance companies and pension funds, are required to have an actuary to assess the financial value of the insurance and pension liabilities, to give professional advice and opinion on pricing, on profit sharing, on the financial strength of the insurer, etc. Besides these "compulsory" duties actuaries are involved in many other activities of the insurer and sometimes also outside insurance. To reflect these wider fields of applications of actuarial knowledge the UK actuarial profession has adopted the slogan "making financial sense of the future".

The word actuary is derived from the Latin word actuarius, which has been given two meanings, a shorthand writer and one who writes out accounts, see Ogborn (1956). It has been concluded that the various acta of the Roman senate were compiled for public use by the actuarius and that, in the preparation of this work, he collected the social events from the official registers and the decisions of the magistrates from the shorthand reports of the notarii who attended the Courts, but that the Acta Senatus were compiled by him from notes of its proceedings which he himself had taken in shorthand (Ogborn 1956).

When the title of actuary first became attached to individuals making insurance mathematical calculations it did not carry the meaning that it has today. The profession grew in response to the demand for persons with the requisite mathematical skill to deal with problems involving life contingencies, especially in connection with life assurance offices and similar provident institutions. However, the present use started to become established in the 18th century when the chief executive of Equitable Life Insurance Society in London, Mr. William Morgan, also performed the insurance technical calculations of the company and held the title actuary, derived from "actuarius" by an antiquary, who was closely involved with the formation of the company (Evans 1998).

2 On the early history of insurance and probability

2.1 Origins of insurance

Risks facing individuals and the community have existed from the earliest times. An obvious method to alleviate the consequences of risks is the use of charitable donations from those who were more fortunate. However, this method cannot be satisfactory because it lacks certainty and may stigmatise the recipient. Therefore it is natural that people very early have looked for some other means which could give the necessary relief as of right, not as charity. The oldest hints of the existence of an early form of insurance and annuities are from ancient Babylonia and Egypt

The following extract (Lewin 1998) from the law code of Hammurabi from Babylonia; eighteenth century BC gives an example of the first forms of cargo insurance:

> "If a merchant lent money to a trader for benefit, and he saw a loss where he went, he shall pay back the principal of the money to the merchant. If, when he went on the road, an enemy made him give up what he was carrying, the trader shall so affirm by God and then shall go free"

The idea was that of mutual insurance. Based on an agreement, a member of the group who had suffered a loss without his own fault was compensated by the others. Later on this developed into more modern insurance involving even an investor to provide the financing. For example, if a sea voyage was successful, the money invested was repaid with a heavy rate of interest. If the voyage failed, no repayment was required. Very early it was observed that the investor's risk was largely reduced if the money was divided between several attempts. Later on in the 14th century the protection element (i.e. the excess interest rate) was separated from the financing element. The insurance protection was no longer necessarily provided by the financers but by a separate "insurer" and so a modern form of (general, non-life) insurance was born. The first genuine insurance policy of this kind known today is from 1350 (Lewin 2001). A cargo of wheat from Sicily to Tunis was insured at a premium of 18%. The insurer, Leonardo Cattanco, undertook to insure all risks from acts of God and perils from the sea.

The two basic forms of life insurance are protection against the risk of death or living long. For the latter the term annuity is often used. Annuity means a series of regular payments contracted to be made to a person or persons as long as they are alive. Pension is an example.

The following presentation on annuities is based on Kopf (1927). It is assumed that in Babylon there existed a fairly wide-spread practice of granting a series of periodic payments secured by land or other property. Legal codes of Egypt give evidence that an annuity was purchased by a Prince ruling in the Middle Empire. There is much evidence that the Romans had the statistical material and the required skill in arithmetic for the construction of crude annuity tables. The purchase and sale of annuities was widely prevalent and some statistical knowledge existed on the effect of mortality on the funds of mutual aid societies, which had wide vogue among civil and military populations. The Romans of the second and third centuries AD were well qualified in the art of calculation. A famous table used to capitalize annuities is attributed to prefect Ulpianus (about 225 AD).

After the fall of Rome in the fourth century AD the money economy almost vanished. One reason for this was the church ban on usury. It was permissible to charge interest whenever the lender was in danger of losing his capital or of exposing himself to a loss or a deprivation of a gain. This was called compensatory interest. The edicts of the Church related primarily to usurius charges on the consumptive needs of the poor and distressed. It was mostly the Church itself that revived public interest in life annuities. Monasteries and other religious bodies gave land in return for annual payments of money.

The annuity practice revived in the late Middle Ages. Probably one contributing factor for that was the abandonment of the system of Roman numeration (about 1150), and the adoption of Arabic numerals as well as the recovery of old Greek and Arabic mathematics.

A new innovation occurred in Germany during the eleventh century. It became customary for barons and counts to finance their wars by hiring mercenaries. Much of this expense was met by hypothecating land, with rents or annuities payable in gold. This way of paying for a war on the installment plan became popular also elsewhere in Europe. For example, in 1470 Genoa had outstanding obligations of this type (loans repayable as annuities and chargeable against the city) for more than 11,000,000 lire. In Germany this form of municipal funding was so lucrative that private undertaking in the annuity field was forbidden in some cities.

The payments to the annuitants were usually made half-yearly. A town official searched out persons entitled to annuity payments, posted a notice on the church door, set up an office and then told the annuitants to call for their money. On the other hand, in Leyden in the middle of the 16th century gratuities were offered to persons who reported deaths of annuitants to the Finance Minister. Rewards were also offered for revealing frauds against the annuity funds.

2.2 Life insurance to scientific basis

The betting on lives and insuring them were long regarded almost as the same activity. It was possible that people betted on the life of the King of the country or on the loss of their own country in war. In order to make insurance a more serious activity the link to gambling had to be broken. In England these two activities were separated legally as late as in 1774. That happened at the same time as life insurance already began to be established on a more scientific basis.

Three prerequisites are needed to put life insurance on a scientific basis: the concept of (compound) interest, numerical theory of probability and relevant statistical data.

The concept of compound interest was well understood at the latest in the 15th century. In 1613 Richard Witt, a London mathematical practitioner, published a landmark work on compound interest. The book delved deeply into the subject in a very practical way, with many tables and examples. It is possible that compound interest tables may have inspired the invention of logarithms, published by Napier in 1614 (Lewin 1998, 2001).

A better understanding of probability also started to emerge. For the Greeks, thinking about games and playing them were separate activities. They understood that more things might happen in the future than actually will happen. The Greeks however had little interest in experimentation (Bernstein 1996). Serious study of risk and probability began during the Renaissance.

Pioneering work on probability was done by Cardano in the 16th century. He studied games of chance and the probabilities involved in dice throws. In the early 17th century a French nobleman Chevaliér de Méré proposed to Blaise Pascal and Pierre Fermat a problem on a fair sharing of stakes if a certain dice throw game will be interrupted. Pascal and Fermat started to solve the problem by combinatorial methods. This start led later on to a rapid development of theory of probability and distributions by many famous names like Christiaan Huygens, Nicholas and Jakob Bernoulli, Leonhard Euler. Although the beginnings of the theory were dealing with empirical problems, the development was very much based on advances in calculus and algebra. As a consequence, for the first time it was possible to make decisions and forecasts about the future with the help of numbers and probability theory. Insurance was one of the obvious areas for applications.

The third pillar of scientific life insurance, the emergence of more reliable statistics on human lives, also started to accelerate in the 17th century. One of the background factors was the need of the governments to know what their resources were e.g. with regard to warfare. And as mentioned above, many governments and cities sold annuities to finance warfare or for property development.

One of the pioneers of mortality studies was James Graunt, a London merchant, who in 1662 published a book entitled "Natural and Political Observations made upon the Bills of Mortality", see Lewin (1998). The Bills of Mortality were weekly printed statements of the numbers of the people who had died in big cities, classified according to the apparent cause of death. The original purpose was to use them as a warning device to detect a possible rise of epidemic diseases. Graunt, however used them to produce a table showing how many of the newborns are expected to be alive at later ages. The table could not be quite reliable among other things for the reason that the age at death was not recorded, but Graunt had estimated it on the basis of the assumed cause of death. Graunt also used the Bills of Mortality to estimate the total population of London, with the result of 384,000 people, which was much less than the commonly asserted one million people.

Graunt's results did not have much influence on the life insurance and annuity practice of that time. Neither was it connected with the calculation of compound interest. That combination was made in 1671 by the Dutch Prime Minister, John de Witt. He had formerly also got a great reputation because of his achievements (both practical and theoretical) in marine warfare (Barnwell 1856).

De Witt based his studies on registers of births and deaths in different towns of Holland. He presented a report to the States-General, giving recommendations for prices of annuities the government was selling in order to raise money for the state. For example, for a person at the age of three years his recommendation (by using a 4 per cent rate of interest) was that the price should be 16 times the annual amount of the annuity. The price charged by the government was independent of the age of the annuitant and 14 times the annual amount. The old practice was not changed because of fear that a price increase would reduce sales.

The first widely circulated work on the value of annuities was published by Edmond Halley in 1693. Halley, a famous astronomer, is perhaps better known because of a comet named after him. Halley's work was based on death statistics from Breslau, which showed for both sexes the numbers of deaths at each age. On the basis of this data and assuming a stationary population Halley constructed a life table showing for each age how many of 1000 newborns were expected to be alive at that age. E.g. for the age of 60 years the figure was 242. Halley combined the life table to compound interest and used the results in the same way as the actuary in traditional life insurance would do today. He listed six possible applications (Halley 1693):

1. "The first use hereof is to shew the Proportion of Men able to bear Arms in any Multitude, which are those between 18 and 56, rather than 16 and 60; the one being generally too weak to bear the Fatigues of War and the Weight of Arms, and the other too crasie and infirm from Age, nonwithstanding particular Instances to the contrary."
2. "The Second Use of this Table is to shew the differing degrees of Mortality, or rather Vitality in all Ages; for if the number of Persons of any Age remaining after one year, be divided by the difference between that and the number of the Age proposed, it shews the odds that there is, that a Person of that Age does not die in a Year."
3. "Use III. But if it be enquired at what number of Years, it is an even Lay that a Person of any Age shall die, this Table readily performs it: For if the number of Persons living of the Age proposed be halved, it will be found by the Table at what Year the said number is reduced to half by Mortality; and that is the Age, to which it is an even Wager, that a Person of the Age proposed shall arrive before he die."
4. "Use IV. By what has been said, the Price of Insurance upon Lives ought to be regulated, and the difference is discovered between the price of ensuring the Live of a Man of 20 and 50, for Example: it being 100 to 1 that a Man of 20 dies not in a year, and but 38 to 1 for a Man of 50 Years of Age."
5. "Use V. On this depends the Valuation of Annuities upon Lives; for it is plain that the Purchaser ought to pay for only such a part of the value of the Annuity, as he has Chances that he is living; and this ought to be computed yearly, and the Sum of all those yearly Values being added together, will amount to the value of the Annuity for the Life of the Person proposed. Now the present value of Money payable after a term of years, at any given rate of Interest, either may be had from Tables already computed; or almost as compendiously, by the Table of

Logarithms: For the Arithmetical Complement of the Logarithm of Unity and its yearly Interest (that is, of 1,06 for Six per Cent. being 9,974694.) being multiplied by the number of years proposed, gives the present value of One Pound payable after the end of so many years. Then by the foregoing Proposition, it will be as the number of Persons living after that term of years, to the number dead; so are the Odds that any one Person is Alive or Dead. And by consequence, as the Sum of both or the number of Persons living of the Age first proposed, to the number remaining after so many years, (both given by the Table) so the present value of the yearly Sum payable after the term proposed, to the Sum which ought to be paid for the Chance the person has to enjoy such an Annuity after so many Years. And this being repeated for every year of the persons Life, the Sum of all the present Values of those Chances is the true Value of the Annuity.

6. "Use VI. Two Lives are likewise valuable by the same Rule."

The principles for calculations were clear but the calculations themselves were laborious. The amount of work was reduced when the numbers of those still living were expressed by a mathematical formula; i.e. by an elementary statistical model. The first to do that was Abraham de Moivre in 1724, who assumed that the number of those living decreased in arithmetical progression.

It still took years before life insurance based on scientific considerations had its breakthrough. In the UK life annuities were traded relatively freely, but their values were still mainly based on rules of thumb. Differences types of insurance against death were mainly very short-term contracts with premiums based on underwriter's experience and judgment. Towards the end of the 18th century the new methods had been developed and they were successfully applied in particular by "Society of Equitable Assurances on Lives and Survivorships", mentioned above as the insurance company to employ the "first" actuary, William Morgan.

Generally life insurance was still to a large extent speculative business and there were a lot of life insurance company bankruptcies and losses of policyholders' money. Above all the reason was the excessive distribution of profits to the entrepreneurs. Speculative business ceased first when a proper insurance supervision was established in the early 19th century. "Equitable" itself survived until the equity bubble in 2000. Its archive is of the highest significance for the history of actuarial science and practice, since it includes original work by Thomas Bayes, James Dodson, William Morgan, and Richard Price, amongst others.

2.3 Law of large numbers, central limit theory

The diversification of risks is one of the very early discovered cornerstones of insurance. Diversification can include two types of effects: pooling of (almost) similar and independent risks or insuring different but independent risks. The law of large numbers (LLN) and the central limit theorem (CLT) are obvious mathematical counterparts for analytic treatment of these effects.

It was thought, long before Bernoulli, that the number of successes in n Bernoulli trials with probability p was approximately equal to np. Italian mathematician Cardano (Ore 1953), for example, applied this formula in calculations connected with games of dice. A second approach to the LLN took shape in astronomy, when during Kepler's lifetime the arithmetic mean became the universal estimator of the constant sought (more on this see e.g. Sheynin (1970, 1977) and Hald (1998)).

The LLN was informally recognized also in collecting the first life tables. The idea was expressed by saying that "if we only collect enough data the irregularities will vanish". E.g. de Witt stated that buying annuities upon many young and apparently healthy lives secured profit "without hazard or risk" (Haberman 1996).

James Bernoulli was one of the most famous mathematicians to treat the LLN with a mathematical rigor. In essence, Bernoulli proved the so-called weak form of the LLN.

The problem of so-called inverse probability (i.e. inferring from the observations the underlying true probability of the event happening) was first not clearly distinguished from the LLN. An elegant solution to the problem, based on the fact that a joint density function of two random variables can be expressed in two different forms of conditional density functions, was developed by Reverend Thomas Bayes (1701–1761), and published posthumously by his colleague and actuary Richard Price in 1763. However, the result was not generally known before Laplace discovered it in 1774. Bayes' result is generally known as Bayes Theorem or as the Law of Inverse Probability

In statistics Bayes Theorem has given rise to a wide branch known under the name Bayesian Statistics (with Empirical Bayesian Statistics as a subset), which is dealing with estimation and prediction by combining prior knowledge and new observations. In actuarial science the parallel (of Empirical Bayesian Statistics) is known as credibility theory.

The problem in applying the LLN to insurance is that insurance portfolios are never infinite and that the variation around that mean is as important as the mean itself. It is used e.g. in assessing the need for capital reserves. Hence the problem of convolution of many individual but not necessarily identical distributions is a central issue in insurance. The CLT was one of the first attempts to provide a theoretical answer to this question. The CLT was a popular subject for mathematical research beginning in the 18th century and it employed many famous mathematicians like Laplace, Cauchy, Poisson, Bessel and Gauss. It is interesting to note that one of the few Finns mentioned in the history of probability theory, J.W. Lindeberg is there because of his version and proof of the CLT. For more on the history of the CLT, see e.g. Hald (1998).

The CLT is applicable when the number of random variables (risks) is large and none of them is dominating the total outcome. This may not always be the case in insurance, where the total loss amount in a portfolio may be heavily dependent on a few big risks. Then other probability distributions are useful, even such which do not possess other finite moments than the first one. A frequently used example is Pareto-distribution. It is also natural that limiting distributions based on the theory of extreme values are useful in types of insurance which are related to natural catastrophes like windstorms, hurricanes, floods and earthquakes. They can also be used in reinsurance based on the idea of cutting the tops of the loss distribution of the insurer buying the reinsurance cover (see e.g. Embrechts et al. (2003)).

2.4 Utility theory

Utility theory deals with the quantification of preferences for risky assets and liabilities, a subject closely related to insurance. Utility theory may be considered to have begun in the 18th century. In the early days of probability theory the expected value (of the game) was used as the main decision-making variable. The invention of the St. Petersburg paradox changed the picture. Daniel Bernoulli was first to suggest assigning a value to consequences and measuring the desirability of lotteries by expected utility. He argued for the logarithmic utility function (instead of a linear utility function as the expected value).

In spite of its close relationship to concepts of insurance, utility theory has not led to any significant practical actuarial applications. However, it is theoretically important for insurance, since it gives economic-philosophical explanation for the existence of insurance. The question is why policyholders are willing to pay more for their policy than the amount of the expected loss; i.e. the expected value for what they receive as return for paying the insurance premium. The explanation provided by utility theory is that the utility function of the policyholder is more concave than that of the insurer, having much more resources than the policyholder.

2.5 Risk theory and stochastic processes

Even if in the development of life insurance described above the randomness of the process was recognized at least implicitly, the practical applications were in essence based on deterministic thinking; i.e. on the calculation of expected values of random variables. In non-life insurance the role of randomness is usually much bigger than in life insurance. However, explicit stochastic methods were seldom applied in practice, where prices in commercial insurance were based on experience and intuition. The continuity of the business was targeted by high security loadings in premiums and in mutual insurance associations by the possibility to resort to supplementary contributions after the losses had occurred. As we will see later in Section 3, a more advanced statistical-theoretical basis for setting non-life premiums started to develop as late as in the early 20th century.

In non-life insurance the policies have a short duration, usually not longer than a year, whereas in life insurance the time horizon is usually very long, even many decades. Thus actuarial calculations in life insurance had from the very beginning a tendency to apply a long-term perspective. However, the calculations were static in nature: the life insurance company was merely seen as the sum of individual (long-term) policies. For a more profound analysis, the insurance company has to be seen as a dynamic entity evolving in time, e.g. new policies continuously flowing into the company. For that analysis we need more than a theory based on fixed risk probabilities and on the calculation of expected values. Even if the theory of probability advanced rapidly, it was also mostly dealing with static phenomena until towards the end of the 19th century, when the theory of stochastic process began to emerge.

One of the early contributors to the theory of stochastic process starting from insurance applications was the Swede Filip Lundberg. In 1903 he published his dissertation (Lundberg 1903) dealing with what was later to become known as collective risk theory. Before Lundberg the insurance portfolios had been analyzed by starting from individual risks and summing them up to form the portfolio level random variable. Exact application of this method required knowledge and convolution of the probability distributions of each risk, which in practice was not possible. The CLT of course allowed approximations to be made.

Lundberg's idea was radical. He started from modeling the total number of claims in a collective of risks without paying attention to individual risks. His model assumed that the occurrence of claims satisfy certain conditions, which in fact were those implying the Poisson process. With each claim is associated a random loss, these random losses being mutually independent and following the same distribution. Then the total loss amount in a given time period follows a compound Poisson distribution.

Without knowing it, Lundberg used the key concept of modern probability theory – the stochastic process – for the first time in an insurance context. At that time there was no exact theory of stochastic processes in the strict mathematical sense.

Although Lundberg's work caught the attention of actuaries, it was understood by few, until Professor Harald Cramér's excellent didactic explanations made the relationship between collective risk theory and the theory of stochastic process apparent to a wide readership, see e.g. Cramér (1930, 1955). At the same time the probability theory was put to a strict theoretical foundation by the Russian mathematician Andrei Kolmogorov, who introduced the axiomatic basis of probability theory using the concepts of measure theory.

Lundberg's collective model could be used e.g. to calculate the probability of ruin of the insurer; i.e. the probability that the resources (premiums and buffer capital, the latter is sometimes called surplus) will not be sufficient to pay all claims. Usually the time horizon was extended to infinity. For most claims size distributions the problem is not analytically tractable, but different approximations are available. This problem, even in its original form, is studied and solutions refined still today.

Later the Lundberg model was enlarged to include a random Poisson parameter and to other types of processes for claim occurrences than Poisson. A Finnish name worth mentioning here is Kari Karhunen, the actuary and later CEO of a Finnish life insurance company, well-known in the theory of stochastic processes from the Karhunen-Loewe expansion. In Section 3.3 recent practically oriented extensions of the Lundberg model will be considered.

3 Common areas of actuarial science, probability and statistics

3.1 Main problems of actuarial practice

The basic practical actuarial problems are the following:

- setting the insurance premiums
- assessing the value for insurance/pension liabilities
- assessing the adequacy of the matching between assets and liabilities
- assessing the financial strength (solvency) of the insurer

More recently these tasks have been extended to building of a comprehensive model (sometimes called internal models) to describe the functioning of the insurer.

In Sections 3.2–3.4 some methodologies used to solve these problems are discussed.

3.2 Premium setting and estimation of claims provisions

The premium setting problem can be approached from different angles. What poses a major practical problem is determination of the premium for a single policyholder belonging to a risk collective, when the total premium of the collective may or may not have been pre-fixed. This problem belongs to the realm of tariff theory (to be briefly discussed in the next section).

Another problem to be considered is: how should the premium for an individual or collective be determined when there is access to certain data on past claims performance of that individual or collective. This is an application area for credibility theory, bonus-malus systems and control theory. Two basic approaches can be distinguished. They could be called a fresh start approach and smoothing over time.

By a fresh start approach I mean the search for a "best" estimate of the claims and other expenses in the future time the insurance policy will cover. Then the premium is set to equal that best estimate. In that context the resulting variability in premiums and in the surplus of the insurer are usually not considered to be relevant. Arguments for this approach are strong. They can be summarized by saying that, due to the free competition in the insurance market, each new policy period should be treated as independent of the former periods: since entry to the market is free, past losses or profits cannot influence the prices that can be charged for future policies; i.e. the new premiums must always be based only on estimates of future risk, giving no regard to the past profitability of the portfolio.

On the other hand, the existence of underwriting cycles (i.e. longer and alternating periods of poor and good profitability) indicates that the fresh start may not always coincide with practical experience. There are also cases where equalizing the premiums over time may be an explicit goal. Thus the second approach to premium rating, smoothing over time, aims to control the variability of at least one of the variables involved, premiums or surplus.

When closing the balance sheet, the insurance company has to estimate what its financial liability is for claims which have already occurred but which have not yet been reported to the company. The reporting delay may be several years. The resulting liability is usually called claims provision. In essence the estimation of the claims provision deals with the same problem as setting premiums. For future premiums mostly an estimate for the claims to occur in the future is needed, whereas in estimation of claims reserves the claims already have occurred in the past but their number and sizes are not yet fully known. So it would be a natural idea to use the same techniques for both premium rating and for estimation of the claims provision. A bit surprisingly, this connection is not always recognized and claims reserving and premium setting are considered as two different exercises.

Tariff theory

As noted above, tariff theory deals with the setting of a premium for an individual risk in a collective and is based on some characteristics of the risk, called tariff factors, but not necessarily on knowledge of the past claims experience from that particular risk. Tariff theory usually refers to the methods for determining the risk part of the premiums, as different from the possible savings element of the premium; in particular in non-life insurance.

A risk premium can be considered to consist of three components: (1) an estimate of the expected claims (for a collective); (2) safety loading, based on the expected variability of the claims, to contribute for maintaining the solvency of the company; and (3) a loading for administrative expenses. In principle it is a mathematical/statistical exercise to determine and to put together these three components to a total premium, but of course market situation, competition and commercial reasons may make the premium actually charged to differ from the actuarial recommendation.

Components 1 and 2 of the premium are clearly a classical application of statistics: estimate the distribution, in particular the expected value of a statistical variable. It is in the company's interest to find tariff factors which classify the collective in such subsets that the risks in each subset are sufficiently similar and that the subsets are reasonably far from each other. In practice the number of available tariff factors is limited by the easiness of collecting relevant data and verifying whether a risk belongs to a certain subset. Often the legislation also forbids the use of certain factors like e.g. race and sex.

In addition to different ad hoc techniques, usual methods of tariff theory include usual multivariate linear statistics as regression techniques, factor analysis, cluster analysis and generalized linear models (see e.g. England and Verrall (2002), Loimaranta et al. (1980), Pitkänen (1975), and van Eeghen et al. (1983)). Techniques of data mining have recently become more and more popular, especially in motor insurance.

Credibility theory

As explained above the term credibility refers to premium rating formulas that combine the individual and the collective claims development. A first major reference is Whitney (1918) who addressed the problem of assessing the risk premium, which he defined as the expected claims expenses per unit of risk exposed, for an individual risk selected from a portfolio (class) of similar risks. Whitney combined the individual risk experience with the class risk experience by a weighted average of the observed mean claim amount per unit of risk exposed for the individual contract and the corresponding overall mean in the insurance portfolio. Whitney considered the risk premium as a random variable which reflects the characteristics of the individual risk. The individual risk is a random selection from a portfolio of similar but not identical risks.

Finding a theoretical basis for rating by credibility type took after Whitney two different ways: one is usually referred to as limited fluctuation credibility theory and the second as greatest accuracy credibility theory. In statistical terms they correspond to the "fixed effect" and the "random effect" models.

In the limited fluctuations approach the goal is to determine the number of observation years needed to make the estimate of the individual risk parameter to be sufficiently close to the true value. Mostly normal approximation was used. Hence the limited fluctuation approach is not actually a theory, but an estimation problem. A survey of the area is given in Longley-Cook (1962).

The greatest accuracy point of view developed in the post World War II era. The rating based on individual experience was now formulated mathematically as estimating the random variable risk parameter with some function of the individual data. The objective is to minimize the mean squared error.

Greatest accuracy credibility theory rapidly developed into a large body of models and methods. Notable works include Bühlmann (1967, 1969), Bühlmann and Straub (1970), Bühlmann and Jewell (1987), and Hachemeister (1975).

In statistical terms the problem setting of credibility theory is equivalent to finding the Bayes estimator under squared loss. Kalman's (1960) linear filtering theory also deals with linear estimation and prediction and it is widely applied e.g. in engineering, control theory, and operations research. Basically it covers many early results in credibility theory and linear Bayesian statistics. However, it goes farther than prediction and estimation as the latent (state) variables are treated as dynamical objects. Thus it is often a central building block in control theory, whose insurance applications will be discussed more in Section 3.3.

Bonus-malus systems

Bonus-malus systems, mostly applied in motor insurance, are another major (and often more practical) technique to combine the individual and collective experience. The basic tariff level is increased by a malus or decreased by a bonus according to which bonus class the policyholder belongs to. If a policyholder has a claim, his/her bonus class will decrease according to a specified rule. Usually the construction of the bonus-malus systems is such that the theory of Markov chains applies for transitions from class to class. For more on bonus-malus systems; see e.g. Lemaire (1995) and Loimaranta (1972).

Models of sickness insurance

Life insurance has extended from the early beginning of insuring against a death or a long life to cover a wide range of human risks like disability, need for long-term care and critical diseases. The actuarial problems of insurance covers based on a person being in a certain health situation can be approached by techniques of Markov chains and processes, both in discrete and continuous time. For example, in disability insurance the benefits are paid when the insured person is disabled and alive. This can be described with the help of states (e.g. active, disabled, dead) and transitions between the states. Being in a state or changing the state usually means that there is a cash flow either from the policyholder to the insurer (e.g. premiums when insured is in state "active") or from the insurer to the insured (e.g. annuity when the insured is in state "disabled"). The transitions between the states are governed by transition probabilities or transition intensities. More on models of person insurance see e.g. Hoem and Aalen (1978) and Haberman and Pitacco (1999).

3.3 Modelling and controlling the long-term performance of an insurer

Dynamic stochastic models

Lundberg's collective risk theory and its extensions did not fully recognize the role of the active decision-making of the company management. It is clear that the management (and shareholders, supervisors and other stakeholders) react to the company's development; e.g. if the company's financial state starts to deteriorate seriously the management most probably takes corrective measures like raising premiums. Even if the management decisions are difficult to model exactly, this type of decisions should be taken into account in models which claim to mimic the real world.

The use of dynamic stochastic simulations to describe the functioning of an insurance company has extended enormously during the 2–3 recent decades. A pioneer in this field has been Teivo Pentikäinen, who has published a series of articles on dynamic stochastic models from 1975 onwards (see e.g. Pentikäinen (1975, 1980), Pentikäinen et al. (1989), and Daykin et al. (1994)). The most recent advancement is that insurance company models are more and more used for insurance supervision purposes too; e.g. to determine the minimum capital the company is required to have in order to be able to fulfill its commitments to policyholders; i.e. the solvency of the company.

The idea is to build a stochastic model to describe an insurance company and to produce by simulation a distribution for a set of indicators of the future financial condition of the insurer. Lundberg's model was very simple: it included 3 variables: risk buffer (surplus), premiums and claims expense (which is composed of the number of claims and claim sizes). In modern models the number of variables can be huge; in particular if the model is meant to describe a financial group operating worldwide via hundreds of subsidiaries and in hundreds of business lines. Many but not all of the variables are stochastic. They are tied to each other on one hand by deterministic equations originating from accounting conventions and on the other hand by statistical dependencies.

Control theory

One of the ways to formalize the decision-making is to apply the methods of control theory. Control theory also expands the scope of credibility theory. In credibility theory the focus is usually on the prediction of future claims expenses and on the fluctuations of premiums. The resulting fluctuation in the insurer's surplus is usually ignored. That means that optimality in its widest sense will not be focused; for example whether a different functional form for the rating rule would give better results in the sense that the same variance of the premiums could be achieved with a smaller variance of the surplus. Control theory provides techniques to look at the problem from this angle and in that way structurise the problem better.

In control theoretical approach, first defining the performance criteria of all the main variables related to the problem should be considered. One has to decide which features of the variables are important and to give appropriate weights to their relative importance. For example, it is clear that the insurer and the policyholders have conflicting interests in deciding how to share the total stochastic variation or "energy" produced by the claims process. It is in the interest of policyholders that the premium variation is minimized, whereas the insurer puts value on smooth flows of surplus and underwriting results. Their common interest is that the fluctuation of the insurer's surplus is minimized, because it also means minimization of the safety loading needed in premiums and minimization of the cost of capital. The reason is that when the variation of surplus is reduced, the average level of the surplus can be lowered. Then the safety loading in premiums needed to support that average level is also lower. Control theory together with appropriate performance criteria provides means to coordinate these different wishes in a coherent and logical way.

Secondly, there may be at disposal a rule by which the premiums are determined. The rule may be an explicit one or it may try to imitate the way the premiums are in practice more or less implicitly determined. Then, by control theoretical methods it is possible to study the behaviour of the main variables when that particular rating rule is used.

Thirdly, the study of control rule may also lead to optimization of the parameter values of the rule. A fourth and more demanding task is to explore what the optimal form of the rating rule would be when the performance criteria are given.

In insurance applications of control theory the system variables may refer e.g. to a part of an insurance portfolio, an insurance line, an insurance company or maybe also to an insurance market. The state variables are a description of the characteristics of the system. The state variables may include e.g. volume, market position, risk exposure, surplus etc. Control variables may also be numerous, as for example premium level, marketing efforts, change of asset mix etc. In the simplest case the state of the insurer is described by one variable only, by the risk buffer, and there is only one control variable: premiums. More on the use of control theory in insurance see e.g. Rantala (2000) and references therein.

Kalman filter technique has proved a useful tool in control theoretical considerations. Another popular theoretical approach is based on Dynamic Programming Principle or Bellman principle.

The practical applications of control theory in insurance are still rare, even if the number of theoretical articles on them has recently increased.

3.4 Financial economics

It is fair to say that actuaries have been pioneers in financial mathematics. The combination of compound interest and mortality tables already 250 years ago was a success. It is equally fair to say that they have not been in the forefront of the most recent development in spite of the fact that finance and insurance are fairly similar in nature, since they both consider the value of a financial instrument or insurance policy to be the discounted present value of the future uncertain cash flows. In fact, as explained in Section 2, when referring to caravan and marine insurance, the financing element and insurance element of a sea loan were not separated before the 14th century. As a curiosity it could be observed that the most recent development in a way has taken us back to where we started: many of the new so-called Alternative Risk Transfers products combine the loan and insurance element again. E.g. in earthquake bonds interests and perhaps a part of the principal of a bond issued by the insurer will be waived in case an earthquake occurs.

The following text is based on Whelan et al. (2002).

The beginning of financial economics is usually traced to Louis Bachelier's theses, Théorie de la Spéculation, which was presented to the Academy of Paris in 1900. The thesis was in mathematical physics and the supervisor was Henri Poincaré. He gave the theses an excellent report, but noted that the topic of modeling the French capital market as a fair game was "somewhat remote from those our candidates are in the habit of treating".

Bachelier studied price changes of equities as a stochastic process. His starting point was that the mathematical expectations of the buyer and the seller are zero (i.e. they form a martingale). He derived an equation, which later became known as the Chapman-Kolmogorov equation (homogenous version) and identified the equation describing the process as the diffusion equation, and showed that (what we now term) the Wiener process is a solution. He solved the probability that a price will exceed (or fall below) a certain level within a given time period, and determined the distribution of the extremes of the price process.

The main practical result of Bachelier's model is that the standard deviation of the distribution of future price changes is directly proportional to the square root of elapsed time. However, this rule was known by French actuaries before Bachelier's dissertation. E.g. The Journal des Actuaires Francáis had noted this empirical rule more than two decades earlier. Apparently this law was widely used on the French bourse, and would, in all likelihood, have been known to Bachelier from when he worked on the Paris Stock Exchange.

Bachelier's theoretical work was relatively well-known and also appreciated by mathematicians with an interest in stochastic processes. His results and methods were also quickly disseminated amongst French actuaries. Bachelier's thesis did not, however, have influence on economic thinking, until it was rediscovered by Savage and Samuelson in the mid-1950s.

The concept of replicating portfolio (i.e. asset portfolio which perfectly matches the cash flows of a given liability portfolio) is a core element in modern financial economics. Among other things it underlies the famous Black–Scholes option-pricing formula. An early predecessor for the concept of replicating portfolio in actuarial mathematics was so-called immunization; introduced in 1952 by the UK actuary Frank Redington (Redington 1952). His approach did not match exactly the asset and liability cash flows as in using the replicating portfolio, but put the durations (discounted mean terms) of the assets and liabilities equal and the spread of the asset cash flows around their discounted means greater than the corresponding spread of liability cash flows. This "immunization" gave the insurance company protection against interest rate movements, since e.g. in the case of a rise in the interest rate the resulting decrease in asset values was offset by a similar decrease in liability values.

Also the constant growth dividend discount model, which as such is mathematically very simple, is often attributed to 20th-century economists. According to Whelan (2002) it can be found much earlier, in 1901, in Todhunter's "The Institute of Actuaries Textbook on Compound Interest and Annuities Certain". According to Whelan it also appears in a footnote as early as 1869 in an article by Sprague published in the Journal of the Institute of Actuaries.

Value at Risk (abbreviated VaR) is a frequently used tool in everyday applications of financial economics. It is also a simple concept, nothing else than a quantile of a probability distribution. This concept was quite early largely used in insurance to assess e.g. the capital needed to attain a sufficiently low ruin probability. For the history of VaR, see e.g. Pradier (2005).

Whelan (2002) and Hardy (2005) list some additional actuarial contributions to financial economics.

Actuaries have also developed stochastic models to describe the investment activities; in particular those of an insurer. One commonly applied model is developed by David Wilkie (Wilkie 1986, 1995). In its simplest form the model simulates the joint distribution of inflation rates, bond yields and equity. These models are calibrated to very long time series of financial variables and consequently they usually have mean reverting characteristics. This empirically observed feature is in contradiction with the random walk assumption of financial economics. The explanation for this discrepancy may be that the long-term behavior of asset prices and in particular equity prices may be different from their short-term behavior.

Other contributions to stochastic investment models include Pukkila et al. (1994).

From an actuarial and mathematical point of view it is remarkable that sometimes the methods of financial economics are in practice applied as "cook book" solutions without paying sufficient attention to verification of the assumptions lying behind the model. On the other hand, if all market participants mechanically follow the rules derived from the models, the model is in a way converted to reality. There is a clear difference to insurance, where the driving factors usually are of a physical nature. But the "virtual" world created by theoretical models may collapse when a human factor comes into the picture. Remember the bankruptcy of the Long Term Capital Management, having as board members Myron Scholes and Robert Merton, who shared the 1997 Bank of Sweden Prize (aka "Nobel Prize in Economics") and who were leading figures behind the Black-Scholes formula or the bubble of ICT share prices round 2000.

4 Actuarial science as a part of the scientific community

The history of actuarial science shows great successes. In particular, the classical paradigm of the life actuary - the deterministic description of the laws of mortality coupled with an assumed fixed interest rate - proved to be a successful tool, on which the business practice of the life insurance companies relied over 200 years. And it is useful still today, the great majority of actuaries worldwide are still working on life and pension insurance using traditional techniques, even if new techniques of financial economics gain more and more popularity. In non-life insurance the extended Lundberg model, rate-making methods and stochastic simulation models of the insurance company have become established methods for solving practical problems.

However, the actuarial science has sometimes been developed in isolation from the rest of the scientific community. This has had two consequences. The achievements in neighboring disciplines have not been taken widely into actuarial use. Similarly, actuarial achievements have not gained a wider audience. For example, credibility theory and Bayesian statistics were developed simultaneously, but independently. Actuarial results on credibility theory were not disseminated to a wider statistical audience. Neither did the applications in financial economics by actuaries in the early 19ties find their way to a more general audience.

Whelan (2002) points to one possible reason: failure to communicate among other things due to differences in jargon. Whelan refers to a Norwegian academic actuary, Karl Borch, who made a similar analysis on actuarial development of stochastic processes, which did not much influence the development of stochastic process theory in probability theory. According to Borch, insurance was for a long time perhaps not the only but certainly a main practical application of probability theory. So actuaries had a field of their own and it was natural that they formulated their mathematical results as solutions to insurance problems and without explaining their more general character. In other applications it was easier to rediscover the results than to find them in existing insurance literature with its own terminology, both probably not very well known to others. Thus lacking communication between actuaries and statisticians caused parallel studies with the result that several ideas were found separately and that there are not many cross-references in the respective literature.

It is also fair to say that actuarial science also has missed important opportunities. One can with good reason ask why actuaries were not in the forefront in developing modern financial economics, which is clearly orientated towards mathematics and probability theory, the home field of actuaries. According to Bühlmann (1997) one of the reasons could be that actuaries were too satisfied with the great success of the life insurance paradigm. Why spend time exploring new ideas, when the old ones seem to work excellently? Actuarial science was thus considered as a "ready-made" theory; all that remained to be done was the fine-tuning of technical details. A result was that actuarial science began to suffer from interested young academics and lack of innovative ideas, the number of actuarial chairs in the universities started to decline and others could take the lead.

Of course this was not the whole truth of actuarial innovation. Bühlmann (1997) himself refers to innovative ideas in other actuarial areas and names some illustrative examples: bonus-malus systems in automobile insurance, the system of pension insurance designed by the Finnish actuaries, the many attempts to modernize fire tariffs, the success stories of Ove Lundberg in sickness insurance and of Hans Ammeter in group life insurance.

Is the communication over boundaries of different disciplines improving? There is at least one example of improvement. Partly for the fear of losing ground to financial engineers, actuaries have began to adopt the terminology used in financial economics and other related sciences, even if there is still hesitation to accept finance theory as an essential tool of actuarial practice. Actuaries also have started to contribute to financial economics, which, taking into account their practical experience, may be beneficial to the sound development of financial economics. In the competition between the two professions, actuaries have the disadvantage of having been somewhat late arrivals in the field. In many countries, however, the training of actuaries concentrates more on mathematics than courses at business schools do. The value of this long-term advantage should not be underestimated.

It is clear that the high-quality education of actuaries, sufficient connection between practice and research, and working communication with allied sciences are necessary prerequisites for a successful development of actuarial science. Here the role of and relation to universities are of great importance.

There is no unique global model for the role of universities in actuarial education or research. In countries where the number of actuaries is relatively large, the professional actuarial organizations are often responsible for a considerable part of the education. There is often cooperation with general university education, with the result that part of the basic training in mathematics and statistics is given by the universities. The specifically actuarial courses remain, however, in the hands of the relevant actuarial organization. In other countries, in particular in smaller ones, the education is almost entirely based on basic university examinations. On top of that there may be a few specific actuarial examinations or requirements for practical experience.

These two traditions to educate actuaries have had some implications for the relationship between practical actuarial work, actuarial science and other mathematical/statistical sciences. The existence of the two traditions may be a cause for, or a consequence of the fact that there is no unique model for the status of actuarial science in universities. In some countries the universities may have departments dedicated to actuarial science, in some countries the actuarial courses, if any, are taught as a part of other syllabuses; usually as a part mathematics, probability or statistics.

Sometimes the actuarial science has suffered from being considered as dealing with too practical problem settings in order to deserve a scientific status. Nowadays the situation looks better. It is not only the education of actuaries, which has began to interest universities but also the actuarial problems are more and more seen to be appropriate for scientific approach. It is worth noting that most authors in Encyclopedia of Actuarial Science seem to come from the academic world. That is very delightful, but a concern may be that contributions from practicing actuaries in the book are so few. I am sure that practicing actuaries will also benefit from close cooperation between practice and research; in particular statistics. That would be beneficial for insurance too. Remember that during the 19th century and the first part of the 20th century in Scandinavian countries a number of outstanding university professors in mathematics played leading roles in the foundation of life insurance companies, and established a tradition that these companies employed highly qualified professional mathematicians as their actuaries.

References

Barnwell, R. G. (1856). *A sketch of the life and times of John de Witt, grandpensionary of Holland, to which is added his treatise on life annuities.* New York: Udney & Russell Publishers.

Beard, R. E., Pentikäinen, T., and Pesonen, E. (1969). *Risk Theory.* London: Chapman & Hall.

Bernstein, P. L. (1996). *Against the Gods, The Remarkable Story of Risk.* New York: Wiley.

Bühlmann, H. (1967). Experience rating and credibility. *Astin Bulletin*, 4, 199–207.

Bühlmann, H. (1969). Experience rating and credibility. *Astin Bulletin*, 5, 157–165.

Bühlmann, H. (1997). The actuary: the role and the limitations of the profession since the mid-19th century. *Astin Bulletin*, 27, 165–171.

Bühlmann, H. and Jewell, W. (1987). Hierarchical credibility revisited. *Mitteilungen der Vereinigung Schweizerischer Versicherungsmathematiker*, pp. 35–54.

Bühlmann, H. and Straub, E. (1970). Glaubwürdigkeit für Schadensätze. *Mitteilungen der Vereinigung Schweizerischer Versicherungsmathematiker*, 70, 111–133.

Cramér, H. (1930). *On the mathematical theory of risk* (Parts I and II). Stockholm: Försäkringsaktiebolaget Skandia.

Cramér, H. (1955). *Collective risk theory: A survey of the theory from the point of view of the theory of stochastic processes.* 7th Jubilee Volume of Skandia Insurance Company, Stockholm.

Daston L. J. (2005). The domestication of risk: mathematical probability and insurance 1650–1830. Presentation from http://www1.fee.uva.nl/ke/act/history.htm.

Daykin C. D., Pentikäinen T., and Pesonen, M. (1994). *Practical Risk Theory for Actuaries.* London: Chapman & Hall.

Embrechts, P., Klueppelberg, C., and Mikosch, T. (2003). *Modelling Extremal Events for Insurance and Finance.* Springer-Verlag.

Encyclopedia of Actuarial Science (2004). Editors in chief J. L. Teugels and B. Sundt. Chichester: Wiley.

England, P. D. and Verrall, R. J (2002). Stochastic claims reserving in general insurance. *British Actuarial Journal,* 8, 443–518.

Evans, J. (1998). Mortality, behold and fear. In *Life, Death and Money.* Ed. D. Renn. Oxford: Blackwell Publishing. Pp. 29–42.

Haberman, S. (1996). Landmarks in the history of actuarial science (up to 1919). Actuarial Research Paper No 84, Department of Actuarial Science and Statistics, City University London.

Haberman, S. and Pitacco, E. (1999). *Actuarial Models for Disability Insurance.* Boca Raton, USA: Chapman & Hall / CRC Press.

Hachemeister, C. (1975). Credibility for regression models with application to trend. In *Credibility: Theory and applications.* Ed. P. M. Kahn. Academic Press. Pp. 129–163.

Hald, A. (1998). *A history of mathematical statistics from 1750 to 1930.* Wiley.

Halley, E. (1693). An Estimate of the Degrees of the Mortality of Mankind, drawn from curious Tables of the Births and Funerals at the City of Breslaw ; with an Attempt to ascertain the Price of Annuities upon Lives. *Philosophical Transactions of the Royal Society of London,* 17, 596–610 & 654–656.

Hardy, M. R. (2005). We are all "actuaries of the third kind" now (editorial). *North American Actuarial Journal,* April 2005, iii–v.

Hoem, J. and Aalen, O.,O. (1978). Actuarial values of payment streams. *Scandinavian Actuarial Journal,* 1978, 38–47.

Kalman, R. (1960). A new approach to linear filtering and prediction problems. *Transactions of the ASME – Journal of Basic Engineering,* 82 (Series D), 35–45.

Kopf, E. W. (1927). The early history of the annuity. *Proceedings of the Casualty Actuarial Society,* 8, 225–266. Available from http://www1.fee.uva.nl/ke/act/history.htm.

Lemaire J. (1995). *Bonus-Malus Systems in Automobile Insurance.* Kluwer Publishers.

Lewin, C. (1998). Earliest days. In *Life, Death and Money.* Ed. D. Renn. Oxford: Blackwell Publishing. Pp. 9–28.

Lewin, C. (2001). Creation of actuarial science. *Zentralblatt für Didaktik der Mathematik,* 33, 61–66.

Longley-Cook, L. H. (1962). An introduction to credibility theory. *Proceedings of the Casualty Actuarial Society,* 49, 194–221.

Loimaranta, K. (1972). Some asymptotic properties of bonus systems. *Astin Bulletin,* 6, 233–245.

Loimaranta, K., Jacobsson, J., and Lonka, H. (1980). On the use of mixture models in clustering multivariate frequency data. *Transactions of International Congress of Actuaries*, 1980, 2, 147–161.

Lundberg, F. (1903). *Approximerad framställning av sannolikhetsfunktionen. Återförsäkring av kollektivrisker*. Akad. Afhandling. Stockholm: Almqvist & Wicksell.

Norberg, R. (2004). Survey of actuarial credibility theory. In *Encyclopedia of Actuarial Science*.

Ogborn, M. E. (1956). The professional name of actuary. *Journal of Institute of Actuaries*, pp. 233–246.

Ore, O. (1953). *Cardano, the Gambling Scholar*. Princeton University Press.

Pentikäinen, T. (1975). A model of stochastic-dynamic prognosis. An application of risk theory to business planning. *Scandinavian Actuarial Journal*, 1975, 29–53.

Pentikäinen, T. (1980). A stochastic-dynamic model for insurance business. *Transactions of the International Congress of Actuaries*, pp. 283–294.

Pentikäinen, T., Bonsdorff, H., Pesonen, M., Rantala, J., and Ruohonen, M. (1989). *Insurance Solvency and Financial Strength*, Helsinki: Finnish Insurance Training and Publishing Company.

Pitkänen, P. (1975). Tariff theory, premium calculation principles. *Astin Bulletin*, 8, 204–208.

Pradier, P.-C. (2005). Value-at-Risk since 1784; a comprehensive history. Available from http://www1.fee.uva.nl/ke/act/history.htm.

Pukkila, T., Ranne, A., and Sarvamaa, S. (1994). On stochastic modeling of inflation. *Actuarial approach for financial risks, AFIR 1994* (Vol. 2). Pp. 589–609.

Rantala, J. (2000). Control theory – a useful actuarial tool? *Giornale dell'istitute italiano degli attuari*, LXIII, 111–127.

Redington, F. M. (1952). Review of the principles of life-office valuations. *Journal of the Institute of Actuaries*, 78, 286–315.

Sheynin, O. (1970). On the early history of the law of large numbers. In *Studies in the History of Statistics and Probability* (Vol. 1). Editors E. S. Pearson and M. G. Kendall. London: Charles Griffin. Pp. 231–239.

Sheynin, O. (1977). Early history of the theory of probability. *Biometrika*, 17, 201–259.

van Eeghen, J., Greup, E., and Nijssen, J. (1983). Rate making. *Surveys of Actuarial Studies*, No 2. Rotterdam: Nationale-Nederlanden N. V.

Whelan, S. (2002). Actuaries' contributions to financial economics, *Actuary*, December 2002, 34–35.

Whelan, S. F, Bowie, D. C, and Hibbert, A. J. (2002). A primer in financial economics. *British Actuarial Journal*, 8, 27–74.

Wilkie, A. D. (1986). A stochastic investment model for actuarial use. *Transactions of the Faculty of actuaries*, 39, 919–954.

Wilkie, A. D. (1995). More on a stochastic asset model for actuarial use. *British Actuarial Journal*, 1, 777–964.

Whitney, A. W. (1918). The theory of experience rating. *Proceedings of the Casualty Actuarial Society*, 4, 274–292.

JUKKA RANTALA
Finnish Centre for Pensions
FI-00065 Eläketurvakeskus
Jukka.Rantala@etk.fi

Festschrift for Tarmo Pukkila on his 60th Birthday
Eds. E. P. Liski, J. Isotalo, J. Niemelä, S. Puntanen, and G. P. H. Styan

Univ. of Tampere, 2006, ISBN 978-951-44-6620-5, pages 285–294

Familial correlations

C. RADHAKRISHNA RAO

Abstract. This paper presents a general discussion of correlation coefficients between measurements taken on members of a family such as brothers, father and son, etc. The correlation coefficient between measurements on a single characteristic (say head length) made on two brothers in a family is known as intraclass correlation coefficient (ICC) of the particular characteristic. We consider the cross correlation coefficient of measurements on two characteristics (say head length (hl) and head breadth (hb), hl taken on one brother and hb on another brother). We call such a coefficient as hetero-ICC and the former based on a single characteristic as homo-ICC. We introduce the concept of canonical intraclass correlations (CIC) based on measurements of multiple characteristics on brothers. We also introduce the concept of homologous canonical correlations (HCC) based on measurements on multiple characteristics taken on father and son. Estimation of various correlation coefficients is considered and some problems which need further investigation are mentioned.

Key words and phrases: Homo-intraclass correlation; Hetero-intraclass correlations; Canonical correlations; Homologous canonical correlation.

1 Introduction

The product moment correlation coefficient was introduced by Galton and Pearson as a measure of resemblance between members of a family, such as brothers, brother and sister, father and son etc., based on certain measurements made on them. There is considerable literature on the subject when measurements are made on a single specified characteristic such as head length or head breadth or stature and so on. We consider problems that arise when measurements on multiple characteristics are available on each individual.

2 Intraclass Correlation Coefficients

2.1 Univariate case

Let $x_1, \ldots, x_k$ be the measurements made on a single characteristic (say head length) on k brothers in a family. A natural covariance structure for the measurements is

$$V(x_i) = \sigma^2, \qquad \mathrm{Cov}(x_i, x_j) = \sigma^2 \rho \tag{2.1.1}$$

where ρ is referred to as the intraclass correlation coefficient (ICC). Given measurements on k brothers in each of n independently chosen families

$$x_1^{(r)}, \ldots, x_k^{(r)}, \qquad r = 1, \ldots, n. \tag{2.1.2}$$

ρ can be estimated as follows. The first step is to set up one way analysis of variance (ANOVA) table, as in Fisher (1925).

ANOVA: One way classification

Source	DF	SS	Expectation
Between families	$n-1$	$b = \frac{1}{k}\sum_{r=1}^{n} T_r^2 - \frac{1}{nk}T^2$	$\sigma^2(n-1)(1+\overline{k-1}\rho)$
Within families	$n(k-1)$	$w = \sum_{r=1}^{n}\sum_{i=1}^{k}\left(x_i^{(r)} - \frac{1}{k}T_r\right)^2$	$\sigma_n^2(k-1)(1-\rho)$

where $T_r = x_1^{(r)} + \cdots + x_k^{(r)}$ and $T = \sum_1^k T_r$. The estimating equations for ρ and σ^2 are

$$b = \sigma^2(n-1)(1+\overline{k-1}\rho), \qquad w = \sigma^2 n(k-1)(1-\rho) \tag{2.1.3}$$

giving an estimate of ρ as

$$\hat{\rho} = \frac{F-1}{k+F-1}, \qquad F = \frac{n(k-1)b}{(n-1)w}. \tag{2.1.4}$$

This estimate differs from what is given in text books as

$$\hat{\rho} = \frac{G-1}{k+G-1}, \qquad G = \frac{(k-1)b}{w}. \tag{2.1.5}$$

Confidence interval for ρ can be obtained by choosing the pivotal statistic

$$\frac{(1-\rho)F}{1+\overline{k-1}\rho} \tag{2.1.6}$$

and equating it to percentile points of Fisher's variance ratio statistic on $(n-1)$ and $n(k-1)$ degrees of freedom.

2.2 Covariance structure in the multivariate case

Let x_{it} be the measurement of the i-th characteristic on the t-th brother in a family for $i = 1, \ldots, p$ (p characteristics) and $t = 1, \ldots, k$ (k brothers in a family). A natural covariance structure for the measurements is

$$\operatorname{Cov}(x_{it}, x_{js}) = \begin{cases} \sigma_i^2 & \text{if } i = j \text{ and } t = s, \\ \sigma_i^2 \rho_{ii} & \text{if } i = j \text{ and } t \neq s, \\ \sigma_i \sigma_j \rho_{ij} & \text{if } i \neq j \text{ and } t \neq s, \\ \sigma_i \sigma_j \rho'_{ij} & \text{if } i \neq j \text{ and } t = s. \end{cases} \tag{2.2.1}$$

In (2.2.1), ρ_{ii} is the usual intraclass correlation coefficient (ICC) which we redesignate as homo-ICC (between the i-th characteristic of two brothers), ρ_{ij} as the hetero-ICC (between the i-th characteristic of one brother and j-th characteristic of another brother), and ρ'_{ij} is the usual correlation between the i-th and j-th characteristics of an individual. (Note that $\rho'_{ii} = 1$).

Denote by

$$x_{i\cdot} = (x_{i1}, \ldots, x_{ik}) \tag{2.2.2}$$

the vector of measurements of the i-th characteristic taken on k brothers. Then we have the following covariance matrices

$$\operatorname{Cov}(x_{i\cdot}, x_{j\cdot}) = \begin{cases} \sigma_i^2[(1-\rho_{ii})I + \rho_{ii}R] & \text{if } i = j, \\ \sigma_i\sigma_j[(\rho'_{ij} - \rho_{ij})I + \rho_{ij}R] & \text{if } i \neq j \end{cases} \tag{2.2.3}$$

where I is $k \times k$ identity matrix and R is $k \times k$ matrix with all its elements as unity.

2.3 Estimation of various correlation coefficients in the multivariate case

We consider independent samples from n families each with k brothers and denote the measurement on the i-th character of the s-th brother in the r-th family by

$$x_{is}^{(r)}, \qquad i = 1, \ldots, p, \quad s = 1, \ldots, k, \quad \text{and} \quad r = 1, \ldots, n. \tag{2.3.1}$$

Based on (2.3.1), we compute the entries of Analysis of Dispersion (MANOVA) table for one way classification as between and within families. The SP (sum of squares and products) matrices of order $p \times p$, B for between families on $(n-1)$ d.f. and W for within families on $n(k-1)$ d.f. are computed as follows (see Rao (1952, pp. 262–263) and Rao (1973, pp. 547–549)).

$$B = (B_{ij}), \qquad B_{ij} = \frac{1}{k}\sum_{r=1}^{n} T_i^{(r)} T_j^{(r)} - \frac{1}{nk} T_i T_j,$$

$$T_i^{(r)} = \sum_{s=1}^{k} x_{is}^{(r)}, \qquad T_i = \sum_{r=1}^{n} T_i^{(r)},$$

$$W = (W_{ij}), \qquad W_{ij} = T_{ij} - B_{ij},$$

$$T_{ij} = \sum_{r=1}^{n}\sum_{s=1}^{k} x_{is}^{(r)} x_{js}^{(r)} - \frac{1}{nk} T_i T_j. \tag{2.3.2}$$

The expectations of B_{ij} and W_{ij} are as follows:

$$E(B_{ij}) = (n-1)\sigma_i\sigma_j[\rho'_{ij} + (k-1)\rho_{ij}],$$
$$E(W_{ij}) = n(k-1)\sigma_i\sigma_j[\rho'_{ij} - \rho_{ij}]. \quad (2.3.3)$$

The estimates of σ_i, $i = 1,\ldots,p$, ρ'_{ij}, $i \neq j$ and ρ_{ij} are obtained from the equations

$$B_{ij} = (n-1)\hat{\sigma}_i\hat{\sigma}_j(\hat{\rho}'_{ij} + (k-1)\hat{\rho}_{ij}),$$
$$W_{ij} = n(k-1)\hat{\sigma}_i\hat{\sigma}_j(\hat{\rho}'_{ij} - \hat{\rho}_{ij}),$$
$$i,j = 1,\ldots,p. \quad (2.3.4)$$

In particular

$$B_{ii} = (n-1)\hat{\sigma}_i^2(1 + \overline{k-1}\hat{\rho}_{ii}),$$
$$W_{ii} = n(k-1)\hat{\sigma}_i^2(1 - \hat{\rho}_{ii}) \quad (2.3.5)$$

from which estimates of σ_i and ρ_{ii} can be obtained. Confidence intervals for ρ_{ii}, the i-th homo-ICC, can be constructed by using the percentage points of the pivotal statistic

$$F = \frac{n(k-1)}{n-1}\,\frac{B_{ii}}{W_{ii}}\,\frac{1-\rho_{ii}}{1+\overline{k-1}\,\rho_{ii}} \quad (2.3.6)$$

which is distributed as Fisher's variance ratio on $(n-1)$ and $n(k-1)$ degrees of freedom.

Estimates of ρ'_{ij} and ρ_{ii} can be obtained from (2.3.4) using estimates of σ_i and σ_j obtained from equations of the type (2.3.5).

Problem 1. How do we construct exact or asymptotic individual and simultaneous confidence intervals for ρ'_{ij} and ρ_{ij}, and tests of significance for specified values?

2.4 Canonical intraclass correlations

Let us replace the measurements on p characteristics of an individual by a linear combination with compounding coefficients $a = (a_1,\ldots,a_p)$, $(\Sigma a_i^2 = 1)$. The data (2.3.1) is transformed to

$$x_s^{(r)} = \sum_{i=1}^{p} a_i x_{is}^{(r)} = a' x_{\cdot s}^{(r)}, \qquad x_{\cdot s}^{(r)} = (x_{1s}^{(r)},\ldots,x_{ps}^{(r)}),$$
$$s = 1,\ldots,k, \qquad r = 1,\ldots,n. \quad (2.4.1)$$

We now use the formula (2.1.4) for the univariate case to compute the ICC.

The expressions for the sum of squares between and within in terms of $x_s^{(r)}$, which depend on a, are

$$b(a) = a'Ba, \qquad w(a) = a'Wa \tag{2.4.2}$$

where B and W are as in (2.3), and $\rho(a)$, the intraclass correlation of the variable $a'x$, is estimated from the equation

$$\frac{b(a)}{w(a)} = \frac{(n-1)[1+\overline{k-1}\rho(a)]}{n(k-1)[1-\rho(a)]}. \tag{2.4.3}$$

We choose a to maximize $\rho(a)$, which is same as maximizing the ratio (2.4.3). The stationary values of (2.4.3) are the roots of the determinantal equation

$$|B - \lambda W| = 0. \tag{2.4.4}$$

Let $\hat{\lambda}_1 \geq \cdots \geq \hat{\lambda}_p$ be the roots of (2.4.4). Corresponding to $\hat{\lambda}_i$, the i-th root, we have $\hat{\rho}_i$ obtained from equation

$$\hat{\lambda}_i = \frac{(n-1)[1+\overline{k-1}\hat{\rho}_i]}{n(k-1)[1-\hat{\rho}_i]}, \qquad i = 1, \ldots, p. \tag{2.4.5}$$

$\hat{\rho}_1, \ldots, \hat{\rho}_p$ are called canonical intraclass correlation coefficients (CICC).

The population values of $\hat{\lambda}_1, \ldots, \hat{\lambda}_p$ are the roots of

$$|(E(B_{ij})) - \lambda(E(W_{ij}))| = 0 \tag{2.4.6}$$

where the (i,j)-th elements of the matrices are as defined in (2.3.3).

It may be noted that under the assumptions made in Section 2.2 on variances and covariances, the matrices $B = (B_{ij})$ and $W = (W_{ij})$ are independently distributed and the distributions of the roots $\hat{\lambda}_1, \ldots, \hat{\lambda}_p$ are known under different hypotheses on ρ_{ij} and ρ'_{ij} (see Anderson (1984), Fisher (1939), Hsu (1938), Roy (1939, 1945)). Some asymptotic tests on CICC are given in Rao (1945).

Problem 2. Exact and asymptotic tests of hypotheses and simultaneous confidence intervals of the population canonical intraclass correlations remain to be worked out in some detail.

3 Canonical Correlations

3.1 Relationship between two sets of variates

Let $x = (x_1, \ldots, x_p)$ be the vector of measurements of p characteristics made on the father and $y = (y_1, \ldots, y_p)$, the vector of corresponding measurements made on the son. Define the covariance matrices:

$$\begin{aligned} \text{Cov}(x,x) &= A \text{ of order } p \times p, \\ \text{Cov}(y,y) &= B \text{ of order } p \times p, \\ \text{Cov}(x,y) &= C \text{ of order } p \times p. \end{aligned} \tag{3.1.1}$$

Canonical correlations between father and son as defined by Hotelling (1936) are obtained by considering linear functions $a'x$ and $b'y$ and finding the stationary values of the correlation coefficient between $a'x$ and $b'y$ by varying a and b. The correlation coefficient between $a'x$ and $b'y$ is

$$\rho(a'x, b'y) = \frac{a'Cb}{\sqrt{(a'Aa)(b'Bb)}}. \tag{3.1.2}$$

The stationary values of ρ, known as canonical correlations, are the singular values of

$$A^{-1/2}CB^{-1/2}. \tag{3.1.3}$$

Problem 3. Under what conditions on A, B and C are the vectors a and b the same at the stationary values of ρ? A sufficient condition for this is that $A = B$ and C is symmetric.

3.2 Homologous canonical correlations

In studying resemblance between father and son, a natural measure is the maximum correlation between $a'x$ and $a'y$, using the same compounding coefficients for the measurements made on the father and son. In such a case,

$$\rho(a'x, a'y) = \frac{a'Da}{\sqrt{(a'Aa)(a'Ba)}} \tag{3.2.1}$$

where $D = 2^{-1}(C + C')$.

To obtain the stationary values of (3.2.1), which are called homologous canonical correlations (HCC), we equate the derivatives of $\rho(a'x, a'y)$ with respect to the elements of a to zero (see Rao (1973, p. 72)). This yields

$$\frac{a'Da}{a'Aa}Aa + \frac{a'Da}{a'Ba}Ba = 2Da \tag{3.2.2}$$

which can be written in the equivalent form

$$\lambda Aa + \mu Ba = 2Da, \qquad \lambda a'Aa = a'Da \tag{3.2.3}$$

introducing two additional variables λ and μ, or in the form

$$\lambda(A + \nu B)a = 2Da, \qquad a'Aa = \nu a'Ba \tag{3.2.4}$$

introducing two additional variables λ and ν.

Since A and B are positive definite matrices there exists a nonsingular matrix S such that

$$A = S\Delta S', \qquad B = SS' \tag{3.2.5}$$

where Δ is a diagonal matrix (see Rao (1973, p. 41)). Then writing b for $S'a$, the equation (3.2.4) takes the simpler form

$$\lambda(\Delta + \nu I)b = 2Eb,$$
$$b'\Delta b = \nu b'b \tag{3.2.6}$$

where $E = S^{-1}D(S^{-1})'$. If $\delta_1, \ldots, \delta_p$ are the diagonal elements of Δ and $b_1, \ldots, b_p$ are the components of b, we have the equations for $b_1, \ldots, b_p$.

$$2b'b[(e_i'Eb)B_i - (e_1'Eb)b_i] = b_1 b_i(\delta_i - \delta_1)b'Eb, \qquad i = 1, \ldots, p \tag{3.2.7}$$

where e_i is the elementary vector with unity as the i-th component and zeros elsewhere. In (3.2.7), we have $(p - 1)$ quartic equations in $(p - 1)$ ratios $(b_2/b_1), \ldots, (b_p/b_1)$. The solution of these equations is in general not easy except in the case of $p = 2$, when there is only one quartic equation, as observed by Kouvaritakis and Cameron (1980).

Rao and Rao (1987) discuss a general computational method for obtaining the stationary values of (3.2.1) using the equation (3.2.4)

$$2Da = \lambda(A + \nu B)a,$$
$$a'Aa = \nu a'Ba. \tag{3.2.8}$$

We observe that $\nu \in [\nu_p, \nu_1]$ where $\nu_1 \geq \cdots \geq \nu_p$ are the eigenvalues of A with respect to B, i.e., the roots of $|A - \nu B| = 0$. For any given $\nu \in [\nu_p, \nu_1]$, the first equation in (3.2.8) provides p eigenvalues

$$\lambda_1(\nu) \geq \cdots \geq \lambda_p(\nu) \tag{3.2.9}$$

of $2D$ with respect to $(A + \nu B)$ and p associated eigenvectors

$$a_1(\nu), \ldots, a_p(\nu). \tag{3.2.10}$$

The pair $(\nu, a_i(\nu))$ will be a solution of (3.2.8) if and only if

$$\nu = a_i'(\nu)Aa_i(\nu)/a_i'(\nu)Ba_i(\nu). \tag{3.2.11}$$

Our computational algorithm is basically a search for ν and an associated eigenvector $a(\nu)$ such that the equation (3.2.11) holds.

However, the complexity of the algorithm depends on the nature of the p eigenvalue functions

$$\lambda_i(\nu), \qquad \nu \in [\nu_p, \nu_1], \qquad i = 1, \ldots, p, \tag{3.2.12}$$

each of which is a continuous function of ν (see Kato (1980, Chapter 2) for various results in this direction). In practical situations, the p eigenvalue functions will be distinct, i.e., no two functions meet at a point, in which case the solution is simple. We start with $\lambda_1(\nu)$. Since $\lambda_1(\nu) \neq \lambda_2(\nu)$ for all ν, there is a unique continuous function $a_1(\nu)$ associated with $\lambda_1(\nu)$. We can then construct the continuous function

$$f_1(\nu) = [a_1'(\nu)Aa_1(\nu)/a_1'(\nu)Ba_2(\nu)] - \nu, \tag{3.2.13}$$

$$f_1(\nu) \geq 0 \quad \text{when } \nu = \nu_p, \qquad f_1(\nu) \leq 0 \quad \text{when } \nu = \nu_1, \tag{3.2.14}$$

so that there is at least one value of ν, say ν_1, for which (3.2.13) vanishes and provides the solution $[\mu_1, a_1(\nu)]$ to (3.2.8). There may be more than one solution to the equation $f_1(\nu) = 0$, each of which leads to a solution of (3.2.8). Since the value of $f_1(\nu)$ for any given ν is uniquely computable, the solution to $f_1(\nu) = 0$ can be easily found through a computer program for solving equations. We then consider $\lambda_2(\nu)$, and since $\lambda_2(\nu) \neq \lambda_3(\nu)$ for all ν, the above procedure can be implemented leading to additional solutions. Then we go to $\lambda_3(\nu)$ and so on. Thus in the case when all the functions $\lambda_i(\nu)$ are distinct, all the solutions, at least p in number, can be obtained.

If $\lambda_i(\nu)$, $i = 1, \ldots, p$, are not all distinct, the computations are more complicated (see Rao and Rao (1987) for a discussion of such cases).

Problem 4. It would be useful to develop a suitable computer program to solve the equation (3.2.8) in generality.

Problem 5. In the context of the above problem, it may be of interest to test on the basis of estimated matrices $\hat{A}$, $\hat{B}$ and $\hat{C}$, the hypothesis $A = B$, where A and B are respectively the covariance matrices of the measurements on father and son, and also whether C is symmetrical. In such a case the vectors a and b we are seeking will be the same.

4 Example

The following table gives the correlation matrix of the measurements on head length (HL), head width (HW), face width (FW) and stature (St) taken on father and son.

Correlation matrix

		Son				Father			
		HL	HW	FW	St.	HL	HW	FW	St.
Son	HL	1.000							
	HW	0.288	1.000						
	FW	0.410	0.604	1.000					
	St.	0.325	0.311	0.219	1.000				
Father	HL	0.341	0.145	0.243	0.055	1.000			
	HW	0.194	0.045	0.066	0.248	0.137	1.000		
	FW	0.057	−0.033	0.111	0.028	0.027	0.657	1.000	
	St.	0.174	0.181	0.187	0.581	0.130	0.325	0.190	1.000

The usual canonical correlations of Hotelling calculated by using the formula (3.1.3), and homologous canonical correlations defined in Section 3.2 following the equation (3.2.1) and computed using an algorithm developed in Rao and Rao (1987) to solve the equation (3.2.4) are given in the following table.

Canonical correlations

	ρ_1	ρ_2	ρ_3	ρ_4
Nonhomo:	0.6077	0.3730	0.2335	0.0862
Homo:	0.5874	0.3564	0.1675	−0.0949

By construction, Nonhomo-canonical correlations are numerically larger than homo-canonical correlations, but the computed values seem to be close.

Acknowledgement

I have great pleasure in contributing to the Festschrift Volume for Dr. Tarmo Pukkila in appreciation of his valuable contributions to statistical theory and practice.

References

Anderson, T.W. (1984). *An Introduction to Multivariate Statistical Analysis* (Second Edition). New York: Wiley.

Fisher, R.A. (1925). *Statistical Methods for Research Workers* (First edition 1925, eleventh edition 1950). Edinburgh: Oliver and Boyd.

Fisher, R.A. (1939). The sampling distribution of some statistics obtained from nonlinear equations. *The Annals of Eugenics*, 9, 238–249.

Hotelling, H. (1936). Relations between two sets of variates. *Biometrika*, 28, 321–377.

Hsu, P.L. (1938). On the distribution of the roots of certain determinantal equations. *The Annals of Eugenics*, 9, 250–258.

Kato, T. (1980). *Perturbation Theory for Linear Operators* (Second Edition). New York: Springer-Verlag.

Kouvaritakis, B. and Cameron, R. (1980). Pole placement with minimized norm controllers. *IEE Proceedings D, Control Theory and Applications*, 127, 32–36.

Rao, C.R. (1945). Familial correlations or the multivariate generalizations of the intraclass correlation. *Current Science*, 3, 66–67.

Rao, C.R. (1952). *Advanced Statistical Methods in Biometric Research.* New York: Wiley.

Rao, C.R. (1973). *Linear Statistical Inference and its Applications* (Second Edition). New York: Wiley.

Rao, C.R. and Rao, Veerendra (1987). Stationary values of the product of two Rayleigh quotients: homologous canonical correlation coefficients. *Sankhyā* B, 49, 113–125.

Roy, S.N. (1939). p-statistics or some generalizations in the analysis of variance. *Sankhyā*, 4, 381–396.

Roy, S. N. (1945). The individual sampling of the maximum, minimum and any intermediate of the p-statistics on the null hypothesis. *Sankhyā*, 7, 133–158.

C. RADHAKRISHNA RAO
Statistics Department
Joab Thomas Building
Pennsylvania State University
University Park, PA 16802
crr1@psu.edu
http://www.stat.psu.edu/people/faculty/crrao.html

Festschrift for Tarmo Pukkila on his 60th Birthday
Eds. E. P. Liski, J. Isotalo, J. Niemelä, S. Puntanen, and G. P. H. Styan

Univ. of Tampere, 2006, ISBN 978-951-44-6620-5, pages 295–300

Normalized Maximum Likelihood models for logit regression

IOAN TABUS & JORMA RISSANEN

Abstract. The relative importance of the influence of different regressor variables to the regressed variable is studied by the Normalized Maximum Likelihood (NML) models for logit regression. The NML models, one for each collection of the regressor variables, maximize the joint probability of the observed values of the regressed and the regressor variables, which provides a direct means for comparison. An efficient algorithm is given for the generally difficult to calculate normalizing coefficient. A numerical example is given.

2000 MSC codes: 62F99, 62J12.

Key words and phrases: Universal model; Sufficient statistic; Model classes; Extended Bernoulli class.

1 Introduction

The observations consist of n pairs $(y^n, \boldsymbol{x}^n) = (y_1, \boldsymbol{x}_1), \dots, (y_n, \boldsymbol{x}_n)$, where the y_i are binary numbers and $\boldsymbol{x}_i \in \mathbb{R}^k$ vectors of numbers $\boldsymbol{x}_i \in \{\boldsymbol{b}_1, \dots, \boldsymbol{b}_\ell\}$ for $\ell \le n$, ranging over a discrete set such as that of quantized real numbers. Unless the discrete set is very large there will be repeated occurrences of the regressor vectors $\boldsymbol{x}_i$, which not only adds information to the statistical relationship $y_i \mid \boldsymbol{x}_i$

$$P(Y_i = 1 \mid \boldsymbol{x}_i; \boldsymbol{\beta}) = \frac{e^{\boldsymbol{\beta}^{\mathsf{T}} \boldsymbol{x}_i}}{1 + e^{\boldsymbol{\beta}^{\mathsf{T}} \boldsymbol{x}_i}}$$

$$P(Y_i = 0 \mid \boldsymbol{x}_i; \boldsymbol{\beta}) = \frac{1}{1 + e^{\boldsymbol{\beta}^{\mathsf{T}} \boldsymbol{x}_i}},$$

where $\boldsymbol{\beta} = \beta_1, \dots, \beta_k$; see Cox (1970) and Hirji et al. (1987), but also greatly simplifies the evaluation of the various formulas needed. Let the number of occurrences of $\boldsymbol{b}_i$ in the string $\boldsymbol{x}_1, \dots, \boldsymbol{x}_n$ be n_i, and let $y_i = 1$ be $m_i(y^n) = m_i$ times of these occurrences. We extend $P(Y_i = 1 \mid \boldsymbol{x}_i; \boldsymbol{\beta})$ to the sequence

$(y^n, \boldsymbol{x}^n)$ by independence so that

$$P(Y^n \mid \boldsymbol{x}^n; \boldsymbol{\beta}) = \frac{\prod_{i=1}^{\ell} e^{m_i \boldsymbol{\beta}^\top \boldsymbol{b}_i}}{\prod_{i=1}^{n}(1 + e^{\boldsymbol{\beta}^\top \boldsymbol{x}_i})} = \frac{e^{\sum_{i=1}^{\ell} m_i \boldsymbol{\beta}^\top \boldsymbol{b}_i}}{\prod_{i=1}^{n}(1 + e^{\boldsymbol{\beta}^\top \boldsymbol{x}_i})} = \frac{e^{\boldsymbol{\beta}^\top \boldsymbol{t}}}{\prod_{i=1}^{\ell}(1 + e^{\boldsymbol{\beta}^\top \boldsymbol{b}_i})^{n_i}}, \tag{1}$$

where $\boldsymbol{t} = \sum_{i=1}^{\ell} m_i \boldsymbol{b}_i$ is a sufficient statistic. Although these logit models may be useful even without repetitions; ie., some or all the numbers n_i equal unity, for their full advantage n_i should exceed unity.

The ML estimate of regression parameters

The following maximum likelihood estimates are well known, but we write them in terms of our notations n_i and m_i, which simplify the subsequent algorithm. We have

$$\log P(y^n \mid \boldsymbol{x}^n; \boldsymbol{\beta}) = \boldsymbol{\beta}^\top \boldsymbol{t} - \sum_{i=1}^{\ell} n_i \log(1 + e^{\boldsymbol{\beta}^\top \boldsymbol{b}_i}) \tag{2}$$

and

$$\frac{d \log P(Y^n \mid \boldsymbol{x}^n; \boldsymbol{\beta})}{d\beta} = \boldsymbol{t} - \sum_{i=1}^{\ell} n_i \boldsymbol{b}_i \frac{e^{\boldsymbol{\beta}^\top \boldsymbol{b}_i}}{(1 + e^{\boldsymbol{\beta}^\top \boldsymbol{b}_i})}. \tag{3}$$

The ML parameter vector $\hat{\boldsymbol{\beta}}$ satisfies

$$\boldsymbol{t} = \sum_{i=1}^{\ell} n_i \boldsymbol{b}_i \frac{e^{\hat{\boldsymbol{\beta}}^\top \boldsymbol{b}_i}}{(1 + e^{\hat{\boldsymbol{\beta}}^\top \boldsymbol{b}_i})}, \tag{4}$$

from which $\hat{\boldsymbol{\beta}}(y^n) = \hat{\boldsymbol{\beta}}_{\boldsymbol{t}}$ can be solved, or equivalently from

$$\sum_{i=1}^{\ell} n_i \boldsymbol{b}_i \left(\frac{m_i}{n_i} - \frac{e^{\hat{\boldsymbol{\beta}}^\top \boldsymbol{b}_i}}{1 + e^{\hat{\boldsymbol{\beta}}^\top \boldsymbol{b}_i}} \right) = 0. \tag{5}$$

Since no closed form solution is known for the ML vector $\hat{\boldsymbol{\beta}}$ it has to be found by numerical means. A number of good algorithms exist.

2 The normalized maximum likelihood model

The normalized maximum likelihood, NML, model is a universal model for a parametric class $\{P(y^n; \theta) : \theta \in \Gamma \subset \mathbb{R}^k\}$, Rissanen (1996), defined as follows

$$\hat{P}(y^n) = \frac{P(y^n; \hat{\theta}(y^n))}{C_{k,n}}$$

$$C_{k,n} = \int P(y^n; \hat{\theta}(y^n))\, dy^n = \int_{\hat{\theta} \in \Gamma} Q(\hat{\theta}; \hat{\theta})\, d\hat{\theta},$$

where $Q(\hat{\theta};\theta)$ is the density function for the ML estimate induced by $P(y^n;\theta)$. This universal model has a number of optimality properties to the effect that it assigns the shortest code length, or equivalently, the maximum density to the data that can be assigned by any model in the class.

In our case the normalized maximum likelihood model for each collection of the retained regressor variables or the corresponding parameters, which define the different model classes, is as follows

$$\hat{P}(y^n \mid \boldsymbol{x}^n) = \frac{P(y^n \mid \boldsymbol{x}^n; \hat{\boldsymbol{\beta}})}{C(X)}, \tag{6}$$

where

$$P(y^n \mid \boldsymbol{x}^n; \hat{\boldsymbol{\beta}}) = \frac{e^{\hat{\boldsymbol{\beta}}^\top \boldsymbol{t}}}{\prod_{i=1}^{\ell}(1+e^{\hat{\boldsymbol{\beta}}^\top \boldsymbol{b}_i})^{n_i}} = P(y^n \mid \boldsymbol{t}; \hat{\boldsymbol{\beta}}_{\boldsymbol{t}}). \tag{7}$$

The normalization constant can be written as

$$\begin{aligned} C(X) &= \sum_{y^n} P(y^n \mid \boldsymbol{x}^n; \hat{\boldsymbol{\beta}}) = \sum_{\boldsymbol{t}\in\Omega} c_n(\boldsymbol{t}, X) P(y^n \mid \boldsymbol{t}; \hat{\boldsymbol{\beta}}_{\boldsymbol{t}}) \\ &= \sum_{\boldsymbol{t}\in\Omega} c_n(\boldsymbol{t}, X) \frac{e^{\hat{\boldsymbol{\beta}}_{\boldsymbol{t}}^\top \boldsymbol{t}}}{\prod_{i=1}^{\ell}(1+e^{\hat{\boldsymbol{\beta}}_{\boldsymbol{t}}^\top \boldsymbol{b}_i})^{n_i}}, \end{aligned} \tag{8}$$

where $c_n(\boldsymbol{t}, X)$ denotes the number of strings y^n such that $\sum_{i=1}^{\ell} m_i(y^n)\boldsymbol{b}_i = \boldsymbol{t}$. The sum is taken over all $\boldsymbol{t}$ such that

$$\boldsymbol{t} = \sum_{i=1}^{\ell} m_i \boldsymbol{b}_i,$$
$$m_i \le n_i, \qquad i = 1,\dots,\ell,$$
$$\sum_{j=1}^{\ell} n_i = n.$$

In Hirji et al. (1987) an algorithm was given to calculate the distribution of $\boldsymbol{t}$, one term in the sum (8) above, for a fixed $\boldsymbol{\beta}$. The algorithm did not take advantage of the fact that $\boldsymbol{t}$ depends only on the distinct repeating regressor vectors $\boldsymbol{b}_i$, which simplifies the calculations.

Computing the counts of the distinct sufficient statistics

There are $\prod_{i=1}^{\ell}(n_i+1)$ possibilities for the numbers $m_1, m_2, \dots, m_\ell$, some of which give the same value for the sufficient statistic $\boldsymbol{t} = \sum_{i=1}^{\ell} m_i \boldsymbol{b}_i$.

We compute recursively in L, $L = 1, 2, \dots, \ell$, the set $\Delta = \{\boldsymbol{t} : \boldsymbol{t} = \sum_{i=1}^{\ell} m_i \boldsymbol{b}_i\}$ of achievable sufficient statistic vectors and the computation of the counts of each. Denote by $\boldsymbol{t}_L = \sum_{i=1}^{L} m_i \boldsymbol{b}_i$ one partial sum up to step L, and $\Delta_L = \{\boldsymbol{t}_L : \boldsymbol{t}_L = \sum_{i=1}^{L} m_i \boldsymbol{b}_i\}$, where $m_i \in \{0, 1, \dots, n_i\}$.

The main recursion for constructing the sufficient statistics vectors is: $\boldsymbol{t}_L^+ = \boldsymbol{t}_{L-1} + j\boldsymbol{b}_L$ where $j \in \{0, 1, \ldots, n_L\}$. The sketch of the algorithm is as follows:

0. Initialize $\Delta_1 = \Delta$ with the vectors $j\boldsymbol{b}_1$, $j = 1 : n_1$
1. For $L = 2 : \ell$
1.1 For $j = 1 : n_L$
1.1.1 For $i = 1 : |\Delta_{L-1}|$
1.1.1.1 $\boldsymbol{t}_L^+ = \boldsymbol{t}_{L-1}(i) + j\boldsymbol{b}_L$
1.1.1.2 For $k = 1 : |\Delta|$
If $\boldsymbol{t}_L^+$ is identical to $\boldsymbol{t}(k)$, the kth vector in Δ,
update counts: $c(\boldsymbol{t}_L(k)) = c(\boldsymbol{t}_L(k)) + \binom{n_L}{j} c(\boldsymbol{t}_{L-1}(i))$
1.1.1.3 If $\boldsymbol{t}_L^+ \notin \Delta_{L-1}$, append $\boldsymbol{t}_L^+$ to Δ and set $c(\boldsymbol{t}_L^+) = \binom{n_L}{j} c(\boldsymbol{t}_{L-1}(i))$
1.1.2 Set $\Delta_L = \Delta$

3 Application

As an example we took the data in Table 3 in Hirji et al. (1987). For $k = 3$ there are $\ell = 8$ distinct (column) regressor vectors 000, 001, ..., 111, repeated 3, 2, 4, 5, 1, 5, 8, 17 times, respectively, at which $y = 1$ occurs 3, 2, 44, 5, 1, 3, 5, 6 times, respectively.

In Table 1 we give the NML code length and the logarithm of the normalizing coefficient in columns 2 and 3, respectively, for all the eight subsets of the retained regressor variables listed in column 1. For instance, the index set $\gamma = 110$ means that the first two variables b_1 and b_2 are retained while the third is ignored and for $k = 2$ there are $\ell = 4$ distinct occurrences of the regressor vectors and the parameters fitted are β_1 and β_2. The NML model for the class defined for this subset is seen to assign the largest probability to the observed data and hence provides the best explanation of the statistical dependency $Y \mid X$. We also see that the first variable is the most important and the third provides little additional information to the first two. We clearly see that the NML models give much more information than the traditional separate testing procedures. In fact, the traditional hypothesis testing procedures consist of 'accept-reject' rules on arbitrarily set levels for the null hypotheses of type $\beta_i = \beta_j = \cdots = 0$ without giving quantitative comparative importance of the various variables.

For the sake of comparison we also give the results in Table 2 when the data are modeled by an extended Bernoulli class, where the errors ε of the model $y = f(\boldsymbol{b}_i) \oplus \varepsilon$ are assumed independent and Bernoulli distributed

$$\mathcal{M}(\theta, k, f) = \{P(y; f, \boldsymbol{b}_i, \theta) = \theta^{(1-y\oplus f(\boldsymbol{b}_i))}(1-\theta)^{(y\oplus f(\boldsymbol{b}_i))}\} \tag{9}$$

Table 1. Logit regression. Optimum in bold face.

y	L_{NML}	$\log_2 C(X)$	$\lvert\Delta_L\rvert$
000	46.91	3.20	47
001	45.21	5.48	572
010	44.88	5.41	512
100	41.18	5.26	407
011	43.84	7.98	6048
101	41.31	7.76	4572
110	**40.49**	7.72	4192
111	41.34	10.47	44280

Table 2. Bernoulli regression. The two best in bold face.

y	L_{NML}	$\log_2 C(X)$
000	46.91	3.20
001	46.97	4.10
010	47.81	4.09
100	47.79	4.07
011	45.41	5.90
101	**45.37**	5.85
110	**45.37**	5.86
111	47.50	9.41

for which the ML is given by

$$P(y^n; \hat{f}_{y^n}, m_1, \ldots, m_\ell) = \left(\frac{\sum_{i=1}^{\ell} \max(m_i, n_i - m_i)}{n}\right)^{\sum_{i=1}^{\ell} \max(m_i, n_i - m_i)} \cdot \left(\frac{\sum_{i=1}^{\ell} \min(m_i, n_i - m_i)}{n}\right)^{\sum_{i=1}^{\ell} \min(m_i, n_i - m_i)} . \quad (10)$$

The computation of the NML for the class $\mathcal{M}(\theta, k, f)$ is described in Tabus et al. (2002).

Although one of the two best results in the Bernoulli regression are obtained with the same retained regressor variables as the optimum in the logit regression, the code lengths in the latter are shorter, and hence the results are more reliable.

References

Cox, D. R. (1970). *The Analysis of Binary Data.* London: Methuen.

Hirji, K. F., Mehta, C. R., and Patel, N. R. (1987). Computing distributions for exact logistic regression. *Journal of the American Statistical Association,* 82, 1110–1117.

Rissanen, J. (1996). Fisher Information and Stochastic Complexity. *IEEE Transactions on Information Theory*, IT-42, 40–47.

Tabus, I., Rissanen, J., and Astola, J. (2002). Normalized maximum likelihood models for Boolean regression with application to prediction and classification in genomics. In *Computational And Statistical Approaches To Genomics*. Eds. W. Zhang and I. Shmulevich. Kluwer Acadmic Publishers. Pp. 173–196.

IOAN TABUS
Institute of Signal Processing
Tampere University of Technology
FI-33101, Tampere, Finland
tabus@cs.tut.fi
http://www.cs.tut.fi/~tabus/

JORMA RISSANEN
Tampere University of Technology, Finland, and
Helsinki Institute for Information Technology
jorma.rissanen@mdl-research.org
http://www.mdl-research.org/jorma.rissanen/

Festschrift for Tarmo Pukkila on his 60th Birthday
Eds. E. P. Liski, J. Isotalo, J. Niemelä, S. Puntanen, and G. P. H. Styan

Univ. of Tampere, 2006, ISBN 978-951-44-6620-5, pages 301–314

Calculating efficient semiparametric estimators for a broad class of missing-data problems

ALASTAIR J. SCOTT & CHRIS WILD

Abstract. We develop efficient methods for computing semiparametric estimates in a wide variety of situations involving missing data and response-selective sampling. The methods are based on the profile likelihood. Estimates of the covariance matrix and associated test statistics are obtained at the same time.

2000 MSC codes: 62G99, 62J99.

Key words and phrases: Missing data; Biased sampling; Profile likelihood.

1 Introduction

We consider a unified method for fitting essentially arbitrary regression models to a large class of missing data and/or response-selective sampling problems using semiparametric maximum likelihood. This paper gives the computational details underlying the profile likelihood methods used, for example, in Scott and Wild (1997), Lawless et al. (1999) and Neuhaus et al. (2002, 2006). However, it covers a much wider range of applications than the situations discussed in those papers.

Suppose that we have a finite population of N individuals under study. Let $\boldsymbol{v}$ represent a set of variables containing easily obtainable information that is available for all N individuals. For our development, $\boldsymbol{v}$ must have finite support, whereas all other variables may be either discrete or continuous. In addition to the information on $\boldsymbol{v}$, we assume that information on a (possibly multivariate) response variable $\boldsymbol{y}$, can be obtained for at least a subset of individuals in the study study, and that a more "expensive" set of explanatory variables $\boldsymbol{z}$ can also obtained for a (possibly different)subset. We may wish to use some of the variables in $\boldsymbol{v}$, say $\boldsymbol{v}_1$, as explanatory variables in our model; other variables in $\boldsymbol{v}$ can play the role of informative surrogates for expensive covariates in $\boldsymbol{z}$. The object is to estimate the parameters, $\boldsymbol{\theta}$, of the regression model $f(\boldsymbol{y} \mid \boldsymbol{z}, \boldsymbol{v}_1; \boldsymbol{\theta})$. Thus we have a parametric regression model for the conditional density of the response given explanatory variables. Our methods can handle situations in which data sources include observations on $\boldsymbol{z}$ and any or all of $(\boldsymbol{z}, \boldsymbol{v})$ $(\boldsymbol{z} \mid \boldsymbol{v})$, $(\boldsymbol{y}, \boldsymbol{v})$, $(\boldsymbol{y} \mid \boldsymbol{v})$, $(\boldsymbol{y}, \boldsymbol{z}, \boldsymbol{v})$, $(\boldsymbol{y}, \boldsymbol{z} \mid \boldsymbol{v})$, $(\boldsymbol{y} \mid \boldsymbol{z}, \boldsymbol{v})$, and $(\boldsymbol{z} \mid \boldsymbol{y}, \boldsymbol{v})$, where " | " refers to information obtained from conditional sampling.

Let $g(\boldsymbol{z}, \boldsymbol{v})$ denote the density of the covariates and $g(\boldsymbol{z} \mid \boldsymbol{v})$ the conditional density of $\boldsymbol{z}$ given $\boldsymbol{v}$. With standard prospective sampling and no missing data, the likelihood factorises into a term involving $\boldsymbol{\theta}$ and a term involving $g()$ so that information on the distribution of the explanatory variables is orthogonal to information on $\boldsymbol{\theta}$. Consequently, we do not need to model the covariate distribution. This is very convenient in practice because we often have far too many covariates of different types for it to be feasible to model their joint distribution in any realistic fashion. Unfortunately, with response-selective sampling, as with most missing data mechanisms, information on $\boldsymbol{\theta}$ and $g()$ is no longer orthogonal and we are forced to use some sort of joint modelling. However, the practical need for methods which do not require parametric modelling of $g()$ is just as great. Thus, we consider semi-parametric methods in which the marginal distribution of $(\boldsymbol{z}, \boldsymbol{v})$ is left unspecified and estimated nonparametrically.

The class of likelihoods that we consider initially consists of all those of the form

$$\prod_{i=1}^{N} f(\boldsymbol{y}_i \mid \boldsymbol{z}_i, \boldsymbol{v}_{1i}; \boldsymbol{\theta})^{\Delta_{1i}} g(\boldsymbol{z} \mid \boldsymbol{v}_i)^{\Delta_{2i}} f(\boldsymbol{y}_i \mid \boldsymbol{v}_i; \boldsymbol{\theta})^{\Delta_{3i}}, \tag{1}$$

where $f(\boldsymbol{y} \mid \boldsymbol{v}; \boldsymbol{\theta}) = \int f(\boldsymbol{y} \mid \boldsymbol{z}, \boldsymbol{v}_1; \boldsymbol{\theta})\, dG(\boldsymbol{z} \mid \boldsymbol{v})$, Δ_{1i} and Δ_{2i} are binary indicators taking values 0 or 1, and Δ_{3i} can take values 0, 1 or -1. Examples where such forms arise in practice are given in the next section. Our estimator of $\boldsymbol{\theta}$, say $\hat{\boldsymbol{\theta}}$, is found by maximizing the *profile* likelihood, obtained by maximizing (1) over the (potentially infinite-dimensional) nuisance parameter $g(\boldsymbol{z} \mid \boldsymbol{v})$. Conditions under which this profile likelihood estimator has full semiparametric efficiency are given by Bickel et al. (1993) and Murphy and van der Vaart (2000) for the i.i.d. case. Simpler conditions that apply directly to our multi-sample likelihood (1) are given in Lee and Hirose (2006). In addition, a consistent estimator of the covariance matrix of $\hat{\boldsymbol{\theta}}$ can be obtained from the inverse profile information matrix. This means that we can produce a single program to cater for all likelihoods in this class and, with minimal modification, a more extended class introduced later. This enables general software to be written whereby a new regression model can be catered for simply by coding a new function to calculate $f(\boldsymbol{y} \mid \boldsymbol{z}, \boldsymbol{v}_1; \boldsymbol{\theta})$ and its derivatives.

Other semiparametric efficient approaches such as those of Robins et al. (1994, 1995) and Holcroft et al. (1997) require complicated modelling over and above finding a suitable model, $f(\boldsymbol{y} \mid \boldsymbol{z}, \boldsymbol{v}_1; \boldsymbol{\theta})$, for the regression of interest. Profile likelihood enables us to obtain standard errors from the inverse Hessian matrix of the likelihood profile without having to consider the intricacies of complex observational schemes that are necessary for the sandwich estimators of variance required by other estimating equation approaches. Analyses based upon the approach here require no modelling effort from the statistician on aspects relating to missingness patterns and thus result in analyses that are much more time-efficient for the statistician.

This paper is organized as follows. Section 2 gives examples showing how likelihoods of the form (1) arise and illustrates the generality of the form. Section 3 describes maximum likelihood estimation for the class described above and the results are extended to a wider class in Section 4. Section 5 describes a much more computationally-efficient specialization of the algorithm that can be used when $\boldsymbol{y}$ is discrete, or for continuous $\boldsymbol{y}$ where we have (or retain) only class-interval information on $(\boldsymbol{y}, \boldsymbol{v})$ when $\boldsymbol{z}$ is missing as in Lawless et al. (1999).

2 Examples

We begin with some examples to illustrate how likelihoods of the form (1) can arise in practice.

Example 1. Case-control designs and generalisations

For case-control studies, y is a binary response variable recording case status as $y = 1$ or control status as $y = 0$. As a typical example, the cases may be those individuals that have contracted a disease of interest and the controls are those that have not.

In a simple case-control study, a random sample of m_1 cases is taken and their covariate values $\boldsymbol{z}$ are subsequently ascertained. The same is done for a sample of m_0 controls. The resulting likelihood is

$$\prod_{\text{cases}} f(\boldsymbol{z} \mid y = 1) \prod_{\text{controls}} f(\boldsymbol{z} \mid y = 0) = \prod_{\text{sample}} f(y \mid \boldsymbol{z}; \boldsymbol{\theta}) g(\boldsymbol{z}) f(y; \boldsymbol{\theta})^{-1}, \quad (2)$$

from Bayes' theorem. This is a very simple example of (1) in which a notional $\boldsymbol{v}$ takes on a single value, $\Delta_1 = \Delta_2 = 1$ if $\boldsymbol{z}$ is observed and 0 otherwise, and $\Delta_3 = -1$ if $\boldsymbol{z}$ is observed and 0 otherwise.

In a population-based study or a two-stage study in which case-control status is ascertained for all population units at the first stage and $\boldsymbol{z}$ is measured for a sample of cases and a sample of controls at the second stage, the likelihood is (Scott and Wild (1991))

$$\Big\{\prod_{\text{cases}} f(\boldsymbol{z} \mid y = 1) \prod_{\text{controls}} f(\boldsymbol{z} \mid y = 0)\Big\} f(y = 1)^{M_1} f(y = 0)^{M_0}$$
$$= \prod_{i=1}^{N} \{f(y \mid \boldsymbol{z}; \boldsymbol{\theta})\}^{\Delta_1} g(\boldsymbol{z})^{\Delta_2} f(y; \boldsymbol{\theta})^{\Delta_3}, \quad (3)$$

where M_1 is the number of cases and M_0 the number of controls in the population or first stage, $\Delta_1 = \Delta_2 = 1$ if $\boldsymbol{z}$ is observed and 0 otherwise, and $\Delta_3 = 0$ if $\boldsymbol{z}$ is observed and $+1$ otherwise. We note that we get the same likelihood whether we take fixed sized samples of cases and controls at the second stage or use a random mechanism as in the missing-data example. However, sandwich estimators of the variance of $\hat{\boldsymbol{\theta}}$ will be different in general although, for the special case of logistic regression, only the variance of the intercept is affected.

With stratified case-control data, as described by Scott and Wild (1997), we have data on $(\boldsymbol{y}, \boldsymbol{v})$ at the first stage and then obtain $\boldsymbol{z}$ for subsamples of cases and controls drawn from strata, $S_1, \ldots, S_L$ say, defined by values of $\boldsymbol{v}$. The likelihood is of the form

$$\prod_{\ell=1}^{L} \prod_{\boldsymbol{v}_i \in S_\ell} \{f(\boldsymbol{y}_i \mid \boldsymbol{z}_i, \boldsymbol{v}_{1i}; \boldsymbol{\theta})\}^{\Delta_1} g(\boldsymbol{z} \mid \boldsymbol{v}_i)^{\Delta_2} f(\boldsymbol{y}_i \mid \boldsymbol{v}_i; \boldsymbol{\theta})^{\Delta_3}, \tag{4}$$

where the Δ_js are as for (3). The same likelihood pertains whether the data is obtained purposefully in this way using subsamples of fixed or random size, or whether we have population $\boldsymbol{y}$ and $\boldsymbol{v}$ data available for the finite population from which the cases and controls were drawn in a simple case-control study. Lawless et al. (1999) discuss a wide variety of other examples and sampling schemes that produce likelihoods of the form (4).

Example 2. Two and three stage missing-at-random

Consider a three stage mechanism in which, at Stage 1, $\boldsymbol{v}$ is observed for a random sample of individuals. At the second stage $\boldsymbol{y}$ is observed for subset of individuals with the ith individual having probability $\pi_1(\boldsymbol{v}_i)$ of being included. At Stage 3, $\boldsymbol{z}$ is observed for a subset of the Stage 2 sample with the ith individual having probability $\pi_2(\boldsymbol{v}_i, \boldsymbol{y}_i)$ of being included in the third stage. Thus, we only have complete $(\boldsymbol{y}, \boldsymbol{z}, \boldsymbol{v})$ information for individuals sampled at Stage 3.

This is a special case of the missing data mechanism considered by Holcroft et al. (1997), which encompasses the mechanisms in Robins et al. (1994, 1995), for a designed study in which π_1 and π_2 would be known. More generally, Holcroft et al. (1997) also allow for missingness by happenstance in which the available data is of the form $\boldsymbol{v}$, $(\boldsymbol{y}, \boldsymbol{v})$ and $(\boldsymbol{y}, \boldsymbol{z}, \boldsymbol{v})$. An assumption that data is missing at random means, in general terms, that the probability that something is missing depends only upon data that is observed, e.g., the probability that $\boldsymbol{z}$ is missing from $(\boldsymbol{y}, \boldsymbol{z}, \boldsymbol{v})$ depends only $(\boldsymbol{y}, \boldsymbol{v})$. Thus, for a missing-at-random analysis, we will still have the same set up as above but with $\pi_1(\ )$ and $\pi_2(\ )$ being unknown. When data is missing at random these probabilities can, however, be estimated from the data, using a binary regression model applied to an observed/missing response. This results in the use of missingness models $\pi_1(\ ;\alpha_1)$ and $\pi_2(\ ;\alpha_2)$ with their own sets of parameters.

Let us write $\tilde{\Delta}_j = 1$ when an observation is included in the $(j+1)$th stage of observation and 0 otherwise. The likelihood for the above scenario is:

$$\begin{aligned}
&\prod[g(\boldsymbol{v})\{1-\pi_1(\boldsymbol{v})\}]^{1-\tilde{\Delta}_1}[g(\boldsymbol{v})\pi_1(\boldsymbol{v})f(\boldsymbol{y}\mid\boldsymbol{v})\{1-\pi_2(\boldsymbol{y},\boldsymbol{v})\}]^{\tilde{\Delta}_1(1-\tilde{\Delta}_2)}\\
&\qquad\cdot[g(\boldsymbol{v})\pi_1(\boldsymbol{v})f(\boldsymbol{y}\mid\boldsymbol{v})\pi_2(\boldsymbol{y},\boldsymbol{v})f(\boldsymbol{z}\mid\boldsymbol{y},\boldsymbol{v})]^{\tilde{\Delta}_1\tilde{\Delta}_2}\\
&=\left\{\prod g(\boldsymbol{v})^{1-\tilde{\Delta}_1}f(\boldsymbol{y},\boldsymbol{v})^{\tilde{\Delta}_1(1-\tilde{\Delta}_2)}f(\boldsymbol{y},\boldsymbol{z},\boldsymbol{v})^{\tilde{\Delta}_1\tilde{\Delta}_2}\right\}\times\mathrm{Term}(\pi_1,\pi_2)\\
&=\left[\prod\{f(\boldsymbol{y}\mid\boldsymbol{z},\boldsymbol{v};\boldsymbol{\theta})g(\boldsymbol{z}\mid\boldsymbol{v})\}^{\tilde{\Delta}_1\tilde{\Delta}_2}f(\boldsymbol{y}\mid\boldsymbol{v}_1;\boldsymbol{\theta})^{\tilde{\Delta}_1(1-\tilde{\Delta}_2)}\right]\\
&\qquad\times\left\{\prod g(\boldsymbol{v})\right\}\times\mathrm{Term}(\pi_1,\pi_2), \qquad (5)
\end{aligned}$$

where $f(\boldsymbol{y}\mid\boldsymbol{v};\boldsymbol{\theta}) = \int f(\boldsymbol{y}\mid\boldsymbol{z},\boldsymbol{v}_1;\boldsymbol{\theta})\,dG_1(\boldsymbol{z}\mid\boldsymbol{v})$. There are several things to note from the form of the likelihood (5). Most importantly, we see that $g(\boldsymbol{v})$ and any missingness model parameters are orthogonal to $\boldsymbol{\theta}$ and the conditional densities $g(\boldsymbol{z}\mid\boldsymbol{v})$ so likelihood-based inferences about $\boldsymbol{\theta}$ use only the first term of (5). This means that: (i) we do not have to construct missingness models and estimate their parameters; (ii) it is only the conditional densities $g(\boldsymbol{z}\mid\boldsymbol{v})$ that we need to estimate nonparametrically; (iii) all of the information on $\boldsymbol{\theta}$ is in the second and third stage data - there is no information on $\boldsymbol{\theta}$ in the data from those individuals for whom we observe $\boldsymbol{v}$ alone; (iv) the likelihood that we end up using is identical to that from a two-stage study in which we obtain data on $(\boldsymbol{y},\boldsymbol{v})$ for all individuals sampled at the first stage and then observe $\boldsymbol{z}$ for a second-stage subsample which individuals enter with probabilities $\pi_2(\boldsymbol{y},\boldsymbol{v})$; and (v) the likelihood we use is the same whether $\boldsymbol{v}$ is random, having been sampled at the first stage, or whether sampling is conditional upon $\boldsymbol{v}$.

We reiterate that only the first term of (1) is relevant for estimation of $\boldsymbol{\theta}$. When $\boldsymbol{v}$ is discrete, which we assume throughout, the first term of (5) is clearly equivalent to (1) with $\Delta_1 = \Delta_2 = \tilde{\Delta}_1\tilde{\Delta}_2$ and $\Delta_3 = \tilde{\Delta}_1(1-\tilde{\Delta}_2)$.

In addition to the examples above, the likelihood (1) allows us to include information that can be treated as independent sampled from any of the following distributions: $f(\boldsymbol{y},\boldsymbol{z},\boldsymbol{v})$, $f(\boldsymbol{y},\boldsymbol{z}\mid\boldsymbol{v})$, $f(\boldsymbol{y}\mid\boldsymbol{z},\boldsymbol{v})$, $f(\boldsymbol{z}\mid\boldsymbol{y},\boldsymbol{v})$, $f(\boldsymbol{y},\boldsymbol{v})$, $f(\boldsymbol{y}\mid\boldsymbol{v})$, $f(\boldsymbol{z},\boldsymbol{v})$, and $f(\boldsymbol{z}\mid\boldsymbol{v})$. Examples of such schemes can be found in Scott and Wild (2001), Neuhaus et al. (2002, 2006) and Lee et al. (2006). This gives a great deal of scope for including supplementary information to cope with the lack of indentifiablity and the ill-conditioning problems that can occur with fitting prospective regressions to retrospectively sampled data.

3 Profile likelihood

3.1 Preliminaries

Recall that $\boldsymbol{v}$ has finite support. Denote the distinct values of $\boldsymbol{v}$ in the observed population by $\tilde{\boldsymbol{v}}_1, \ldots, \tilde{\boldsymbol{v}}_S$ and let S_s be the stratum containing all units with $\boldsymbol{v}_i = \tilde{\boldsymbol{v}}_s$. Then (1) can be written in the form

$$L[\boldsymbol{\theta}, \{g(\cdot \mid \boldsymbol{v}_s)\}] = \prod_{s=1}^{S} \prod_{i \in S_s} f(\boldsymbol{y}_i \mid \boldsymbol{z}_i, \tilde{\boldsymbol{v}}_{1s}; \boldsymbol{\theta})^{\Delta_{1i}} g(\boldsymbol{z}_i \mid \tilde{\boldsymbol{v}}_s)^{\Delta_{2i}} f(\boldsymbol{y}_i \mid \tilde{\boldsymbol{v}}_s; \boldsymbol{\theta})^{\Delta_{3i}}. \tag{6}$$

We wish to maximize this as a function of $\boldsymbol{\theta}$ and the S conditional densities $g(\boldsymbol{z} \mid \tilde{\boldsymbol{v}}_s)$. As is standard in semiparametric maximum likelihood, we treat these densities as discrete with all of the mass being placed at the observed $\boldsymbol{z}$ values.

For simplicity, we write $\boldsymbol{x} = (\boldsymbol{z}, \boldsymbol{v}_1)$ to include all covariates that are to be used in the model. Note that, when we consider only the sizes of probability atoms, $g(\boldsymbol{x} \mid \boldsymbol{v}) = g(\boldsymbol{z}, \boldsymbol{v}_1 \mid \boldsymbol{v}) = g(\boldsymbol{z} \mid \boldsymbol{v})$. The only remaining role of $\boldsymbol{v}$ in (6) is to divide the data set up into the S strata with separate conditional distributions of $\boldsymbol{x}$ to be estimated for each stratum.

Our problem is now to maximize

$$\ell(\boldsymbol{\theta}, g_1, \ldots, g_S) = \prod_{s=1}^{S} \prod_{i \in S_s} f(\boldsymbol{y}_i \mid \boldsymbol{x}_i; \boldsymbol{\theta})^{\Delta_{1i}} g(\boldsymbol{x}_i \mid S_s)^{\Delta_{2i}} f(\boldsymbol{y}_i \mid S_s; \boldsymbol{\theta})^{\Delta_{3i}},$$

with $f(\boldsymbol{y} \mid S_s; \boldsymbol{\theta}) = \int f(\boldsymbol{y} \mid \boldsymbol{z}, \tilde{\boldsymbol{v}}_{s1}; \boldsymbol{\theta})\, dG(\boldsymbol{z} \mid \tilde{\boldsymbol{v}}_s)$. The corresponding log-likelihood is of the form $\ell(\boldsymbol{\theta}, \boldsymbol{g}_1, \ldots, \boldsymbol{g}_S) = \sum_s \ell_s(\boldsymbol{\theta}, \boldsymbol{g}_s)$, where $\boldsymbol{g}_s = \boldsymbol{g}(\boldsymbol{x} \mid S_s)$ Thus, the profile log-likelihood, in which we maximise out the $\boldsymbol{g}_s$'s for fixed $\boldsymbol{\theta}$, is of the form

$$\ell_P(\boldsymbol{\theta}) = \ell\{\boldsymbol{\theta}, \hat{\boldsymbol{g}}_1(\cdot\,; \boldsymbol{\theta}), \ldots, \hat{\boldsymbol{g}}_S(\cdot\,; \boldsymbol{\theta})\} = \sum_s \ell_s\{\boldsymbol{\theta}, \hat{\boldsymbol{g}}_s(\cdot\,; \boldsymbol{\theta})\} = \sum_s \ell_{Ps}(\boldsymbol{\theta}).$$

This means that we need only to be able to solve the problem of obtaining the profile for $\boldsymbol{\theta}$ (and its derivatives) for a single stratum, i.e. to maximize

$$L(\boldsymbol{\theta}, \boldsymbol{g}) = \prod_i f(\boldsymbol{y}_i \mid \boldsymbol{x}_i; \boldsymbol{\theta})^{\Delta_{1i}} g(\boldsymbol{x}_i)^{\Delta_{2i}} f(\boldsymbol{y}_i; \boldsymbol{\theta})^{\Delta_{3i}}. \tag{7}$$

In terms of implementation in software, we need to write a function to find $\ell_P(\boldsymbol{\theta}) = \sup_{\boldsymbol{g}}\{\log L(\boldsymbol{\theta}, \boldsymbol{g})\}$ where $L(\boldsymbol{\theta}, \boldsymbol{g})$ is given by (7). When we have multiple strata, we can send the data from each stratum in turn to that function and accumulate the results.

3.2 Basic profile likelihood algorithm

In essence, we will let $\delta_i = g(\boldsymbol{x}_i)$ and work with $\ell(\boldsymbol{\theta}, \boldsymbol{\delta})$ with $\boldsymbol{\delta} = (\delta_1, \delta_2, \ldots)$ as if it were an ordinary parametric log-likelihood. One of the problems with this, however, is that it often results in working with very large arrays. It is particularly important to keep the dimension of $\boldsymbol{\delta}$ as small as possible. Trapping replicate data points is one way of reducing the size of these arrays. Thus, we will write in terms of replicated data. Whether or not we do this makes no difference at all to the profile that we obtain for $\boldsymbol{\theta}$, but it can substantially reduce storage.

Let $A = \{i : \Delta_{1i} = 1\}$, $B = \{i : \Delta_{2i} = 1\}$, and $C = \{i : \Delta_{3i} \neq 0\}$. Let $\tilde{\boldsymbol{x}}_1, \ldots, \tilde{\boldsymbol{x}}_J$ be the distinct values of $\boldsymbol{x}$ in B, m_j be the multiplicity of $\tilde{\boldsymbol{x}}_j$ in B and $\delta_j = g(\tilde{\boldsymbol{x}}_j)$. Let $\tilde{\boldsymbol{y}}_1, \ldots, \tilde{\boldsymbol{y}}_K$ be the distinct values of $\boldsymbol{y}$ in C and let $r_k = \sum_{\{i:\boldsymbol{y}_i=\tilde{\boldsymbol{y}}_k\}} \Delta_{3i}$. Note that r_k can be positive, negative or zero. On noting that $f(y) = \sum f(\boldsymbol{y} \mid \tilde{\boldsymbol{x}}_j)\delta_j$, the log-likelihood from (7) can be written in the form

$$\ell(\boldsymbol{\theta}, \boldsymbol{\delta}) = \sum_A \log f(\boldsymbol{y}_i \mid \boldsymbol{x}_i; \boldsymbol{\theta}) + \sum_j m_j \log \delta_j + \sum_k r_k \log\left\{ \sum_{j=1}^{J} f(\tilde{\boldsymbol{y}}_k \mid \tilde{\boldsymbol{x}}_j; \boldsymbol{\theta})\delta_j \right\}. \tag{8}$$

Since the δ_j parameters have to satisfy the constraints $0 < \delta_j < 1$ and $\sum \delta_j = 1$, we reparameterize in terms of $\rho_j = \log(\delta_j/\delta_J)$ and work with $\ell(\boldsymbol{\theta}, \boldsymbol{\rho})$. With this parametrization $\delta_j = \exp(\rho_j)/\sum \exp(\rho_\ell)$ (with $\rho_J \equiv 0$) and the constraints are satisfied automatically. The profile log-likelihood is then $\ell_P(\boldsymbol{\theta}) = \ell(\boldsymbol{\theta}, \hat{\boldsymbol{\rho}}(\boldsymbol{\theta}))$, where $\hat{\boldsymbol{\rho}}(\boldsymbol{\theta})$ satisfies $\partial\ell(\boldsymbol{\theta}, \boldsymbol{\rho})/\partial\boldsymbol{\rho} = \boldsymbol{0}$, and ℓ_P has profile score vector

$$\boldsymbol{U}_P(\boldsymbol{\theta}) = \frac{\partial \ell_P(\boldsymbol{\theta})}{\partial \boldsymbol{\theta}} = \left.\frac{\partial \ell(\boldsymbol{\theta}, \boldsymbol{\rho})}{\partial \boldsymbol{\theta}}\right|_{\boldsymbol{\rho}=\hat{\boldsymbol{\rho}}(\boldsymbol{\theta})}$$

(see Seber and Wild (1989), equation (2.69)) and observed profile information matrix

$$\boldsymbol{\mathcal{I}}_P = \left(-\frac{\partial^2 \ell_P(\boldsymbol{\theta})}{\partial \boldsymbol{\theta}\, \partial \boldsymbol{\theta}^{\mathsf{T}}}\right) = \left.\{\boldsymbol{\mathcal{J}}_{\theta\theta} - \boldsymbol{\mathcal{J}}_{\theta\rho}\boldsymbol{\mathcal{J}}_{\rho\rho}^{-1}\boldsymbol{\mathcal{J}}_{\theta\rho}^{\mathsf{T}}\}\right|_{\boldsymbol{\rho}=\hat{\boldsymbol{\rho}}(\boldsymbol{\theta})} \tag{9}$$

written in terms of the blocks of $\boldsymbol{\mathcal{J}}$, the observed information matrix obtained from $\ell(\boldsymbol{\theta}, \boldsymbol{\rho})$ (see Seber and Wild (1989), just prior to equation (2.72)).

We apply a Newton–Raphson based algorithm, with updating steps $\boldsymbol{\theta}^{(a+1)} = \boldsymbol{\theta}^{(a)} + \boldsymbol{\mathcal{I}}_P^{-1}\boldsymbol{U}_P \mid_{\boldsymbol{\theta}=\boldsymbol{\theta}^{(a)}}$ for $a = 1, 2, \ldots$ to maximize the profile log-likelihood $\ell_P(\boldsymbol{\theta})$. At each iteration we solve for the accompanying $\hat{\boldsymbol{\rho}}(\boldsymbol{\theta}^{(a+1)})$ also by using Newton–Raphson to maximise $\ell(\boldsymbol{\theta}^{(a+1)}, \boldsymbol{\rho})$ with respect to $\boldsymbol{\rho}$. The derivatives required for all of this are given in Appendix A. Our "Newton–Raphson based algorithm" employs simple versions of the hill-climbing techniques discussed in Section 13.3.1 of Seber and Wild (1989) to improve robustness. We have been surprised by how stable and reliable the method has turned out to be in practice, despite the often very large dimensions of the parameter vectors involved.

A clear disadvantage with the algorithm discussed in this section is that the dimension of the parameter vectors can be very large indeed (equal to the sample size n in the worst case), requiring substantial storage. For example, using Newton–Raphson for the maximization requires that we store $\mathcal{J}_{\rho\rho}$. This is also necessary if we wish to calculate the profile information matrix to obtain variance estimates for $\hat{\boldsymbol{\theta}}$. We will find in the next section that we can obtain a substantial reduction in dimensionality, and consequent increase in speed, when $\boldsymbol{y}$ is discrete. In particular, for binary regression models we can work with a nuisance parameter of dimension 1 rather than $\boldsymbol{\rho}$, which has dimension $J-1$ where J is the number of distinct values observed for $\boldsymbol{x}$. The same sort of reduction can be made for continuous $\boldsymbol{y}$ in situations where only class interval information on $\boldsymbol{y}$ is available for those data points for which $\boldsymbol{x}$ is not fully observed.

Before going on, however, we do note that when we have several strata, the method discussed in the current subsection never needs to store a $\mathcal{J}_{\rho\rho}$ matrix for more than one stratum. These matrices are used to find the contribution of the current stratum to the overall information matrix $\mathcal{I}_P$ and then discarded when we move on to process the data from the next stratum; see the discussion surrounding (7). This makes it feasible to handle reasonably large data sets. For example, Jiang (2004) was able to run simulations fitting linear models to two-phase samples with strata of size $N = 5000$ and sub-sample sizes of $n = 1000$ using these methods.

4 An extension to the class of likelihoods

There are important extensions of the likelihood class (1) which do not affect the essential nature of the maximization problem. (We have postponed consideration of these in the interests of intelligibility.) For example, Lawless et al. (1999) discuss failure time data in which whether of not a data point is fully observed depends on membership of strata defined in terms of both $\boldsymbol{y}$ and $\boldsymbol{x}$. They also used strata involving both $\boldsymbol{y}$ and $\boldsymbol{x}$ to avoid the problem of empty or near-empty strata. Neuhaus et al. (2002) deals with retrospectively sampled family data. Here, $\boldsymbol{y}$ records the set of binary responses for each member of a cluster (or family) and sampling is conditional upon observation of some specified pattern in the responses from a cluster. This data can also be supplemented in various ways, for example by knowledge of stratum sizes in the finite population from which the individuals were sampled.

We can expand (1) to cater for such examples as follows. Let $\boldsymbol{h}_v(\boldsymbol{y},\boldsymbol{x})$ be a known function of the data, where we may use different functions for different $\boldsymbol{v}$. Imagine that the probability of being observed depends upon the value of $\boldsymbol{h}$. We may, for example, sample conditionally upon $\boldsymbol{h}$ values and then observe $(\boldsymbol{y},\boldsymbol{x})$. We may also use a random mechanism by which $\boldsymbol{h}$ values are obtained according to some probability, $\pi_4(\boldsymbol{h})$ say, and then $(\boldsymbol{y},\boldsymbol{x})$ are sampled obtained from the conditional distribution of $(\boldsymbol{y},\boldsymbol{x})$ given $\boldsymbol{h}$.

We may supplement such data with finite population data, or data from a random sample of $\boldsymbol{h}$ values. Alternatively, we may may have data produced by a random process, observe the $\boldsymbol{h}$ values as they arise and then further observe $(\boldsymbol{y}, \boldsymbol{x})$ with probability $\pi_5(\boldsymbol{h})$. In all of these situations, the likelihood is of the form,

$$\prod_{s=1}^{S} \prod_{i:\boldsymbol{v}_i=\boldsymbol{v}_s} f(\boldsymbol{y}_i \mid \boldsymbol{z}_i, \boldsymbol{v}_{1s}; \boldsymbol{\theta})^{\Delta_{1i}} g(\boldsymbol{z}_i \mid \boldsymbol{v}_s)^{\Delta_{2i}} f\{\boldsymbol{h}_s^{[i]} \mid \boldsymbol{v}_s; \boldsymbol{\theta}\}^{\Delta_{3i}}, \tag{10}$$

where $\boldsymbol{h}_s^{[i]} = \boldsymbol{h}_{\boldsymbol{v}_s}(\boldsymbol{y}_i, \boldsymbol{x}_i)$, for suitably chosen Δ_{ji}s. This is a simple generalization of (6) and almost all the work in Section 3.2 applies directly. Again we need only consider the profiling problem for a single stratum, and (7) becomes

$$L(\boldsymbol{\theta}, g) = \prod f(\boldsymbol{y}_i \mid \boldsymbol{x}_i; \boldsymbol{\theta})^{\Delta_{1i}} g(\boldsymbol{x}_i)^{\Delta_{2i}} f\{\boldsymbol{h}(\boldsymbol{y}, \boldsymbol{z}) = \boldsymbol{h}^{[i]}; \boldsymbol{\theta}\}^{\Delta_{3i}}, \tag{11}$$

where $f\{\boldsymbol{h}; \boldsymbol{\theta}\} = \int_{\boldsymbol{h}(\boldsymbol{y},\boldsymbol{x})=\boldsymbol{h}} dF(\boldsymbol{y} \mid \boldsymbol{x}; \boldsymbol{\theta})\, dG(\boldsymbol{x})$. Suppose that $\tilde{\boldsymbol{h}}_k$ occurs with multiplicity r_k. Then (8), the form we use for computation, becomes

$$\begin{aligned} \ell(\boldsymbol{\theta}, \boldsymbol{\delta}) = \sum_A \log f(\boldsymbol{y}_i \mid \boldsymbol{x}_i; \boldsymbol{\theta}) + \sum_j m_j \log \delta_j \\ + \sum_k r_k \log\Big\{\sum_j f(\tilde{\boldsymbol{h}}_k \mid \tilde{\boldsymbol{x}}_j; \boldsymbol{\theta}) \delta_j\Big\}, \end{aligned} \tag{12}$$

and $f\{\tilde{\boldsymbol{h}}_k \mid \boldsymbol{x}; \boldsymbol{\theta}\} = \int_{S_k(\boldsymbol{x})} dF(\boldsymbol{y} \mid \boldsymbol{x}; \boldsymbol{\theta})$ with $S_k(\boldsymbol{x}) = \{\boldsymbol{y} : \boldsymbol{h}(\boldsymbol{y}, \boldsymbol{x}) = \tilde{\boldsymbol{h}}_k\}$. The profile likelihood algorithm for the larger class of likelihoods in this subsection differs from that in Section 3.2 only in that $f\{\tilde{\boldsymbol{h}}_k \mid \boldsymbol{x}; \boldsymbol{\theta}\}$ replaces $f(\tilde{\boldsymbol{y}}_k \mid \boldsymbol{x}; \boldsymbol{\theta})$ in the last term of the log-likelihood. In computational terms, this means that to accommodate a new model $f(\boldsymbol{y} \mid \boldsymbol{x}; \boldsymbol{\theta})$ when $\boldsymbol{h}(\boldsymbol{y}, \boldsymbol{x})$ is more complicated than simply $\boldsymbol{h}(\boldsymbol{y}, \boldsymbol{x}) = \boldsymbol{y}$, an additional function must be written to evaluate $f\{\boldsymbol{h} \mid \boldsymbol{x}; \boldsymbol{\theta}\}$ and its derivatives with respect to $\boldsymbol{\theta}$.

5 Exploiting discreteness

As we noted in Section 3.2, a big disadvantage of the brute-force approach outlined there is the dimension of the maximization problem. A substantial reduction of this dimension can be achieved in some important special cases, specifically whenever the $\boldsymbol{h}(\boldsymbol{y}, \boldsymbol{x})$ can take only a finite set of values, $(\tilde{\boldsymbol{h}}_1, \tilde{\boldsymbol{h}}_2, \ldots, \tilde{\boldsymbol{h}}_K)$ say.

If we maximise (12) with respect to $\boldsymbol{\delta}$ for fixed $\boldsymbol{\theta}$, using a Lagrange multiplier to cater for the constraint $\sum_j \delta_j = 1$, cf. Scott and Wild (1997, circa equation (A1.2)) we find that $\hat{\boldsymbol{\delta}}(\boldsymbol{\theta})$ satisfies the set of equations

$$\delta_j = m_j \Big/ \left\{ (m_+ + r_+) - \sum_k \frac{r_k f(\tilde{\boldsymbol{h}}_k \mid \tilde{\boldsymbol{x}}_j; \boldsymbol{\theta})}{\sum_{j'} f(\tilde{\boldsymbol{h}}_k \mid \tilde{\boldsymbol{x}}_{j'}; \boldsymbol{\theta}) \delta_{j'}} \right\}, \qquad j = 1, \ldots, J, \tag{13}$$

where $m_+ = \sum_j m_j$ is the total number of observations in B and $r_+ = \sum r_k$. Suppose that all possible values have been observed at least once so that $\sum_{k=1}^{K} f(\tilde{\boldsymbol{h}}_k \mid \boldsymbol{x}; \boldsymbol{\theta}) = 1$. If $r_k \neq 0$, set

$$Q_k = \sum_j f(\tilde{\boldsymbol{h}}_k \mid \tilde{\boldsymbol{x}}_j; \boldsymbol{\theta})\delta_j$$

and write

$$\tilde{p}_k = \tilde{p}_k(Q_k) = (m_+ + r_+) - \frac{r_k}{Q_k}. \tag{14}$$

Then the system (13) can be written in the form

$$\delta_j = \frac{m_j}{(m_+ + r_+) - \sum_k r_k \frac{f(\tilde{\boldsymbol{h}}_k \mid \tilde{\boldsymbol{x}}_j; \boldsymbol{\theta})}{Q_k}} = \frac{m_j}{\sum_k \tilde{p}_k f(\tilde{\boldsymbol{h}}_k \mid \tilde{\boldsymbol{x}}_j; \boldsymbol{\theta})}, \tag{15}$$

where the set of Q_k's corresponding to nonzero r_k satisfy the system

$$Q_k = \sum_j \frac{m_j f(\tilde{\boldsymbol{h}}_k \mid \tilde{\boldsymbol{x}}_j; \boldsymbol{\theta})}{(m_+ + r_+) - \sum_k \frac{m_k}{Q_k} f(\tilde{\boldsymbol{h}}_k \mid \tilde{\boldsymbol{x}}_j; \boldsymbol{\theta})} = \sum_j \frac{m_j f(\tilde{\boldsymbol{h}}_k \mid \tilde{\boldsymbol{x}}_j; \boldsymbol{\theta})}{\sum_k \tilde{p}_k f(\tilde{\boldsymbol{h}}_k \mid \tilde{\boldsymbol{x}}_j; \boldsymbol{\theta})}. \tag{16}$$

The system of equations (16) is equivalent to the set of 'score' equations, $\partial \ell^* / \partial \boldsymbol{Q} = \boldsymbol{0}$ for fixed $\boldsymbol{\theta}$, where

$$\begin{aligned} \ell^*(\boldsymbol{\theta}, \boldsymbol{Q}) = &\sum_A \log f(\boldsymbol{y}_i \mid \boldsymbol{x}_i; \boldsymbol{\theta}) \\ &- \sum_j m_j \log\Big\{\sum_k \tilde{p}_k(Q_k) f(\tilde{\boldsymbol{h}}_k \mid \tilde{\boldsymbol{x}}_j; \boldsymbol{\theta})\Big\} + \sum r_k \log Q_k. \end{aligned} \tag{17}$$

Thus we can either obtain the profile log-likelihood using $\ell_P(\boldsymbol{\theta}) = \ell(\boldsymbol{\theta}, \hat{\boldsymbol{\delta}}(\boldsymbol{\theta}))$, where $\boldsymbol{\delta}$ has dimension $(J-1)$, or using $\ell_P(\boldsymbol{\theta}) = \ell^*(\boldsymbol{\theta}, \hat{\boldsymbol{Q}}(\boldsymbol{\theta}))$, where $\boldsymbol{Q}$ has dimension $(K-1)$.

Further, and perhaps more importantly, it follows from Theorem 2.2 in Seber and Wild (1989) that

$$\frac{\partial^2 \ell_P(\boldsymbol{\theta})}{\partial \boldsymbol{\theta}\, \partial \boldsymbol{\theta}^\top} = \frac{\partial^2 \ell^*(\boldsymbol{\theta}, \boldsymbol{Q})}{\partial \boldsymbol{\theta}\, \partial \boldsymbol{\theta}^\top} - \frac{\partial^2 \ell^*(\boldsymbol{\theta}, \boldsymbol{Q})}{\partial \boldsymbol{\theta}\, \partial \boldsymbol{Q}^\top} \left(\frac{\partial^2 \ell^*(\boldsymbol{\theta}, \boldsymbol{Q})}{\partial \boldsymbol{Q}\, \partial \boldsymbol{Q}^\top} \right)^{-1} \frac{\partial^2 \ell^*(\boldsymbol{\theta}, \boldsymbol{Q})}{\partial \boldsymbol{Q}\, \partial \boldsymbol{\theta}^\top}.$$

Recalling the standard form for the inverse of a partitioned matrix, it follows that the inverse profile information, $-(\partial^2 \ell_P(\boldsymbol{\theta}) / \partial \boldsymbol{\theta}\, \partial \boldsymbol{\theta}^\top)^{-1}$ is equal to the leading $p \times p$ submatrix of $\boldsymbol{\mathcal{J}}^{*-1}$, where $\boldsymbol{\mathcal{J}}^* = \partial^2 \ell^*(\boldsymbol{\phi}) / \partial \boldsymbol{\phi}\, \partial \boldsymbol{\phi}^\top$, with $\boldsymbol{\phi} = \binom{\boldsymbol{\theta}}{\boldsymbol{Q}}$. This means that, for making inferences about $\boldsymbol{\theta}$, we can proceed as if $\ell^*(\boldsymbol{\phi})$ was the log-likelihood. We can obtain the semiparametric maximum likelihood estimator of $\boldsymbol{\theta}$ by setting $\partial \ell^*(\boldsymbol{\theta}, \boldsymbol{Q}) / \partial \boldsymbol{\phi} = 0$, we can estimate its covariance matrix with the appropriate block of $\boldsymbol{\mathcal{J}}^{*-1}$ and we can test hypotheses about $\boldsymbol{\theta}$ using appropriate differences in $-2\ell^*$. (This last statement needs some justification but the general case follows in exactly the same way as the special case treated in Scott and Wild (1989).)

Since K is almost always very much less than J, using $\ell^*(\boldsymbol{\theta}, \boldsymbol{Q})$ in place of $\ell(\boldsymbol{\theta}, \boldsymbol{\delta})$ can result in large reductions in storage requirements and in computing time. For example, in the important special case of fitting a binary regression model to case-control data, $K = 2$ and we have essentially reduced the problem from one involving a vector of n nuisance parameters to one involving a single scalar nuisance parameter.

We note that, although we can treat $\ell^*(\boldsymbol{\phi})$ as if it were a log-likelihood for many purposes, it is not in fact a true log-likelihood. In particular, ℓ^* typically has a minimum rather than a maximum in $\boldsymbol{Q}$ when the nonzero r_ks are all positive as is the case with missing data problems.

We have experimented with several reparameterizations of $\boldsymbol{Q}$ to take care of positivity constraints including $Q_k = \exp(\rho_k)/\{1 + \sum \exp(\rho_\ell)\}$ and

$$Q_k = \exp(\xi_k)/\{1 + \exp(\xi_k)\} \quad \text{or} \quad \xi_k = \text{logit}(Q_k).$$

The former, which also takes care of the summation constraint, leads to singular information matrices when two or more $r_k = 0$, whereas both parameterizations lead to the identical sets of derivatives when at most one $r_k = 0$. Thus, we routinely use $\ell^*(\boldsymbol{\theta}, \boldsymbol{\xi})$, where $\boldsymbol{\xi}$ contains only those ξ_k for which $r_k \neq 0$, for computation. Now,

$$\ell_P(\boldsymbol{\theta}) = \ell^*(\boldsymbol{\theta}, \hat{\boldsymbol{\xi}}(\boldsymbol{\theta})),$$

where $\hat{\boldsymbol{\xi}}(\boldsymbol{\theta})$ satisfies $\partial\ell(\boldsymbol{\theta}, \boldsymbol{\xi})^*/\partial\boldsymbol{\xi} = \mathbf{0}$. We then calculate the profile score vector and profile information matrix of $\ell_P(\boldsymbol{\theta})$ using

$$\boldsymbol{U}_P(\boldsymbol{\theta}) = \left.\frac{\partial\ell^*(\boldsymbol{\theta}, \boldsymbol{\xi})}{\partial\boldsymbol{\theta}}\right|_{\boldsymbol{\xi}=\hat{\boldsymbol{\xi}}(\boldsymbol{\theta})} \quad \text{and} \quad \mathcal{I}_P = \left.\{\mathcal{J}^*_{\theta\theta} - \mathcal{J}^*_{\theta\xi}\mathcal{J}^{*-1}_{\xi\xi}\mathcal{J}^{*\mathsf{T}}_{\theta\xi}\}\right|_{\boldsymbol{\xi}=\hat{\boldsymbol{\xi}}(\boldsymbol{\theta})}.$$

Expressions for the required derivatives are given in Appendix B.

6 Conclusion

The computational procedures outlined in this paper enable us to make efficient inferences about parameters of interest in a large number of situations involving missing data and response-biased sampling. In many of these situations it has simply not been feasible to implement efficient procedures before this and people have proposed a variety of *ad hoc* alternatives. Most of these alternatives should become obsolete when software to implement the methods described in this paper is available. Such software is currently under development and a prototype package is available from Chris Wild (c.wild@auckland.ac.nz) on request. A more polished version should soon be available on his web site at http://www.stat.auckland.ac.nz.

Appendix A. Derivatives of $\ell(\boldsymbol{\theta}, \boldsymbol{\rho})$

We give results for the general case described in Section 4. Equation (8) is the special case of equation (12) in which $\boldsymbol{h}(\boldsymbol{y}, \boldsymbol{x}) = \boldsymbol{y}$, and $f(\tilde{h}_k \mid \tilde{\boldsymbol{x}}_j; \boldsymbol{\theta}) = f(\tilde{\boldsymbol{y}}_k \mid \tilde{\boldsymbol{x}}_j; \boldsymbol{\theta})$ so that its derivatives with respect to $\boldsymbol{\theta}$ are simply the derivatives of the regression model $f()$. The user needs to specify

$$D_{kj}^{(\theta)} = \frac{\partial f(\tilde{h}_k \mid \tilde{\boldsymbol{x}}_j; \boldsymbol{\theta})}{\partial \boldsymbol{\theta}} \quad \text{and} \quad D_{kj}^{\theta\theta} = \frac{\partial D_{kj}^{(\theta)}}{\partial \boldsymbol{\theta}^{\mathsf{T}}}.$$

We repeat (12) more compactly as

$$\begin{aligned} \ell(\boldsymbol{\theta}, \boldsymbol{\delta}) &= \ell(\boldsymbol{\theta}, \boldsymbol{\rho}) \\ &= \sum_A \log f_i + \sum_j m_j \log \delta_j + \sum_k r_k \log\Big\{\sum_j f(\tilde{h}_k \mid \tilde{\boldsymbol{x}}_j; \boldsymbol{\theta})\delta_j\Big\}, \qquad (18) \end{aligned}$$

where, $f_i = f(\boldsymbol{y}_i \mid \boldsymbol{x}_i; \boldsymbol{\theta})$ and $\delta_j = \exp(\rho_j)/\sum_\ell \exp(\rho_\ell)$ with $\rho_K \equiv 0$. After some manipulation, we find that

$$\begin{aligned} \frac{\partial \ell}{\partial \boldsymbol{\theta}} &= \sum_A \frac{\partial \log f_i}{\partial \boldsymbol{\theta}} + \sum_k r_k \frac{\boldsymbol{D}_k^{(\theta)}}{D_k}, \\ \frac{\partial \ell}{\partial \rho} &= \check{\boldsymbol{m}} + \sum_k r_k \check{\boldsymbol{R}}_k - (m_+ + r_+)\check{\boldsymbol{\delta}} \\ \boldsymbol{\mathcal{J}}^{(\theta\theta)} &= \sum_A \frac{\partial^2 \log f_i}{\partial \boldsymbol{\theta}\, \partial \boldsymbol{\theta}^{\mathsf{T}}} - \sum_k r_k \left\{ \frac{\boldsymbol{D}_k^{(\theta\theta)}}{D_k} - \left(\frac{\boldsymbol{D}_k^{(\theta)}}{D_k}\right)\left(\frac{\boldsymbol{D}_k^{(\theta)}}{D_k}\right)^{\mathsf{T}} \right\} \\ \boldsymbol{\mathcal{J}}^{(\theta\rho_j)} &= \sum_k r_k \left\{ \frac{Q_{kj}^* \delta_j}{D_k} \frac{\boldsymbol{D}_k^{(\theta)}}{D_k} - \frac{Q_{kj}^{*(\theta)} \delta_j}{D_k} \right\}, \qquad j = 1, \ldots, J-1 \\ \boldsymbol{\mathcal{J}}^{(\rho\rho)} &= (m_+ + r_+)\{\operatorname{diag}(\check{\boldsymbol{\delta}}) - \check{\boldsymbol{\delta}}\check{\boldsymbol{\delta}}^{\mathsf{T}}\} - \sum_k r_k \{\operatorname{diag}(\check{\boldsymbol{R}}_k) - \check{\boldsymbol{R}}_k \check{\boldsymbol{R}}_k^{\mathsf{T}}\} \end{aligned}$$

Here, $D_k = \sum_j f(\tilde{h}_k \mid \tilde{\boldsymbol{x}}_j; \boldsymbol{\theta})\delta_j$, $\check{\boldsymbol{R}}_k$ is the vector with elements $D_{kj}^{(\theta)}\delta_j/D_k$, $j = 1, \ldots, J-1$, $\check{\boldsymbol{m}} = (m_1, \ldots, m_{J-1})$, $\check{\boldsymbol{\delta}} = (\delta_1, \ldots, \delta_{J-1})$, $\boldsymbol{D}_k^{(\theta)} = \sum_j D_{kj}^{(\theta)}\delta_j$, $\boldsymbol{D}_k^{(\theta\theta)} = \sum_j D_{kj}^{(\theta\theta)}\delta_j$, and $\sum_j$ denotes sums from 1 to J.

Appendix B. Derivatives of $\ell^*(\boldsymbol{\theta}, \boldsymbol{\xi})$

$$\begin{aligned} \ell^*(\boldsymbol{\theta}, \boldsymbol{\xi}) &= \ell^*(\boldsymbol{\theta}, \boldsymbol{Q}) \\ &= \sum_A \log f_i - \sum_j m_j \log\Big\{\sum_k \tilde{p}_k f(\tilde{h}_k \mid \tilde{\boldsymbol{x}}_j; \boldsymbol{\theta})\Big\} + \sum_k r_k \log Q_k, \qquad (19) \end{aligned}$$

where $\tilde{p}_k = \tilde{p}_k(Q_k) = (m_+ + r_+) - r_k/Q_k$, and $\xi_k = \text{logit}(Q_k)$. We find that

$$\frac{\partial \ell}{\partial \boldsymbol{\theta}} = \sum_A \frac{\partial \log f_i}{\partial \boldsymbol{\theta}} - \sum_j m_j \frac{\partial}{\partial \boldsymbol{\theta}} \log\Big(\sum_k \tilde{p}_k f(\tilde{h}_k \mid \tilde{\boldsymbol{x}}_j; \boldsymbol{\theta})\Big),$$

$$\frac{\partial \ell^*}{\partial \xi_k} = r_k e^{-\xi_k}\left(Q_k - \sum_j \frac{m_j f(\tilde{h}_k \mid \tilde{\boldsymbol{x}}_j; \boldsymbol{\theta})}{\sum_{k'} \tilde{p}_{k'} f(\tilde{h}_k \mid \tilde{\boldsymbol{x}}_j; \boldsymbol{\theta})}\right), \qquad k = 1, \ldots, K,$$

$$\boldsymbol{\mathcal{J}}^{(\theta\theta)} = -\sum_A n_i \frac{\partial^2 \log f_i}{\partial \boldsymbol{\theta}\, \partial \boldsymbol{\theta}^{\mathsf{T}}} + \sum_j m_j \left[\frac{E_j^{*(\theta\theta)}}{E_j} - \left\{\frac{E_j^{*(\theta)}}{E_j}\right\}\left\{\frac{E_j^{*(\theta)}}{E_j}\right\}^{\mathsf{T}}\right],$$

$$\boldsymbol{\mathcal{J}}^{(\theta\xi_k)} = r_k e^{-\xi_k} \sum_j m_j \left[\frac{D_{kj}^{*(\theta)}}{E_j} - \left(\frac{f(\tilde{h}_k \mid \tilde{\boldsymbol{x}}_j; \boldsymbol{\theta})}{E_j}\right)\left\{\frac{E_j^{(\theta)}}{E_j}\right\}\right], \qquad k = 1, \ldots, K,$$

$$\boldsymbol{\mathcal{J}}^{(\xi\xi)} = \text{diag}()\{\text{diag}(\boldsymbol{Q}) - \boldsymbol{Q}\boldsymbol{Q}^{\mathsf{T}}\} - \sum_j m_j\{\text{diag}(\boldsymbol{F}_j) + \boldsymbol{F}_j \boldsymbol{F}_j^{\mathsf{T}}\},$$

where $E_j = \sum_{k'} \tilde{p}_{k'} f(\tilde{h}_k \mid \tilde{\boldsymbol{x}}_j; \boldsymbol{\theta})$, $E_j^{(\theta)} = \sum_{k'} \tilde{p}_{k'} D_{k'j}^{*(\theta)}$ and $\boldsymbol{F}_j$ is the vector with kth element $r_k e^{-\xi_k} f(\tilde{h}_k \mid \tilde{\boldsymbol{x}}_j; \boldsymbol{\theta})/E_j$.

References

Bickel, P. J., Klaassen, C. A., Ritov, Y., and Wellner, J. A. (1993). *Efficient and Adaptive Estimation for Semiparametric Models.* Baltimore: Johns Hopkins University Press.

Holcroft, C. A., Rotnitzky, A., and Robins, J. M. (1997). Efficient estimation of regression parameters from multistage studies with validation of outcome and covariates. *Journal of Statistical Planning and Inference*, 65, 349–374.

Jiang, Y. (2004). *Semiparametric maximum likelihood for multi-phase response-selective sampling and missing data problems.* PhD Thesis, University of Auckland.

Lawless, J. F., Wild, C. J., and Kalbfleish (1999). Semiparametric methods for response-selective and missing data problems in regression. *Journal of the Royal Statistical Society: Series B*, 61, 413–38.

Lee, A. J. and Hirose, Y. (2006). Semiparametric efficiency bounds for regression models under generalized case-control sampling. Under review for *Annals of Statistics.*

Lee, A. J., Scott, A. J., and Wild, C. J. (2006). Fitting binary regression models with case-augmented samples. *Biometrika*, 97, 23–37.

Murphy, S. A. and van der Vaart, A. W. (2000). On profile likelihood (with discussion). *Journal of the American Statistical Association*, 95, 449–485.

Neuhaus, J., Scott, A. J., and Wild, C. J. (2002). The analysis of retrospective family studies. *Biometrika*, 89, 23–37.

Neuhaus, J., Scott, A. J., and Wild, C. J. (2006). Family-specific approaches to the analysis of case-control family data. *Biometrics*, 62, to appear.

Robins, J. M., Rotnitzky, A., Zhao, L. P., and Lipsitz, S. (1994). Estimation of regression coefficients when some regressors are not always observed. *Journal of the American Statistical Association*, 89, 846–866.

Robins, J. M., Hsieh, F., and Newey, W. (1995). Semiparametric efficient estimation of a conditional density with missing or mismeasured covariates. *Journal of the Royal Statistical Society: Series B*, 57, 409–424.

Scott, A. J. and Wild, C. J. (1989). Hypothesis testing in case-control studies. *Biometrika*, 76, 806–808.

Scott, A. J. and Wild, C. J. (1991). Fitting logistic models in stratified case-control studies. *Biometrics*, 47, 497–510.

Scott, A. J. and Wild, C. J. (1997). Fitting regression models to case-control data by maximum likelihood. *Biometrika*, 84, 57–71.

Scott, A. J. and Wild, C. J. (2001). Maximum likelihood for generalised case-control studies. *Journal of Statistical Planning and Inference*, 96, 3–27.

Seber, G. A. F. and Wild, C. J. (1989). *Nonlinear Regression*. New York: Wiley.

ALASTAIR SCOTT
Department of Statistics
University of Auckland
Auckland, New Zealand
a.scott@auckland.ac.nz

CHRIS WILD
Department of Statistics
University of Auckland
Auckland, New Zealand
c.wild@auckland.ac.nz

Festschrift for Tarmo Pukkila on his 60th Birthday
Eds. E. P. Liski, J. Isotalo, J. Niemelä, S. Puntanen, and G. P. H. Styan

Univ. of Tampere, 2006, ISBN 978-951-44-6620-5, pages 315–326

Universal optimality for the joint estimation of parameters

KIRTI R. SHAH & BIKAS K. SINHA

Abstract. The concept of universal optimality is applied to the joint estimation of sets of parameters and it is shown that optimality for the joint estimation implies optimality for the estimation of the individual sets of parameters. This result is applied to some special settings of interest which leads to some new optimality results in these settings.

2000 MSC codes: 62K05, 62K10.

Key words and phrases: Crossover designs; Split-block designs; Designs for a competing effects model.

1 Introduction

In a landmark paper Kiefer (1975) pioneered the concept of universal optimality. Rather than proving the optimality of a design w.r.t. a specific criterion, Kiefer proposed that one should consider the class of *all* optimality criteria which satisfy certain reasonable requirements and attempt to establish optimality w.r.t. all the criteria in this class.

The formulation given by Kiefer was somewhat modified by Shah and Sinha (1989b). In Section 2 of this paper, we deal with a slightly altered version of this formulation and re-state a sufficient condition for universal optimality given by Shah and Sinha (2001).

In Section 3 we deal with the situation where one is interested in the joint estimation of sets of parameters. It is shown that universal optimality for the joint estimation of sets of parameters implies universal optimality for the individual sets of parameters.

This result is applied to various settings in Section 4. First we deal with the cross-over designs. It is shown that a completely balanced design is universally optimal within the class of binary designs as well as within the class of restricted non-binary designs but it is not universally optimal in the unrestricted class. To show this, we present an optimality functional which satisfies all the requirements of universal optimality and for which a non-binary design has a smaller criterion value.

We also deduce some new optimality results for split-block designs and for designs for a competing effects model.

2 Universal optimality

The notion of universal optimality was first introduced by Kiefer (1975). Shah and Sinha (1989a,b) gave a somewhat different formulation of UO. Here, we present a modified version of this formulation.

Let $\mathcal{D}$ denote the class of designs under consideration ($\mathcal{D}$ might contain as few as two designs). Let C denote the class of information matrices corresponding to the designs in $\mathcal{D}$. It is understood that the information matrix is for a set of parameters of interest eliminating the remaining parameters.

We consider a class of optimality functionals $\phi(\boldsymbol{C})$ defined for all matrices in C which satisfy the following conditions:

1. $\phi(\boldsymbol{C}_g) = \phi(\boldsymbol{C})$ where $\boldsymbol{C}_g$ is obtained from $\boldsymbol{C}$ by applying permutation $g \in \mathcal{G}$ on a specified set of elements. Here $\mathcal{G}$ is a group of permutations.

   Exact nature of $\mathcal{G}$, the group of permutations and the manner in which g operates on $\boldsymbol{C}$ would depend upon the problem at hand.

2. If $\boldsymbol{C}_1 \geq \boldsymbol{C}_2$ i.e. if $\boldsymbol{C}_1 - \boldsymbol{C}_2$ is n.n.d. then $\phi(\boldsymbol{C}_1) \leq \phi(\boldsymbol{C}_2)$.

   This is a natural requirement.

3. $\phi(\alpha \boldsymbol{C}_{g_1} + (1-\alpha)\boldsymbol{C}_{g_2}) \leq \phi(\boldsymbol{C})$ where g_1 and g_2 are any permutations and α is a rational number between 0 and 1.

   Here, we require convexity only on permuted versions of the same information matrix $\boldsymbol{C}$. We require that $\phi(\cdot)$ is defined for such convex combinations.

The above requirements on $\phi(\cdot)$ are somewhat less restrictive because we do *not* impose convexity requirement on the set of *all* $\boldsymbol{C}$-matrices. Further, requirement 2 is a natural one. It is not clear if Kiefer's requirements on optimality functionals imply condition 2 stated above.

A design d^* is said to be universally optimal (UO) within the design class $\mathcal{D}$ if

$$\phi(\boldsymbol{C}_{d^*}) \leq \phi(\boldsymbol{C}_d)$$

for all $d \in \mathcal{D}$.

We now present a theorem giving a sufficient condition for a design to be UO.

Theorem 2.1. *A design d^* is UO if for any $d \in \mathcal{D}$*

$$\boldsymbol{C}_{d^*} \geq \sum_g t_g(\boldsymbol{C}_{dg})$$

where $\boldsymbol{C}_{dg}$ is obtained by application of g on $\boldsymbol{C}_d$ and t_g are non-negative rational numbers such that $\sum_g t_g = 1$.

Proof. Using requirements 2 and 3 stated above, it can be seen that

$$\phi(C_{d^*}) \le \phi\left(\sum t_g C_{dg}\right) \le \phi(C_d).$$

□

The above theorem provides a very powerful tool for establishing UO of designs in many settings. Optimality of a balanced incomplete block design (BIBD) or of a most symmetrically allocated (MSA) completely randomized design as well as many other optimality results can all be obtained very simply by an application of the above theorem. This was proved by Shah and Sinha (2001) in a slightly different formulation of universal optimality. This was obtained as a refinement of Proposition 1 by Kiefer (1975) and a result by Yeh (1986).

3 UO for the joint estimation of parameters

We consider the situation where a design d^* is UO for the estimation of $(\boldsymbol{\theta}', \boldsymbol{\eta}')'$ where $\boldsymbol{\theta}$ is $k \times 1$ and $\boldsymbol{\eta}$ is $s \times 1$. We shall now examine the consequences of this for the estimation of $\boldsymbol{\theta}$.

Before we embark on this we shall note a few properties of the information matrix $\boldsymbol{C}$. We partition $\boldsymbol{C}$ in accordance with the dimensions of $\boldsymbol{\theta}$ and $\boldsymbol{\eta}$ as

$$\boldsymbol{C} = \begin{pmatrix} \boldsymbol{C}_{11} & \boldsymbol{C}_{12} \\ \boldsymbol{C}_{21} & \boldsymbol{C}_{22} \end{pmatrix}.$$

A generalized inverse of $\boldsymbol{C}$ is given by

$$\boldsymbol{C}^- = \begin{pmatrix} \boldsymbol{C}_{11.2}^- & -\boldsymbol{C}_{11.2}^-\boldsymbol{C}_{12}\boldsymbol{C}_{22}^- \\ -\boldsymbol{C}_{22}^-\boldsymbol{C}_{21}\boldsymbol{C}_{11.2}^- & \boldsymbol{C}_{22}^- + \boldsymbol{C}_{22}^-\boldsymbol{C}_{21}\boldsymbol{C}_{11.2}^-\boldsymbol{C}_{12}\boldsymbol{C}_{22}^- \end{pmatrix}$$

where $\boldsymbol{C}_{11.2} = \boldsymbol{C}_{11} - \boldsymbol{C}_{12}\boldsymbol{C}_{22}^-\boldsymbol{C}_{21}$ and for $\boldsymbol{C}_{22}^-$ and $\boldsymbol{C}_{11.2}^-$ we take any symmetric g-inverses. Since $\boldsymbol{C}^-$ can be formally used as the dispersion matrix of $(\boldsymbol{\theta}', \boldsymbol{\eta}')'$, $\boldsymbol{C}_{11.2}$ can be regarded as the information matrix for $\boldsymbol{\theta}$. $\boldsymbol{C}_{11.2}$ is called the Schur complement of $\boldsymbol{C}_{22}$. We note here two important properties of Schur complements. Let $\boldsymbol{C}_{11.2} = \boldsymbol{F}(\boldsymbol{C})$. Then

$$\boldsymbol{F}((1-\alpha)\boldsymbol{A} + \alpha\boldsymbol{B}) \ge (1-\alpha)\boldsymbol{F}(\boldsymbol{A}) + \alpha\boldsymbol{F}(\boldsymbol{B}) \quad \text{for } 0 \le \alpha \le 1 \tag{3.1}$$

and

$$\boldsymbol{A} \ge \boldsymbol{B} \implies \boldsymbol{F}(\boldsymbol{A}) \ge \boldsymbol{F}(\boldsymbol{B}) \tag{3.2}$$

where $\boldsymbol{A}$ and $\boldsymbol{B}$ are information matrices. For a proof of these and a description of some other properties of Schur complements one may refer to Pukelsheim (1993).

We shall now prove the following theorem which has many applications.

Theorem 3.1. *If d^* is UO for the estimation of $(\boldsymbol{\theta}', \boldsymbol{\eta}')'$ in a design class $\mathcal{D}$ then it is UO for the estimation of $\boldsymbol{\theta}$ within the same design class $\mathcal{D}$.*

Proof. UO for the joint estimation of $\boldsymbol{\theta}$ and $\boldsymbol{\eta}$ imply that it minimizes $\phi(\boldsymbol{C})$ for every $\phi(\cdot)$ which satisfies conditions (1), (2) and (3) for UO stated in the previous section.

We define $\boldsymbol{F}(\boldsymbol{C}) = \boldsymbol{C}_{11.2}$ and let $\phi_1(\boldsymbol{F})$ be a real valued functional defined on the space of these $\boldsymbol{F}$ matrices. Let $\phi_1(\cdot)$ denote one such functional satisfying the three conditions. We now define $\phi(\boldsymbol{C}) = \phi_1(\boldsymbol{F}(\boldsymbol{C}))$ and then show that $\phi(\boldsymbol{C})$ so defined satisfies the three conditions. This would imply that $\phi(\boldsymbol{C}) = \phi_1(\boldsymbol{F}(\boldsymbol{C}))$ is minimized by d^* and hence d^* is UO for the estimation of $\boldsymbol{\theta}$.

Let $\boldsymbol{C}_g$ denote the matrix obtained by the action of permutation g on $\boldsymbol{C}$. It is easy to see that $\boldsymbol{F}(\boldsymbol{C}_g) = \boldsymbol{F}_g$ where $\boldsymbol{F}_g$ is obtained by the action of g on $\boldsymbol{F}$. Thus,

$$\phi(\boldsymbol{C}_g) = \phi_1\big(\boldsymbol{F}(\boldsymbol{C}_g)\big) = \phi_1(\boldsymbol{F}_g) = \phi(\boldsymbol{F}) = \phi(\boldsymbol{C}).$$

This shows that $\phi(\cdot)$ satisfies condition (1).

To examine if condition (2) holds, we note that if $\boldsymbol{C}_1 \geq \boldsymbol{C}_2$ then $\boldsymbol{F}(\boldsymbol{C}_1) \geq \boldsymbol{F}(\boldsymbol{C}_2)$ and hence

$$\phi(\boldsymbol{C}_1) = \phi_1\big(\boldsymbol{F}(\boldsymbol{C}_1)\big) \leq \phi_1\big(\boldsymbol{F}(\boldsymbol{C}_2)\big) = \phi(\boldsymbol{C}_2).$$

Thus, condition (2) holds. For the verification of condition (3), we first note that from the concavity of the Schur complement, $\boldsymbol{F}(\sum w_g \boldsymbol{C}_g) \geq \sum w_g \boldsymbol{F}(\boldsymbol{C}_g) = \sum w_g \boldsymbol{F}(\boldsymbol{C}) = \boldsymbol{F}(\boldsymbol{C})$ and hence

$$\phi\Big(\sum w_g \boldsymbol{C}_g\Big) = \phi_1\Big(\boldsymbol{F}\Big(\sum w_g \boldsymbol{C}_g\Big)\Big) \leq \phi_1(\boldsymbol{F}(\boldsymbol{C})) = \phi(\boldsymbol{C}).$$

This completes the proof of the theorem. □

The above theorem shows that UO for the joint estimation of $\boldsymbol{\theta}$ and $\boldsymbol{\eta}$ is a very strong property and that it implies UO for the estimation of the individual components.

We note that UO for the joint estimation of $\boldsymbol{\theta}$ and $\boldsymbol{\eta}$ also implies UO for the estimation of $\boldsymbol{\theta}(\boldsymbol{\eta})$ in a model which ignores $\boldsymbol{\eta}(\boldsymbol{\theta})$. This can be proved using arguments similar to the ones used in the proof of the above theorem.

Shah et al. (2005) demonstrated that UO for the estimation of $\boldsymbol{\eta}$ eliminating $\boldsymbol{\theta}$ and that for $\boldsymbol{\theta}$ eliminating $\boldsymbol{\eta}$ jointly lead to UO for their joint estimation only in a restricted class of designs. In the most general class of competing designs, this does not necessarily hold true. This we demonstrate in the application section below with reference to crossover designs. On the other hand, one might be tempted to think that UO for the estimation of $\boldsymbol{\eta}$ ignoring $\boldsymbol{\theta}$ and for the estimation of $\boldsymbol{\theta}$ eliminating $\boldsymbol{\eta}$ implies UO for the joint estimation of $\boldsymbol{\theta}$ and $\boldsymbol{\eta}$. However, the following example shows that this does not seem to be true.

We consider the framework of designs where there are b blocks of size k for comparing v treatments and where a balanced incomplete block design (BIBD) exists. It is well known that the BIBD is UO for the estimation of block effects ignoring the treatment effects and for the estimation of treatment effects eliminating the block effects. However, if the design is UO for the estimation of the block and treatment effects, by the above theorem it would imply that a BIBD is UO for the estimation of the block effects. This would be equivalent to UO of a linked block design for the estimation of the treatment effects in a design class where all treatments are equally replicated but the block sizes may be unequal. This does not seem to be true.

It may be noted that there are optimality functionals of practical interest which involve precision of estimation of functions involving both the sets of parameters and which satisfy the conditions of UO set out in the previous section. Thus UO for the joint estimation also implies optimality w.r.t. such functionals. For an example of this in the setting of crossover designs one may refer to a recent paper by Shah et al. (2005) and also to Shah and SahaRay (2005).

In the following section we shall deal with some applications of the results of this section.

4 Applications to some design settings

4.1 Crossover designs

Let us consider class $\mathcal{D}$ of crossover designs where v treatments are arranged in p rows and n columns in such a way that no treatment is applied on the same unit in successive periods. The rows correspond to periods whereas the columns correspond to the units. We shall assume that the parameter values are such that a balanced crossover design exists. A crossover design is said to be balanced if

(a) every treatment occurs t times in each period

(b) the design with units as blocks forms a balanced incomplete block design (BIBD)

(c) the design with units as blocks and where the last period is omitted also forms a BIBD

(d) every ordered pair of distinct treatments occur in consecutive periods in a unit the same number of times

(e) in the set of t units containing a particular treatment in the last period, each of the remaining $(v-1)$ treatment is applied λ times.

Existence of a balanced crossover design implies

$$n = vt, \qquad \lambda = t(p-1)/(v-1)$$

where t and λ are positive integers.

For simplicity of presentation, we shall assume that $p \leq v$. However, the results of this paper hold even when $p > v$.

Let $d(i,j)$ be the treatment assigned to the jth unit in the ith period and let y_{ij} denote the response obtained from that unit in that period. We assume that the y_{ij} are uncorrelated with common variance σ^2 and

$$E(y_{ij}) = \mu + \rho_i + \gamma_j + \tau_{d(i,j)} + \delta_{d(i-1,j)} \tag{4.1}$$

$i = 1,2,\ldots,p$; $j = 1,2,\ldots,n$; $\delta_{d(0,j)} = 0$ for all j, where $E(.)$ denotes the expected value of the variable in the parenthesis, μ is the general mean, ρ, γ, τ and δ are the period, unit, direct and residual treatment effects respectively.

Let $\boldsymbol{N}_u(\bar{\boldsymbol{N}}_u)$ denote the incidence matrix of direct (residual) treatment effects and units and let $\boldsymbol{S}$ be the incidence matrix of direct and residual treatment effects.

For a balanced crossover design, $\boldsymbol{S} = \lambda(\boldsymbol{J}_v - \boldsymbol{I}_v)$ where $\boldsymbol{J}_v$ is a $v \times v$ matrix with each element unity. Further, for a balanced crossover design each of $\boldsymbol{N}_u\boldsymbol{N}_u'$ and $\bar{\boldsymbol{N}}_u\bar{\boldsymbol{N}}_u'$ is completely symmetric i.e. is of the form $\alpha\boldsymbol{I}_v + \beta\boldsymbol{J}_v$.

Initially, we shall assume that there are no period effects in the model.

For $d \in \mathcal{D}$, let $\boldsymbol{C}_d$ denote the $2v \times 2v$ information matrix for direct and residual effects eliminating the period and unit effects. Dropping the suffix d, we may write $\boldsymbol{C}_d$ as

$$\boldsymbol{C} = \begin{pmatrix} \boldsymbol{C}_{11} & \boldsymbol{C}_{12} \\ \boldsymbol{C}_{21} & \boldsymbol{C}_{22} \end{pmatrix} \tag{4.2}$$

where $\boldsymbol{C}_{11}$ corresponds to the part for direct effects. $\boldsymbol{C}_{12}$, $\boldsymbol{C}_{21}$ and $\boldsymbol{C}_{22}$ are described similarly.

For the balanced crossover design d^* it is shown in Shah (2002) that

$$\boldsymbol{C}_{11}^* = \frac{vt(p-1)}{(v-1)}\boldsymbol{H}, \qquad \boldsymbol{C}_{12}^* = -\frac{vt(p-1)}{p(v-1)}\boldsymbol{H}$$

and

$$\boldsymbol{C}_{22}^* = \frac{t(p-1)(pv-v-1)}{p(v-1)}\boldsymbol{H} + \frac{t(p-1)}{pv}\boldsymbol{J}_v \tag{4.3}$$

where $\boldsymbol{H} = \boldsymbol{I}_v - \boldsymbol{J}_v/v$.

It has been shown by Shah et al. (2005) that d^* is UO for the joint estimation of $\boldsymbol{\tau}$ and $\boldsymbol{\delta}$ within the class of binary designs.

They also showed that d^* is UO for estimation of the direct effects or of the residual effects.

Here, we shall show that (a) d^* is UO within the class of restricted non-binary designs (to be specified below) and that (b) d^* is *not* UO within the unrestricted class $\mathcal{D}$. Again, we refer to UO for the joint estimation of $\boldsymbol{\tau}$ and $\boldsymbol{\delta}$.

We define below the following functions of design parameters.

$$\beta = \sum_i \sum_u n_{iu}^2,$$

$$l = \sum_i \text{(sum of } n_{iu}\text{'s for units with treatment } i \text{ in the last period)} \tag{4.4}$$

It is shown in Shah et al. (2005) that $\beta - 2l \geq vt(p-2)$ and $l \geq vt$. These imply $\beta - l \geq vt(p-1)$ and $\beta \geq pvt$. Let $x = \beta - 2l - vt(p-2)$ and $y = l - vt$. Clearly, $x \geq 0$, $y \geq 0$. We note that for a binary design, $x = y = 0$. A design with $x > 0$ and $y = 0$ will be called restricted non-binary. Thus, a restricted non-binary design is characterized by the property that a treatment which occurs in the last period does *not* occur in any earlier period.

Let $\boldsymbol{C}_{dg}$ denote that $\boldsymbol{C}_d$ matrix where in each of $\boldsymbol{C}_{11}$, $\boldsymbol{C}_{12}$, $\boldsymbol{C}_{21}$ and $\boldsymbol{C}_{22}$, the rows and columns are permuted by a permutation g in $\{1, 2, \ldots, v\}$. Further, let $\bar{\boldsymbol{C}}_d = \sum_g \boldsymbol{C}_{dg}/v!$ where the summation is over all $v!$ permutations. It is easy to see that each of $\bar{\boldsymbol{C}}_d$ and $\bar{\boldsymbol{C}}_{d^*}$ has the form

$$\begin{pmatrix} a\boldsymbol{H} & b\boldsymbol{H} \\ b\boldsymbol{H} & c\boldsymbol{H} + \frac{t(p-1)}{pv}\boldsymbol{J}_v \end{pmatrix}$$

where for $\boldsymbol{C}_{d^*}$

$$a = a^* = \frac{pvt(p-1)}{p(v-1)}, \qquad b = b^* = \frac{-vt(p-1)}{p(v-1)},$$
$$c = c^* = \frac{t(p-1)(pv-v-1)}{p(v-1)}.$$

For $\bar{\boldsymbol{C}}_d$ the corresponding expressions are

$$\bar{a} = a^* - \frac{x+2y}{p(v-1)}, \qquad \bar{b} = b^* - \frac{x+y}{p(v-1)}, \qquad \bar{c} = c^* - \frac{x}{p(v-1)}.$$

Thus, we get

$$\boldsymbol{C}^* - \bar{\boldsymbol{C}} = \frac{1}{p(v-1)}\begin{pmatrix} (x+2y)\boldsymbol{H} & -(x+y)\boldsymbol{H} \\ -(x+y)\boldsymbol{H} & x\boldsymbol{H} \end{pmatrix}.$$

When $y = 0$, $\boldsymbol{C}^* - \bar{\boldsymbol{C}}$ is n.n.d. and hence by Theorem 3.1, d^* is UO.

When the period effects are taken into account, $\boldsymbol{C}^*$ is reduced by

$$\begin{pmatrix} \boldsymbol{0} & \boldsymbol{0} \\ \boldsymbol{0} & \frac{t(p-1)}{pv}\boldsymbol{J}_v \end{pmatrix}$$

which has no effect in the estimation of the contrasts. On the other hand, $\bar{\boldsymbol{C}}$ gets reduced by a n.n.d. matrix. Hence $\boldsymbol{C}^* - \bar{\boldsymbol{C}}$ is n.n.d. when period effects are included in the model.

If $y \neq 0$, it can be shown that $\boldsymbol{C}^* - \bar{\boldsymbol{C}}$ has $(v-1)$ positive eigenvalues and $(v-1)$ negative eigenvalues. Thus, when $y \neq 0$, $\boldsymbol{C}^* - \bar{\boldsymbol{C}}$ is not n.n.d. regardless of the value of x.

To demonstrate a situation where d^* can actually be improved upon w.r.t. some contrasts we consider the following two designs

$$d_1: \begin{matrix} 1 & 2 & 3 & 4 & 4 & 3 & 2 & 1 & 2 & 4 & 3 & 1 \\ 2 & 3 & 4 & 1 & 1 & 4 & 3 & 2 & 4 & 1 & 2 & 3 \\ 1 & 1 & 2 & 2 & 3 & 3 & 4 & 4 & 1 & 2 & 3 & 4 \end{matrix}$$

$$d_2: \begin{matrix} 1 & 2 & 3 & 1 & 4 & 2 & 4 & 1 & 3 & 2 & 4 & 3 \\ 2 & 3 & 1 & 4 & 2 & 1 & 1 & 3 & 4 & 4 & 3 & 2 \\ 3 & 1 & 2 & 2 & 1 & 4 & 3 & 4 & 1 & 3 & 2 & 4 \end{matrix}$$

We note that d_2 is balanced whereas d_1 is non-binary with $y > 0$.

Consider repeating d_1 with different permutations of $\{1, 2, 3, 4\}$ giving in all $24 \times 12 = 288$ units. Call the resulting design $\tilde{d}_1$. Also consider 24 repetitions of d_2 and denote it by $\tilde{d}_2$. Since d_2 is completely balanced, $\tilde{d}_2$ is also completely balanced and hence has $x = y = 0$. However for d_1 and hence for $\tilde{d}_1$, $y \neq 0$. It turns out that for the full model including the period effects,

$$\boldsymbol{C}_{\tilde{d}_1} = 24 \begin{pmatrix} \frac{22}{3}\boldsymbol{H} & -3\boldsymbol{H} \\ -3\boldsymbol{H} & \frac{14}{3}\boldsymbol{H} \end{pmatrix} \quad \text{and} \quad \boldsymbol{C}_{\tilde{d}_2} = 24 \begin{pmatrix} 8\boldsymbol{H} & -\frac{8}{3}\boldsymbol{H} \\ -\frac{8}{3}\boldsymbol{H} & \frac{14}{3}\boldsymbol{H} \end{pmatrix}$$

where, $\boldsymbol{H} = \boldsymbol{I}_4 - \boldsymbol{J}_4/4$. This gives

$$\boldsymbol{C}^+_{\tilde{d}_1} = \frac{1}{24} \begin{pmatrix} .1845\boldsymbol{H} & .1194\boldsymbol{H} \\ .1194\boldsymbol{H} & .2914\boldsymbol{H} \end{pmatrix}, \qquad \boldsymbol{C}^+_{\tilde{d}_2} = \frac{1}{24} \begin{pmatrix} .1544\boldsymbol{H} & .0882\boldsymbol{H} \\ .0822\boldsymbol{H} & .2647\boldsymbol{H} \end{pmatrix}.$$

This shows that $\tilde{d}_2$ is superior to $\tilde{d}_1$ for the estimation of each of direct and residual effects. However, there are three functions involving both direct and residual effects for which $\tilde{d}_1$ is superior to $\tilde{d}_2$ and another three functions for which $\tilde{d}_2$ is superior to $\tilde{d}_1$. In fact, we shall show here that there is an optimality functional satisfying the three requirements for UO, for which the non-binary design $\tilde{d}_1$ is *better* than the *best* binary design $\tilde{d}_2$.

We note that

$$\boldsymbol{C}^+_{\tilde{d}_1} - \boldsymbol{C}^+_{\tilde{d}_2} = \begin{pmatrix} .0301\boldsymbol{H} & .0312\boldsymbol{H} \\ .0312\boldsymbol{H} & .0267\boldsymbol{H} \end{pmatrix}.$$

We consider a matrix of the form

$$\begin{pmatrix} a\boldsymbol{H} & b\boldsymbol{H} \\ b\boldsymbol{H} & c\boldsymbol{H} \end{pmatrix}.$$

Let $\boldsymbol{x}_1$, $\boldsymbol{x}_2$, $\boldsymbol{x}_3$ denote three orthonormal eigenvectors of $\boldsymbol{H}$ associated with the eigenvalue unity. It is easy to see that for $i = 1$, 2, or 3, $(\boldsymbol{x}_i', \theta\boldsymbol{x}_i')'$ is an eigenvector of $\left(\begin{smallmatrix} a\boldsymbol{H} & b\boldsymbol{H} \\ b\boldsymbol{H} & c\boldsymbol{H} \end{smallmatrix}\right)$ when θ is appropriately chosen. The eigenvalues are

$$\frac{a + c \pm \sqrt{(a+c)^2 - 4(ac - b^2)}}{2}$$

each with multiplicity 3. If $ac - b^2 < 0$, there is a negative eigenvalue of multiplicity 3. It turns out that the value of θ does not depend upon i. Let θ^- denote the value of θ which corresponds to the negative eigenvalues.

We now consider the optimality functional given by

$$\phi(\boldsymbol{C}) = \sum_i (\boldsymbol{x}_i', \theta^- \boldsymbol{x}_i')\boldsymbol{C}^+ \begin{pmatrix} \boldsymbol{x}_i \\ \theta^- \boldsymbol{x}_i \end{pmatrix}.$$

Since $\sum_{i=1}^3 \boldsymbol{x}_i \boldsymbol{x}_i' = \boldsymbol{H}$, it is easy to see that $\phi(\boldsymbol{C}_g) = \phi(\boldsymbol{C})$. It is easy to verify that the other two conditions also hold.

Since $\boldsymbol{C}_{\tilde{d}_1}^+ - \boldsymbol{C}_{\tilde{d}_2}^+$ has negative eigenvalues corresponding to eigenvectors $(\boldsymbol{x}_i', \theta^- \boldsymbol{x}_i')'$ for $i = 1, 2, 3$, it follows that $\phi(\boldsymbol{C}_{\tilde{d}_1}^+) < \phi(\boldsymbol{C}_{\tilde{d}_2}^+)$.

Thus $\tilde{d}_2$ is *not* UO for the estimation of $(\boldsymbol{\tau}', \boldsymbol{\delta}')'$.

4.2 Split block designs

Ozawa et al. (2001) introduced a design known as split-block design. The basic structure is as follows. We have a set of b blocks each having p rows and q columns. We also have two factors called F_1 and F_2. F_1 is at v_1 levels with $v_1 \geq p$ and F_2 is at v_2 levels with $v_2 \geq q$. In each block, the design assigns p levels of F_1 to the p rows and q levels of F_2 to the q columns. Let m_{pi} (n_{qi}) denote the number of times level p of F_1 (q of F_2) is used in block i. We assume that $m_{pi} = 0$ or 1 and $n_{qi} = 0$ or 1. We also define some design parameters as follows.

$\lambda(p, p'; q, q')$ = # of blocks in which levels p and p' of F_1 occur *and* levels q and q' of F_2 occur ($p \neq p'; q \neq q'$),

$\lambda(p, p'; q)$ = # of blocks in which levels p and p' of F_1 occur *and* level q of F_2 occurs ($p \neq p'$),

$\lambda(p; q, q')$ = # of blocks in which level p of F_1 occurs *and* levels q and q' of F_2 occur ($q \neq q'$),

$\lambda(p; q)$ = # of blocks in which level p of F_1 occurs *and* level q of F_2 occurs.

A design for which $\lambda(p, p'; q, q')$ is the same for all $p \neq p'$ and $q \neq q'$ is termed a balanced incomplete split block design (BISBD) by Ozawa et al.

It is easy to see that if one eliminates both row and column effects in each block, one can only estimate F_1F_2 interaction. Analysis of row totals (within blocks) enables estimation of F_1 and of F_1F_2. Similarly, the analysis of column totals (within blocks) enables estimation of F_2 and of F_1F_2. Finally, the analysis of block totals gives information on F_1, F_2 and F_1F_2. It can be shown that for each of the four models described above, the overall $\boldsymbol{C}$ matrix for the BISBD is the average of the $\boldsymbol{C}_d$ matrix over $v_1!\,v_2!$ permutations of the levels of F_1 and F_2 for *any* binary design. Thus, for the analysis of block totals we see that the BISBD is UO for the *joint* estimation of F_1, F_2 and of F_1F_2. By the results of the previous section it follows that the BISBD is also UO for the estimation of *each* of F_1, F_2 and F_1F_2. Shah (2002) had established UO property of these designs only for the estimation of F_1F_2 and that too under severe restrictions on the class of competing designs. Here, we only require that the competing design is binary i.e. $m_{pi} = 0$ or 1 and $n_{qi} = 0$ or 1

Similarly, it follows that for the analysis based on the row totals (column totals) within each block, the BISBD is UO for the estimation of $F_1\,(F_2)$ and of F_1F_2 jointly as well as separately.

Thus, our approach establishes very strong optimality properties of BISBD within a much broader class of competing designs.

4.3 Designs for a competing effects model

Raghavarao et al. (1986) introduced a model where in a block design every observation is affected by "competition" effects from other treatments in the same block. A related paper by Bhaumik (1995) focuses on optimality aspects of the designs.

We consider binary block designs for v treatments in b blocks of sizes k_1, $k_2, \ldots, k_b$ respectively. Thus, the design class is denoted by $\mathcal{D}(b, v, k_1, k_2, \ldots, k_b)$. For a design $d \in \mathcal{D}$, let $S_{t(d)}$ denote the set of treatments in the tth block. When d is understood, we shall simply write S_t. For every $i \in S_t$, our model postulates

$$y_i(S_t) = \tau_i + \sum_{\substack{j \in S_t \\ j \neq i}} \gamma_{i(j)} + e_i(S_t); \qquad i \in S_t, \;\; t = 1, 2, \ldots, b \tag{4.5}$$

where y_i is the observation on the ith treatment in block t, τ_i is the effect of the ith treatment, $\gamma_{i(j)}$ is the competition effect of the jth treatment on the ith treatment and $e_i(S_t)$'s are random errors assumed to be uncorrelated having a common variance σ^2.

We now introduce some notation for the design d, again dropping the suffix d. Let r_i denote the number of blocks containing treatment i and j. Finally let δ_{ijm} denote the number of blocks containing treatments i, j and m. A design is said to be a 3-design if r_i, λ_{ij}, δ_{ijm} are all independent of their respective suffixes.

We now write

$$\begin{aligned}
\boldsymbol{\gamma}_{(i)} &= (\gamma_{i(1)}, \ldots, \gamma_{i(i-1)}, \gamma_{i(i+1)}, \ldots, \gamma_{i(v)})', \\
\bar{\gamma}_i &= \sum_{j \neq i} \gamma_{i(j)}/(v-1), \qquad i = 1, 2, \ldots, v, \\
\boldsymbol{\beta}_i &= (\tau_i, \boldsymbol{\gamma}'_{(i)})', \\
\boldsymbol{\beta} &= (\boldsymbol{\beta}'_{(1)}, \ldots, \boldsymbol{\beta}'_{(i)}, \ldots, \boldsymbol{\beta}'_{(v)})'.
\end{aligned}$$

Raghavarao and Zhou (1998) showed that designs with constant block sizes do not have non-singular information matrix for $\boldsymbol{\beta}$. They considered UO formulation where a permutation g on treatments $\{1, 2, \ldots, v\}$ determine a $v^2 \times v^2$ matrix $\boldsymbol{G}_g$ such that when the treatments are re-labelled according to g, $\boldsymbol{C}$, the information matrix for $\boldsymbol{\beta}$ gets transformed to $\boldsymbol{G}'_g \boldsymbol{C} \boldsymbol{G}_g$.

Raghavarao and Zhou showed that if a 3-design with unequal block sizes exits, it is UO for the estimation of the entire vector $\boldsymbol{\beta}$. For a detailed discussion of this, one may refer to Raghavarao and Zhou (1998) or to Liski et al. (2001).

By the results of the previous section it follows that such a design is also UO for (i) the estimation of the τ_i's, (ii) a permutation invariant set of contrasts in the τ_i's (iii) for the estimation of the $\bar{y}_i$'s or (iv) all contrasts in the elements of the $\boldsymbol{y}_{(i)}$'s. (We note that in each of the above, the parameter set is invariant when the treatments are re-labelled according to a permutation g.) Thus, we can deduce very strong optimality properties of a 3-design with unequal block sizes. These were not previously known.

Acknowledgement

This was partial supported by a research grant from the Natural Sciences and Engineering Research Council of Canada. This support is gratefully acknowledged.

References

Bhaumik, D. K. (1995). Optimality in the competing effects model. *Sankhyā*, 57, 48–56.

Kiefer, J. (1975). Construction and optimality of generalized Youden designs. In *A Survey of Statistical Design and Linear Models.* Ed. J. N. Srivastava. Amsterdam: North Holland. Pp. 333–353.

Liski, E. P., Mandal, N. K., Shah, K. R., and Sinha, B. K. (2001). *Topics in Optimal Designs.* Lecture Notes in Statistics, 163. Springer-Verlag.

Ozawa, K., Jimbo, M., Kageyama, S., and Mejza, S. (2001). Optimality and construction of incomplete split-block designs. *Journal of Statistical Planning and Inference*, to appear.

Pukelsheim, F. (1993). *Optimal design of experiments.* New York: Wiley.

Raghavarao, D., Federer, W. T., and Schwager, S. J. (1986). Characteristics for distinguishing balanced incomplete block designs with repeated blocks. *Journal of Statistical Plannng and Inference*, 13, 151–163.

Raghavarao, D. and Zhou, B. (1998). Universal optimality of UE 3-designs for a competing effects model. *Communications in Statistics - Theory and Methods*, 27, 153–164.

Shah, K. R. (2002). Optimal split-block designs. *Calcutta Statistical Association Bulletin*, 52, 279–295.

Shah, K. R., Bose, M., and Raghavarao, D. (2005). Universal optimality of Patterson's cross-over designs. *The Annals of Statistics*, 33, 2854–2872.

Shah, K. R. and SahaRay, R. (2005). Optimal crossover designs for comparing mixed carryover effects. Submitted.

Shah, K. R. and Sinha, B. K. (1989a). On the choice of optimality criteria in comparing statistical design. *The Canadian Journal of Statistics*, 17, 345–348.

Shah, K. R. and Sinha, B. K. (1989b). *Theory of Optimal Designs*. Lecture Notes in Statistics, 54. Springer-Verlag.

Shah, K. R. and Sinha, B. K. (2001). Discrete optimal designs: Criteria and characterizations. *Recent Advances in Experimental Designs and Related Topics* (Proceedings of a Symposium held in Honour of Professor D. Raghavarao in Temple University in October, 1999). Nova Science Publishers. Pp. 115–133.

Yeh, M. (1986). Conditions for universal optimality of block designs. *Biometrika*, 73, 701–706.

KIRTI R. SHAH
University of Waterloo
Waterloo, ON N2L 3G1, Canada

BIKAS K. SINHA
Indian Statistical Institute
Kolkata, 700108, India
bksinha@isical.ac.in
http://www.isical.ac.in/~bksinha/

Festschrift for Tarmo Pukkila on his 60th Birthday
Eds. E. P. Liski, J. Isotalo, J. Niemelä, S. Puntanen, and G. P. H. Styan

Univ. of Tampere, 2006, ISBN 978-951-44-6620-5, pages 327–346

Some statistical aspects of assessing agreement: theory and applications

PORNPIS YIMPRAYOON MONTIP TIENSUWAN BIMAL K. SINHA

Abstract. When two experts employ measurements on a continuous scale on a common set of contestants, assessing their agreement is of vital importance to ensure consistency, and it essentially boils down to testing for equality of some parameters in their joint distribution under a parametric set-up. In this paper, three test procedures are applied in testing agreement under a bivariate normal set-up for small and large sample sizes. Some results of the simulation study based on a small sample size are presented. All test procedures in this paper are also illustrated using an application to a real data set of a large sample size.

2000 MSC codes: 62H12, 62H15.

Key words and phrases: Bivariate normal; Concordance correlation coefficient; Continuous scale; Likelihood ratio test; Mean squared difference.

1 Introduction

Assessing agreement plays an important role in examining the acceptability of a new or generic process, methodology and formulation in both science and non-science fields of laboratory performance, instrument or assay validation, method comparisons, statistical process control, goodness of fit, and individual bioequivalence (Lin et al. 2002). It has been used very often to measure the agreement between different data-generating sources referred to as observers or experts. An observer could be a chemist, a psychologist, a radiologist, a clinician, a nurse, a rating system, a diagnosis, a treatment, an instrument, a method, a process, a technique or a formula. There are numerous examples that illustrate these situations, and here we list some of them. In clinical and medical measurement comparison of a newly developed measurement method with an established one is often used to see whether they agree sufficiently for the new to replace the old. It makes sure the new method of measurement is cheap, quick and optimal. In criminal trials, a group of jurors is used and sentencing depends on the complete agreement among the jurors. Hotels receive five stars only after several visitors agree on the service. The medals and ranking in sport games are based on the ratings of several judges.

Evaluation of agreement has received considerable attention in the literature. Cohen (1960) proposed kappa statistic which is a basic method for measuring agreement among observers when the categories of response are nominal. It assigns the same score to any pair of assessments that differ. Later, Cohen (1968) extended the original kappa statistic by presenting the weighted kappa which assigns unequal scores to such pairs. Moreover, in the work of Landis and Koch (1977), it was found that weighted kappa is appropriate for measuring agreement when the categories of response are ordinal. Bland and Altman (1986) introduced an alternative approach based on graphical techniques, leading to a simple calculation for assessing the agreement between two methods of clinical measurement. In addition, there are several usual approaches for evaluating agreement when the data are measured on a continuous scale such as Pearson correlation coefficient, regression analysis, paired t-tests, least squares analysis for slope and intercept, within-subject coefficient of variation, and intra-class correlation coefficient. The concordance correlation coefficient (CCC) was first proposed by Lin (1989) for assessment of agreement in continuous data. It represents a breakthrough in assessing agreement between two distinct methods for continuous data in that it appears to avoid all the shortcomings associated with usual approaches in some situations.

The CCC measures agreement between alternative methods by measuring the variation of their linear relationship from 45° line (the identity line) through the origin. This coefficient not only measures how far each observation pair deviates from the line fit to the data (precision), but also how far this line deviates from the 45° line through the origin (accuracy). That is, the CCC has meaningful components of both precision and accuracy. In short, Lin (1989) expresses the degree of concordance between two variables X and Y by the mean of their squared difference (MSD), $E(Y-X)^2$, and defines the CCC as

$$\rho_c = 1 - \frac{E(Y-X)^2}{E_{\text{indep}}(Y-X)^2} = \frac{2\sigma_{xy}}{\sigma_x^2 + \sigma_y^2 + (\mu_y - \mu_x)^2}$$

where $E_{\text{indep}}(\cdot)$ represents expectation under the assumption of independence of X and Y, $\mu_x = E(X)$, $\mu_y = E(Y)$, $\sigma_x^2 = \text{Var}(X)$, $\sigma_y^2 = \text{Var}(Y)$, and $\sigma_{xy} = \text{Cov}(X,Y) = \rho\sigma_x\sigma_y$. Lin (1989) estimates this CCC with data by substituting the sample moments of a bivariate sample into above formula to compute the sample counterpart of CCC (r_c). The CCC translates the MSD into a correlation coefficient that measures the agreement along the identity line. It has the properties of a CCC in that it ranges between -1 and $+1$, with -1 indicating perfect reversed agreement ($Y = -X$), 0 indicating no agreement, and +1 indicating perfect agreement ($Y = X$).

Extending Lin's ideas, Chinchilli et al. (1996) suggested a weighted CCC for repeated measures design. Vonesh et al. (1996) and Vonesh and Chinchilli (1997) have modified Lin's approach to assessing goodness-of-fit for choosing models that have better agreement between the observed and the predicted values. Barnhart and Williamson (2001) proposed a generalized estimating equations approach to model the CCC via three sets of estimating equations. King and Chinchilli (2001a) developed a robust version of the CCC. King and Chinchilli (2001b) proposed a generalized CCC for categorical data and continuous data. They also show that the generalized CCC is actually equivalent to the kappa statistic for binary data and equivalent to the weight kappa statistic for ordinal data. Barnhart et al. (2002) presented an overall CCC in terms of the inter-observer variability for assessing agreement among multiple fixed observers. Lin et al. (2002) gave a review and comparison of various measures, including the CCC, of developments in this field by comparing the powers of the tests: 1) $\mu_x = \mu_y$, 2) $\sigma_x = \sigma_y$, and 3) $\rho = \rho_0$ where ρ_0 is a given value. Their calculation is illustrated using two real data examples.

In the context of bioequivalence, many similar studies can be found in Mandallaz and Mau (1981), Schuirmann (1987), Anderson and Hauck (1990), Sheiner (1992), Holder and Hsuan (1993), Schall and Luus (1993), Schall (1995), Schall and Williams (1996), and Lin (2000).

Our study applies and extends the work of Lin et al. (2002) by combining the problems of testing for $\mu_x = \mu_y$, $\sigma_x = \sigma_y$, and $\rho = \rho_0$ into one overall testing problem. We offer solutions based on the Likelihood Ratio Test (LRT), CCC, and MSD, all based on a bivariate normal set up.

The paper is organized as follows. In section 2 we illustrate the three test procedures, and indicate the computation of their cut-off points and power in section 3 and section 4, respectively, via simulation for small sample size. The cut-off points of the test procedures for large sample size are indicated in section 5, following standard large sample theory. Section 6 contains illustration of the test procedures mentioned in this paper by analyzing a real data set with a large sample size. We conclude this paper with some comments in section 7. Section 8 contains some tables showing simulated power of our proposed test procedures and some technical details.

2 Derivation of test procedures

Let X and Y denote random variables representing paired observations for assessing the agreement. We assume that X and Y have a bivariate normal distribution with means μ_x and μ_y, variances σ_x^2 and σ_y^2, correlation coefficient ρ and the covariance of X and Y is $\sigma_{xy} = \rho\sigma_x\sigma_y$. We denote this by

$$\begin{pmatrix} X \\ Y \end{pmatrix} \sim N_2\left[\begin{pmatrix} \mu_x \\ \mu_y \end{pmatrix}, \begin{pmatrix} \sigma_x^2 & \rho\sigma_x\sigma_y \\ \rho\sigma_x\sigma_y & \sigma_y^2 \end{pmatrix}\right], \tag{2.1}$$

where $-\infty < \mu_x, \mu_y < \infty$, $\sigma_x, \sigma_y > 0$, $-1 < \rho < 1$.

We wish to combine the problems of testing equality of means, equality of variances, and a high value of correlation coefficient into one overall testing problem:

$$H_0\colon \mu_x = \mu_y,\ \sigma_x = \sigma_y,\ \rho = \rho_0 \quad \text{versus} \quad H_1\colon H_0 \text{ is not true}, \tag{2.2}$$

where ρ_0 is a given high value.

We propose three test procedures for testing H_0 versus H_1.

First test procedure: we use the statistic λ_1^* from the LRT defined by

$$\lambda_1 = \frac{\max_{H_0\colon \mu_x=\mu_y, \sigma_x=\sigma_y, \rho=\rho_0} L(\mu_x, \mu_y, \sigma_x^2, \sigma_y^2, \rho \mid \text{data})}{\max_{\text{Unrestricted}} L(\mu_x, \mu_y, \sigma_x^2, \sigma_y^2, \rho \mid \text{data})},$$

where $L(\mu_x, \mu_y, \sigma_x^2, \sigma_y^2, \rho \mid \text{data})$ is the standard likelihood function.

To evaluate $\max_{H_0\colon \mu_x=\mu_y, \sigma_x=\sigma_y, \rho=\rho_0} L(\mu_x, \mu_y, \sigma_x^2, \sigma_y^2, \rho \mid \text{data})$, it can be easily shown that the maximum likelihood estimators of μ_x and σ_x^2 are obtained by solving the equations

$$(1-\rho_0)\bar{x} + (1-\rho_0)\bar{y} - 2(1-\rho_0)\mu_x = 0 \tag{2.3}$$

and

$$-2n(1-\rho_0^2)\sigma_x^2 + n[(\bar{x}-\mu_x)^2 + (\bar{y}-\mu_x)^2 - 2\rho_0(\bar{x}-\mu_x)(\bar{y}-\mu_x)] + S_x^2 + S_y^2 - 2\rho_0 S_{xy} = 0. \tag{2.4}$$

Hence the estimators are given by

$$\hat{\mu}_x = \frac{\bar{x}+\bar{y}}{2} \tag{2.5}$$

and

$$\hat{\sigma}_x^2 = \frac{1}{2n(1-\rho_0^2)}\left(\frac{n}{2}(1+\rho_0)(\bar{x}-\bar{y})^2 + S_x^2 + S_y^2 - 2\rho_0 S_{xy}\right). \tag{2.6}$$

where $\bar{x} = \sum_{i=1}^n x_i/n$, $\bar{y} = \sum_{i=1}^n y_i/n$, $S_x^2 = \sum_{i=1}^n (x_i-\bar{x})^2$, $S_y^2 = \sum_{i=1}^n (y_i-\bar{y})^2$, $S_{xy}^2 = \sum_{i=1}^n (x_i-\bar{x})(y_i-\bar{y})$. Substituting the above estimators, we obtain

$$\max_{H_0\colon \mu_x=\mu_y, \sigma_x=\sigma_y, \rho=\rho_0} L(\mu_x, \mu_y, \sigma_x^2, \sigma_y^2, \rho \mid \text{data}) = \left(\frac{n\sqrt{1-\rho_0^2}}{\pi\left[\frac{n}{2}(1+\rho_0)(\bar{x}-\bar{y})^2 + S_x^2 + S_y^2 - 2\rho_0 S_{xy}\right]}\right)^n e^{-n}. \tag{2.7}$$

To find $\max_{\text{Unrestricted}} L(\mu_x, \mu_y, \sigma_x^2, \sigma_y^2, \rho \mid \text{data})$, it is well known that $\hat{\hat{\mu}}_x = \bar{x}$, $\hat{\hat{\mu}}_y = \bar{y}$, $\hat{\hat{\sigma}}_x^2 = S_x^2/n = s_x^2$, $\hat{\hat{\sigma}}_y^2 = S_y^2/n = s_y^2$, and $\hat{\hat{\rho}} = S_{xy}/(S_x S_y) = r$ which gives

$$\max_{\text{Unrestricted}} L(\mu_x, \mu_y, \sigma_x^2, \sigma_y^2, \rho \mid \text{data}) = \left(\frac{n}{2\pi\sqrt{S_x^2 S_y^2 - S_{xy}^2}} \right)^n e^{-n}. \tag{2.8}$$

Hence λ_1 is obtained as

$$\lambda_1 = \left(\frac{4\sqrt{(1-\rho_0^2)(S_x^2 S_y^2 - S_{xy}^2)}}{n(1+\rho_0)(\bar{x}-\bar{y})^2 + 2(S_x^2 + S_y^2 - 2\rho_0 S_{xy})} \right)^n. \tag{2.9}$$

Our first test procedure thus rejects H_0 if

$$\lambda_1^* = \frac{\sqrt{S_x^2 S_y^2 - S_{xy}^2}}{n(1+\rho_0)(\bar{x}-\bar{y})^2 + 2(S_x^2 + S_y^2 - 2\rho_0 S_{xy})} < d_1, \tag{2.10}$$

where d_1 is a generic constant to be obtained from the size condition.

Our second test procedure is based essentially following Lin et al. (2002) by noting that the sample counterpart of CCC is given by

$$r_c = \frac{2 r s_x s_y}{s_x^2 + s_y^2 + (\bar{y}-\bar{x})^2}, \tag{2.11}$$

Replacing r by ρ_0 in (2.11), our second test rejects H_0 if

$$\lambda_2^* = \frac{2\rho_0 S_x S_y}{S_x^2 + S_y^2 + n(\bar{y}-\bar{x})^2} < d_2, \tag{2.12}$$

where d_2 is a generic constant to be obtained from the size condition. This is justified as λ_2^* is expected to be large under H_0.

Remark. It is quite interesting to compare the two test statistics λ_1^* and λ_2^*. It turns out that for ρ nearly unity, the two are almost equivalent in large samples!

Our third test procedure is again based on Lin (2000) who showed that

$$W = \log e^2 \sim N(\log \varepsilon^2, \sigma_W^2) \tag{2.13}$$

where

$$\varepsilon^2 = (\mu_y - \mu_x)^2 + \sigma_y^2 + \sigma_x^2 - 2\sigma_{yx}, \tag{2.14}$$

$$e^2 = (\bar{y} - \bar{x})^2 + s_y^2 + s_x^2 - 2s_{yx}, \tag{2.15}$$

and

$$\sigma_W^2 = \frac{2[1 - (\mu_y - \mu_x)^4/e^4]}{n-2}. \tag{2.16}$$

Under H_0, it then follows that

$$\frac{\sqrt{n-2}}{\sqrt{2}}(\log[(\bar{y}-\bar{x})^2+s_y^2+s_x^2-2s_{xy}]-\log[2\sigma_x^2(1-\rho)]) \sim N(0,1). \quad (2.17)$$

Using $\rho = \rho_0$ and the fact that $\sigma_x^2 = \sigma_y^2$ under H_0, our third test rejects H_0 if

$$\lambda_3^* = \frac{n(\bar{y}-\bar{x})^2 - 2\rho_0 S_x S_y}{S_x^2 + S_y^2} > d_3, \quad (2.18)$$

where d_3 is a generic constant. Again, its justification follows as λ_3^* is expected to be small under H_0 since ρ is generally positively large.

Below we summarize the three test procedures for our testing problem (2.2).

Test procedure 1: Reject H_0 if $\lambda_1^* = \frac{\sqrt{S_x^2 S_y^2 - S_{xy}^2}}{n(1+\rho_0)(\bar{x}-\bar{y})^2+2(S_x^2+S_y^2-2\rho_0 S_{xy})} < d_1$.

Test procedure 2: Reject H_0 if $\lambda_2^* = \frac{2\rho_0 S_x S_y}{S_x^2+S_y^2+n(\bar{y}-\bar{x})^2} < d_2$.

Test procedure 3: Reject H_0 if $\lambda_3^* = \frac{n(\bar{y}-\bar{x})^2-2\rho_0 S_x S_y}{S_x^2+S_y^2} > d_3$.

3 Computation of the cut-off points in small samples

In this section we briefly illustrate computation of d_1, d_2, and d_3 for test procedures 1, 2 and 3, respectively, when the sample size n is small. This is done by first expressing λ_1^*, λ_2^*, and λ_3^* in term of V_1, V_2, and V_3, where $S_x^2 \sim \sigma_x^2 V_1$, $S_y^2 \sim \sigma_x^2 V_2$, $S_{xy} \sim \rho_0 \sigma_x^2 V_3$, and noting that $\frac{n(\bar{x}-\bar{y})^2}{2\sigma_x^2(1-\rho_0)} \sim \chi^2_{1\text{ d.f.}}$.

Expressed in terms of V_i's, our test statistics take the form

$$\lambda_1^* = \frac{\sqrt{V_1 V_2 - \rho_0^2 V_3^2}}{2[(1-\rho_0^2)\chi_1^2 + (V_1 + V_2 - 2\rho_0^2 V_3)]}, \quad (3.1)$$

$$\lambda_2^* = \frac{2\rho_0\sqrt{V_1 V_2}}{V_1 + V_2 + 2(1-\rho_0)\chi_1^2}, \quad (3.2)$$

and

$$\lambda_3^* = \frac{2[(1-\rho_0)\chi_1^2 - \rho_0\sqrt{V_1 V_2}\,]}{V_1 + V_2}. \quad (3.3)$$

We now use the following six steps to compute d_1, d_2, and d_3.

1. Generate a standard normal variable $N(0,1)$ for computing the chi-square distribution with 1 degree of freedom.
2. Simulate $n-1$ independent paired samples of bivariate normal distribution subject to

$$\begin{pmatrix} u_i \\ w_i \end{pmatrix} \sim N_2\left[\begin{pmatrix} 0 \\ 0 \end{pmatrix}, \begin{pmatrix} 1 & \rho_0 \\ \rho_0 & 1 \end{pmatrix}\right] \quad \text{for } i = 1, \ldots, n-1.$$

3. Evaluate V_1, V_2, and V_3 by using the formulae:

$$V_1 = u_1^2 + \cdots + u_{n-1}^2,$$
$$V_2 = w_1^2 + \cdots + w_{n-1}^2,$$
$$V_3 = \sum_{i=1}^{n-1} u_i w_i.$$

4. Calculate λ_1^*, λ_2^*, and λ_3^* from equations (3.1), (3.2), and (3.3) respectively.
5. Repeat steps 1 through 4 based on 1000 simulations using $\rho_0 = 0.7, 0.8, 0.9$ and $n = 5, 10, 15, 20$.
6. Find values of d_1, d_2, and d_3 for the level $\alpha = 1\%, 5\%$.

The simulated cut-off points are shown in Table 3.1 for above values of n and ρ_0 when $\alpha = 1\%, 5\%$.

Table 3.1. Cut-off points for $n = 5, 10, 15, 20$, $\rho_0 = 0.7, 0.8, 0.9$, $\alpha = 1\%, 5\%$.

α	ρ_0	n	d_1	d_2	d_3
0.01	0.7	5	0.07511	0.24412	0.32555
		10	0.19177	0.47031	−0.34353
		15	0.24732	0.56630	−0.48796
		20	0.25930	0.58928	−0.53550
	0.8	5	0.19761	0.33229	0.02564
		10	0.23335	0.61392	−0.53683
		15	0.29783	0.69065	−0.65005
		20	0.29864	0.70689	−0.68809
	0.9	5	0.10886	0.49368	−0.33277
		10	0.30697	0.77020	−0.75790
		15	0.39237	0.82741	−0.82235
		20	0.43414	0.84570	−0.84041
0.05	0.7	5	0.14232	0.38018	−0.10107
		10	0.23567	0.55079	−0.49281
		15	0.28048	0.61116	−0.56915
		20	0.28995	0.62845	−0.60987
	0.8	5	0.16282	0.50348	−0.33914
		10	0.27801	0.67172	−0.64366
		15	0.32988	0.72762	−0.70742
		20	0.34401	0.74499	−0.73653
	0.9	5	0.20953	0.67620	−0.62293
		10	0.38359	0.82106	−0.81179
		15	0.45357	0.85600	−0.85189
		20	0.48275	0.86883	−0.86680

4 Power computation

In this section power calculation for all three test procedures is illustrated by using simulation.

First test:

$$\text{Power} = \Pr[\lambda_1^* < d_1] \tag{4.1}$$

where

$$\lambda_1^* = \frac{\sqrt{S_x^2 S_y^2 - S_{xy}^2}}{n(1+\rho_0)(\bar{x}-\bar{y})^2 + 2(S_x^2 + S_y^2 - 2\rho_0 S_{xy})}. \tag{4.2}$$

Second test:

$$\text{Power} = \Pr[\lambda_2^* < d_2] \tag{4.3}$$

where

$$\lambda_2^* = \frac{2\rho_0 S_x S_y}{S_x^2 + S_y^2 + n(\bar{y}-\bar{x})^2}. \tag{4.4}$$

Third test:

$$\text{Power} = \Pr[\lambda_3^* > d_3] \tag{4.5}$$

where

$$\lambda_3^* = \frac{n(\bar{y}-\bar{x})^2 - 2\rho_0 S_x S_y}{S_x^2 + S_y^2}. \tag{4.6}$$

To compute power of the test procedures 1–3, we use the following steps.

1. Simulate n independent paired samples of bivariate normal distribution subject to

$$\begin{pmatrix} x_i \\ y_i \end{pmatrix} \sim N_2\left[\begin{pmatrix} 0 \\ \delta_1 \end{pmatrix}, \begin{pmatrix} 1 & \rho_1\sqrt{\delta_2} \\ \rho_1\sqrt{\delta_2} & \delta_2 \end{pmatrix}\right] \quad \text{for } i = 1, \ldots, n,$$

   under the alternative hypothesis H_1.

2. Calculate $\bar{x}$, $\bar{y}$, S_x^2, S_y^2, and S_{xy} and hence empirical power for test procedure 1–3.

3. Repeat steps 1 and 2 based on 1000 simulations using $\delta_1 = 0.5, 1, 1.5, 2$; $\delta_2 = 0.5, 0.7, 0.9$; ρ_1 (for $\rho_0 = 0.7$) $= 0.6, 0.65, 0.75, 0.8$, ρ_1 (for $\rho_0 = 0.8$) $= 0.6, 0.7, 0.85, 0.9$ and ρ_1 (for $\rho_0 = 0.9$) $= 0.7, 0.8, 0.95$.

Some simulated powers of the tests for testing problem (2.2) under a variety of alternatives are shown in Section 8.1.

5 Derivation of cut-off points for large sample size

In this section we discuss derivation of the cut-off points for large values of n. This is essentially done by computing the large sample means and variances of the test statistics λ_1^*, λ_2^*, and λ_3^*, under H_0, by applying large sample theory, and then using a normal approximation. It is shown in Section 8.2 that, under H_0,

$$E(\lambda_1^*) \approx \frac{1}{4\sqrt{1-\rho_0^2}} + \frac{1}{4n\sqrt{1-\rho_0^2}}, \tag{5.1}$$

$$\mathrm{Var}(\lambda_1^*) \approx \frac{1-\rho_0^6-3\rho_0^2+3\rho_0^4}{16n^2(\rho_0^2-1)^4} = \frac{1-\rho^2}{16n^2}, \tag{5.2}$$

$$E(\lambda_2^*) \approx \rho_0 + \frac{\rho_0(\rho_0^2+2\rho_0-3)}{2n}, \tag{5.3}$$

$$\mathrm{Var}(\lambda_2^*) \approx \frac{\rho_0^2(\rho_0^4+2\rho_0^2-8\rho_0+5)}{2n^2}, \tag{5.4}$$

$$E(\lambda_3^*) \approx -\rho_0 + \frac{2-\rho_0-\rho_0^3}{2n}, \tag{5.5}$$

$$\mathrm{Var}(\lambda_3^*) \approx \frac{\rho_0^6-2\rho_0^4+5\rho_0^2-8\rho_0+4}{2n^2}. \tag{5.6}$$

Hence, for large n, the test procedures are carried out as follows.

Test procedure 1: Reject H_0 if

$$\lambda_1^* < d_1 \Leftrightarrow \frac{\lambda_1^* - E(\lambda_1^*)}{\sqrt{\mathrm{Var}(\lambda_1^*)}} < \frac{d_1 - E(\lambda_1^*)}{\sqrt{\mathrm{Var}(\lambda_1^*)}} = -z_\alpha. \tag{5.7}$$

Test procedure 2: Reject H_0 if

$$\lambda_2^* < d_2 \Leftrightarrow \frac{\lambda_2^* - E(\lambda_2^*)}{\sqrt{\mathrm{Var}(\lambda_2^*)}} < \frac{d_2 - E(\lambda_2^*)}{\sqrt{\mathrm{Var}(\lambda_2^*)}} = -z_\alpha. \tag{5.8}$$

Test procedure 3: Reject H_0 if

$$\lambda_3^* > d_3 \Leftrightarrow \frac{\lambda_3^* - E(\lambda_3^*)}{\sqrt{\mathrm{Var}(\lambda_3^*)}} > \frac{d_3 - E(\lambda_3^*)}{\sqrt{\mathrm{Var}(\lambda_3^*)}} = z_\alpha. \tag{5.9}$$

Obviously, the constants d_1, d_2 and d_3 are obtained above from normal approximations.

6 Numerical results

This section presents an example based on a real large data set which compares the agreement of two instruments in measuring blood counts in human samples (Lin et al. 2002). The data set described here deals with Diaspirin crosslinked hemoglobin (DCLHb) of 299 patients, collected by two different methods. The first one is based on HemoCue method (X) and the second one is based on the modificaton of HemoCue method (Y), namely Sigma

Table 6.1. Data on DCLHb of 299 patients, measured by HemoCue method (X) and Sigma (Y).

X	Y	X	Y	X	Y	X	Y	X	Y	X	Y	X	Y
1340	1330	100	100	180	180	50	50	50	50	320	310	270	270
100	100	1610	1600	50	50	60	60	1170	1180	1430	1430	80	80
80	80	150	140	70	70	1610	1600	330	330	90	90	70	70
1340	1340	1380	1380	1550	1560	200	200	60	60	210	220	210	200
530	550	520	510	80	80	90	90	90	90	1770	1770	50	50
240	240	1430	1420	90	90	160	160	310	310	600	600	1200	1220
60	60	330	330	70	70	50	50	90	90	360	350	1070	1080
70	80	90	90	1560	1560	1040	1040	360	360	70	70	400	400
50	50	90	90	710	720	1250	1250	1120	1120	130	130	120	120
1720	1770	1920	1950	190	190	150	150	1200	1210	680	680	80	90
460	460	70	60	100	100	1530	1530	210	210	110	110	790	790
130	140	880	990	720	720	440	440	60	60	360	360	680	680
50	50	1490	1490	710	710	1680	1740	1450	1450	70	70	80	80
60	60	330	320	80	80	500	500	100	100	70	70	850	850
270	270	1440	1420	670	670	100	100	360	360	60	60	340	340
80	80	1150	1130	270	280	80	70	950	940	130	130	450	450
910	910	810	820	80	70	50	60	80	80	420	420	130	130
650	700	400	400	1380	1380	1180	1230	1120	1170	340	340	850	850
90	80	110	120	670	670	80	70	450	460	230	220	240	240
900	890	1510	1520	440	430	1180	1160	150	150	400	400	430	430
130	140	1030	1010	140	140	460	460	740	750	140	130	50	50
80	80	370	370	90	80	190	190	880	880	390	380	50	50
1840	1830	150	150	1510	1380	1150	1150	540	540	50	70	360	360
430	430	800	800	860	870	530	520	230	230	570	560	400	400
80	90	580	580	90	90	450	450	1180	1180	530	540	110	110
90	100	220	240	160	160	200	200	1500	1510	410	420	980	980
160	160	90	90	230	240	1380	1300	760	760	60	60	200	200
500	500	530	530	520	510	320	320	130	130	460	460	50	50
60	60	470	470	1000	1010	170	180	1060	1080	50	50	480	480
200	200	200	210	450	450	1250	1250	770	770	330	340	100	100
130	130	100	100	300	270	580	580	360	380	690	690	160	160
110	110	1080	1080	150	150	430	430	450	460	120	120	80	80
90	90	50	50	280	280	180	180	50	50	90	90	760	760
910	910	570	570	80	80	1040	1040	230	230	790	790	590	590
770	770	360	370	820	790	420	420	460	460	570	520	700	700
800	810	240	240	510	520	870	870	360	370	130	140	130	130
50	50	50	60	130	130	1260	1230	640	640	1430	1400	230	230
620	610	1660	1740	1610	1610	840	840	110	110	420	420	50	50
210	210	50	60	70	70	320	320	1590	1590	670	680	500	500
190	190	1190	1150	50	50	70	70	500	510	80	80	500	500
90	90	70	80	1420	1440	70	60	810	810	300	300	60	60
140	140	1640	1660	330	330	1410	1440	80	90	210	220		
110	110	880	820	90	90	450	450	580	580	130	120		

Table 6.2. Summary statistics for DCLHb data.

n	299	S_x^2	67068066.22	s_d^2	322.6100
$\bar{x}$	489.3311	S_y^2	67249378.60	$\bar{u}$	979.5987
$\bar{y}$	490.2676	S_{xy}	67110653.51	r_{uv}	−0.0357
s_x^2	225060.6249	r	0.9993		
s_y^2	225669.0557	$\bar{d}$	−0.9365		

method. All paired data (x_i, y_i); $i = 1, \ldots, 299$ and its summary statistics are displayed in Table 6.1 and Table 6.2, respectively.

We apply our test procedures to analyze this data set for testing (2.2) by replacing $\rho_0 = 0.7, 0.8, 0.9$ into equations (5.1)-(5.6). We then get means and variances for λ_1^*, λ_2^*, and λ_3^* as shown in Table 6.3.

Table 6.3. Means and variances for λ_1^*, λ_2^*, and λ_3^* when $\rho_0 = 0.7, 0.8, 0.9$.

	ρ_0	Mean	Variance
λ_1^*	0.7	0.34890	0.13708×10^{-5}
	0.8	0.41527	0.19419×10^{-5}
	0.9	0.57162	0.36795×10^{-5}
λ_2^*	0.7	0.69870	0.16994×10^{-5}
	0.8	0.79898	0.10366×10^{-5}
	0.9	0.89941	0.34474×10^{-6}
λ_3^*	0.7	−0.69840	0.27262×10^{-5}
	0.8	−0.79885	0.13587×10^{-5}
	0.9	−0.89938	0.38725×10^{-6}

The values of T_1, T_2, T_3, T_4, and T_5 are obtained by substituting the statistics in Table 6.2 into (8.1). Next we replace these values into equations (4.2), (4.4), and (4.6) where $\rho_0 = 0.7, 0.8, 0.9$, then the values of the estimates λ_1^*, λ_2^*, and λ_3^* are obtained as shown in Table 6.4.

Table 6.4. Values of the estimates λ_1^*, λ_2^*, and λ_3^* for $\rho_0 = 0.7, 0.8, 0.9$.

ρ_0	λ_1^*	λ_2^*	λ_3^*
0.7	0.34973	0.6999	−0.6999
0.8	0.41606	0.7999	−0.7999
0.9	0.57187	0.8999	−0.8999

It is then obvious that, based on $\rho_0 = 0.7, 0.8, 0.9$, we accept H_0 for all test procedures 1–3 at significance level $\alpha = 0.01, 0.05$, that is, we conclude that $\mu_x = \mu_y$, $\sigma_x = \sigma_y$, $\rho = \rho_0$, hence implying agreement.

7 Conclusion

In this paper we focus on evaluating the agreement between two observers who employ measurements on a continuous scale. Three test procedures based on the LRT, CCC and MSD are proposed for testing agreement under a bivariate normal set up and the computation of their cut-off points and power is indicated via simulation for small sample size. We also indicate the computation of the cut-off points of the test procedures for large sample size, thus making inference in testing agreement feasible for both small and large sample sizes. An application to a real data set with a large sample size illustrates the proposed test procedures. The methods suggested in this paper under a bivariate normal set up can be extended to evaluate the agreement between two observers when the data set may be based on other meaningful bivariate distributions such as bivariate exponential, bivariate lognormal, bivariate gamma, etc. We propose to undertake these studies in the future.

8 Appendix

8.1 Simulated power of the test for testing (2.2)

Table 8.1. Simulated powers of the tests for testing H_0: $\mu_x = \mu_y$, $\sigma_x = \sigma_y$, $\rho = \rho_0$ with $\mu_x = 0$, $\mu_y = 0.5$, $\sigma_x^2 = 1$, $\sigma_y^2 = 0.7$ for $\rho_0 = 0.7$.

ρ_1	n	Power of λ_1^*		Power of λ_2^*		Power of λ_3^*	
		$\alpha = 0.01$	$\alpha = 0.05$	$\alpha = 0.01$	$\alpha = 0.05$	$\alpha = 0.01$	$\alpha = 0.05$
0.6	5	0.097	0.336	0.072	0.241	0.127	0.186
	10	0.305	0.557	0.200	0.424	0.263	0.496
	15	0.432	0.749	0.432	0.654	0.444	0.652
	20	0.576	0.814	0.544	0.763	0.549	0.805
0.65	5	0.095	0.335	0.067	0.229	0.121	0.267
	10	0.311	0.599	0.185	0.420	0.251	0.492
	15	0.432	0.756	0.420	0.657	0.430	0.667
	20	0.579	0.823	0.530	0.764	0.547	0.816
0.75	5	0.100	0.357	0.057	0.193	0.106	0.240
	10	0.344	0.620	0.146	0.404	0.232	0.480
	15	0.459	0.778	0.414	0.669	0.426	0.671
	20	0.666	0.891	0.519	0.781	0.545	0.837
0.8	5	0.109	0.391	0.050	0.185	0.098	0.224
	10	0.406	0.680	0.140	0.385	0.219	0.468
	15	0.592	0.878	0.391	0.674	0.407	0.686
	20	0.758	0.944	0.507	0.797	0.553	0.860

Table 8.2. Simulated powers of the tests for testing H_0: $\mu_x = \mu_y, \sigma_x = \sigma_y, \rho = \rho_0$ with $\mu_x = 0, \mu_y = 0.5, \sigma_x^2 = 1, \sigma_y^2 = 0.7$ for $\rho_0 = 0.8$.

ρ_1	n	Power of λ_1^*		Power of λ_2^*		Power of λ_3^*	
		$\alpha = 0.01$	$\alpha = 0.05$	$\alpha = 0.01$	$\alpha = 0.05$	$\alpha = 0.01$	$\alpha = 0.05$
0.6	5	0.095	0.383	0.123	0.349	0.186	0.359
	10	0.469	0.763	0.389	0.580	0.386	0.628
	15	0.724	0.925	0.615	0.791	0.605	0.787
	20	0.852	0.989	0.703	0.876	0.740	0.883
0.7	5	0.090	0.383	0.104	0.314	0.166	0.349
	10	0.456	0.753	0.358	0.575	0.381	0.619
	15	0.711	0.934	0.625	0.804	0.618	0.808
	20	0.840	0.986	0.720	0.896	0.762	0.815
0.85	5	0.106	0.448	0.073	0.255	0.131	0.305
	10	0.584	0.865	0.305	0.551	0.337	0.632
	15	0.850	0.987	0.642	0.843	0.646	0.851
	20	0.954	1.000	0.743	0.944	0.792	0.961
0.9	5	0.129	0.521	0.061	0.228	0.124	0.275
	10	0.722	0.944	0.281	0.548	0.324	0.646
	15	0.956	1.000	0.645	0.863	0.650	0.884
	20	0.995	1.000	0.749	0.968	0.824	0.980

Table 8.3. Simulated powers of the tests for testing H_0: $\mu_x = \mu_y, \sigma_x = \sigma_y, \rho = \rho_0$ with $\mu_x = 0, \mu_y = 0.5, \sigma_x^2 = 1, \sigma_y^2 = 0.7$ for $\rho_0 = 0.9$

ρ_1	n	Power of λ_1^*		Power of λ_2^*		Power of λ_3^*	
		$\alpha = 0.01$	$\alpha = 0.05$	$\alpha = 0.01$	$\alpha = 0.05$	$\alpha = 0.01$	$\alpha = 0.05$
0.7	5	0.142	0.352	0.227	0.509	0.288	0.531
	10	0.785	0.981	0.624	0.819	0.675	0.830
	15	0.993	1.000	0.844	0.930	0.865	0.929
	20	0.999	1.000	0.919	0.978	0.927	0.980
0.8	5	0.133	0.344	0.191	0.481	0.255	0.506
	10	0.790	0.988	0.626	0.838	0.692	0.845
	15	0.993	1.000	0.863	0.966	0.886	0.967
	20	1.000	1.000	0.947	0.990	0.966	0.993
0.95	5	0.241	0.543	0.124	0.403	0.192	0.453
	10	0.975	1.000	0.624	0.887	0.717	0.906
	15	1.000	1.000	0.954	0.994	0.966	0.997
	20	1.000	1.000	0.994	1.000	0.995	1.000

8.2 General result on mean and variance for large sample size

Assume $\phi(T_1,T_2,T_3,T_4,T_5) = \phi(\boldsymbol{T})$ to be a smooth function of $\boldsymbol{T}$ where $\boldsymbol{T}$ is defined as:

$$T_1 = \bar{x}, \qquad T_2 = \bar{y}, \qquad T_3 = \frac{S_x^2}{n-1} = \frac{\sum(x_i-\bar{x})^2}{n-1},$$
$$T_4 = \frac{S_y^2}{n-1} = \frac{\sum(y_i-\bar{y})^2}{n-1}, \qquad T_5 = \frac{S_{xy}}{n-1} = \frac{\sum(x_i-\bar{x})(y_i-\bar{y})}{n-1}. \tag{8.1}$$

Obviously the following holds in our case:

$$\begin{pmatrix}\bar{x}\\ \bar{y}\end{pmatrix} = \begin{pmatrix}T_1\\ T_2\end{pmatrix} \sim N_2\left[\begin{pmatrix}\mu_1\\ \mu_2\end{pmatrix}, \frac{1}{n}\begin{pmatrix}\sigma_1^2 & \rho\sigma_1\sigma_2\\ \rho\sigma_1\sigma_2 & \sigma_2^2\end{pmatrix}\right]; \tag{8.2}$$

$$(n-1)\begin{pmatrix}T_3 & T_5\\ T_5 & T_4\end{pmatrix} = \begin{pmatrix}S_x^2 & S_{xy}\\ S_{xy} & S_y^2\end{pmatrix} \sim W(\Sigma, n-1) \tag{8.3}$$

where

$$\Sigma = \begin{pmatrix}\sigma_1^2 & \rho\sigma_1\sigma_2\\ \rho\sigma_1\sigma_2 & \sigma_2^2\end{pmatrix}$$

and W represents Wishart distribution;

$$\begin{pmatrix}T_1\\ T_2\end{pmatrix} \perp \begin{pmatrix}T_3 & T_5\\ T_5 & T_4\end{pmatrix}. \tag{8.4}$$

Let $E(T_1) = \theta_1$, $E(T_2) = \theta_2$, $E(T_3) = \theta_3$, $E(T_4) = \theta_4$, and $E(T_5) = \theta_5$. By a Taylor expansion it readily follows that

$$\begin{aligned}
\phi(\boldsymbol{T}) &= \phi(\theta_1,\theta_2,\theta_3,\theta_4,\theta_5)\\
&\quad + \Bigg[(T_1-\theta_1)\frac{\partial\phi}{\partial T_1}\bigg|_{\boldsymbol{T}=\boldsymbol{\theta}} + (T_2-\theta_2)\frac{\partial\phi}{\partial T_2}\bigg|_{\boldsymbol{T}=\boldsymbol{\theta}} + (T_3-\theta_3)\frac{\partial\phi}{\partial T_3}\bigg|_{\boldsymbol{T}=\boldsymbol{\theta}}\\
&\qquad + (T_4-\theta_4)\frac{\partial\phi}{\partial T_4}\bigg|_{\boldsymbol{T}=\boldsymbol{\theta}} + (T_5-\theta_5)\frac{\partial\phi}{\partial T_5}\bigg|_{\boldsymbol{T}=\boldsymbol{\theta}}\Bigg]\\
&\quad + \frac{1}{2}\Bigg[(T_1-\theta_1)^2\frac{\partial^2\phi}{\partial T_1^2}\bigg|_{\boldsymbol{T}=\boldsymbol{\theta}}\\
&\qquad + (T_2-\theta_2)^2\frac{\partial^2\phi}{\partial T_2^2}\bigg|_{\boldsymbol{T}=\boldsymbol{\theta}} + (T_3-\theta_3)^2\frac{\partial^2\phi}{\partial T_3^2}\bigg|_{\boldsymbol{T}=\boldsymbol{\theta}}\\
&\qquad + (T_4-\theta_4)^2\frac{\partial^2\phi}{\partial T_4^2}\bigg|_{\boldsymbol{T}=\boldsymbol{\theta}} + (T_5-\theta_5)^2\frac{\partial^2\phi}{\partial T_5^2}\bigg|_{\boldsymbol{T}=\boldsymbol{\theta}}\\
&\qquad + 2(T_1-\theta_1)(T_2-\theta_2)\frac{\partial^2\phi}{\partial T_1\,\partial T_2}\bigg|_{\boldsymbol{T}=\boldsymbol{\theta}}\\
&\qquad + 2(T_1-\theta_1)(T_3-\theta_3)\frac{\partial^2\phi}{\partial T_1\,\partial T_3}\bigg|_{\boldsymbol{T}=\boldsymbol{\theta}}
\end{aligned}$$

$$
\begin{aligned}
&+ 2(T_1-\theta_1)(T_4-\theta_4)\frac{\partial^2\phi}{\partial T_1\,\partial T_4}\bigg|_{\boldsymbol{T}=\boldsymbol{\theta}}\\
&+ 2(T_1-\theta_1)(T_5-\theta_5)\frac{\partial^2\phi}{\partial T_1\,\partial T_5}\bigg|_{\boldsymbol{T}=\boldsymbol{\theta}}\\
&+ 2(T_2-\theta_2)(T_3-\theta_3)\frac{\partial^2\phi}{\partial T_2\,\partial T_3}\bigg|_{\boldsymbol{T}=\boldsymbol{\theta}}\\
&+ 2(T_2-\theta_2)(T_4-\theta_4)\frac{\partial^2\phi}{\partial T_2\,\partial T_4}\bigg|_{\boldsymbol{T}=\boldsymbol{\theta}}\\
&+ 2(T_2-\theta_2)(T_5-\theta_5)\frac{\partial^2\phi}{\partial T_2\,\partial T_5}\bigg|_{\boldsymbol{T}=\boldsymbol{\theta}}\\
&+ 2(T_3-\theta_3)(T_4-\theta_4)\frac{\partial^2\phi}{\partial T_3\,\partial T_4}\bigg|_{\boldsymbol{T}=\boldsymbol{\theta}}\\
&+ 2(T_3-\theta_3)(T_5-\theta_5)\frac{\partial^2\phi}{\partial T_3\,\partial T_5}\bigg|_{\boldsymbol{T}=\boldsymbol{\theta}}\\
&+ 2(T_4-\theta_4)(T_5-\theta_5)\frac{\partial^2\phi}{\partial T_4\,\partial T_5}\bigg|_{\boldsymbol{T}=\boldsymbol{\theta}}\Bigg] + \cdots.
\end{aligned}
$$

After taking the expectations of both sides of the above equation and using fact (8.4), the general result for mean of $\phi(\boldsymbol{T})$, up to $O(1/n)$, is

$$
\begin{aligned}
E(\phi(\boldsymbol{T})) = \phi(\boldsymbol{\theta}) + \frac{1}{2}\Bigg[&\operatorname{Var}(T_1)\frac{\partial^2\phi}{\partial T_1^2}\bigg|_{\boldsymbol{T}=\boldsymbol{\theta}}\\
&+ \operatorname{Var}(T_2)\frac{\partial^2\phi}{\partial T_2^2}\bigg|_{\boldsymbol{T}=\boldsymbol{\theta}} + \operatorname{Var}(T_3)\frac{\partial^2\phi}{\partial T_3^2}\bigg|_{\boldsymbol{T}=\boldsymbol{\theta}}\\
&+ \operatorname{Var}(T_4)\frac{\partial^2\phi}{\partial T_4^2}\bigg|_{\boldsymbol{T}=\boldsymbol{\theta}} + \operatorname{Var}(T_5)\frac{\partial^2\phi}{\partial T_5^2}\bigg|_{\boldsymbol{T}=\boldsymbol{\theta}}\Bigg]\\
&+ \operatorname{Cov}(T_1,T_2)\frac{\partial^2\phi}{\partial T_1\,\partial T_2}\bigg|_{\boldsymbol{T}=\boldsymbol{\theta}} + \operatorname{Cov}(T_3,T_4)\frac{\partial^2\phi}{\partial T_3\,\partial T_4}\bigg|_{\boldsymbol{T}=\boldsymbol{\theta}}\\
&+ \operatorname{Cov}(T_3,T_5)\frac{\partial^2\phi}{\partial T_3\,\partial T_5}\bigg|_{\boldsymbol{T}=\boldsymbol{\theta}} + \operatorname{Cov}(T_4,T_5)\frac{\partial^2\phi}{\partial T_4\,\partial T_5}\bigg|_{\boldsymbol{T}=\boldsymbol{\theta}}.
\end{aligned}
$$

We now consider $\operatorname{Var}(\phi(\boldsymbol{T}))$, up to $O(1/n)$, as consisting of three parts given by

$$
\begin{aligned}
&\operatorname{Var}(\phi(\boldsymbol{T}))\\
&= \operatorname{Var}\Bigg[\Bigg((T_1-\theta_1)\frac{\partial\phi}{\partial T_1}\bigg|_{\boldsymbol{T}=\boldsymbol{\theta}}\\
&\qquad + (T_2-\theta_2)\frac{\partial\phi}{\partial T_2}\bigg|_{\boldsymbol{T}=\boldsymbol{\theta}} + (T_3-\theta_3)\frac{\partial\phi}{\partial T_3}\bigg|_{\boldsymbol{T}=\boldsymbol{\theta}}\\
&\qquad + (T_4-\theta_4)\frac{\partial\phi}{\partial T_4}\bigg|_{\boldsymbol{T}=\boldsymbol{\theta}} + (T_5-\theta_5)\frac{\partial\phi}{\partial T_5}\bigg|_{\boldsymbol{T}=\boldsymbol{\theta}}\Bigg) \quad \to \text{(1st part)}\\
&\quad + \frac{1}{2}\Bigg((T_1-\theta_1)^2\frac{\partial^2\phi}{\partial T_1^2}\bigg|_{\boldsymbol{T}=\boldsymbol{\theta}}
\end{aligned}
$$

$$+ (T_2-\theta_2)^2\frac{\partial^2\phi}{\partial T_2^2}\bigg|_{\boldsymbol{T}=\boldsymbol{\theta}} + (T_3-\theta_3)^2\frac{\partial^2\phi}{\partial T_3^2}\bigg|_{\boldsymbol{T}=\boldsymbol{\theta}}$$

$$\left. + (T_4-\theta_4)^2\frac{\partial^2\phi}{\partial T_4^2}\bigg|_{\boldsymbol{T}=\boldsymbol{\theta}} + (T_5-\theta_5)^2\frac{\partial^2\phi}{\partial T_5^2}\bigg|_{\boldsymbol{T}=\boldsymbol{\theta}}\right) \to \text{(2nd part)}$$

$$+\left((T_1-\theta_1)(T_2-\theta_2)\frac{\partial^2\phi}{\partial T_1\,\partial T_2}\bigg|_{\boldsymbol{T}=\boldsymbol{\theta}}\right.$$

$$+ (T_1-\theta_1)(T_3-\theta_3)\frac{\partial^2\phi}{\partial T_1\,\partial T_3}\bigg|_{\boldsymbol{T}=\boldsymbol{\theta}}$$

$$+ (T_1-\theta_1)(T_4-\theta_4)\frac{\partial^2\phi}{\partial T_1\,\partial T_4}\bigg|_{\boldsymbol{T}=\boldsymbol{\theta}}$$

$$+ (T_1-\theta_1)(T_5-\theta_5)\frac{\partial^2\phi}{\partial T_1\,\partial T_5}\bigg|_{\boldsymbol{T}=\boldsymbol{\theta}}$$

$$+ (T_2-\theta_2)(T_3-\theta_3)\frac{\partial^2\phi}{\partial T_2\,\partial T_3}\bigg|_{\boldsymbol{T}=\boldsymbol{\theta}}$$

$$+ (T_2-\theta_2)(T_4-\theta_4)\frac{\partial^2\phi}{\partial T_2\,\partial T_4}\bigg|_{\boldsymbol{T}=\boldsymbol{\theta}}$$

$$+ (T_2-\theta_2)(T_5-\theta_5)\frac{\partial^2\phi}{\partial T_2\,\partial T_5}\bigg|_{\boldsymbol{T}=\boldsymbol{\theta}}$$

$$+ (T_3-\theta_3)(T_4-\theta_4)\frac{\partial^2\phi}{\partial T_3\,\partial T_4}\bigg|_{\boldsymbol{T}=\boldsymbol{\theta}}$$

$$+ (T_3-\theta_3)(T_5-\theta_5)\frac{\partial^2\phi}{\partial T_3\,\partial T_5}\bigg|_{\boldsymbol{T}=\boldsymbol{\theta}}$$

$$\left.\left. + (T_4-\theta_4)(T_5-\theta_5)\frac{\partial^2\phi}{\partial T_4\,\partial T_5}\bigg|_{\boldsymbol{T}=\boldsymbol{\theta}}\right)\right] \to \text{(3rd part)}$$

This can be rewritten in the form

$$\begin{aligned}\operatorname{Var}(\phi(\boldsymbol{T})) &= \operatorname{Var}(\text{1st part}) + \operatorname{Var}(\text{2nd part})\\ &\quad + \operatorname{Var}(\text{3rd part}) + 2\operatorname{Cov}(\text{1st part, 2nd part})\\ &\quad + 2\operatorname{Cov}(\text{1st part, 3rd part}) + 2\operatorname{Cov}(\text{2nd part, 3rd part}).\end{aligned}$$

The above variances and covariances are computed by using some standard properties of a bivariate normal distribution, Helmert's orthogonal transformation and the following theorem (Anderson 2003).

Theorem. *Let*

$$S = \begin{pmatrix} S_x^2 & S_{xy} \\ S_{xy} & S_y^2 \end{pmatrix} \sim W(\Sigma, n-1),$$

where

$$\Sigma = \begin{pmatrix} \sigma_1^2 & \rho\sigma_1\sigma_2 \\ \rho\sigma_1\sigma_2 & \sigma_2^2 \end{pmatrix}$$

and W represents Wishart distribution. Then

(i) $E(S_{ij}) = (n-1)\sigma_{ij}$.

(ii) $\mathrm{Cov}(S_{ij}, S_{kl}) = (n-1)(\sigma_{ik}\sigma_{jl} + \sigma_{il}\sigma_{jk})$.

(iii) $E(SAS) = n(n-1)(\Sigma A \Sigma) + (n-1)(\mathrm{tr}\,\Sigma A)\Sigma$, *where* $A > 0$, *a matrix of constants.*

It immediately follows that

$$\mathrm{Var}(T_1) = \frac{\sigma_1^2}{n}, \qquad \mathrm{Var}(T_2) = \frac{\sigma_2^2}{n}, \qquad \mathrm{Var}(T_3) \approx \frac{2\sigma_1^4}{n},$$

$$\mathrm{Var}(T_4) \approx \frac{2\sigma_2^4}{n}, \qquad \mathrm{Var}(T_5) \approx \frac{\sigma_1^2\sigma_2^2(1+\rho^2)}{n},$$

$$\mathrm{Cov}(T_1, T_2) = \frac{\rho\sigma_1\sigma_2}{n}, \qquad \mathrm{Cov}(T_3, T_4) \approx \frac{2\sigma_1^2\sigma_2^2\rho^2}{n},$$

$$\mathrm{Cov}(T_3, T_5) \approx \frac{2\rho\sigma_1^3\sigma_2}{n}, \qquad \mathrm{Cov}(T_4, T_5) \approx \frac{2\rho\sigma_1\sigma_2^3}{n},$$

$$\mathrm{Var}(T_1-\theta_1)^2 = \frac{2\sigma_1^4}{n^2}, \qquad \mathrm{Var}(T_2-\theta_2)^2 = \frac{2\sigma_2^4}{n^2},$$

$$\mathrm{Var}(T_3-\theta_3)^2 \approx \frac{8\sigma_1^8}{n^2}, \qquad \mathrm{Var}(T_4-\theta_4)^2 \approx \frac{8\sigma_2^8}{n^2},$$

$$\mathrm{Var}(T_5-\theta_5)^2 \approx \frac{2\sigma_1^4\sigma_2^4(1+\rho^2)^2}{n^2},$$

$$\mathrm{Cov}((T_1-\theta_1)^2, (T_2-\theta_2)^2) = \frac{2\rho^2\sigma_1^2\sigma_2^2}{n^2},$$

$$\mathrm{Cov}((T_3-\theta_3)^2, (T_4-\theta_4)^2) \approx \frac{8\rho^4\sigma_1^4\sigma_2^4}{n^2},$$

$$\mathrm{Cov}((T_3-\theta_3)^2, (T_5-\theta_5)^2) \approx \frac{8\rho^2\sigma_1^6\sigma_2^2}{n^2},$$

$$\mathrm{Cov}((T_4-\theta_4)^2, (T_5-\theta_5)^2) \approx \frac{8\rho^2\sigma_1^2\sigma_2^6}{n^2},$$

$$\mathrm{Var}(T_1-\theta_1)(T_2-\theta_2) = \frac{\sigma_1^2\sigma_2^2(1+\rho^2)}{n^2},$$

$$\mathrm{Var}(T_1-\theta_1)(T_3-\theta_3) \approx \frac{2\sigma_1^6}{n^2},$$

$$\mathrm{Var}(T_1-\theta_1)(T_4-\theta_4) \approx \frac{2\sigma_1^2\sigma_2^4}{n^2},$$

$$\mathrm{Var}(T_1-\theta_1)(T_5-\theta_5) \approx \frac{\sigma_1^4\sigma_2^2(1+\rho^2)}{n^2},$$

$$\mathrm{Var}(T_2-\theta_2)(T_3-\theta_3) \approx \frac{2\sigma_1^4\sigma_2^2}{n^2},$$

$$\mathrm{Var}(T_2-\theta_2)(T_4-\theta_4) \approx \frac{2\sigma_2^6}{n^2},$$

$$\mathrm{Var}(T_2-\theta_2)(T_5-\theta_5) \approx \frac{\sigma_1^2\sigma_2^4(1+\rho^2)}{n^2},$$

$$E((T_3-\theta_3)^2(T_4-\theta_4)^2) \approx \frac{4\sigma_1^4\sigma_2^4(1+2\rho^4)}{n^2},$$

$$\mathrm{Var}(T_3-\theta_3)(T_4-\theta_4) \approx \frac{4\sigma_1^4\sigma_2^4(1+\rho^4)}{n^2},$$

$$E((T_3-\theta_3)^2(T_5-\theta_5)^2) \approx \frac{2\sigma_1^6\sigma_2^2(1+5\rho^2)}{n^2},$$

$$\mathrm{Var}(T_3-\theta_3)(T_5-\theta_5) \approx \frac{2\sigma_1^6\sigma_2^2(1+3\rho^2)}{n^2},$$

$$E((T_4-\theta_4)^2(T_5-\theta_5)^2) \approx \frac{2\sigma_1^2\sigma_2^6(1+5\rho^2)}{n^2},$$

$$\mathrm{Var}(T_4-\theta_4)(T_5-\theta_5) \approx \frac{2\sigma_1^2\sigma_2^6(1+3\rho^2)}{n^2},$$

$$E((T_3-\theta_3)^2(T_4-\theta_4)(T_5-\theta_5)) \approx \frac{4\sigma_1^5\sigma_2^3\rho(1+2\rho^2)}{n^2},$$

$$E((T_3-\theta_3)(T_4-\theta_4)^2(T_5-\theta_5)) \approx \frac{4\sigma_1^3\sigma_2^5\rho(1+2\rho^2)}{n^2},$$

$$E((T_3-\theta_3)(T_4-\theta_4)(T_5-\theta_5)^2) \approx \frac{2\sigma_1^4\sigma_2^4\rho^2(5+\rho^2)}{n^2},$$

$$E(T_3-\theta_3)^3 \approx \frac{8\sigma_1^6}{n^2}, \qquad E(T_4-\theta_4)^3 \approx \frac{8\sigma_2^6}{n^2},$$

$$E(T_5-\theta_5)^3 \approx \frac{2\sigma_1^3\sigma_2^3\rho(3+\rho^2)}{n^2},$$

$$E((T_3-\theta_3)(T_4-\theta_4)^2) \approx \frac{8\sigma_1^2\sigma_2^4\rho^2}{n^2},$$

$$E((T_3-\theta_3)(T_5-\theta_5)^2) \approx \frac{2\sigma_1^4\sigma_2^2(1+3\rho^2)}{n^2},$$

$$E((T_3-\theta_3)^2(T_4-\theta_4)) \approx \frac{8\sigma_1^4\sigma_2^2\rho^2}{n^2},$$

$$E((T_4-\theta_4)(T_5-\theta_5)^2) \approx \frac{2\sigma_1^2\sigma_2^4(1+3\rho^2)}{n^2},$$

$$E((T_3-\theta_3)^2(T_5-\theta_5)) \approx \frac{8\sigma_1^5\sigma_2\rho}{n^2},$$

$$E((T_4-\theta_4)^2(T_5-\theta_5)) \approx \frac{8\sigma_1\sigma_2^5\rho}{n^2},$$

$$E((T_3-\theta_3)(T_4-\theta_4)(T_5-\theta_5)) \approx \frac{4\sigma_1^3\sigma_2^3\rho(1+\rho^2)}{n^2},$$

$$E((T_1-\theta_1)^3(T_2-\theta_2)) = \frac{3\sigma_1^3\sigma_2\rho}{n^2},$$

$$E((T_1-\theta_1)(T_2-\theta_2)^3) = \frac{3\sigma_1\sigma_2^3\rho}{n^2},$$

$$E((T_3-\theta_3)^3(T_4-\theta_4)) \approx \frac{12\sigma_1^6\sigma_2^2\rho^2}{n^2},$$

$$E((T_3-\theta_3)^3(T_5-\theta_5)) \approx \frac{12\sigma_1^7\sigma_2\rho}{n^2},$$

$$E((T_4-\theta_4)^3(T_5-\theta_5)) \approx \frac{12\sigma_1\sigma_2^7\rho}{n^2},$$

$$E((T_3-\theta_3)(T_4-\theta_4)^3) \approx \frac{12\sigma_1^2\sigma_2^6\rho^2}{n^2},$$

$$E((T_3-\theta_3)(T_5-\theta_5)^3) \approx \frac{6\sigma_1^5\sigma_2^3\rho(1+\rho^2)}{n^2},$$

$$E((T_4-\theta_4)(T_5-\theta_5)^3) \approx \frac{6\sigma_1^3\sigma_2^5\rho(1+\rho^2)}{n^2}.$$

Equations (5.1)-(5.6) readily follow from the above computations.

Acknowledgements

Our sincere thanks are due to a referee for some critical and constructive comments which improved the presentation of the paper. We also thank the Staff Development Project of the Commission on Higher Education, Thailand for a scholarship, and the Thailand Research Fund (TRF) for a research grant.

References

Anderson, S. and Hauck, W.W. (1990). Considersation of individual bioequivalence. *Journal of Pharmacokinetics and Biopharmaceutics*, 18, 259-273.

Anderson, T.W. (2003). *An Introduction to Multivariate Statistical Analysis*. New York: John Wiley and Sons.

Barnhart, H.X. and Williamson, J.M. (2001). Modeling concordance correlation via GEE to evaluate reproducibility. *Biometrics*, 57, 931-940.

Barnhart, H.X., Haber, M., and Song, J. (2002). Overall concordance correlation coefficient for evaluating agreement among multiple observers. *Biometrics*, 58, 1020-1027.

Bland, J.M. and Altman, D. (1986). Statistical methods for assessing agreement between two methods of clinical measurement. *Lancet*, 1, 307-310.

Chinchilli, V.M., Martel, J.K. Kumanyika, S., and Lloyd, T. (1996). A weighted concordance correlation coefficient for repeated measurement designs. *Biometrics*, 52, 341-353.

Cohen, J. (1960). A coefficient of agreement for nominal scales. *Educational and Psychological Measurement*, 20, 37-46.

Cohen, J. (1968). Weighted kappa: Nominal scale agreement with provision for scaled disagreement or partial credit. *Psychological Bulletin*, 70, 213-220.

Holder, D.J. and Hsuan, F. (1993). Moment-based criteria for determining bioequivalence. *Biometrika*, 80, 835-846.

King, T.S. and Chinchilli, V.M. (2001a). Robust estimators of the concordance correlation coefficient. *Journal of Biopharmaceutical Statistics*, 11, 83-105.

King, T. S. and Chinchilli, V. M. (2001b). A generalized concordance correlation coefficient for continuous and categorical data. *Statistics in Medicine*, 20, 2131–2147.

Landis, J. R. and Koch, G. G. (1977). The measurement of observer agreement for categorical data. *Biometrics*, 33, 159–174.

Lin, L., Hedayat, A. S., Sinha, B. K., and Yang, M. (2002). Statistical methods in assessing agreement: models, issues, and tools. *Journal of the American Statistical Association*, 97, 257–270.

Lin, L. I. K. (1989). A concordance correlation coefficient to evaluate reproducibility. *Biometrics*, 45, 255–268.

Lin, L. I. K. (2000). Total deviation index for measuring individual agreement with application in laboratory performance and bioequivalence. *Statistics in Medicine*, 19, 255–270.

Mandallaz, D. and Mau, J. (1981). Comparison of different methods for decision makimg in bioequivalence assessment. *Biometrics*, 37, 213–222.

Schall, R. (1995). Assessment of individual and population bioequivalence using the probability that bioavilities are similar. *Biometrics*, 51, 615–626.

Schall, R. and Luus, H. G. (1993). On population and individual bioequivalence. *Statistics in Medicine*, 12, 1109–1124.

Schall, R. and Williams, R. L. (1996). Towards a practical strategy for assessing individual bioequivalence. *Journal of Pharmacokinetics and Biopharmaceutics*, 24, 133–149.

Schuirmann, D. J. (1987). A comparison of the two one-sided tests procedure and the power approach for assessing the equivalence of average bioavailability. *Journal of Pharmacokinetics and Biopharmaceutics*, 15, 657–680.

Sheiner, L. B. (1992). Bioequivalence revisted. *Statistics in Medicine*, 11, 1777–1788.

Vonesh, E. F. and Chinchilli, V. M. (1997). *Linear and Nonlinear Models for the Analysis of Repeated Measurements*. New York: Marcel Dekker.

Vonesh, E. F., Chinchilli, V. M., and Pu, K. (1996). Goodness-of-fit in generalized nonlinear mixed-effect models. *Biometrics*, 52, 572–587.

PORNPIS YIMPRAYOON
Department of Mathematics, Faculty of Science
Mahidol University, Rama 6 Road, Bangkok 10400, Thailand

MONTIP TIENSUWAN
Department of Mathematics, Faculty of Science
Mahidol University, Rama 6 Road, Bangkok 10400, Thailand

BIMAL K. SINHA
Department of Mathematics and Statistics
University of Maryland
Baltimore County, 1000 Hilltop Circle,
Baltimore, MD 21250, USA
sinha@math.umbc.edu

Festschrift for Tarmo Pukkila on his 60th Birthday
Eds. E. P. Liski, J. Isotalo, J. Niemelä, S. Puntanen, and G. P. H. Styan

Univ. of Tampere, 2006, ISBN 978-951-44-6620-5, pages 347–365

Mean square error optimal linear plus quadratic combination of forecasts

Sven-Oliver Troschke & Götz Trenkler

Abstract. This paper deals with linear plus quadratic approaches aiming at finding a combined forecast for a scalar random variable from several individual forecasts for that variable. When combining forecasts linear approaches have been used predominantly. One reason may be the well-known fact that the linear approach with constant term is optimal with respect to the mean square prediction error loss, if the single forecasts and the target variable follow a joint normal distribution. In this paper no assumption is made on the type of the joint distribution. Its moments up to order four, however, are assumed to be given for the derivation of the optimal combination parameters. Three versions for the quadratic part of the combined forecast are discussed. As a by-product a linear plus quadratic adjustment of a single forecast is obtained. In order to apply these methods to empirical data the moments of the joint distribution have to be estimated. First results on the comparison of the new methods to some of the classical linear approaches are given. It is found that there are situations where the linear plus quadratic approaches may be employed beneficially, but further investigations have to be carried out.

2000 MSC codes: 62M20, 62P20.

Key words and phrases: Combination of forecasts; Linear plus quadratic combination.

1 Introduction

Suppose that we are given k forecasts $f_1, \dots, f_k$ for a scalar random variable y. The forecasts are gathered in a random vector $\mathbf{f}$, i.e. $\mathbf{f} = (f_1, \dots, f_k)^{\mathsf{T}}$. Our aim is to obtain combined forecasts f_{comb} from the single forecasts f_i which are optimal within certain given classes of combinations.

Optimality in this paper is always understood as optimality with respect to the mean square prediction error (MSPE). Given a forecast f for a random variable y the MSPE is given by

$$\mathrm{MSPE}(f, y) = \mathrm{E}[(y - f)^2] = \mathrm{Var}(y - f) + [\mathrm{E}(y - f)]^2. \tag{1.1}$$

It is a well-known fact (see e.g. Thiele 1993) that a linear combination $f_{\mathbf{b},c} = \mathbf{b}^\mathsf{T}\mathbf{f} + c$ with suitably chosen $\mathbf{b} = (b_1, \dots, b_k)^\mathsf{T} \in \mathbb{R}^k$ and $c \in \mathbb{R}$ is optimal among all combinations if y and $\mathbf{f}$ follow a joint normal distribution.

In the absence of joint normality, however, it is worthwhile to consider nonlinear forecast combinations. Stimulated by Taylor's series expansion formula we may try to 'approximate' the target variable y by a *linear plus quadratic* function in $\mathbf{f}$

$$f_{\mathbf{A},\mathbf{b},c} = \mathbf{f}^\mathsf{T}\mathbf{A}\mathbf{f} + \mathbf{b}^\mathsf{T}\mathbf{f} + c, \tag{1.2}$$

rather than by a linear function. Here $c \in \mathbb{R}$, $\mathbf{b} = (b_1, \dots, b_k)^\mathsf{T} \in \mathbb{R}^k$ and

$$\mathbf{A} = \begin{pmatrix} a_{11} & a_{12} & \dots & a_{1k} \\ a_{12} & a_{22} & \dots & a_{2k} \\ \vdots & \vdots & \ddots & \vdots \\ a_{1k} & a_{2k} & \dots & a_{kk} \end{pmatrix} \in \mathbb{R}^{k\times k} \tag{1.3}$$

may be assumed to be symmetric without loss of generality, because it only appears within the quadratic form $\mathbf{f}^\mathsf{T}\mathbf{A}\mathbf{f}$.

In order to apply such a linear plus quadratic combination of forecasts *two steps* have to be taken:

In the *first step* we derive the theoretically optimal combination parameters $\mathbf{A}_{\mathrm{opt}}$, $\mathbf{b}_{\mathrm{opt}}$ and c_{opt} such that

$$\mathrm{MSPE}(f_{\mathbf{A}_{\mathrm{opt}},\mathbf{b}_{\mathrm{opt}},c_{\mathrm{opt}}}, y) \le \mathrm{MSPE}(f_{\mathbf{A},\mathbf{b},c}, y) \tag{1.4}$$

for all symmetric matrices $\mathbf{A}$, vectors $\mathbf{b}$ and scalars c. Clearly, the optimal linear plus quadratic combination also outperforms the optimal linear combination $\mathbf{f}_{\mathbf{b}^*_{\mathrm{opt}},c^*_{\mathrm{opt}}}$ since the latter may be regarded as a linear plus quadratic combination with $\mathbf{A} = \mathbf{0}$, $\mathbf{b} = \mathbf{b}^*_{\mathrm{opt}}$ and $c = c^*_{\mathrm{opt}}$.

For the determination of the optimal combination parameters we will assume that the first to fourth order moments of the joint distribution of y and $\mathbf{f}$ exist and are known. We will see that the optimal linear plus quadratic combination parameters depend on these moments.

In practical applications, however, such moments will hardly be known. Consequently, in the *second step* we have to estimate the necessary moments from a sample of observations on the variables of interest. Then we plug these estimators into the formulae for the optimal combinations. In this paper we will apply the ordinary sample moments as estimators, but of course one might think of using alternatives for this step, e.g. robust estimators.

We will investigate three versions of the linear plus quadratic approach: The combined forecast in Equation (1.2) with no additional restriction (besides symmetry) imposed on the matrix $\mathbf{A}$ is referred to as the *strong version*.

Consequently, the strong linear plus quadratic approach involves $k(k+1)/2$ parameters for the quadratic part and $(k+1)(k+2)/2$ parameters in total.

Since the number of observations from which the unknown parameters are to be estimated is not so large in general, it is reasonable to consider reduced linear plus quadratic approaches as well, which involve less parameters. In order to achieve this goal we may restrict $\mathbf{A}$ to be a diagonal matrix or even to be a multiple of the $k \times k$ identity matrix.

Restricting $\mathbf{A}$ to be diagonal leads to the *medium version* of the linear plus quadratic approach

$$f_{\mathbf{a},\mathbf{b},c} = \mathbf{f}^{\mathsf{T}} \operatorname{dg}(\mathbf{a})\mathbf{f} + \mathbf{b}^{\mathsf{T}}\mathbf{f} + c = \sum_{i=1}^{k} a_i f_i^2 + \mathbf{b}^{\mathsf{T}}\mathbf{f} + c, \tag{1.5}$$

where $\mathbf{a} = (a_1, \ldots, a_k)^{\mathsf{T}} \in \mathbb{R}^k$,

$$\operatorname{dg}(\mathbf{a}) = \begin{pmatrix} a_1 & 0 & \ldots & 0 \\ 0 & a_2 & \ldots & 0 \\ \vdots & \vdots & \ddots & \vdots \\ 0 & 0 & \ldots & a_k \end{pmatrix} \in \mathbb{R}^{k \times k}, \tag{1.6}$$

is a diagonal matrix, $\mathbf{b} = (b_1, \ldots, b_k)^{\mathsf{T}} \in \mathbb{R}^k$ and $c \in \mathbb{R}$. Thereby the number of the elements in $\mathbf{A}$ is reduced to k and the total of unknown parameters is reduced to $2k + 1$.

Restricting $\mathbf{A}$ to be a multiple of the identity matrix, i.e. $\mathbf{A} = \alpha \mathbf{I}_k$, leads to the *weak version* of the linear plus quadratic approach which is

$$f_{\alpha,\mathbf{b},c} = \alpha \mathbf{f}^{\mathsf{T}}\mathbf{f} + \mathbf{b}^{\mathsf{T}}\mathbf{f} + c, \tag{1.7}$$

where $\alpha \in \mathbb{R}$, $\mathbf{b} = (b_1, \ldots, b_k)^{\mathsf{T}} \in \mathbb{R}^k$ and $c \in \mathbb{R}$. Thus there only remains one single parameter for the quadratic part and $k + 2$ unknown parameters in total.

As we will see later, the optimal choice of the combination parameters within the linear plus quadratic approaches requires knowledge about the first to fourth order moments of the joint distribution of y and $\mathbf{f}$. We will now introduce our notation:

Extending the approach from Harville (1985) and utilizing the notation from Rao and Kleffe (1988) we will assume the following setting: The expectations of y and $\mathbf{f}$ are given by $\mathrm{E}(y) = \mu_0$ and $\mathrm{E}(\mathbf{f}) = \boldsymbol{\mu}_{\mathbf{f}} := (\mu_1, \ldots, \mu_k)^{\mathsf{T}}$, respectively, which gives rise to the model:

$$\begin{pmatrix} y \\ \mathbf{f} \end{pmatrix} = \begin{pmatrix} \mu_0 \\ \boldsymbol{\mu}_{\mathbf{f}} \end{pmatrix} + \begin{pmatrix} \varepsilon_0 \\ \boldsymbol{\varepsilon}_{\mathbf{f}} \end{pmatrix} =: \boldsymbol{\mu} + \boldsymbol{\varepsilon}, \tag{1.8}$$

where $\boldsymbol{\varepsilon}_{\mathbf{f}} := (\varepsilon_1, \ldots, \varepsilon_k)^{\mathsf{T}}$. Consequently, $\mathrm{E}(\boldsymbol{\varepsilon}) = \mathbf{0}$ and the higher order moments of $\boldsymbol{\varepsilon}$ are the centered moments of $(y, \mathbf{f}^{\mathsf{T}})^{\mathsf{T}}$.

First, let us turn to the second order moments:

$$\boldsymbol{\Sigma} := \mathrm{E}(\boldsymbol{\varepsilon}\boldsymbol{\varepsilon}^\top) = \mathrm{E}\left[\begin{pmatrix}\varepsilon_0\\ \boldsymbol{\varepsilon}_{\mathbf{f}}\end{pmatrix}\begin{pmatrix}\varepsilon_0\\ \boldsymbol{\varepsilon}_{\mathbf{f}}\end{pmatrix}^\top\right] =: \begin{pmatrix}\Sigma_{00} & \boldsymbol{\Sigma}_{0\mathbf{f}}\\ \boldsymbol{\Sigma}_{\mathbf{f}0} & \boldsymbol{\Sigma}_{\mathbf{ff}}\end{pmatrix} \tag{1.9}$$

and

$$\mathrm{E}(\boldsymbol{\varepsilon}\boldsymbol{\varepsilon}^\top) = \mathrm{E}\left[\left(\begin{pmatrix}y\\ \mathbf{f}\end{pmatrix} - \begin{pmatrix}\mu_0\\ \boldsymbol{\mu}_{\mathbf{f}}\end{pmatrix}\right)\left(\begin{pmatrix}y\\ \mathbf{f}\end{pmatrix} - \begin{pmatrix}\mu_0\\ \boldsymbol{\mu}_{\mathbf{f}}\end{pmatrix}\right)^\top\right] = \mathrm{Cov}\begin{pmatrix}y\\ \mathbf{f}\end{pmatrix}. \tag{1.10}$$

The lower left $(k \times 1)$-submatrix $\boldsymbol{\Sigma}_{\mathbf{f}0}$ and the lower right $(k \times k)$-submatrix $\boldsymbol{\Sigma}_{\mathbf{ff}}$ of $\boldsymbol{\Sigma}$ read explicitly

$$\boldsymbol{\Sigma}_{\mathbf{f}0} = \begin{pmatrix}\Sigma_{10}\\ \Sigma_{20}\\ \vdots\\ \Sigma_{k0}\end{pmatrix} \quad \text{and} \quad \boldsymbol{\Sigma}_{\mathbf{ff}} = \begin{pmatrix}\Sigma_{11} & \Sigma_{12} & \dots & \Sigma_{1k}\\ \Sigma_{21} & \Sigma_{22} & \dots & \Sigma_{2k}\\ \vdots & \vdots & \ddots & \vdots\\ \Sigma_{k1} & \Sigma_{k2} & \dots & \Sigma_{kk}\end{pmatrix}. \tag{1.11}$$

We will assume invertibility of the centered second order moment matrix of $\mathbf{f}$ throughout, i.e. we assume invertibility of $\boldsymbol{\Sigma}_{\mathbf{ff}} = \mathrm{Cov}(\mathbf{f})$ and hence also invertibility of the non-centered second order moment matrix $\boldsymbol{\Sigma}_{\mathbf{ff}} + \boldsymbol{\mu}_{\mathbf{f}}\boldsymbol{\mu}_{\mathbf{f}}^\top = \mathrm{E}(\mathbf{f}\mathbf{f}^\top)$ is granted. Note that vectors and matrices are represented by bold face letters.

Analogously, the third order moments of $\boldsymbol{\varepsilon}$ are given by

$$\boldsymbol{\Phi} := \mathrm{E}(\boldsymbol{\varepsilon} \otimes \boldsymbol{\varepsilon}\boldsymbol{\varepsilon}^\top) = \begin{pmatrix}\boldsymbol{\Phi}_0\\ \boldsymbol{\Phi}_1\\ \vdots\\ \boldsymbol{\Phi}_k\end{pmatrix}, \tag{1.12}$$

where

$$\boldsymbol{\Phi}_i = \mathrm{E}(\varepsilon_i\boldsymbol{\varepsilon}\boldsymbol{\varepsilon}^\top) = \begin{pmatrix}\Phi_{i00} & \boldsymbol{\Phi}_{i0\mathbf{f}}\\ \boldsymbol{\Phi}_{i\mathbf{f}0} & \boldsymbol{\Phi}_{i\mathbf{ff}}\end{pmatrix}, \qquad i = 0, \dots, k \tag{1.13}$$

and the fourth order moments are given by

$$\boldsymbol{\Psi} = \mathrm{E}(\boldsymbol{\varepsilon}\boldsymbol{\varepsilon}^\top \otimes \boldsymbol{\varepsilon}\boldsymbol{\varepsilon}^\top) = \begin{pmatrix}\boldsymbol{\Psi}_{00} & \boldsymbol{\Psi}_{01} & \dots & \boldsymbol{\Psi}_{0k}\\ \boldsymbol{\Psi}_{10} & \boldsymbol{\Psi}_{11} & \dots & \boldsymbol{\Psi}_{1k}\\ \vdots & \vdots & \ddots & \vdots\\ \boldsymbol{\Psi}_{k0} & \boldsymbol{\Psi}_{k1} & \dots & \boldsymbol{\Psi}_{kk}\end{pmatrix}, \tag{1.14}$$

where

$$\boldsymbol{\Psi}_{ij} = \mathrm{E}(\varepsilon_i\varepsilon_j\boldsymbol{\varepsilon}\boldsymbol{\varepsilon}^\top) = \begin{pmatrix}\Psi_{ij00} & \boldsymbol{\Psi}_{ij0\mathbf{f}}\\ \boldsymbol{\Psi}_{ij\mathbf{f}0} & \boldsymbol{\Psi}_{ij\mathbf{ff}}\end{pmatrix}, \qquad i, j = 0, \dots, k. \tag{1.15}$$

Note that $\boldsymbol{\Sigma}$, $\boldsymbol{\Phi}_i$ and $\boldsymbol{\Psi}_{ij}$ are symmetric matrices of order $(k+1) \times (k+1)$. Furthermore $\boldsymbol{\Psi}_{ij} = \boldsymbol{\Psi}_{ji}$ such that the matrix $\boldsymbol{\Psi}$ is symmetric as well.

The elements of $\mathbf{\Phi}$ are $\Phi_{ijl} = \mathrm{E}(\varepsilon_i\varepsilon_j\varepsilon_l)$ and the elements of $\mathbf{\Psi}$ are $\Psi_{ijlm} = \mathrm{E}(\varepsilon_i\varepsilon_j\varepsilon_l\varepsilon_m)$.

Section 2 deals with some of the classical linear approaches within the framework of this paper whereas Section 3 investigates the linear plus quadratic approaches. Setting $k = 1$ we obtain and investigate adjustments of individual forecasts in Section 4. First results on the comparison of the linear plus quadratic to the classical approaches are presented in Section 5. An empirical application as well as theoretical results based on a given set of moments $\boldsymbol{\mu}$, Σ, $\mathbf{\Phi}$ and $\mathbf{\Psi}$ are reported. Section 6 concludes the paper.

Appendix B cites two results from the literature which are essential for the subsequent sections.

2 The linear approach

Linearly combined forecasts are of the form $\mathbf{b}^{\mathsf{T}}\mathbf{f} + c$, where it may be appropriate to impose certain restrictions on the combination parameters $\mathbf{b}$ and c. Linear approaches have been widely discussed in the literature, compare e.g. Clemen (1989) or Thiele (1993) for good overviews on the topic.

To derive the theoretically optimal combination parameters within the linear approaches we only need the first and second order moments of the joint distribution of y and $\mathbf{f}$ to exist and to be known.

We will restrict ourselves to consider only two prominent versions of the linear approach. Additional results can be found in Troschke and Trenkler (2000a) and Troschke (2002). The first version is

$$f_{\mathbf{b},c} = \mathbf{b}^{\mathsf{T}}\mathbf{f} + c, \tag{2.1}$$

i.e. the linear combination with constant term c and without restrictions on the vector $\mathbf{b}$. Its expectation is given by

$$\mathrm{E}(f_{\mathbf{b},c}) = \mathbf{b}^{\mathsf{T}}\boldsymbol{\mu}_{\mathbf{f}} + c. \tag{2.2}$$

From Harville (1985), Equation (2.1) we know that the mean square prediction error of such a combined forecast is minimized if we choose the combination parameters $\mathbf{b}$ and c according to

$$\mathbf{b}_{\mathrm{opt}} = \mathbf{\Sigma}_{\mathbf{ff}}^{-1}\mathbf{\Sigma}_{\mathbf{f}0} \quad \text{and} \quad c_{\mathrm{opt}} = \mu_0 - \mathbf{\Sigma}_{\mathbf{f}0}^{\mathsf{T}}\mathbf{\Sigma}_{\mathbf{ff}}^{-1}\boldsymbol{\mu}_{\mathbf{f}} \tag{2.3}$$

leading to the optimal value of the MSPE-function

$$\mathrm{MSPE}(f_{\mathbf{b}_{\mathrm{opt}},c_{\mathrm{opt}}}, y) = \Sigma_{00} - \mathbf{\Sigma}_{\mathbf{f}0}^{\mathsf{T}}\mathbf{\Sigma}_{\mathbf{ff}}^{-1}\mathbf{\Sigma}_{\mathbf{f}0}. \tag{2.4}$$

As stated in Section 1, $f_{\mathbf{b}_{\mathrm{opt}},c_{\mathrm{opt}}}$ is not only MSPE-optimal within the class of linear combinations $f_{\mathbf{b},c}$ but also within the class of all combined forecasts under joint normality of y and $\mathbf{f}$. Obviously, the combined forecast $f_{\mathbf{b}_{\mathrm{opt}},c_{\mathrm{opt}}}$ is unbiased even if the single forecasts are biased.

The second linear combination we will consider is the arithmetic mean of the individual forecasts. It is a very simple and empirically very powerful statistic:

$$f_{\mathrm{am}} = \frac{1}{k}\sum_{i=1}^{k} f_i = \frac{1}{k}\mathbf{1}^{\mathsf{T}}\mathbf{f}. \tag{2.5}$$

Its expectation is

$$\mathrm{E}(f_{\mathrm{am}}) = \frac{1}{k}\mathbf{1}^{\mathsf{T}}\boldsymbol{\mu}_{\mathbf{f}} \tag{2.6}$$

and thus the unweighted average is not unbiased in general. If, however, each individual forecast is unbiased, then so is f_{am}. The corresponding MSPE-value is given by

$$\mathrm{MSPE}(f_{\mathrm{am}}, y) = \Sigma_{00} - \frac{2}{k}\mathbf{1}^{\mathsf{T}}\Sigma_{\mathbf{f}0} + \frac{1}{k^2}\mathbf{1}^{\mathsf{T}}\Sigma_{\mathbf{ff}}\mathbf{1} + \left(\frac{1}{k}\mathbf{1}^{\mathsf{T}}\boldsymbol{\mu}_{\mathbf{f}} - \mu_0\right)^2. \tag{2.7}$$

We now turn to the linear plus quadratic approaches to the combination of forecasts. They are of the general form $\mathbf{f}^{\mathsf{T}}\mathbf{A}\mathbf{f} + \mathbf{b}^{\mathsf{T}}\mathbf{f} + c$, and the versions analyzed here differ with respect to the choice of the matrix $\mathbf{A}$ in the quadratic part of this expression. Since the linear combination $f_{\mathbf{b},c} = \mathbf{b}^{\mathsf{T}}\mathbf{f} + c$, with weights chosen according to (2.3), is MSPE-optimal among all combined forecasts under joint normality of y and $\mathbf{f}$, employment of linear plus quadratic approaches only deserves attention under non-normality. Hence we will assume non-normality in the following.

3 The linear plus quadratic approach

The strong linear plus quadratic approach $f_{\mathbf{A},\mathbf{b},c} = \mathbf{f}^{\mathsf{T}}\mathbf{A}\mathbf{f} + \mathbf{b}^{\mathsf{T}}\mathbf{f} + c$ is based on a full $k \times k$ real symmetric matrix $\mathbf{A}$ to build the quadratic part, a k-dimensional real vector $\mathbf{b}$ as well as a real constant term c.

The expectation of $f_{\mathbf{A},\mathbf{b},c}$ is immediately derived from Lemma 1 (a) in the Appendix. Setting $\tilde{\mathbf{Y}} = \mathbf{f}$, $\tilde{\boldsymbol{\mu}} = \boldsymbol{\mu}_{\mathbf{f}}$ and $\tilde{\boldsymbol{\varepsilon}} = \boldsymbol{\varepsilon}_{\mathbf{f}}$ we obtain $\tilde{\Sigma} = \Sigma_{\mathbf{ff}}$. Setting further $\tilde{\mathbf{A}} = \mathbf{A}$ and $\tilde{\mathbf{a}} = \mathbf{b}$ we arrive at

$$\mathrm{E}(f_{\mathbf{A},\mathbf{b},c}) = \boldsymbol{\mu}_{\mathbf{f}}^{\mathsf{T}}\mathbf{A}\boldsymbol{\mu}_{\mathbf{f}} + \mathrm{tr}(\mathbf{A}\Sigma_{\mathbf{ff}}) + \mathbf{b}^{\mathsf{T}}\boldsymbol{\mu}_{\mathbf{f}} + c. \tag{3.1}$$

To determine how the combination parameters $\mathbf{A}$, $\mathbf{b}$ and c should be chosen in order to minimize the mean square prediction error, we have performed the following three steps (compare Section A in the Appendix for details): In the first step the general MSPE-function of a combined forecast $f_{\mathbf{A},\mathbf{b},c}$ is calculated explicitly. In the second step this function is differentiated with respect to $\mathbf{A}$, $\mathbf{b}$ and c. In the final step the derivatives are simultaneously set to zero resulting in a linear equation system. The unique solution $(\mathbf{A}_{\mathrm{opt}}, \mathbf{b}_{\mathrm{opt}}, c_{\mathrm{opt}})$ of this equation system yields the desired minimum of the

MSPE-function:

$$c_{\text{opt}} = \mu_0 - \mathbf{b}_{\text{opt}}^{\top}\boldsymbol{\mu}_{\mathbf{f}} - \boldsymbol{\mu}_{\mathbf{f}}^{\top}\mathbf{A}_{\text{opt}}\boldsymbol{\mu}_{\mathbf{f}} - \text{tr}(\mathbf{A}_{\text{opt}}\boldsymbol{\Sigma}_{\mathbf{ff}}), \tag{3.2}$$

$$\mathbf{b}_{\text{opt}} = \boldsymbol{\Sigma}_{\mathbf{ff}}^{-1}(\boldsymbol{\Sigma}_{\mathbf{f}0} - \boldsymbol{\varphi}_{\mathbf{A}_{\text{opt}}}) - 2\mathbf{A}_{\text{opt}}\boldsymbol{\mu}_{\mathbf{f}} \tag{3.3}$$

and

$$\begin{aligned} 4\boldsymbol{\psi}_{\mathbf{A}_{\text{opt}}} &- 2\,\text{diag}(\boldsymbol{\psi}_{\mathbf{A}_{\text{opt}}}) - 4\boldsymbol{\Phi}_{0\mathbf{ff}} + 2\,\text{diag}(\boldsymbol{\Phi}_{0\mathbf{ff}}) \\ &+ \sum_{i=1}^{k} \boldsymbol{\xi}_i^{(k)\top}\boldsymbol{\Sigma}_{\mathbf{ff}}^{-1}(\boldsymbol{\Sigma}_{\mathbf{f}0} - \boldsymbol{\varphi}_{\mathbf{A}_{\text{opt}}})[4\boldsymbol{\Phi}_{i\mathbf{ff}} - 2\,\text{diag}(\boldsymbol{\Phi}_{i\mathbf{ff}})] \\ &- 4\,\text{tr}(\mathbf{A}_{\text{opt}}\boldsymbol{\Sigma}_{\mathbf{ff}})\boldsymbol{\Sigma}_{\mathbf{ff}} + 2\,\text{tr}(\mathbf{A}_{\text{opt}}\boldsymbol{\Sigma}_{\mathbf{ff}})\,\text{diag}(\boldsymbol{\Sigma}_{\mathbf{ff}}) = \mathbf{0}. \end{aligned} \tag{3.4}$$

Here $\boldsymbol{\xi}_i^{(k)}$ denote the k-dimensional unit vectors, i.e. the ith component of $\boldsymbol{\xi}_i^{(k)}$ is equal to 1 whereas the other entries are equal to 0.

Equation (3.4) represents a linear equation system with the unknowns being the $k(k+1)/2$ different elements of the symmetric matrix $\mathbf{A}_{\text{opt}}$. Unfortunately, we cannot write down its solution explicitly, and hence we cannot give the optimal combination parameters $(\mathbf{A}_{\text{opt}}, \mathbf{b}_{\text{opt}}, c_{\text{opt}})$ in an explicit form. In practical applications we have to solve Equation (3.4) in order to obtain $\mathbf{A}_{\text{opt}}$, then insert this solution into Equation (3.3) and thus get $\mathbf{b}_{\text{opt}}$ and finally insert these two results into Equation (3.2) to obtain c_{opt}.

Provided that Equations (3.4), (3.3) and (3.2) have a common unique solution $(\mathbf{A}_{\text{opt}}, \mathbf{b}_{\text{opt}}, c_{\text{opt}})$, it can be seen that this solution describes a minimum of the MSPE-function within the considered class of combined forecasts. The mean square prediction error

$$\begin{aligned} \text{MSPE}(f_{\mathbf{A},\mathbf{b},c}, y) &= \text{E}[(y - f_{\mathbf{A},\mathbf{b},c})^2] \\ &= \text{E}[(y - \mathbf{f}^{\top}\mathbf{A}\mathbf{f} - \mathbf{b}^{\top}\mathbf{f} - c)^2] \\ &= \text{E}\left[\left(y - \sum_{i=1}^{k}\sum_{j=1}^{k} a_{ij}f_if_j - \sum_{i=1}^{k} b_if_i - c\right)^2\right] \\ &= \text{E}\left[\left(y - \sum_{i=1}^{k} a_{ii}f_i^2 - 2\sum_{i<j}\sum a_{ij}f_if_j - \sum_{i=1}^{k} b_if_i - c\right)^2\right] \end{aligned} \tag{3.5}$$

is a quadratic function in the unknown parameters bounded below by the value 0.

Since we cannot express the optimal combination parameters $\mathbf{A}_{\text{opt}}$, $\mathbf{b}_{\text{opt}}$ and c_{opt} explicitly, we cannot give an expression for the optimal value $\text{MSPE}(f_{\mathbf{A}_{\text{opt}},\mathbf{b}_{\text{opt}},c_{\text{opt}}}, y)$ of the MSPE-function either.

We can conclude, however, that $f_{\mathbf{A}_{\text{opt}},\mathbf{b}_{\text{opt}},c_{\text{opt}}}$ is an unbiased forecast: Following Equation (3.1) the expectation of $f_{\mathbf{A}_{\text{opt}},\mathbf{b}_{\text{opt}},c_{\text{opt}}}$ is given by

$$\text{E}(f_{\mathbf{A}_{\text{opt}},\mathbf{b}_{\text{opt}},c_{\text{opt}}}) = \boldsymbol{\mu}_{\mathbf{f}}^{\top}\mathbf{A}_{\text{opt}}\boldsymbol{\mu}_{\mathbf{f}} + \text{tr}(\mathbf{A}_{\text{opt}}\boldsymbol{\Sigma}_{\mathbf{ff}}) + \mathbf{b}_{\text{opt}}^{\top}\boldsymbol{\mu}_{\mathbf{f}} + c_{\text{opt}}. \tag{3.6}$$

Then unbiasedness is guaranteed by the optimal choice of the constant term as can be seen by inserting

$$c_{\text{opt}} = \mu_0 - \mathbf{b}_{\text{opt}}^{\mathsf{T}}\boldsymbol{\mu}_{\mathbf{f}} - \boldsymbol{\mu}_{\mathbf{f}}^{\mathsf{T}}\mathbf{A}_{\text{opt}}\boldsymbol{\mu}_{\mathbf{f}} - \operatorname{tr}(\mathbf{A}_{\text{opt}}\boldsymbol{\Sigma}_{\mathbf{ff}}) \tag{3.7}$$

into Equation (3.6).

The fact that the optimal combination parameters $\mathbf{A}_{\text{opt}}$, $\mathbf{b}_{\text{opt}}$ and c_{opt} are not obtainable by explicit formulae, but have to be calculated from Equations (3.2), (3.3) and (3.4) not only makes further theoretical considerations impossible, but also impedes the application of the strong linear plus quadratic combination technique. Consequently, it is desirable to find an easier way to apply linear plus quadratic combination.

This is indeed possible: Granger and Ramanathan (1984) observe that the linear combination problems from Section 2 may be treated from a regression viewpoint. Analogously, a regression approach may be followed for strong linear plus quadratic combination: Minimization of (3.5) corresponds to regressing y on $f_1^2, \ldots, f_k^2, (f_i f_j)_{i,j=1,\ldots,k,i<j}, f_1, \ldots, f_k$ using a constant term, cf. Rao (1965, pp. 222 f.).

This permits easy implementation and makes standard computer software applicable. It can be shown that using the common least squares estimator in the regression leads to the same results as replacing the true moments $\boldsymbol{\mu}$, $\boldsymbol{\Sigma}$, $\boldsymbol{\Phi}$ and $\boldsymbol{\Psi}$ by their respective sample moments in the above formulae for the optimal combination parameters. The regression approach is thoroughly dealt with in Troschke (2002), compare also Troschke and Trenkler (2000b).

Likewise we can determine equation systems and regression approaches for the medium and weak linear plus quadratic combinations $f_{\mathbf{a},\mathbf{b},c} = \sum_{i=1}^{k} a_i f_i^2 + \mathbf{b}^{\mathsf{T}}\mathbf{f} + c$ and $f_{\alpha,\mathbf{b},c} = \alpha\mathbf{f}^{\mathsf{T}}\mathbf{f} + \mathbf{b}^{\mathsf{T}}\mathbf{f} + c$. In the latter case the equation system even has an explicit solution.

In Section 5 we will report about first investigations on the quality of the linear plus quadratic approaches in the case of $k = 2$ forecasts. But first we turn to the special case $k = 1$.

4 The special case $k = 1$: Adjustment of forecasts

There is no reason why the special case $k = 1$ should be ruled out in the above considerations. Of course, this "combination of one forecast" should rather be addressed as *adjustment of single forecasts*. Exploiting the moment structure of the joint distribution of the target variable y and a single forecast f_i the performance of f_i can be improved with respect to the mean square prediction error basing on this adjustment.

The MSPE of the forecast f_i is given by

$$\begin{aligned} \operatorname{MSPE}(f_i, y) &= \mathrm{E}[(y - f_i)^2] = \operatorname{Var}(y - f_i) + [\mathrm{E}(y - f_i)]^2 \\ &= \Sigma_{00} + \Sigma_{ii} - 2\Sigma_{i0} + \mu_0^2 + \mu_i^2 - 2\mu_0\mu_i. \end{aligned} \tag{4.1}$$

All of the linear and linear plus quadratic combination approaches described above may be applied in this case. Some of them, however, are identical to others. For instance all three linear plus quadratic combined forecasts coincide in the present situation, i.e. we only need to consider one *linear plus quadratic adjustment*

$$(f_i)_{\alpha,b,c} = \alpha f_i^2 + b f_i + c \tag{4.2}$$

with $\alpha, b, c \in \mathbb{R}$. The optimal choices for the unknown parameters may be derived as

$$\alpha_{\text{opt}} = \frac{\Phi_{0ii} - \Sigma_{i0}\Sigma_{ii}^{-1}\Phi_{iii}}{\Psi_{iiii} - \Phi_{iii}^2\Sigma_{ii}^{-1} - \Sigma_{ii}^2}, \tag{4.3}$$

$$b_{\text{opt}} = \frac{\Sigma_{i0}}{\Sigma_{ii}} - \alpha_{\text{opt}}\left(\frac{\Phi_{iii}}{\Sigma_{ii}} + 2\mu_i\right) \tag{4.4}$$

and

$$c_{\text{opt}} = \mu_0 - b_{\text{opt}}\mu_i - \alpha_{\text{opt}}(\mu_i^2 + \Sigma_{ii}) \tag{4.5}$$

leading to the MSPE-value of the optimal linear plus quadratic adjusted forecast

$$\text{MSPE}((f_i)_{\alpha_{\text{opt}},b_{\text{opt}},c_{\text{opt}}}, y) = \Sigma_{00} - \frac{\Sigma_{i0}^2}{\Sigma_{ii}} - \frac{(\Phi_{0ii} - \Sigma_{i0}\Sigma_{ii}^{-1}\Phi_{iii})^2}{\Psi_{iiii} - \Phi_{iii}^2\Sigma_{ii}^{-1} - \Sigma_{ii}^2}. \tag{4.6}$$

The *unrestricted linear adjustment with constant term* is

$$(f_i)_{b,c} = b f_i + c \tag{4.7}$$

with $b, c \in \mathbb{R}$. Granger (1989, p. 169) points out the usefulness of such an adjustment. The optimal choices for the parameters are obtained as special cases of Equations (2.3), namely

$$b_{\text{opt}} = \frac{\Sigma_{i0}}{\Sigma_{ii}} \quad \text{and} \quad c_{\text{opt}} = \mu_0 - \frac{\Sigma_{i0}}{\Sigma_{ii}}\mu_i \tag{4.8}$$

with corresponding optimal MSPE-value

$$\text{MSPE}((f_i)_{b_{\text{opt}},c_{\text{opt}}}, y) = \Sigma_{00} - \frac{\Sigma_{i0}^2}{\Sigma_{ii}}. \tag{4.9}$$

Following the results from the previous sections both of these adjusted forecasts are unbiased.

Finally, the adjustment counterpart of the arithmetic mean equals the original single forecast f_i and needs no special consideration.

The two different ways of adjusting a single forecast introduced above will be included in our first comparison of the methods carried out in Section 5.

5 Empirical and theoretical comparisons

In this section we will present an empirical example illustrating the adjustments of single forecasts as well as the combination of $k = 2$ forecasts on the basis of the new methods. This will be followed by a theoretical comparison of these methods based on a given set of moments $\boldsymbol{\mu}$, $\boldsymbol{\Sigma}$, $\boldsymbol{\Phi}$ and $\boldsymbol{\Psi}$ obtained from the data of the example. The corresponding results for the additional linear combinations mentioned in Section 2 can be found in Troschke and Trenkler (2000b). It should be pointed out, however, that these comparisons are only meant to provide a first impression of the possible usefulness of the linear plus quadratic approaches. More details can be found in Troschke (2002).

The data for the numerical example are taken from a larger data set of German macro economic variables and corresponding forecasts investigated by Klapper (1998). We picked out the DIW (Deutsches Institut für Wirtschaftsforschung, f_1) and Ifo (Ifo-Institut für Wirtschaftsforschung, f_2) forecasts for the target variable 'real change of private consumption' (y). These yearly data are available for a period of 21 years from 1976 to 1996. They are given in Table 1.

Table 1. Real change of German private consumption (y) and corresponding DIW and Ifo forecasts (f_1, f_2) for the period from 1976 to 1996.

	Year						
	1976	1977	1978	1979	1980	1981	1982
y	3.6	3.1	3.4	3.2	1.7	−1.2	−2.2
f_1	3.0	4.5	3	3.5	2.0	1	−0.5
f_2	2.5	4.5	3	3.5	1.5	1	0.0
	1983	1984	1985	1986	1987	1988	1989
y	1.1	0.6	1.8	4.3	3.5	2.7	1.7
f_1	−0.5	0	1.5	3.5	3.0	3.0	2.0
f_2	−0.5	1	1.5	3.0	3.5	2.5	2.5
	1990	1991	1992	1993	1994	1995	1996
y	4.7	3.6	1.7	0.2	0.6	1.8	1.3
f_1	3.5	3.5	2	0	−1.5	0.5	2.0
f_2	4.0	3.0	2	0	−1.0	0.5	2.5

When evaluating the data it is important to take their availability into account: The forecasts f_1 and f_2 for year t, say, are made at the end of year $t-1$ and the true value of the target variable y for the year $t-2$ are not published by the Statistisches Bundesamt before the end of year $t-1$.

Consequently, at the time when the individual forecasts for year t are to be combined, namely at the end of year $t - 1$, we can only use the past data up to year $t - 2$.

These past data serve to estimate the optimal combination parameters at each point of time. Due to structural changes in the data set the optimal combination parameters may not be stable over time. A common procedure in this situation is to use only the latest observations for parameter estimation. Of course the amount of past data should not be too small either so that the estimation of the moments of the joint distribution is at least fairly reliable. As a compromise we chose a history of 10 data points for parameter estimation.

Altogether we will use the data from 1976 to 1985 to estimate the combination parameters for the 1987 forecasts, the data from 1977 to 1986 to estimate the combination parameters for the 1988 forecasts, and so on. This leads to a time span of 10 years (1987 to 1996) in which the performance of the various methods is evaluated by means of the average of the squared forecast errors. This is the empirical counterpart of mean square prediction error and will consequently be denoted as $\widehat{\text{MSPE}}$.

A very simple strategy for the combination of the single forecasts is their arithmetic mean. Since it is easy to apply and also quite successful in empirical investigations, any other combination technique is measured against the arithmetic mean. Therefore we decided to present all $\widehat{\text{MSPE}}$-values relative to the $\widehat{\text{MSPE}}$-value of the arithmetic mean, which is 0.7538 in the considered time period. All decimals have been deleted following the second decimal such that methods outperforming the arithmetic mean can be identified immediately. Proceeding in this way makes the results directly comparable to those in Klapper (1998).

The results of this evaluation are presented in Table 2. It can be seen that in this example the weak linear plus quadratic combination is the best of all combination methods followed by the medium linear plus quadratic combination technique. Only these two combinations perform better than both individual forecasts. Their $\widehat{\text{MSPE}}$-values are about two third of the value for the arithmetic mean. The linear unrestricted combination with constant term is about as good as the arithmetic mean. The strong linear plus quadratic combination performs like the worse of the two individual forecasts which is 14% worse than the arithmetic mean.

The better adjustments of individual forecasts in this example are the linear plus quadratic adjustments. Both of them have $\widehat{\text{MSPE}}$-values of about 60% of the value belonging to the arithmetic mean. Thus they are the best of the considered techniques, even better than all combination methods. Also the linear unrestricted adjustments with constant term perform quite well.

The forecasts for the years 1987 to 1996 produced by the weak linear plus quadratic combination of f_1 and f_2 are given by 2.4075, 2.9264, 1.6082, 4.2094, 4.1306, 1.4047, 0.0789, 1.6358, 0.5785 and 1.9407. Together with the

Table 2. $\widehat{\text{MSPE}}$-values of adjusted and combined forecasts in an empirical application (all values relative to the $\widehat{\text{MSPE}}$ of the arithmetic mean)

Forecast $f_.$		$\widehat{\text{MSPE}}(f_., y)$
DIW forecast	$f_1 = f_{\text{DIW}}$	1.14
Adjustments:	$f_{\text{DIW},\hat{\alpha}_{\text{opt}},\hat{b}_{\text{opt}},\hat{c}_{\text{opt}}}$	0.61
	$f_{\text{DIW},\hat{b}_{\text{opt}},\hat{c}_{\text{opt}}}$	0.83
Ifo forecast	$f_2 = f_{\text{Ifo}}$	0.97
Adjustments:	$f_{\text{Ifo},\hat{\alpha}_{\text{opt}},\hat{b}_{\text{opt}},\hat{c}_{\text{opt}}}$	0.60
	$f_{\text{Ifo},\hat{b}_{\text{opt}},\hat{c}_{\text{opt}}}$	0.93
Linear combination	$f_{\hat{\mathbf{b}}_{\text{opt}},\hat{c}_{\text{opt}}}$	1.03
LPQ combinations:	$f_{\hat{\mathbf{A}}_{\text{opt}},\hat{\mathbf{b}}_{\text{opt}},\hat{c}_{\text{opt}}}$	1.14
	$f_{\hat{\mathbf{a}}_{\text{opt}},\hat{\mathbf{b}}_{\text{opt}},\hat{c}_{\text{opt}}}$	0.66
	$f_{\hat{\alpha}_{\text{opt}},\hat{\mathbf{b}}_{\text{opt}},\hat{c}_{\text{opt}}}$	0.64

target variable, the individual forecasts and their arithmetic mean they are visualized in Figure 1.

It should be pointed out that the preceding analysis represents only a single example and cannot be generalized. In our first investigations there have been cases where the linear plus quadratic techniques, especially the strong linear plus quadratic technique, perform significantly worse. Presumably this is due to the very small amount of past data available for the estimation of moments. Especially for the higher moments only 10 data points seem to be very few. Again we must refer to a more detailed analysis of the performance of the linear plus quadratic techniques in Troschke (2002).

To judge the potential of the linear plus quadratic techniques it is interesting to compare the optimal MSPE-values within the various approaches for the case where the moments $\boldsymbol{\mu}$, $\boldsymbol{\Sigma}$, $\boldsymbol{\Phi}$ and $\boldsymbol{\Psi}$ of the joint distribution of y, f_1 and f_2 are known. In order to base these considerations on realistic grounds we are now going to use the sample moments, which may be calculated from the whole set of 21 data points in Table 1, as the true moments.

From these moments we may determine the optimal adjustment or combination parameters belonging to the different methods. Following the formulae from Section 3 we obtain, for example, the optimal parameters for the strong linear plus quadratic approach:

$$\mathbf{A}_{\text{opt}} = \begin{pmatrix} 2.3910 & -2.7544 \\ -2.7544 & 3.3331 \end{pmatrix}, \quad \mathbf{b}_{\text{opt}} = \begin{pmatrix} 3.3049 \\ -3.3753 \end{pmatrix}, \quad \mathbf{c}_{\text{opt}} = 0.6113. \quad (5.1)$$

Inserting the respective optimal combination parameters into the general MSPE-formula (A.4) (for linear plus quadratic combination) or by direct calcu-

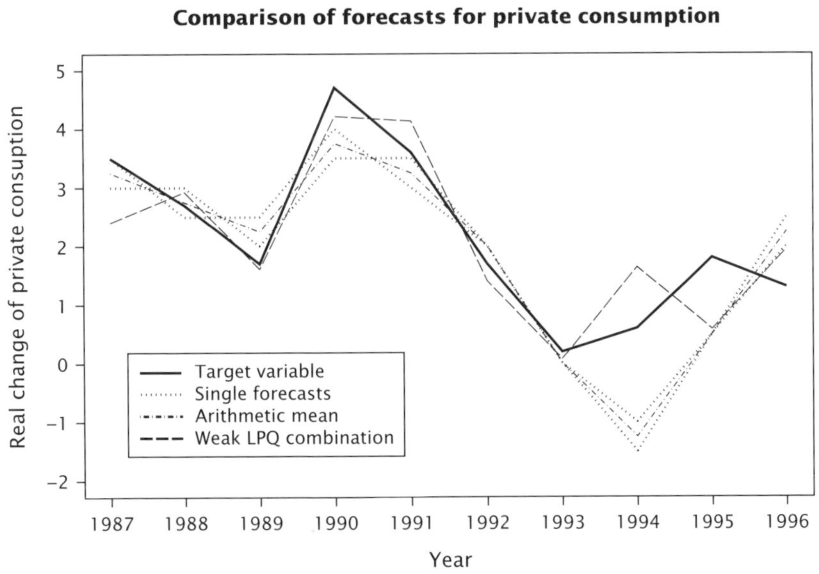

Figure 1. Target variable *real change of private consumption*, together with its DIW and Ifo forecasts, their arithmetic mean and their weak linear plus quadratic combination.

lation from the respective formulae for the optimal MSPE-value (for all other combinations and all adjustments) we derive the optimal MSPE-values for all the considered methods. Again we report all these MSPE-values relative to the MSPE of the arithmetic mean, which is 1.0894. All values in Table 3 have been deleted after the second decimal.

Since the moments $\boldsymbol{\mu}$, $\boldsymbol{\Sigma}$, $\boldsymbol{\Phi}$ and $\boldsymbol{\Psi}$ are assumed to be known, the calculations can be done on a theoretical basis and, hence, the MSPE-values reflect the theoretical ranking of the various methods: strong linear plus quadratic combination is not worse than medium linear plus quadratic combination, which in turn is not worse than weak linear plus quadratic combination, which in turn is not worse than the linear unrestricted combination with constant term, and so on.

In the situation under consideration the expected squared error loss of the strong linear plus quadratic combination is 27% less than that of the arithmetic mean. Medium and weak linear plus quadratic combinations are expected to be only 14% better than the arithmetic mean. We may conclude that in the above application medium and weak linear plus quadratic combinations performed much better than might have been expected, especially when taking into consideration that the necessity to estimate the optimal combination parameters leads to an even worse theoretical MSPE. In addition the linear plus quadratic adjustments performed much better in the application than might have been expected.

Table 3. MSPE-values of adjusted and combined forecasts for certain known moments $\boldsymbol{\mu}$, $\boldsymbol{\Sigma}$, $\boldsymbol{\Phi}$ and $\boldsymbol{\Psi}$ (all values relative to the MSPE of the arithmetic mean)

Forecast $f_{\cdot}$		MSPE$(f_{\cdot}, y)$
DIW forecast	$f_1 = f_{\text{DIW}}$	0.98
Adjustments:	$f_{\text{DIW},\alpha_{opt},b_{opt},c_{opt}}$	0.88
	$f_{\text{DIW},b_{opt},c_{opt}}$	0.93
Ifo forecast	$f_2 = f_{\text{Ifo}}$	1.09
Adjustments:	$f_{\text{Ifo},\alpha_{opt},b_{opt},c_{opt}}$	1.04
	$f_{\text{Ifo},b_{opt},c_{opt}}$	1.06
Linear combination	$f_{\mathbf{b}_{opt},c_{opt}}$	0.92
LPQ combinations:	$f_{\mathbf{A}_{opt},\mathbf{b}_{opt},c_{opt}}$	0.73
	$f_{\mathbf{a}_{opt},\mathbf{b}_{opt},c_{opt}}$	0.86
	$f_{\alpha_{opt},\mathbf{b}_{opt},c_{opt}}$	0.86

It can be seen that there is some potential in the linear plus quadratic approaches to outperform the arithmetic mean. How well this potential is exploited will depend on how good the moments of the joint distribution can be estimated. Clearly, the more suitable data are available for that purpose the better. Consequently, the linear plus quadratic approaches should be more valuable for monthly, weekly or even daily data (e.g. from the stock market) than they are for yearly data. Also the data should not be subject to extreme structural changes during the period under study.

6 Conclusions

In this paper we have introduced the linear plus quadratic approach for the combination of forecasts. Three versions of this approach have been considered. The strong version depends on the largest number of unknown combination parameters followed by the medium and then the weak version. We have derived equation systems from which the respective optimal combination parameters can be calculated. Each of the linear plus quadratic approaches requires knowledge about the first to fourth order moments of the joint distribution of $\mathbf{y}$ and $\mathbf{f}$. In practical applications these moments have to be estimated. Alternatively, regression approaches may be pursued. We have also considered some classical linear approaches as competitors to the new approaches.

Additionally, we have investigated the special case $k = 1$ which means adjustment of an individual forecast. Furthermore we have reported on first comparisons of the classical and the new approaches in these cases. We have seen that employing linear plus quadratic adjustments and combinations may be beneficial, but also that this is not always the case. Due to the smaller number of parameters involved the weak linear plus quadratic combination seems to be suitable if only a small amount of data is available for combination parameter estimation.

A much more detailed analysis of the possible benefits of the linear plus quadratic approaches has to follow, as was explained in Section 5. A point of special interest would be to find a guideline for potential users identifying situations beforehand in which linear plus quadratic combination of forecasts is promising. Especially the question of how much data should be available is interesting. Troschke (2002) addresses these questions in detail.

A Derivation of optimal parameters for strong linear plus quadratic combination

In Section 3 the equations determining the optimal combination parameters $\mathbf{A}_{\text{opt}}$, $\mathbf{b}_{\text{opt}}$ and c_{opt} for the strong linear plus quadratic approach are given. The purpose of this Appendix is to provide some intermediate results from the omitted proof. As outlined in Section 3 the proof is carried out in three steps:

Step 1: Explicit calculation of the MSPE-function. Since $\text{MSPE}(f_{\mathbf{A},\mathbf{b},c}, y) = \text{E}[(y - f_{\mathbf{A},\mathbf{b},c})^2] = \text{Var}(y - f_{\mathbf{A},\mathbf{b},c}) + [\text{E}(y - f_{\mathbf{A},\mathbf{b},c})]^2$ we may split the necessary calculations in two parts.

While the calculation of $[\text{E}(y - f_{\mathbf{A},\mathbf{b},c})]^2$ is quite easily done with the help of (3.1) and $\text{E}(y) = \mu_0$, the calculation of $\text{Var}(y - f_{\mathbf{A},\mathbf{b},c})$ requires much more effort.

Setting

$$\tilde{\mathbf{Y}} = \begin{pmatrix} y \\ \mathbf{f} \end{pmatrix}, \quad \tilde{\boldsymbol{\mu}} = \begin{pmatrix} \mu_0 \\ \boldsymbol{\mu}_{\mathbf{f}} \end{pmatrix} = \boldsymbol{\mu} \quad \text{and} \quad \tilde{\boldsymbol{\varepsilon}} = \begin{pmatrix} \varepsilon_0 \\ \boldsymbol{\varepsilon}_{\mathbf{f}} \end{pmatrix} = \boldsymbol{\varepsilon} \tag{A.1}$$

we obtain

$$\tilde{\Sigma} = \Sigma, \quad \tilde{\boldsymbol{\Phi}} = \boldsymbol{\Phi} \quad \text{and} \quad \tilde{\boldsymbol{\Psi}} = \boldsymbol{\Psi} \tag{A.2}$$

as defined in (1.9) and (1.12)–(1.15). Setting further

$$\tilde{\mathbf{A}} = \tilde{\mathbf{B}} = \begin{pmatrix} 0 & \mathbf{0} \\ \mathbf{0} & -\mathbf{A} \end{pmatrix} \quad \text{and} \quad \tilde{\mathbf{a}} = \tilde{\mathbf{b}} = \begin{pmatrix} 1 \\ -\mathbf{b} \end{pmatrix} \tag{A.3}$$

we may then apply Lemma 1 (b).

Joining the two parts of the calculation and performing some simplifications we finally arrive at the following expression for the mean square prediction error of $f_{\mathbf{A},\mathbf{b},c}$, where the terms have been ordered with respect to the occurring unknowns:

$$
\begin{aligned}
&\mathrm{MSPE}(f_{\mathbf{A},\mathbf{b},c}, y) \\
&\quad = 4\boldsymbol{\mu}_{\mathrm{f}}^{\mathsf{T}}\mathbf{A}\Sigma_{\mathrm{ff}}\mathbf{A}\boldsymbol{\mu}_{\mathrm{f}} + 4\boldsymbol{\varphi}_{\mathrm{A}}^{\mathsf{T}}\mathbf{A}\boldsymbol{\mu}_{\mathrm{f}} + \mathrm{tr}(\mathbf{A}\boldsymbol{\psi}_{\mathrm{A}}) + (\boldsymbol{\mu}_{\mathrm{f}}^{\mathsf{T}}\mathbf{A}\boldsymbol{\mu}_{\mathrm{f}})^2 + 2\boldsymbol{\mu}_{\mathrm{f}}^{\mathsf{T}}\mathbf{A}\boldsymbol{\mu}_{\mathrm{f}}\,\mathrm{tr}(\mathbf{A}\Sigma_{\mathrm{ff}}) \\
&\qquad - 4\Sigma_{\mathrm{f}0}^{\mathsf{T}}\mathbf{A}\boldsymbol{\mu}_{\mathrm{f}} - 2\,\mathrm{tr}(\mathbf{A}\boldsymbol{\Phi}_{0\mathrm{ff}}) - 2\mu_0\boldsymbol{\mu}_{\mathrm{f}}^{\mathsf{T}}\mathbf{A}\boldsymbol{\mu}_{\mathrm{f}} - 2\mu_0\,\mathrm{tr}(\mathbf{A}\Sigma_{\mathrm{ff}}) \\
&\qquad + 4\mathbf{b}^{\mathsf{T}}\Sigma_{\mathrm{ff}}\mathbf{A}\boldsymbol{\mu}_{\mathrm{f}} + 2\mathbf{b}^{\mathsf{T}}\boldsymbol{\varphi}_{\mathrm{A}} + 2\boldsymbol{\mu}_{\mathrm{f}}^{\mathsf{T}}\mathbf{A}\boldsymbol{\mu}_{\mathrm{f}}\mathbf{b}^{\mathsf{T}}\boldsymbol{\mu}_{\mathrm{f}} + 2\,\mathrm{tr}(\mathbf{A}\Sigma_{\mathrm{ff}})\mathbf{b}^{\mathsf{T}}\boldsymbol{\mu}_{\mathrm{f}} \\
&\qquad + \mathbf{b}^{\mathsf{T}}\Sigma_{\mathrm{ff}}\mathbf{b} + \mathbf{b}^{\mathsf{T}}\boldsymbol{\mu}_{\mathrm{f}}\boldsymbol{\mu}_{\mathrm{f}}^{\mathsf{T}}\mathbf{b} \\
&\qquad - 2\mathbf{b}^{\mathsf{T}}\Sigma_{\mathrm{f}0} - 2\mu_0\mathbf{b}^{\mathsf{T}}\boldsymbol{\mu}_{\mathrm{f}} \\
&\qquad + 2\boldsymbol{\mu}_{\mathrm{f}}^{\mathsf{T}}\mathbf{A}\boldsymbol{\mu}_{\mathrm{f}}c + 2\,\mathrm{tr}(\mathbf{A}\Sigma_{\mathrm{ff}})c \\
&\qquad + 2\mathbf{b}^{\mathsf{T}}\boldsymbol{\mu}_{\mathrm{f}}c \\
&\qquad + c^2 \\
&\qquad - 2\mu_0 c \\
&\qquad + \Sigma_{00} + \mu_0^2,
\end{aligned}
\tag{A.4}
$$

where

$$
\boldsymbol{\varphi}_{\mathrm{A}} = \begin{pmatrix} \mathrm{tr}(\mathbf{A}\boldsymbol{\Phi}_{1\mathrm{ff}}) \\ \vdots \\ \mathrm{tr}(\mathbf{A}\boldsymbol{\Phi}_{k\mathrm{ff}}) \end{pmatrix}
\tag{A.5}
$$

is a k-dimensional vector and

$$
\boldsymbol{\psi}_{\mathrm{A}} = \begin{pmatrix} \mathrm{tr}(\mathbf{A}\boldsymbol{\Psi}_{11\mathrm{ff}}) & \dots & \mathrm{tr}(\mathbf{A}\boldsymbol{\Psi}_{1k\mathrm{ff}}) \\ \vdots & \ddots & \vdots \\ \mathrm{tr}(\mathbf{A}\boldsymbol{\Psi}_{k1\mathrm{ff}}) & \dots & \mathrm{tr}(\mathbf{A}\boldsymbol{\Psi}_{kk\mathrm{ff}}) \end{pmatrix}
\tag{A.6}
$$

is a symmetric $k \times k$ matrix.

Step 2: Differentiation. Since the parameter **b** is a vector and **A** even is a matrix the concept of matrix differential calculus (Magnus and Neudecker 1999, see especially pp. 177 f.) proves most helpful.

Applying common differential calculus we immediately get

$$
\frac{\partial\,\mathrm{MSPE}(f_{\mathbf{A},\mathbf{b},c}, y)}{\partial c} = 2[c - \mu_0 + \mathbf{b}^{\mathsf{T}}\boldsymbol{\mu}_{\mathrm{f}} + \boldsymbol{\mu}_{\mathrm{f}}^{\mathsf{T}}\mathbf{A}\boldsymbol{\mu}_{\mathrm{f}} + \mathrm{tr}(\mathbf{A}\Sigma_{\mathrm{ff}})].
\tag{A.7}
$$

With the help of matrix differential calculus it is not difficult to show

$$
\begin{aligned}
\frac{\partial\,\mathrm{MSPE}(f_{\mathbf{A},\mathbf{b},c}, y)}{\partial \mathbf{b}} = 2[&\Sigma_{\mathrm{ff}}\mathbf{b} + \boldsymbol{\mu}_{\mathrm{f}}\boldsymbol{\mu}_{\mathrm{f}}^{\mathsf{T}}\mathbf{b} - \Sigma_{\mathrm{f}0} - \mu_0\boldsymbol{\mu}_{\mathrm{f}} + 2\Sigma_{\mathrm{ff}}\mathbf{A}\boldsymbol{\mu}_{\mathrm{f}} \\
&+ \boldsymbol{\varphi}_{\mathrm{A}} + \boldsymbol{\mu}_{\mathrm{f}}^{\mathsf{T}}\mathbf{A}\boldsymbol{\mu}_{\mathrm{f}}\boldsymbol{\mu}_{\mathrm{f}} + \mathrm{tr}(\mathbf{A}\Sigma_{\mathrm{ff}})\boldsymbol{\mu}_{\mathrm{f}} + c\boldsymbol{\mu}_{\mathrm{f}}].
\end{aligned}
\tag{A.8}
$$

Differentiation with respect to **A** is the hard part of this second step. Since **A** is symmetric we have to apply Lemma 2. After some tedious calculations we finally arrive at

$$\begin{aligned}
&\frac{\partial\,\mathrm{MSPE}(f_{\mathbf{A},\mathbf{b},c}, y)}{\partial \mathbf{A}} \\
&\quad = 2[\boldsymbol{\mu}_{\mathrm{f}}\boldsymbol{\mu}_{\mathrm{f}}^{\mathsf{T}}\mathbf{A}(4\boldsymbol{\Sigma}_{\mathrm{ff}} + \boldsymbol{\mu}_{\mathrm{f}}\boldsymbol{\mu}_{1}^{\mathsf{T}}) + (4\boldsymbol{\Sigma}_{\mathrm{ff}} + \boldsymbol{\mu}_{\mathrm{f}}\boldsymbol{\mu}_{1}^{\mathsf{T}})\mathbf{A}\boldsymbol{\mu}_{\mathrm{f}}\boldsymbol{\mu}_{\mathrm{f}}^{\mathsf{T}} \\
&\qquad - \mathrm{diag}(\boldsymbol{\mu}_{\mathrm{f}}\boldsymbol{\mu}_{\mathrm{f}}^{\mathsf{T}}\mathbf{A}(4\boldsymbol{\Sigma}_{\mathrm{ff}} + \boldsymbol{\mu}_{\mathrm{f}}\boldsymbol{\mu}_{1}^{\mathsf{T}}))] \\
&\qquad + \mathrm{tr}(\mathbf{A}\boldsymbol{\Sigma}_{\mathrm{ff}})[4\boldsymbol{\mu}_{\mathrm{f}}\boldsymbol{\mu}_{\mathrm{f}}^{\mathsf{T}} - 2\,\mathrm{diag}(\boldsymbol{\mu}_{\mathrm{f}}\boldsymbol{\mu}_{1}^{\mathsf{T}})] \\
&\qquad + \mathrm{tr}(\mathbf{A}\boldsymbol{\mu}_{\mathrm{f}}\boldsymbol{\mu}_{1}^{\mathsf{T}})[4\boldsymbol{\Sigma}_{\mathrm{ff}} - 2\,\mathrm{diag}(\boldsymbol{\Sigma}_{\mathrm{ff}})] \\
&\qquad + 4[\boldsymbol{\varphi}_{\mathbf{A}}\boldsymbol{\mu}_{\mathrm{f}}^{\mathsf{T}} + \boldsymbol{\mu}_{\mathrm{f}}\boldsymbol{\varphi}_{\mathbf{A}}^{\mathsf{T}} - \mathrm{diag}(\boldsymbol{\varphi}_{\mathbf{A}}\boldsymbol{\mu}_{\mathrm{f}}^{\mathsf{T}})] \\
&\qquad + 4\boldsymbol{\psi}_{\mathbf{A}} - 2\,\mathrm{diag}(\boldsymbol{\psi}_{\mathbf{A}}) \\
&\qquad + \sum_{i=1}^{k}\sum_{j=1}^{k} a_{ij}\mu_j[8\boldsymbol{\Phi}_{i\mathrm{ff}} - 4\,\mathrm{diag}(\boldsymbol{\Phi}_{i\mathrm{ff}})] \\
&\qquad + 4[\boldsymbol{\Sigma}_{\mathrm{ff}}\mathbf{b}\boldsymbol{\mu}_{\mathrm{f}}^{\mathsf{T}} + \boldsymbol{\mu}_{\mathrm{f}}\mathbf{b}^{\mathsf{T}}\boldsymbol{\Sigma}_{\mathrm{ff}} - \mathrm{diag}(\boldsymbol{\Sigma}_{\mathrm{ff}}\mathbf{b}\boldsymbol{\mu}_{\mathrm{f}}^{\mathsf{T}})] \\
&\qquad + (\mathbf{b}^{\mathsf{T}}\boldsymbol{\mu}_{\mathrm{f}} + c - \mu_0)[4(\boldsymbol{\Sigma}_{\mathrm{ff}} + \boldsymbol{\mu}_{\mathrm{f}}\boldsymbol{\mu}_{1}^{\mathsf{T}}) - 2\,\mathrm{diag}(\boldsymbol{\Sigma}_{\mathrm{ff}} + \boldsymbol{\mu}_{\mathrm{f}}\boldsymbol{\mu}_{\mathrm{f}}^{\mathsf{T}})] \\
&\qquad + \sum_{i=1}^{k} b_i[4\boldsymbol{\Phi}_{i\mathrm{ff}} - 2\,\mathrm{diag}(\boldsymbol{\Phi}_{i\mathrm{ff}})] \\
&\qquad - 4[\boldsymbol{\Sigma}_{\mathrm{f}0}\boldsymbol{\mu}_{\mathrm{f}}^{\mathsf{T}} + \boldsymbol{\mu}_{\mathrm{f}}\boldsymbol{\Sigma}_{\mathrm{f}0}^{\mathsf{T}} - \mathrm{diag}(\boldsymbol{\Sigma}_{\mathrm{f}0}\boldsymbol{\mu}_{\mathrm{f}}^{\mathsf{T}})] \\
&\qquad - 4\boldsymbol{\Phi}_{0\mathrm{ff}} + 2\,\mathrm{diag}(\boldsymbol{\Phi}_{0\mathrm{ff}}),
\end{aligned} \tag{A.9}$$

where for a $k \times k$-matrix $\mathbf{M} = (m_{ij})$ we define

$$\mathrm{diag}(\mathbf{M}) = \begin{pmatrix} m_{11} & 0 & \ldots & 0 \\ 0 & m_{22} & \ldots & 0 \\ \vdots & \vdots & \ddots & \vdots \\ 0 & 0 & \ldots & m_{kk} \end{pmatrix} \in \mathbb{R}^{k\times k}. \tag{A.10}$$

Step 3: Equating to zero. Setting Equations (A.7), (A.8) and (A.9) simultaneously to zero we arrive at Equations (3.2), (3.3) and (3.4) from Section 3. They determine the optimal choices for $\mathbf{A}$, $\mathbf{b}$ and c.

B Two fundamental lemmas

This Appendix cites two results from the literature which are essential for our considerations.

The first result is concerned with the first and second order moments of quadratic forms. Clearly, it is most important for our derivations. It should be pointed out that no distributional assumption is made. Assuming (multivariate) normality would lead to much simpler formulae on the one hand. But on the other hand the normality assumption would render the whole linear plus quadratic approach to the combination of forecasts unnecessary, as has been made clear in the introduction.

Lemma 1 (Rao and Kleffe 1988, p. 32, (iv)). *Let* $\tilde{\mathbf{Y}} = \tilde{\boldsymbol{\mu}} + \tilde{\boldsymbol{\varepsilon}}$ *where* $\tilde{\boldsymbol{\mu}}$ *is a constant vector and* $\tilde{\boldsymbol{\varepsilon}}$ *is a vector random variable with moments* $\mathrm{E}(\tilde{\boldsymbol{\varepsilon}}) = \mathbf{0}$, $\mathrm{E}(\tilde{\boldsymbol{\varepsilon}}\tilde{\boldsymbol{\varepsilon}}^{\mathsf{T}}) = \tilde{\boldsymbol{\Sigma}}$, $\mathrm{E}(\tilde{\boldsymbol{\varepsilon}} \otimes \tilde{\boldsymbol{\varepsilon}}\tilde{\boldsymbol{\varepsilon}}^{\mathsf{T}}) = \tilde{\boldsymbol{\Phi}}$ *and* $\mathrm{E}(\tilde{\boldsymbol{\varepsilon}}\tilde{\boldsymbol{\varepsilon}}^{\mathsf{T}} \otimes \tilde{\boldsymbol{\varepsilon}}\tilde{\boldsymbol{\varepsilon}}^{\mathsf{T}}) = \tilde{\boldsymbol{\Psi}}$. *Further let* $\tilde{\mathbf{a}}$ *and* $\tilde{\mathbf{b}}$ *be vectors and let* $\tilde{\mathbf{A}}$ *and* $\tilde{\mathbf{B}}$ *be symmetric matrices of appropriate dimensions. Then*

(a) $\mathrm{E}(\tilde{\mathbf{a}}^{\mathsf{T}}\tilde{\mathbf{Y}} + \tilde{\mathbf{Y}}^{\mathsf{T}}\tilde{\mathbf{A}}\tilde{\mathbf{Y}}) = \tilde{\mathbf{a}}^{\mathsf{T}}\tilde{\boldsymbol{\mu}} + \tilde{\boldsymbol{\mu}}^{\mathsf{T}}\tilde{\mathbf{A}}\tilde{\boldsymbol{\mu}} + \mathrm{tr}(\tilde{\mathbf{A}}\tilde{\boldsymbol{\Sigma}})$,

(b)
$$\begin{aligned}
&\mathrm{Cov}(\tilde{\mathbf{a}}^{\mathsf{T}}\tilde{\mathbf{Y}} + \tilde{\mathbf{Y}}^{\mathsf{T}}\tilde{\mathbf{A}}\tilde{\mathbf{Y}}, \tilde{\mathbf{b}}^{\mathsf{T}}\tilde{\mathbf{Y}} + \tilde{\mathbf{Y}}^{\mathsf{T}}\tilde{\mathbf{B}}\tilde{\mathbf{Y}}) \\
&\quad = \tilde{\mathbf{b}}^{\mathsf{T}}[2\tilde{\boldsymbol{\Sigma}}\tilde{\mathbf{A}}\tilde{\boldsymbol{\mu}} + \tilde{\boldsymbol{\Sigma}}\tilde{\mathbf{a}} + \tilde{\boldsymbol{\Phi}}^*(\tilde{\mathbf{A}})] + \mathrm{tr}(\tilde{\mathbf{B}}[4\tilde{\boldsymbol{\mu}}\tilde{\boldsymbol{\mu}}^{\mathsf{T}}\tilde{\mathbf{A}}\tilde{\boldsymbol{\Sigma}} + 2\tilde{\boldsymbol{\Phi}}(\tilde{\mathbf{A}}\tilde{\boldsymbol{\mu}}) + 2\tilde{\boldsymbol{\Phi}}^*(\tilde{\mathbf{A}})\tilde{\boldsymbol{\mu}}^{\mathsf{T}} \\
&\qquad + \tilde{\boldsymbol{\Psi}}(\tilde{\mathbf{A}}) + 2\tilde{\boldsymbol{\mu}}\tilde{\mathbf{a}}^{\mathsf{T}}\tilde{\boldsymbol{\Sigma}} + \tilde{\boldsymbol{\Phi}}(\tilde{\mathbf{a}}) - \mathrm{tr}(\tilde{\mathbf{A}}\tilde{\boldsymbol{\Sigma}})\tilde{\boldsymbol{\Sigma}}]).
\end{aligned}$$

Here the following abbreviations have been used: For a vector $\tilde{\mathbf{c}} = (\tilde{c}_i)$ *and a matrix* $\tilde{\mathbf{C}} = (\tilde{c}_{ij})$ *we define*

$$\begin{aligned}
\tilde{\boldsymbol{\Psi}}(\tilde{\mathbf{C}}) &= \sum_i \sum_j \tilde{c}_{ij}\tilde{\boldsymbol{\Psi}}_{ij}, \\
\tilde{\boldsymbol{\Phi}}(\tilde{\mathbf{c}}) &= \sum_i \tilde{c}_i\tilde{\boldsymbol{\Phi}}_i, \\
\tilde{\boldsymbol{\Phi}}^*(\tilde{\mathbf{C}}) &= (\mathrm{tr}(\tilde{\mathbf{C}}\tilde{\boldsymbol{\Phi}}_i))_i,
\end{aligned}$$

i.e. the first two quantities are matrices, whereas the last one is a vector.

In matrix differential calculus it is a special and difficult situation when the derivative is to be taken with respect to a symmetric matrix. The following lemma shows how to proceed correctly in this case.

Lemma 2 (Rao and Rao 1998, p. 230). *Let* f *be a scalar valued function of a matrix variable* $\mathbf{A}$, *where* $\mathbf{A}$ *is symmetric. Then*

$$\frac{\partial f(\mathbf{A})}{\partial \mathbf{A}} = \left\{ \frac{\partial f(\mathbf{B})}{\partial \mathbf{B}} + \left(\frac{\partial f(\mathbf{B})}{\partial \mathbf{B}}\right)^{\mathsf{T}} - \mathrm{diag}\left(\frac{\partial f(\mathbf{B})}{\partial \mathbf{B}}\right) \right\}\Bigg|_{\mathbf{B}=\mathbf{A}}.$$

This is meant to indicate that f *is regarded as a function of an arbitrary matrix* $\mathbf{B}$ *which has the same size as* $\mathbf{A}$, *but all the components of* $\mathbf{B}$ *are regarded as independent variables. Then the derivative of* f *is formed with respect to* $\mathbf{B}$, *the above expression is calculated and in this expression* $\mathbf{B}$ *is replaced by the symmetric matrix* $\mathbf{A}$ *again.*

Here for a square matrix $\mathbf{M} = (m_{ij})$ we define $\mathrm{diag}(\mathbf{M})$ as the diagonal matrix of the same dimension with the elements m_{ii} on its diagonal (cf. Equation (A.10)).

Acknowledgements

The authors wish to thank Jürgen Groß for his helpful comments and suggestions. Special thanks go to an anonymous referee who helped to improve the paper considerably. Financial support of the Deutsche Forschungsgemeinschaft (SFB 475, "Reduction of complexity in multivariate data structures") is gratefully acknowledged.

References

Clemen, R. T. (1989). Combining forecasts: a review and annotated bibliography. *International Journal of Forecasting*, 5, 559–583.

Granger, C. W. J. (1989). Combining forecasts – twenty years later. *Journal of Forecasting*, 8, 167–173.

Granger, C. W. J. and Ramanathan, R. (1984). Improved methods of combining forecasts. *Journal of Forecasting*, 3, 197–204.

Harville, D. A. (1985). Decomposition of prediction error. *Journal of the American Statistical Association*, 80, 132–138.

Klapper, M. (1998). Combining German Macro Economic Forecasts Using Rank-Based Techniques. Technical Report 19/1998, Sonderforschungsbereich 475, University of Dortmund.

Magnus, J. R. and Neudecker, H. (1999). *Matrix Differential Calculus with Applications in Statistics and Econometrics*, Revised Edition. Chichester: Wiley.

Rao, C. R. (1965). *Linear statistical inference and its applications.* New York: Wiley.

Rao, C. R. and Kleffe, J. (1988). *Estimation of Variance Components and Applications.* Amsterdam: North-Holland.

Rao, C. R. and Rao, M. B. (1998). *Matrix Algebra and Its Applications to Statistics and Econometrics.* Singapore: World Scientific.

Thiele, J. (1993). *Kombination von Prognosen* (Wirtschaftswissenschaftliche Beiträge, Band 74). Heidelberg: Physica-Verlag.

Troschke, S. O. (2002). *Enhanced Approaches to the Combination of Forecasts* (Reihe Quantitative Ökonomie, Band 127). Lohmar; Cologne: Josef Eul Verlag.

Troschke, S. O. and Trenkler, G. (2000). Linear Plus Quadratic Approach to the Mean Square Error Optimal Combination of Forecasts. Technical Report 54/2000, Sonderforschungsbereich 475, University of Dortmund.

Troschke, S. O. and Trenkler, G. (2000). Regression Approach to the Linear Plus Quadratic Combination of Forecasts. Technical Report 55/2000, Sonderforschungsbereich 475, University of Dortmund.

The articles appearing in the Technical Report series of the Sonderforschungsbereich 475 "Reduction of complexity in multivariate data structures" can be found in the world wide web: http://www.sfb475.uni-dortmund.de/dienst/en/content/veroeff-e/veroeff-e.html.

SVEN-OLIVER TROSCHKE
Hülser Straße 7, 47906 Kempen, Germany
taeger-troschke@freenet.de

GÖTZ TRENKLER
Department of Statistics, University of Dortmund
44221 Dortmund, Germany
trenkler@statistik.uni-dortmund.de
http://www.statistik.uni-dortmund.de/de/content/einrichtungen/lehrstuehle/personen/trenkler.html

Festschrift for Tarmo Pukkila on his 60th Birthday
Eds. E. P. Liski, J. Isotalo, J. Niemelä, S. Puntanen, and G. P. H. Styan
© Dept. of Mathematics, Statistics and Philosophy,
Univ. of Tampere, 2006, ISBN 978-951-44-6620-5, pages 367–383

A photo album for Tarmo Mikko Pukkila

SIMO PUNTANEN & GEORGE P. H. STYAN

Abstract. We present a set of photographs showing Dr. Tarmo Mikko Pukkila (b. 1946) and his friends, colleagues and family, taken from 1980 through 1993. In 1980, Dr. Pukkila was appointed Professor of Statistics at the University of Tampere. He has served in numerous administrative positions at the University of Tampere: Head of the Department, Dean of the Faculty, and as Rector from 1987 through 1993.

2000 MSC codes: 01A60, 01A65, 01A74, 62-03.

Key words and phrases: University of Tampere; Gustav Elfving (1908–1984); First International Tampere Seminar on Linear Statistical Models and their Applications (Tampere 1983); Eino Haikala (1913–1993); International Workshop on Linear Models, Experimental Designs, and Related Matrix Theory (Tampere 1990); Chinubhai Ghelabhai Khatri (1931–1989); Second International Tampere Conference in Statistics (Tampere 1987).

Simo Puntanen

Figure 1. Haikala's farm, 1983: Soile Puntanen, Johan and Ulla Fellman, Leena and Erkki Liski, Gustav Elfving, Kaisa Huuhtanen, Helena Pukkila, Pentti Huuhtanen, Tarmo Pukkila, Bill Farebrother, C. R. Rao, Bimal K. Sinha.

University of Tampere

Figure 2. After the Inaugural Lecture for the Professorship Tampere 1980: Tarmo Pukkila and family.

University of Tampere

Figure 3. The Doctoral Convocation of Kalle Kaihari in 1980: Reino Erma, Kalle Kaihari, Pekka Paavola, Armas Nieminen, Tarmo Pukkila, Olavi J. Mattila, Urpo Levo.

Figure 4. Tampere 1983: Bhargavi Rao, Gustav Elfving, Timo Mäkeläinen, Tarmo Pukkila, Eino Haikala.

Figure 5. Tampere 1983: Bhargavi Rao, Soile Puntanen, Helena Pukkila, Marja Haikala.

Figure 6. Tampere 1983: Tarmo Pukkila thanking the Keynote Speakers for their performances.

Figure 7. Chez Pukkila in 1983: Evelyn M. Styan, Tarmo Pukkila (back to camera), George P. H. Styan, Soile Puntanen, Bill Farebrother.

Simo Puntanen

Figure 8. Sauna Party in Tampere, 1983.

Figure 9. Prague 1984: Harri Hietikko, Simo Puntanen, Tarmo Pukkila, and Pentti Huuhtanen are thirsty after the talks in COMPSTAT 84.

Figure 10. The Doctoral Convocation in 1985: Arvo Ylppö (97 years!), C.R. Rao, Tarmo Pukkila.

Simo Puntanen

Figure 11. C. R. Rao hosting Tarmo Pukkila in Pittsburgh, May 1986.

University of Tampere

Figure 12. Tarmo Pukkila stepping towards the City Reception in Raatihuone, Tampere 1987. Try to spot, e.g., Tim Dunne, Johan Fellman, Bryan Manly, Heinz Neudecker, Kenneth Nordström.

Figure 13. Tampere 1987: Tarmo Pukkila, (Paula Hietala and Johan Fellman in the background), George E. P. Box, Friedrich Pukelsheim.

Figure 14. Conference Dinner, Tampere 1987: George E.P. Box, Evelyn M. Styan, T.W. Anderson, Tarmo Pukkila, George P. H. Styan.

University of Tampere

Figure 15. Sauna Party, Tampere 1987: Roy E. Welsch, Daryl Pregibon, Tarmo Pukkila.

Simo Puntanen

Figure 16. Tampere 1987: Laura and Elina Pukkila, Chinubhai Ghelabhai Khatri.

University of Bergen

Figure 17. Bergen, Norway, 1988: Nordic Conference of University Rectors.

Sitra

Figure 18. Finnish National Fund for Research and Development (Sitra), a course on economic policy in 1988.

University of Łódź

Figure 19. Tarmo Pukkila in Łódź with Matti Parjanen, 1988.

Figure 20. Neuchâtel 1989: Sheila and Sujit Kumar Mitra, Friedrich Pukelsheim, Erkki Liski (back to camera), George P. H. Styan, Tarmo Pukkila, Jerzy K. Baksalary.

Figure 21. Neuchâtel 1989: A preliminary programme of the Tampere 1990 Workshop.

Figure 22. Celebrating the 350th anniversary of the first Finnish university, Turku 1990.

Figure 23. Rowing competition in Sulkava, 1990.

Figure 24. VIPs of the University of Tampere, 1991: Kauko Sipponen, Erkki Pystynen, Jaakko Uotila, Armas Nieminen, Lauri Seppänen, Tarmo Pukkila.

Figure 25. Finnish rectors in the Berlin Olympic Stadium, 1991: Bengt Stenlund (Åbo Akademi), Juhani Oksman (University of Oulu), Tarmo Pukkila, Päiviö Tommila (University of Helsinki).

Figure 26. Tampere 1992: Kauko Sipponen, Tarmo Pukkila, Mrs. Fulbright, William Fulbright.

Figure 27. At the Pukkila home in 1992: David Brillinger, Helena and Laura Pukkila, Lorie Brillinger, Soile Puntanen, Tarmo Pukkila.

Figure 28. Tampere 1993: Helena Pukkila.